introduction to the structure of the earth

introduction to the structure of the earth

Edgar W. Spencer
Professor and Chairman
Department of Geology
Washington and Lee University

McGraw-Hill Book Company
New York   St. Louis   San Francisco
London   Sydney   Toronto
Mexico   Panama

introduction to the structure of the earth

Library of Congress Catalog Card Number 68-9049
60196
2 3 4 5 6 7 8 9 0 VHVH 7 6 5 4 3 2 1 0

This book is dedicated to the memory of two outstanding teachers
Arie Poldervaart
Walter Bucher

preface

This book is designed for use in introductory structural geology courses in which the emphasis is placed on basic principles. Brief treatments of selected aspects of regional structural geology, structure of ocean basins, the earth's interior, and tectonics are included to broaden the student's conception of the importance, application, and relation of structural principles to other aspects of earth science.

Students using this book should be familiar with the principles of physical and historical geology, and they should have a working knowledge of algebra and plane geometry. Each topic is developed from elementary concepts, and particular care has been taken where mathematical concepts are involved.

A broad-ranging coverage of all aspects of structural geology—principles, regional structure, and tectonics—has been selected in preference to great depth of treatment. Selected techniques of structural analysis are briefly described in appendixes, and a set of problems is included to illustrate the application of the methods.

It has been my pleasure and good fortune to have been associated as a student, colleague, and friend with a number of outstanding structural geologists, and I am grateful for the help and encouragement these friends have given me. I am indebted particularly to my former teachers Walter Bucher, Arie Poldervaart, Marshall Kay, and Marcellus Stow, who stimulated my interest in problems of structural geology, and to Arnold Lillie and S. Warren Carey, with whom I recently studied.

I wish to acknowledge with thanks the many reprints, photographs, and line drawings which have been made available to me for use in the preparation of this book. Illustrations have been directly acknowledged in the captions, and sources of research materials are acknowledged in the reference sections. A special note of gratitude is due Mrs. Stuart Brewbaker for her careful assistance in preparation of the manuscript.

Edgar W. Spencer

contents

1
introduction

"Structural geology is the study of the structural (as opposed to compositional) features of rocks, of the geographic distribution of the features and their causes. A structural feature is one produced in rock by movements after deposition and commonly after consolidation of the rock."* These definitions are drawn independently of the size of the structural features considered, and the range of sizes involved is great. Study of structural features of submicroscopic size has been carried on primarily in the field of solid state physics although features of this size are doubtless important in their aggregate effect on rock deformation. Geologists have long been concerned with structural features of microscopic size; the field of petrofabrics deals largely with such features.

Petrofabrics, the study of rock fabric, involves analysis of the component parts of a rock—the fragments, crystal grains, and their sizes, shapes, arrangements, orientations in space, relations to one another, internal structure, and the movements and process which played a part in the formation of the fabric.

Most geologists are concerned with structural features which range in size from those encountered in an outcrop (mesoscopic size) to those of regional size which must be represented on geologic or structural maps. Still larger-scale features are considered in *tectonics*—"the study of the broader features of the earth and their causes."†

The name of this book implies an all-encompassing study of the earth. The student interested in the formation of structures such as we see in a folded mountain belt or in subsurface investigation over a salt dome, or the student with an eye for larger structural features may grow impatient with a discussion of physical principles and wonder at the long description of the nature of materials. But we shall see that the behavior of materials is one important aspect of structural geology and that knowledge derived from the

* As defined in Am. Geol. Inst., © 1960, Glossary of geology and related sciences.
† Am. Geol. Inst., © 1960, Glossary of geology and related sciences.

behavior of natural materials under varying conditions and over long times is critical to an understanding of the origin of most structural features and is no less important in tectonic theory.

The study of the behavior of material; the description of microscopic and mesoscopic structural features; the mapping and detailing of the structural, petrologic, and stratigraphic relations in regional geology; and the analysis of the earth's interior are all parts of any global view of the structure of the earth. Any satisfactory tectonic synthesis of these many aspects of structural geology must be internally consistent with regard to what is known from all these sources. It is precisely for this reason that geotectonics is the most vulnerable aspect of the field.

Because the structure of rock bodies is so basic to the understanding of other aspects of geology, structural features are studied with many purposes in mind. Structural knowledge is vital in applied fields of geology, such as ground water hydrology, engineering geology, petroleum geology, and mining geology, where it is of critical importance to learn the subsurface configuration of rock bodies as well as to know their surface distribution. Many petroleum traps are structural features (e.g., anticlines, fault traps), and the geologist must know the structural setting of stratigraphic traps such as pinch-outs, unconformities, reefs, and porosity traps in order to locate and develop production intelligently. The evaluation of shape and size of an ore body or an economically important rock body such as coal or limestone may determine the economic feasibility of mining it. Knowledge of the existence of a fault which displaces the ore or coal may well mean the difference between financial success and failure. Many of the failures of large engineering structures can be directly attributed to faulty evaluation of the structure of the foundation rock. Dams have been built on active faults without taking precautions to prevent failure in the event of movement, and dam and bridge abut-

ments have been founded on schistose rocks in which the orientation of the schistosity had led to failure under load pressure.

Stratigraphers must understand the structure of a region and its age in order to go about removing the effects of deformation in making restoration of the paleogeography. The details of the pattern in a salt mine located in a salt dome or a study of the behavior of halite under high confining pressure may lead to a better understanding of the formation of salt structures. In short, structure is studied by many different techniques, on scales ranging from microscopic to global, and for reasons ranging from understanding the way a single crystal of calcite is deformed to seeking a synthesis of global structural patterns.

STRUCTURAL METHODS

The methods used to obtain structural knowledge may be classified as follows:

1. Geologic mapping
2. Aerial photograph interpretation and geomorphic analysis
3. Subsurface methods (interpretation of well logs; construction of subsurface maps; interpretation of geophysical data)
4. Geophysical methods
5. Mesoscopic analysis of rock structure and fabric
6. Microscopic analysis of rock fabric—petrofabrics
7. Experimental study
8. Theoretical method—mathematical theory of deformation
9. Synthesis

Geologic mapping is by far the main source of structural data. The map shows the distribution of rock units; from the map the attitude of contacts between units can be found, and interpretation of the form of the units at depth can be made. Maps in igneous and metamorphic terranes may show the geographic distribution of planar and linear structures in the rock. The larger-scale structure of the rock body can be interpreted from this pattern.

Subsurface structural methods may be construed to include all the means by which the configuration of a rock body below the ground surface is obtained. Subsurface methods include the construction of cross sections and other projections at depth based on geometry of the rock at the surface, or by means of actual control points obtained by drilling, geophysical methods, or in mine shafts. Among the most powerful of these tools are structure contour and isopach or thickness maps, which we will consider later.

Geophysics is of great significance not only as a means of determining depth to stratigraphic horizons and their attitude in space, but as our best source of information about the crust as a structural unit, and about the deeper structure and composition of the interior of the earth. A very large part of what we know about the structure of ocean basins is derived from geophysical methods. Geophysical methods help us locate anomalous and thus potentially interesting areas for detailed study.

Mesoscopic methods of structural analysis encompass those techniques of the study of structure which are based on field observations of rock fabric, and the relations of the various elements of the rock structure to one another. Such studies may include geometrical analysis of joints, rock cleavages, foliations in metamorphic rocks, flow lines in igneous intrusions, bedding surfaces, or the relations of any of these planar and linear elements to one another. Such analyses have proved fruitful in metamorphic rocks and in regions subjected to multiple deformations where conventional methods of geologic mapping have failed to resolve the more complex geometries of the rock bodies. Some techniques of mesoscopic analysis have been carried over from microscopic petrofabric studies employing statistical methods and symmetry concepts.

Petrofabric studies have been useful in establishing the changes of fabric when rocks are deformed or metamorphosed, such as the alignment of crystallographic axes in stress fields and the effects of recrystallization during and after deformation. Petrofabrics has proved particularly significant in connection with experimental methods of studying rock deformation.

Experiments are being used to discover the behavior of minerals and rocks under high confining pressures, under various temperatures, and in stress fields. The specimens thus deformed are analyzed by petrofabric methods, and the geometric relationships among crystallographic orientations, slip planes, etc., of the minerals and the known applied stresses are established. *Dynamic structural geology* is the name applied to studies in which strains are related to stress fields. When this relation is not considered the approach is *kinematic*—based on the movement pattern without reference to force. This field has provided new understanding of conditions of deformation at depth in the earth's crust. Other very different experiments employing scale models and synthetic materials have been used to simulate large-scale structural features ranging from folds to mountain systems. Experiments of this type are also used to test theoretical work.

Mathematical theories of stress, strain, and elasticity have been applied to try to gain a better understanding of the manner of rock yield and failure. The large number of variables involved in natural rock deformation make rigid theoretical analysis very difficult, but some interesting conclusions have been reached through theory concerning the mechanisms of folding and faulting. These methods are particularly valuable in combination with experiments and comparative field studies.

Synthesis implies the bringing together of information and integrating it into a coherent picture. As such, synthesis is important as a method of structural analysis. This bringing together of the details of regional geology, subsurface configuration, lithology, and age is an important part of the reconstruction or synthesis of structural evolution which has led to so many major discoveries both for the exploration geologist and for the theorist. The concepts of geosynclines, continental drift, and orogeny are products of this approach.

THE PROBLEM OF DISTINGUISHING PRIMARY AND SECONDARY FEATURES

Chapters 3 to 9 are devoted to discussion of the shape, internal and external structure, and mode of origin of structural features in rock bodies. Some of the features we will examine were formed during deposition of sediment or during emplacement and crystallization of igneous rocks. Other features result from postdepositional or postcrystallization deformation. Sometimes it is not easy to distinguish these later, secondary structural features from the earlier, primary features. This is particularly true when a distinction is to be drawn between syndepositional and postdepositional deformation in soft sediment. It may also be difficult to distinguish features formed in unconsolidated sediment from those formed in compacted rock. This problem arises because very high confining pressure and elevated temperature induce plastic behavior in consolidated rock not unlike the behavior of clay near the ground surface. The problem becomes acute in metamorphic rocks in which the whole fabric of the rock is likely to have changed. Some structures such as cross bedding and ripple marks are created during deposition, and others develop during lithification and compaction as in the case of compaction folds. We are hardly justified in classing as secondary those features which are formed during deposition, but secondary structural features may form at any time after deposition including the stage during which the sediment is unconsolidated. This is significant because unconsolidated sediment is subject to the development of slump and compaction features which may closely resemble structures formed in response to externally applied force. There are numerous cases in which soft sediment features resemble those also developed in metamorphic or consolidated sedimentary rock as a result of stresses other than those which can be directly attributed to gravity. Pinch and swell structures may form either as a result of differential compaction or as a result of the pulling apart of a sequence of interbedded units of different physical properties. They are known in sediment and in sedimentary and metamorphic rocks (Fig. 7-14). Cross bedding and shear fractures (horsetail fractures) are sometimes similar in appearance and may be easily confused in metamorphic rocks. Complex folds may develop in slump masses. Flowage in clay or salt layers interbedded with other rock types during compaction may closely resemble deformation involving sliding of units over a shale or salt layer along a bedding fault at depth or drag folds formed in flexure folding (Figs. 6-13 and 9-8).

The resolution of the problem of distinguishing primary from secondary features usually depends on establishing the relation of the structure in question to the larger-scale features with which it is associated. It is examined to see that its shape, its geometry, is in harmony with that of related structures.

Diastrophism is defined as a general term applied to those processes by which the rocks in the crust and mantle of the earth are deformed, producing strains such as folds, fractures, and faults. The term may also be applied to the formation of mountain systems, continents, and ocean basins. An attempt has often been made to distinguish features formed as a result of stresses resulting from the gravity field from "deformational" structural features due to other causes such as uplift and crustal compression. It is increasingly evident that the determination of origin of such features is not so obvious as it might appear.

Horace de Saussure (1776) recorded the observation in the Alps which led him to conclude that a conglomerate was not in its original position. He clearly distinguishes primary from secondary features as follows:

. . . there, what was my surprise to find the beds in a vertical attitude.

The reason of that astonishment will be easily understood when one considers that it is impossible that this puddingstone could have been formed in such a position.

That particles of the most extreme tenuity, suspended in a liquid, could agglutinate and form vertical beds is easy to conceive, and it is demonstrated in alabaster, in agate, and even in artificial crystallizations. But that a stone already formed, of the size of a man's head, should arrest itself in the middle of a vertical wall, and should stay in such a position while small particles of stone surround it, weld it and fix it in that position is an absurd and impossible hypothesis. One must therefore admit as a demonstrated fact that these puddingstones were formed in a horizontal position, or almost such, and upturned later, after having been hardened.

The possibility that stratification in sedimentary rocks might be formed at high angles (above the angle of repose) is no longer given serious consideration by geologists, and though the formation of layering in many metamorphic rocks is still debated, the presence of high dips and folds in layered rocks is taken as a strong indication of diastrophism. Similarly, breaks in the continuity of the physical properties of rocks, fractures, or cleavages are usually interpreted as evidence of deformation even though it is well recognized that fractures also form from cooling in magma or from desiccation in fine sediment, and the possibility is recognized that many fractures may develop in rocks that otherwise show little evidence of strain. A similar dichotomy exists with respect to faults. Compare a mass of rock that becomes separated along fractures and slides downslope with a block that is moved laterally as a result of regional compressive stresses. What criteria can we use to distinguish the phenomena of large-scale mass movement from diastrophism, or are the two the same? These examples serve to emphasize the need for great care in the assignation of terms with connotations of genesis in the description of structural features.

KEY INDICATORS OF ROCK DEFORMATION

Deformation of rocks usually proceeds with changes in shape of the rock mass involved and this is accomplished through changes in the

Fig. 1-1 Cataclastic texture in calcite, $\times$ 29. (*Courtesy of Alan Spry.*)

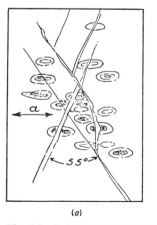
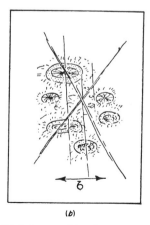

(a)   (b)

Fig. 1-2 Deformed oolites and related shear and tension fractures from South Mountain area, Maryland. (*From Cloos, 1947.*)

fabric of the component parts of the mass. Involved are such processes as the development of twinning in rocks composed of calcite; rotation and rearrangement of grains in clastic rocks (Fig. 1-1); granulation; recrystallization; flattening; elongation; and slip in clays and shales.

All of these processes result in creation of diagnostic fabrics which are studied and analyzed in the field of structural petrology or petrofabrics.

The deformation of geological objects provides some of the most significant clues to rock

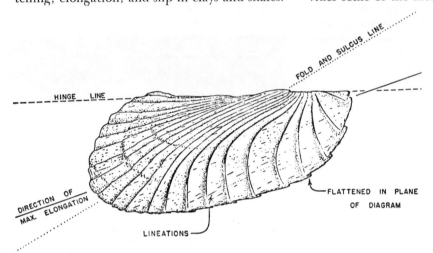

Fig. 1-3 Deformed brachipod, Middlebury synclinorium, Vermont. (*Crosby, Ph.D. dissertation, Columbia University.*)

Fig. 1-4 Snowball garnet, × 22. (*Courtesy of Alan Spry.*)

deformation. For information to be useful, the original shape of such objects must be known. Among the best known of these studies is that of deformed oolites (Fig. 1-2). Fossils, because of their regular geometrical features, have proven especially useful for this purpose also.

Crosby (1963) used deformed brachiopods (Fig. 1-3) to help differentiate effects of different deformations in western Vermont. This was accomplished by relating the maximum elongations to particular fold mechanisms.

In another example of the use of deformed geological objects, studies of "rolled" garnet porphyroblasts in schists (Fig. 1-4) can reveal the sense of rotation. This provides a key to the movement plan within the schist at the time the garnets became deformed. Pressure fringes around pyrite crystals (Fig. 1-6) can be used in the same way.

In summary, the study of rock deformation in the field is based on analysis of changes in shape of rock masses as in folding and development of pinch and swell structures, on analysis of failure of the rock as in development of fractures and faults, on analysis of changes in rock fabric and in the deformation of geological objects such as fossils and oolites. Other approaches to rock deformation are found in theoretical and experimental analysis.

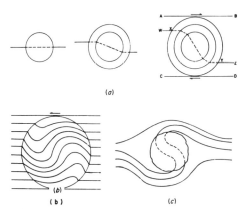

Fig. 1-5 Hypotheses for the origin of rotational structure. [*From Spry, 1964: (a) after Schmidt, 1918; (b) after Mugge, 1930, p. 493; (c) after Mugge, 1930.*]

Fig. 1-6 Pressure fringe on pyrite, × 80. (*Courtesy of Alan Spry.*)

GENERAL REFERENCES

Badgley, P. C., 1965, Structural and tectonic principles: New York, Harper & Row, 521 p.

Bailey, E. B., 1935, Tectonic essays: Oxford, Clarendon.

Beloussov, V. V., and Maxwell, J. C., 1962, Basic problems in geotectonics: New York, McGraw-Hill, 820 p.

Billings, M. P., 1954, Structural geology, 2d ed.: Englewood Cliffs, N.J., Prentice-Hall, 514 p.

Bucher, W. H., 1933, The deformation of the earth's crust: Princeton, N.J., Princeton Univ.

Cloos, Ernst, 1947, Oolite deformation in the South Mountain fold, Maryland: Geol. Soc. America Bull., v. 58, p. 843–918.

Crosby, G. W., 1963, Structural evolution of the Middlebury synclinorium, west-central Vermont: Ph.D. thesis, Columbia Univ.

Daly, R. A., 1940, Strength and structure of the earth: Englewood Cliffs, N.J., Prentice-Hall.

De Saussure, Horace, 1796, Voyages dans les Alpes, v. iv: Neuchâtel.

De Sitter, L. U., 1964, Structural geology, 2d. ed.: New York, McGraw-Hill, 587 p.

Eardley, A. J., 1951, Structural geology of North America: New York, Harper & Row.

Fairburn, H. W., 1942, Structural petrology of deformed rocks: Cambridge, Mass., Addison-Wesley.

Geikie, James, 1940, Structural and field geology, 5th ed.: Edinburgh, Oliver & Boyd.

Goguel, Jean, 1965, Tectonics, 2d ed.: San Francisco, Freeman.

Griggs, D. T., and Handin, John, eds., 1960, Rock deformation: Geol. Soc. America Mem. 79, 382 p.

Hills, E. S., 1953, Outlines of structural geology, 3d ed.: London, Methuen.

———— 1963, Elements of structural geology: New York, Wiley, 483 p.

Irvine, T. N., ed., 1965, The world rift system: Geol. Survey Canada Paper 66–14, Dept. Mines and Technical Surveys, Ottawa.

Jeffreys, H., 1929, The earth, 2d ed.: London, Cambridge.

Kay, G. M., 1951, North American geosynclines: Geol. Soc. America Mem. 48.

Lotze, Franz, 1956, Geotektonisches symposium en ehren von Hans Stille: Stuttgart, Kommissions—verlag von Ferdinand Enke.

Nevin, C. M., 1942, Principles of structural geology, 3d ed.: New York, Wiley.

Poldervaart, Arie, ed., 1955, The crust of the earth: Geol. Soc. America Spec. Paper 62.

Poole, W. H., ed., 1965, Continental margins and island arcs: Geol. Survey Canada Paper 66–15, Dept. Mines and Technical Surveys, Ottawa.

Ramsay, J. G., 1967, Folding and fracturing of rocks: New York, McGraw-Hill, 560 p.

Sander, B., 1930, Gefügekunde der Gesteine: Vienna, Springer, 352 p.

———— 1948, Einfuhrung in die Gefugekunde der geologischen Korper, pt. I: Vienna, Springer, 215 p.

Schmidt, Walter, 1932, Tektonik und Verformungslehre: Berlin, Borntraeger, 208 p.

Sonder, R. A., 1956, Mechanik der Erde: Stuttgart, E. Schweizerbartsche Verlags.

Spry, Allen, 1964, The origin and significance of snowball structures in garnet: Jour. Petrology, v. 4.

Stočes, Bohuslav, and White, C. H., 1935, Structural geology: London, Macmillan.

Turner, F. J., and Verhoogen, John, 1960, Igneous and metamorphic petrology: New York, McGraw-Hill, 694 p.

Turner, F. J., and Weiss, L. E., 1963, Structural analysis of metamorphic tectonites: New York, McGraw-Hill, 560 p.

Umbgrove, J. H. F., 1947, The pulse of the earth, 2d ed.: The Hague, Nijhoff.

Whitten, E. H. Timothy, 1966, Structural geology of folded rocks: Chicago, Rand McNally, 663 p.

Willis, Bailey, and Willis, Robin, 1934, Geologic structures, 3d ed.: New York, McGraw-Hill.

part one
principles of
structural geology

2
concepts of stress and strain

STRESS IN THE EARTH'S CRUST

A rock mass is in a state of stress when a force is applied, in any manner whatsoever, to it. If the force is applied externally to the surface of a body, then *stress* on the surface is defined as the force per unit area of that surface. *Force,* in turn, is defined in terms of the effect a "force" has on a body; it is defined as the product of mass and acceleration ($F = ma$). These effects are of two types—a change in the shape of the body or a change in the state of motion of the body. It is often convenient to think of forces as "pushes" or "pulls" exerted by one body on another. When a geologist studies structural features in the field he observes strains—changes in shape and changes in position that have arisen as a result of applied stresses. Sometimes it is possible to infer what stresses have acted to create the strains we see in folds, faults, fractures, and other structural features, but such inferences are often fraught with the danger of misinterpretation. Yet, the assignation of the sources of stress is one of our ultimate aims, and a number of primary sources are recognized. Determining which of these sources are the correct ones will be one of our objectives.

The force of gravity has been widely recognized in recent years as an important factor in crustal deformation. It is of paramount importance in isostatic adjustments of the crust. Normal faults are sometimes called gravity faults, and it is clear in some cases that normal faults are the result of collapse or slump due to failure in the gravity field. Gravity is being increasingly called on as a motive force in some thrust faults, called *gravity-glide faults.* Its function in such cases is similar to that in the inclined plane problems in elementary physics. When the inclination of the plane is sufficient the block is able to overcome the frictional resistance holding the block in place and the block slides. By analogy, gravity-glide faults occur where a rock mass is uplifted until the units slide over some potential "gliding" plane, usually an incompetent layer such as salt or shale. A gravity-glide fault is formed if a break occurs along and through the moving plate of rock and units are displaced. If movement occurs in sedimentary rocks without such a break, disharmonic folds are formed. If the fault forms, it defines the leading edge of the plate.

Even in such a vastly simplified situation as the one described above, it becomes obvious that we are dealing with a complicated interrelationship of stress patterns. Gravity provides the motive force for the slippage of the block, but some other undesignated stress initiated the process by causing the block to be uplifted bringing the downslope component of gravity into operation. Also, the stresses responsible for the development of the fault on the edge of the plate were secondary. They were set up as a consequence of the block's initial movement.

The assignment of the origin of stresses thought to be responsible for different structures figures importantly in the consideration of the origin of the large-scale tectonic features of the earth.

In addition to gravity we should consider two other conditions which may be responsible for primary generation of stress in the crust. These are volume changes and drag caused by relative movement of materials within the earth.

Changes in volume of materials within the earth could be caused by a number of processes which, though largely hypothetical, have been invoked in tectonic theories. Among these are:

1. Heat gain or loss may be a cause of change. It has been suggested both that the earth is cooling and contracting and that it is warming and expanding. In either case changes in volume would necessarily result in stress fields in the crustal rocks, which are forced to become accommodated to the larger or smaller interior. To enliven the argument it should be pointed out that there are many crustal features which indicate crustal tension, such as the great grabens and midocean rift zones and others which seem to point to crustal compression as do the folded mountain belts. The generation of magma is certainly of at least local importance. The volume increases associated with the melting are surely a factor in creating the structures associated with forceful intrusions.

2. Phase changes of minerals at depth have been offered as a possible explanation for some of the seismic discontinuities. These changes are thought to involve changes in the packing of atoms within minerals of the mantle. Such changes would be accompanied by changes in density and volume.

3. It is clear that the crust is not homogeneous throughout, and we know that unusual seismic velocities occur deep in the crust in some places, notably the island arcs and under the midocean ridges. Although we know very little directly about the homogeneity or lack of it within the mantle and even less about possible physical or chemical processes in action in the contact zone between the crust and mantle, processes are going on in this contact zone which are creating a material of seismic velocity that is intermediate between that of normal crustal and mantle materials (probably serpentine).

Frictional drag on the crust due to relative movement of crustal and subcrustal material is one of the most popular of current ideas regarding the primary sources of crustal stress. This type of movement might be generated by the following:

1. Convection currents due to temperature differences between the earth's interior and surface might cause frictional drag. Tem-

perature differences should cause hotter material to rise against the force of gravity; gravity would cause the cooler displaced materials to sink. This process would take place within the mantle.

2. Drag would be set up as a result of movements due to changes in volume. Such movements would occur if the process of volume change did not occur uniformly throughout the earth.

3. Movements of crustal materials could be caused by imbalances in the distribution of continental masses on the earth. The system is analogous to that of a rotating sphere which has masses distributed in an irregular manner on its surface. Forces are set up on a rotating body which tend to move the masses into a balanced position.

These possible primary sources of stress in the crust are not considered to be equally important by any geologist, but it is not easy to establish criteria which exclude all but one or even most of them as likely causes. Arguments about their importance abound in geologic literature and we will later consider the cases for and against them. Let it suffice here to say that it is possible to find among these various ideas origins for stress fields necessary to elevate, depress, compress, and pull apart crustal rocks.

For a fuller understanding of structural features we must turn to theoretical and experimental methods of analysis. From these we may expect to gain an appreciation of the physical conditions under which earth materials yield in different ways, and to develop some insight into the possible stress conditions which might promote development of certain types of structures in the crust. We have not yet reached the point in the development of theoretical and experimental analysis at which we can explain most structural features with a high degree of certainty, but the origin of many earth structures can be inferred by analogy from simplified models.

ANALYSIS OF ROCK DEFORMATION

The most significant handicap in the theoretical analysis of rock deformation as it occurs in nature is the fact that large bodies of rock are not homogeneous. Not only is there a great variety of rock types, each of which has a unique range of mineral composition, there also are many fabric types. Variations in rock type, thickness, original structural configuration, and physical conditions under which deformation occurs leads to a very high order of possible natural combinations. One approach to this problem is to break the problem into its simplest component parts and then to evaluate them. For example, many rocks are crystalline aggregates. Thus it makes sense to examine the structure of common single crystals and determine how they may be deformed. Then experiments may be run on small statistically homogeneous specimens of crystalline aggregates. These are deformed in tension, in compression, in torsion, under a variety of temperature and confining pressure conditions, in the presence of a variety of fluids, under various amounts of directed stress, and for differing amounts of time. The effects of varying each of these conditions are observed and evaluated.

Unfortunately the nature of the conditions favoring deformation of solid rocks, particularly the high confining pressures required and the long times involved, make deformations of large bodies of rock impossible on an experimental basis. Almost all experiments have been run on specimens no more than 1 in. in diameter and 2 in. long. What can be learned from these experiments is the change in fabric which results under certain specific conditions. Similar fabrics may be found in nature and the character of the deformation inferred by analogy.

Two viewpoints are used to make interpretations of the observed fabric of a naturally occurring rock, kinematic and dynamic. Dynamic interpretations are primarily concerned with the nature of the stresses that were acting in the rocks at the time of deformation. Mechanisms of deformation, faulting, fracture, flow, etc., are inferred from the observed rock fabric, and these mechanisms are interpreted in terms of the stress field that acted within the rock body. Recent experimental and theoretical study has put this approach on a much firmer footing.

The kinematic approach proceeds from the observed fabric and determination of the geometry and symmetry of the fabric to a plan of movement which took place during deformation.

Other subsidiary approaches are used in the problem of analyzing rock deformation. One is the use of stress analysis as it has been developed in engineering materials studies. In this field theoretical stress-strain analysis has been made of the deformation mainly of metals and to a lesser degree of ceramics and polycrystalline aggregates. The stress in flexed elastic metal bars and plates is an example. This has been extended to include treatment of plastic and pseudoviscous materials under various types of lateral restraint and when the layers are enclosed in media of different kinds.

Still another approach to rock deformation is made through the use of model studies. These are intriguing because scale models have been constructed so that they faithfully reproduce many features of naturally deformed rock sequences. They have the significant value of helping us visualize what may happen, but many geologists are highly critical of this approach on the grounds that the materials used in the scale models are not rocks and their analogy to nature is superficial.

In summary, the state of geologic analysis of large-scale rock deformation in nature involves a combination of studies of overall structural form, of detailed examination of rock fabric which is interpreted in terms of our experience with the fabric of experimentally deformed rocks, of theoretical stress analysis of idealized configurations and materials, and of the behavior of simplified models.

In the following chapters we will consider the nature of the behavior of rocks and minerals under various conditions which may be reasonably expected to exist in the earth. We know at the onset that rocks will not behave at depth within the earth as they do in our common experience at the surface. Such normally brittle rocks as quartzite and limestone can be found in folded sequences where fracturing is of only minor importance. It would be reasonable to expect that the behavior of rocks would depend on such conditions as temperature; the types of solutions present; the confining pressure due to the depth at which the rock is buried; the type of rock involved, its composition and texture; the nature of the forces acting on the rock, the way they are applied, their magnitude, and their duration. All of these factors are important, and fortunately there is sufficient theoretical and experimental knowledge of them to allow us to grasp some aspects of the most significant interrelationships.

Some understanding of at least a few of the elementary principles and definitions of mechanics are necessary before undertaking the study of rock deformation.

Vectors—Visualization of Applied Force

Forces may be represented graphically as vector quantities having magnitude and direction. In preparing such a graphical representation the direction of the line is indicated by its position in space, and its length is drawn proportional to the magnitude of the force as determined by a selected scale. An arrow is used to indicate the direction of the force, and the tip of the arrow indicates the point of application of the force.

When several forces act at a given point they can be replaced by a single "resultant" force. This can be represented with vectors by use of vector addition. The vector sum is found by drawing the vectors in one of the ways illustrated in Fig. 2-1. A parallelogram is constructed in one of these methods, and the vector sum is the diagonal. In the simplest case, where two vectors act along the same line, they are added or subtracted depending on direction. If a number of vectors are involved they may be reduced one at a time until a final resultant is obtained, or they may be added by the method illustrated.

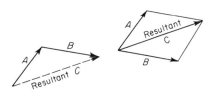

Fig. 2-1 Vector addition.

The above method has certain obvious limitations in its application to three-dimensional space. For these purposes it is best to work with vector components. Any vectors which yield a particular vector when added may be considered its vector components. If we select three mutually perpendicular axes so situated that a vector passes through the point of origin, then the vector can be broken into three vector components that are parallel to the three axes. The components are (Fig. 2-3):

Component x = vector magnitude $\times \cos \alpha$
Component y = vector magnitude $\times \cos \gamma$
Component z = vector magnitude $\times \cos \beta$

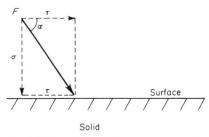

Fig. 2-2 Resolving a force vector acting on a surface at an angle α into a normal component σ and a shearing component τ. $\sigma = F \sin \alpha$; $\tau = F \cos \alpha$.

Using similar methods all other vectors passing through that point of origin can be broken into components parallel to the three axes. The resultant can then be found by adding and subtracting the vector components parallel to each axis and then determining the resultant of the quantities remaining.

NOTION OF STRESS

A rock is in a state of stress when a force is applied, in any manner whatsoever, to it. These forces are of two types: those like the force of gravity which act throughout the body, called *body forces;* and those that act on surfaces and cause neighboring parts of the medium to act on one another, called *surface forces,* as when a bar is compressed in a vise, pulled apart, twisted, or submerged in a liquid or at depth in the earth. The stress on a surface is the force across a unit area of the particular surface. Stresses may have the effect of changing the volume or the shape of the body. These changes may be recoverable as in elastic deformation, or they may result in permanent nonelastic

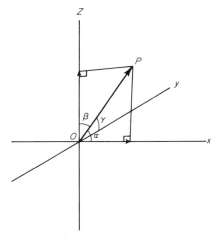

Fig. 2-3 Resolving a vector *OP* into three mutually perpendicular components.

changes. To describe completely the stress in a body, we must consider the stress at each point in the body. The problem is greatly simplified if it can be assumed that a homogeneous state of stress exists, such that the stress has the same magnitude and direction at every point in the body. This unfortunately is not the case in the formation of some earth structures, but it is necessary for us to make this assumption in order to understand simple stress situations, and it is an assumption that appears to be reasonable in many natural circumstances, especially if a small volume is considered.

Assuming that a homogeneous state of stress does exist within a body, consider the stresses acting on a very small cube, point size, in that body. If the cube is oriented so that its edges lie along the coordinate axes of an orthogonal coordinate system, one with three mutually

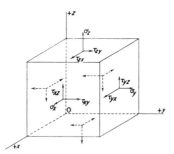

Fig. 2-4 Stresses on a cubical element in equilibrium. (*From Varnes, 1962.*)

perpendicular axes, then regardless of the orientation of the force acting on the cube it can be resolved into three components (parallel to the coordinate axes) for each of the faces of the cube. For each face of the cube one component will be normal to the face (normal stresses are designated σ) and two acting within the plane of the face (called *shearing stresses* and designated τ by convention). All nine of these stresses for the cube are shown in Fig. 2-4, and these can be summed as shown. These completely define the state of stress for the cube; however, several of the components are dependent. As a result of the equilibrium condition, no rotation, the components of stress that are tending to make the cube rotate must be zero or counterbalanced. Consider rotation about the z axis, for example. Shearing stresses τ_{xy} and τ_{yx} tend to cause such rotation. They must both be zero or equal since they have opposite senses of rotation. Similarly, $\tau_{yz} = \tau_{zy}$, and $\tau_{xz} = \tau_{zx}$. Thus only six of the nine stress components are independent, and the state of stress at a point can be expressed in terms of six components.

If the cube is in equilibrium (is not rotating) all of the stresses acting at this point can be resolved into normal stresses acting along three mutually perpendicular directions, known as the principal stress axes or directions. The shear stresses along these directions are zero. In the general case when the three are of different magnitudes they are referred to as the:

Maximum stress direction	σ_1
Intermediate stress direction	σ_2
Least stress direction	σ_3

The states of stress in homogeneous jacketed cylindrical specimens are illustrated in Fig. 2-5 for compression and extension tests. Such tests, with variable temperature, confining pressure, pore pressure, and strain rates, have been the basis for much of the modern dynamic structural approach.

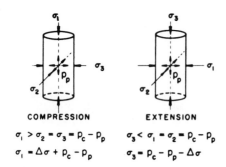

COMPRESSION

EXTENSION

$$\sigma_1 > \sigma_2 = \sigma_3 = P_c - P_p$$

$$\sigma_1 = \Delta\sigma + P_c - P_p$$

$$\sigma_3 < \sigma_1 = \sigma_2 = P_c - P_p$$

$$\sigma_3 = P_c - P_p - \Delta\sigma$$

$\sigma_1, \sigma_2, \sigma_3$ = MAXIMUM, INTERMEDIATE, MINIMUM EFFECTIVE PRINCIPAL STRESSES.

$P_c - P_p$ = EFFECTIVE CONFINING PRESSURE.

Fig. 2-5 Sketch of states of stress in homogeneous cylindrical jacketed specimens in compression and extension tests. (*From Handin, in Clark, 1966.*)

Condition of Plane Stress

Two-dimensional stress does not exist in nature, but the analysis of such a state is much simpler than the three-dimensional case which has the same general form. It will be instructive to consider some two-dimensional situations in which we will assume that the quantities involved are independent of the z axis. Under these conditions the stress at a point o exerted across the plane $x = O$ (Fig. 2-6a) by the material on the right-hand side of this plane has two components, σ_x and τ_{xy}. Similarly, the components of stress on the plane $y = 0$ would be τ_{yx} and σ_y.

Now let us consider the relations between these components. Assume that the material is at rest and that all quantities vary slowly from point to point so that the stresses at a point a very short distance from o are nearly equal to those at o. The forces acting on the faces of a very small square of this material are:

On the side AB Area $\times\, \sigma_x$ + area τ_{xy}
On the side OC Area $\times\, \sigma_x$ − area τ_{xy}

Since the square is in equilibrium and not rotating,

$$\tau_{xy} = \tau_{yx}$$

Thus, of the four stress components with which we started, only three are independent.

Next we will consider the stress across some plane which passes through the point of origin O. In order to define the position of this plane in space, it is specified that the normal to this plane makes an angle ϕ with the x axis (Fig. 2-6) and that the plane is very close to O so that the stresses on it are the same as those on a parallel plane through O. The triangle is considered to be in equilibrium, and we will calculate the normal and shear stresses σ and τ across the plane AB. The normal stresses to the plane AB can be found by resolving the stresses parallel to the x and y axes onto the line OP. It is necessary to remember that the amount of stress on a surface is a function of the area of the surface. Thus if we assume that all sides of the triangle OAB are of unit width, the areas of OA and OB can be expressed in terms of the area of AB:

$$OA = AB \sin \phi$$
$$OB = AB \cos \phi$$

Then the stress components acting in the x direction become

$$S_x = \sigma_x \cos \phi + \tau_{xy} \sin \phi$$

and those acting in the y direction are

$$S_y = \sigma_y \sin \phi + \tau_{xy} \cos \phi$$

Resolving these stresses onto OP, the normal stress to AB becomes

$$(AB)\sigma = (AB) \sin \phi(\tau_{yx} \cos \phi + \sigma_y \sin \phi) \\ + (AB) \cos \phi(\sigma_x \cos \phi + \tau_{xy} \sin \phi)$$

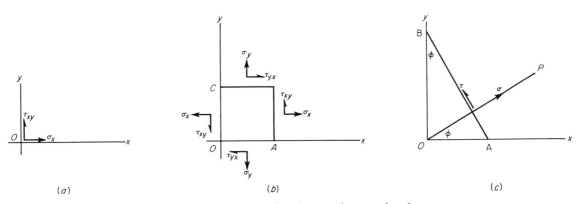

(a)   (b)   (c)

Fig. 2-6 Conditions of plane stress. (a) Stress at a point O exerted across the plane $x = O$; (b) stresses on a small cube; (c) stresses across a plane AB inclined at angle ϕ. (*Redrawn after Jaeger, 1956.*)

The shearing stresses along the plane AB are found by resolving the stress components in the direction of AB as follows:

$$\tau = (\sigma_y - \sigma_x) \sin \phi \cos \phi + \tau_{xy}(\cos^2 \phi - \sin^2 \phi)$$

since $\tau_{xy} = \tau_{yx}$, the above expressions become

$$\tau = (\sigma_y - \sigma_x) \sin \phi \cos \phi + \tau_{xy}(\cos^2 \phi - \sin^2 \phi)$$
$$\sigma = \sigma_x \cos^2 \phi + 2\tau_{xy} \sin \phi \cos \phi + \sigma_y \sin^2 \phi$$

These equations give a description of the way in which the stress at a point varies with direction. If we differentiate the equation above for the value of the normal stress with respect to the angle of inclination of the plane,

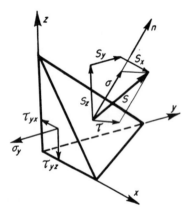

Fig. 2-7 Stress components acting on a tetrahedron. (*From Nádai, 1950.*)

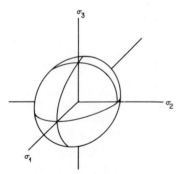

Fig. 2-8 Stress ellipsoid showing principal stress axes.

$$\frac{d\sigma}{d\phi} = 2(\sigma_y - \sigma_x) \sin \phi \cos \phi + 2\tau_{xy}(\cos^2 \phi - \sin^2 \phi)$$

which reduces to

$$\frac{d\sigma}{d\phi} = 2\tau$$

The normal stress is a maximum or a minimum when ϕ has the following value (Jaeger, 1956):

$$\tan 2\phi = \frac{2\tau_{xy}}{\sigma_x - \sigma_y} \tag{1}$$

This equation yields two angles (or directions) at right angles to one another, for which the normal stress is a maximum and a minimum when the shear stresses across them are zero. These two directions, one a maximum and one a minimum normal stress direction for which shear stresses are zero, are called the *principal axes of stress,* and the stresses in these directions are called the *principal stresses.*

Three-dimensional Stress

For the more general case, Nadai (1950) has shown that three stress axes like the ones defined for the cube exist for stress components acting on a tetrahedron (Fig. 2-7). If a stress, S, is acting on the oblique face of the tetrahedron, it can be resolved first into a normal stress, σ, and a shearing stress, τ. The normal and shearing stress can be resolved into stress components, paralleling the reference axes, and the resultant stress components can be summed for the oblique surface as follows (the area of the oblique surface is taken as unity for simplicity). The component of stress parallel to the z axis, S_z, is equal to the sum of:

1. The normal stress to the surface multiplied by the cosine of the angle between the normal and the z axis
2. The shearing stress component in the yz plane multiplied by the cosine of the angle between this component and the z axis
3. The shearing stress component in the xz plane multiplied by the cosine of the angle between this component and the z axis

Similarily, the components of stress parallel to each of the coordinate axes may be summed as shown below:

$$S_x = \sigma_x \cos \alpha + \tau_{yx} \cos \beta + \tau_{xz} \cos \gamma$$
$$S_y = \tau_{xy} \cos \alpha + \sigma_y \cos \beta + \tau_{zy} \cos \gamma \qquad (2)$$
$$S_z = \tau_{xz} \cos \alpha + \tau_{yz} \cos \beta + \sigma_z \cos \gamma$$

The normal stress on this oblique surface can be expressed in terms of these components. The normal stress on this oblique surface is the sum of the projections of the above stress components on the normal to the surface:

$$\sigma = S_x \cos \alpha + S_y \cos \beta + S_z \cos \gamma$$

If the principal axes of the state of stress are selected as the coordinate axes, then the shearing stress components disappear and the equations in Eq. (2) above reduce to

$$S_x = \sigma_1 \cos \alpha$$
$$S_y = \sigma_2 \cos \beta \qquad (3)$$
$$S_z = \sigma_3 \cos \gamma$$

From trigonometry we know that the squares of the direction cosines are equal to unity:

$$\cos^2 \alpha + \cos^2 \beta + \cos^2 \gamma = 1$$

By substituting from Eq. (3),

$$\frac{S_x^2}{\sigma_1^2} + \frac{S_y^2}{\sigma_2^2} + \frac{S_z^2}{\sigma_3^2} = 1 \qquad (4)$$

Equation (4) is the form of the equation of an ellipsoid, and it is called the stress ellipsoid. Thus the three-dimensional state of stress at a point can be defined in terms of three mutually perpendicular normal stresses which are related to one another as the axes of an ellipsoid (Fig. 2-8).

Variation of Shearing and Normal Stresses on an Inclined Plane

Evidence of extension and shortening is commonly encountered among structural features in the field. In its simplest form we may envision a cylinder or bar in the state of stress illustrated in Fig. 2-9. The shortening in this case is due to compression in the direction of

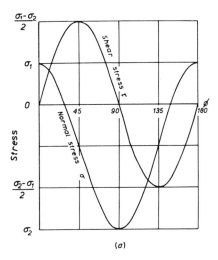

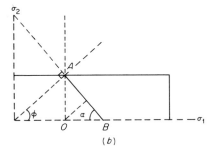

Fig. 2-9 Variations of normal stress σ and shear stress τ with changes in ϕ. [*Part (a) from Ramsay, 1967.*]

the maximum principal stress, and the extension is due to tension in the direction of the least principal stress. Consider the stresses on various planes through a cylinder or bar under compression or tension. Imagine that the plane is oriented so that it makes an angle α with the long axis of the bar and so that the normal to the plane makes an angle ϕ with the axis of the bar (Fig. 2-9).

A plane-stress state can be resolved into two perpendicular principal normal stresses. The stresses acting on the arbitrarily selected plane may be found by first rotating the coordinate axes until they coincide with the principal normal stress directions. Assume that the inclined plane is of unit length. Then $AO =$

l cos ϕ and $OB = $ l sin ϕ, resolving the normal stresses σ_1 and σ_2 on to AB.

$$\sigma = \cos \phi(\sigma_1 \cos \phi) + \sin \phi(\sigma_2 \sin \phi)$$
$$\sigma = \sigma_1 \cos^2 \phi + \sigma_2 \sin^2 \phi$$

which can be rewritten

$$\sigma = \frac{\sigma_1 + \sigma_2}{2} + \frac{\sigma_1 - \sigma_2}{2} \cos 2\phi$$

Similarly, the principal stresses can be resolved into shearing components along AB:

$$\tau = \cos \phi(\sigma_1 \sin \phi) - \sin \phi(\sigma_2 \cos \phi)$$
$$= (\sigma_1 - \sigma_2) \sin \phi \cos \phi$$
$$= \frac{\sigma_1 - \sigma_2}{2} \sin 2\phi$$

These equations can be plotted out as shown in Fig. 2-9. Shearing stress is seen to reach a maximum at 45 and 135° orientations of the inclined plane and normal stresses are a maximum at 0 and 90° orientations.

Mohr's Representation of Stress

Otto Mohr (1882), a German engineer, demonstrated one of the most useful of the various methods of representation of a state of plane stress. He made use of a circle plotted on a two-axis coordinate system in which the abscissa is the normal stress σ and the ordinate is the shearing stress τ (Fig. 2-10). From this plot it is possible to read directly the magnitude of both the normal and shear stresses which are acting upon any arbitrarily chosen plane making an angle, α, with the direction of the least stress provided the magnitude of the maximum and minimum principal stresses at the point are known. The derivation of the equations on which the Mohr circle construction is based is given later in this chapter in a footnote.

It is shown that the values for the normal and shearing stresses on an arbitrary plane can be expressed in terms of the following three values:

$$\frac{\sigma_1 + \sigma_3}{2} \qquad \frac{\sigma_1 - \sigma_3}{2} \qquad 2\alpha$$

If the point on the abscissa described in the first of these terms is taken as the origin of a radius vector which makes an angle 2α with the positive direction of the abscissa, and if the second of the above terms is taken as the length of the radius vector, it is found that for every value of the angle α the coordinates of the end of the vector satisfy the equations for the values of the normal and shearing stresses on the plane

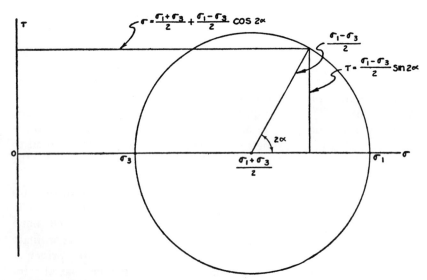

Fig. 2-10 Mohr's stress circle. (*From Hubbert, 1951.*)

which makes an angle α with the axis of least stress. As α is changed the radius vector describes a circle which is the locus of all of the values for normal and shearing stress for all orientations of the reference plane.

The Mohr circle can be easily read. Note for example that when the reference plane is normal to the principal stress direction (the angle α is equal to zero), the normal stress on the plane is the maximum principal stress, and the shearing stresses vanish. When the reference plane is perpendicular to the least principal stress the normal stress on the plane is equal to the least principal stress, and the shearing stresses vanish. It is also seen that shearing stresses reach a maximum when $2\alpha = 90°$ ($\alpha = 45°$), and that the magnitude of the maximum shearing stress is $\tau = (\sigma_1 - \sigma_3)/2$. This condition is obtained at two orientations of the reference

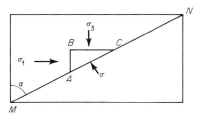

Fig. 2-11 Stresses on an inclined plane.

plane when $2\alpha = 90°$ and $2\alpha = 270°$. The two shear stresses thus produced are of equal magnitude but of opposite sense.*

It is also possible to use Mohr's technique to show stresses in several planes (Fig. 2-12). This representation is analogous to using the three mutually perpendicular reference ellipses (the xy, xz, and yz planes) of a stress ellipsoid, and the planes formed by the maximum and least

---

* Derivation of equations for the Mohr circle. The following derivation is adapted from the discussion of Hubbert (1951):

The purpose of the following is to determine equations which may be used to find the value of the normal and shearing stresses acting on a plane of arbitrary orientation to the principal stress direction. Figure 2-11 shows such an arbitrarily selected plane, MN, which is inclined at an angle, α, to the least stress direction. The intermediate stress direction lies perpendicular to the page; and the cross section thus illustrated is taken to be of unit thickness. Let ABC be a small right-triangular prism whose sides are respectively perpendicular to the axes of the maximum and least principal stresses. Let dS be the area of the hypotenuse, and let σ and τ be, respectively, the normal and shear stresses which act on this surface.

If the prism is taken small enough so that its weight is negligible as compared with the surface forces which act upon it, it will be accordingly in equilibrium under the influence of the surface forces due to the stresses σ_1, σ_3, σ, and τ. Resolving these forces into horizontal and vertical components, the sum of the vertical components must be zero, and also the sum of the horizontal components must be zero.

The forces acting upon the prism are the products of the stresses and the areas acted upon. The areas of three sides are as follows:

Side $AB = dS$
Side $BC = dS \sin \alpha$
Side $CA = dS \cos \alpha$

The sums of the horizontal and vertical components are, respectively,

$$\sigma_1 \, dS \cos \alpha - \sigma \cos \alpha \, dS - \tau \sin \alpha \, dS = 0$$
$$\sigma_3 \, dS \sin \alpha - \sigma \sin \alpha \, dS + \tau \cos \alpha \, dS = 0 \tag{5}$$

If we eliminate dS and solve Eq. (5) for the two unknowns τ and σ, we obtain

$$\sigma = \sigma_1 \cos^2 \alpha + \sigma_3 \sin^2 \alpha$$
$$\tau = (\sigma_1 - \sigma_3) \sin \alpha \cos \alpha \tag{6}$$

From trigonometry,

$$\cos^2 \alpha = \frac{1 + \cos 2\alpha}{2}$$
$$\sin^2 \alpha = \frac{1 - \cos 2\alpha}{2}$$
$$\sin \alpha \cos \alpha = \frac{\sin 2\alpha}{2}$$

When these values are substituted into Eq. (6), those reduce to the simpler forms

$$\sigma = \frac{\sigma_1 + \sigma_3}{2} + \frac{\sigma_1 - \sigma_3}{2} \cos 2\alpha$$
$$\tau = \frac{\sigma_1 - \sigma_3}{2} \sin 2\alpha$$

wherein τ and σ are expressed as simple functions of σ_1 and σ_3 and the angle 2α. These equations are capable of a simple geometrical representation if plotted as shown in Fig. 2-10 on coordinates of σ and τ.

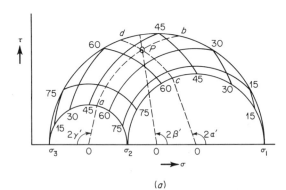

(a)

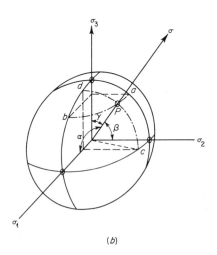

(b)

Fig. 2-12 (a) Mohr circles for three planes of the stress ellipsoid; (b) an ellipsoid showing location of a point P. (*Modified after Nádai, 1950, and Jaeger, 1956.*)

principal stresses, etc., are labeled. The reading of this diagram is clarified if it is compared with the stress ellipsoid (Fig. 2-12b) and each of the following features is noted:

1. The least principal stress is greater than zero: $\sigma_1 > \sigma_2 > \sigma_3$.
2. The points σ_1, σ_2, σ_3 correspond to points of intersection of the lines of principal stress with the surface of the stress ellipsoid.
3. O is the center of the Mohr diagrams for each of the three planes.

4. The $\sigma_1\sigma_3$ plane contains the largest range of stress differences, and the difference between the maximum and least stress is exactly equal to the sum of the stress differences of the maximum and intermediate and the intermediate and least stress.
5. The normal and shear stresses for all directions lying in the principal stress planes can be read directly by projecting the corresponding point from the circumference of the circle to the coordinate axes σ and τ.
6. Point P, which corresponds to an arbitrary stress direction OP, lies outside the principal stress planes. The stresses in this or any other direction can be read from the diagram. The point P is located in the stress ellipsoid by the angles between the line OP and the coordinate axes. The same point may be located in the Mohr diagram.

Figure 2-12a shows the projection of the concentric axes (dotted) to each of the smaller circles which may be used as coordinates in plotting points that do not fall in the principal stress planes. The solid lines and degree markings on the outside of the major circle are guides to the angle 2β. To locate a point P determine the angle between the projection of the line OP in the XY plane and the X axis, angle γ; repeat for ZY plane. Draw radii in the corresponding circles on the Mohr diagram, extending lines first to the edge of the circle, points A and C, and then along the concentric arcs which intersect those points. P is located where the two arcs intersect.

Stress Trajectories

One of the best ways of illustrating the stress within a body is to show by means of orthogonal lines the directions of the maximum and least principal stress directions in some plane through the body. Such lines are called *stress trajectories* (Fig. 4-5). The lines are closely spaced at positions of stress concentration; they are widely spaced where the value of the stress is lower. A set of lines showing the lines or planes of maximum shearing stress can be readily prepared from stress trajectories (drawn on a plane normal to the intermediate principal stress direction) because the direction of maximum shearing stress makes a 45° angle with the maximum principal stress.

STRAIN

A body is said to be strained when either its size or its shape is altered under an applied force. Thus strain is based on geometrical considerations. If a bar is strained so that the original length is increased (a linear strain) the ratio of the change of length to the original length is a measure of the strain. The measure of a strain in this case is a nondimensional figure, a percentage. Similarly, the strain in cases of changes of volume is the ratio of the change in volume to the original volume. Shear strains are measured by the change of angle between a plane and a line that was normal to the plane before strain occurred.

Much of the theory of strains deals with cases of homogeneous strain in which straight lines remain straight and parallel lines remain parallel after strain (Fig. 2-13). Only two of many possible strains are illustrated.

Strains are broadly classed into two categories: (1) dilation—changes in volume and

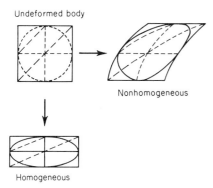

Undeformed body

Nonhomogeneous

Homogeneous

Fig. 2-13 Examples of homogeneous and nonhomogeneous strain.

(2) distortion—changes in shape. Sometimes changes in position and changes in orientation are also considered to be strains.

Dilation

When all three of the principal stresses are equal the normal stresses that act on any plane are also equal and no shearing stresses exist in the material. Strain under this condition is purely dilational, change in volume only, and the state of stress is hydrostatic stress.

Even when the three principal stresses are unequal, a portion of the stress system acts as though it is hydrostatic. This portion, the mean stress, is one-third of the sum of the principal stresses. The part of the stress system that deviates from the hydrostatic condition is called the *deviatoric stress,* and it is this part of the system that produces distortion. The dilations or distortions may be elastic or permanent in either case.

Distortion includes:

1. Simple extension along one axis (uniextensional strain)
2. Extension along two axes (biextensional strain)
3. Pure shear
4. Simple shear

Translation and rotation are kinds of displacement while dilation and distortion may be thought of as kinds of deformation. Translational and rotational displacements may occur during deformation. In fact all these kinds of displacements and deformation may be associated in a single outcrop.

In pure dilation there is no change of shape, but a change of volume. The principal stresses are equal.

Pure and simple shear must be clearly differentiated. The cases of uniextensional and biextensional strain are special cases of pure shear. In pure shear, reference lines parallel to the three principal strain axes remain straight, but reference lines drawn at an angle to these axes will be rotated. If these lines are drawn as conjugate pairs one of each pair will be rotated sinistrally, the other dextrally. Compare this with the case of simple shear in which all reference lines are rotated and all in the same sense (e.q., clockwise). Uniextensional strain may be visualized as the case of a stretched cylinder in which the long axis is lengthened (the diameter is reduced). Biextensional strain may be represented by a rectangular bar in which two dimensions increase in length while the third is reduced (Fig. 2-14).

The external form of a strain ellipse can be derived by either pure shear, dextral simple shear, or sinistral simple shear (Fig. 2-15). Although the external shape of the strain ellipses deformed by pure and by simple shear are the same, there are significant differences in the internal changes (Fig. 2-16). In simple shear the

rhomb is shown with an external couple, but it is clear that movements within the ellipse have taken place by a process of slippage along closely spaced laminae. Note the offset of one diagonal marker and the lack of offset of the other diagonal marker. Compare this with similar markers in pure shear. The outer edges of the original square were subjected to a couple, but the outer boundaries of the square constrained internal rotations. By analogy the simple shear is like laminar flow in which a viscous material is forced through a container with fixed boundaries such as glacier ice in a valley, or salt movement in rising salt domes.

From the foregoing it should be clear that significant problems are involved in trying to deduce the stress system responsible for a particular strain. Unique solutions to this problem are rarely obtained. However, it is frequently

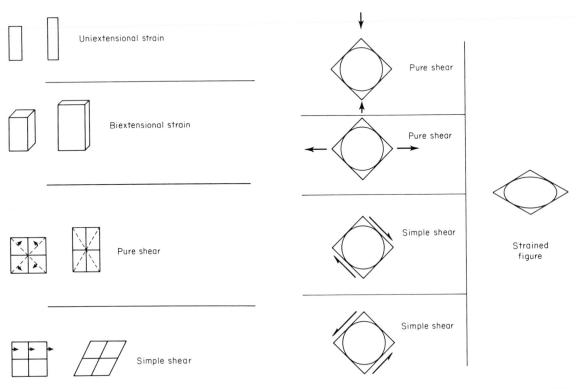

Fig. 2-14 Types of strain.

Fig. 2-15 The external form of a strained figure, right, could be formed by any of the ways shown at left.

possible to make a reasonable judgment of the original shape and position of a deformed body of rock by making use of elongated oolites, deformed fossils, rolled garnets, and deformed primary structures. The distinction drawn between pure and simple shear provides a useful guide to the manner of deformation. Some success has been achieved through petrofabric studies in which it has been shown that the gliding plane has a preferred orientation relative to the principal stress direction, and a positive relationship also exists between the formation of certain types of fractures and the principal stress directions.

Measurement of Strain

The value of a strain is determined by measurement of changes which take place in the lengths of lines and angles between lines. Changes in shape and position of fossils, primary sedimentary structures, primary rock textures, and other features from known original orientations provide the most direct means of measuring strain in rocks. The strain in a given extension or shortening of a given length is expressed as the ratio of the change in length to the original length.

$$e = \frac{\Delta L}{L_0}$$

Shear strain (Fig. 2-16) is measured in terms of the change in angular relation between two lines that were originally normal to one another.

γ (shear strain) $= \tan \phi$ (angular shear)

Strain Ellipsoid

Hooke's law states that stress is proportional to strain for elastic behavior; therefore, a strain ellipsoid must exist which is the reciprocal of the stress ellipsoid. The maximum principal stress axis is the least principal strain axis, etc. This strain ellipsoid is useful in describing elastic deformation. The principal axes of the strain ellipsoid are $A > B > C$, and A is the longest by convention.

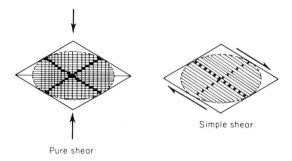

Fig. 2-16 Internal distinction between pure and simple shear.

The strain ellipsoid is used much more commonly as a representation of the total (largely nonelastic) change of shape in a body after deformation, ideally illustrated by the deformation of spherical oolites to ellipsoids or deformation of pebbles or fossils the original shape of which was known. Such a use is valid if the strain is homogeneous, if straight lines remain straight, and if parallel lines remain parallel. This strain ellipsoid has no unique relation to the stress ellipsoid. Thus it can not be used to determine the exact stress history of the deformed rock, the manner of stress application, its duration, or its direction. It is valuable as a guide to visualizing relationships of various fabric elements of a deformed rock or a region.

The total deformation strain ellipsoid must not be used to infer regional stress systems, and its use for estimating even local stresses is of dubious value.

Photoelastic Technique of
In Situ Stress Measurement

Photoelastic strain gauges can be used to determine the orientations of the principal directions of residual stress in rocks. Strain gauges are made of thin plates of polished optical strain-sensitive material. The gauge is irradiated with visible light through a film so that the light passes through the gauge and is reflected back by a mirror through the gauge and film. Variations in strain affect the birefringence of

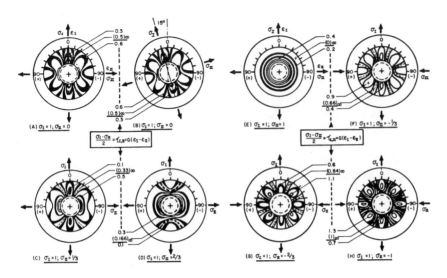

Fig. 2-17 Calculated theoretical shear stress distribution in the biaxial gage. (*a*) Axes of symmetry coincide with directions of tensile stress; (*b*) uniaxial at 15° inclination; (*c*), (*d*), (*f*) and (*g*) biaxial loading at various orientations; (*e*) equal biaxial tensile or compressive stresses; (*h*) pure shear. (*After Oppel, 1961.*)

the gauge material and show up as changes in the shape and number of visible interference fringes. One method of using the gauge consists of drilling a hole in fresh rock and cementing the gauge to the bottom of the hole; then a core drill is used to (overcore) drill a cylindrical hole around the gauge releasing *in situ* strain, and the pattern in the gauge is then observed. The symmetry of the pattern is used to identify the principal directions of stress and strain, and the type of pattern (Fig. 2-17) identifies the principal stress ratio. Determination of the type is done by making comparisons between the observed gauge and calculated theoretical stress distributions in the gauge for known ratios of two principal stresses (Fig. 2-17). Recent discussions of necessary corrections and techniques are available in the works of Voight (1967), Roberts (1964), and Oppel (1961).

STRESS-STRAIN RELATIONSHIPS FOR IDEAL MATERIALS

The behavior of various materials, both natural (rocks) and artificial (metals), is most frequently described in terms of the relationships between forces applied to the material (the stresses created within the material) and the resulting strain, and the way strain varies with time—all under carefully specified conditions of temperature, pressure, strain rate, and duration of load. Most of the early ideas in this field of material science grew out of studies of the physics of fluids and the properties of engineering materials. Later, as experimental work at higher temperatures and pressures became possible, the field was extended to include rocks and the effects of long-term experiments. The evaluation of the time factor is of paramount importance in geologic considerations. From these experimental studies a number of "ideal" models of material behavior have been established. Elastic, viscous, and plastic behavior are the simplest of these models; elasticoviscous, firmoviscous, and plasticoviscous models represent materials which combine characteristics of the first three.

Elastic Behavior

Robert Hooke described elastic behavior, finding that strain in an elastic body is reversible (the strain disappears when the stress system applied to the body is removed) and the amount of strain is directly proportional to the load applied (Fig. 2-18). This relation holds true provided the load does not exceed a certain value (dependent on the material involved), called the *yield point*. If loads are applied above the yield point, strain is no longer proportional to stress—much larger strains occur with small increases in load, and at least part of the strain is a permanent deformation. Hooke's law states that stress σ is proportional to strain ε, or $\sigma = E\varepsilon$ where E is a constant of proportionality dependent on the material, called *Young's modulus.*

Young's modulus, also called the *stretch modulus,* may be determined in experiments by subjecting a material to longitudinal tensile or compressive stresses and strains. It is found that Young's modulus, which is the ratio of

tensile stress to tensile strain, is equal to the ratio of compressive stress to compressive strain for a given material.

Another elastic modulus is the *shear modulus,* the ratio of shearing stress to shearing strain, which is also known as the *rigidity or torsion modulus* and applied to bodies deformed in shear. The *bulk modulus* relates to dilation in response to pressure changes. The bulk modulus is the ratio of the pressure to the fractional change in volume $(\Delta V / V_0)$. Compressibility is the reciprocal of the bulk modulus, and is defined as the fractional change in volume per unit increase in pressure. Elastic moduli for several rocks are given in Table 2-1. These moduli are constant for isotropic materials, but rocks are rarely isotropic. The values therefore

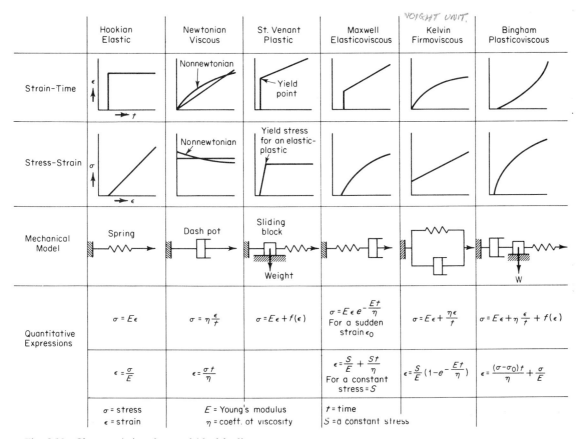

Fig. 2-18 Characteristics of several ideal bodies.

Table 2-1 Elastic Moduli for Selected Rocks

Rock	E*	G*
Basalt, Michigan	0.85	0.34
Marble, Cockeysville	0.49	0.26
Dunite, New Zealand	1.52	0.60
Gabbro	1.08	0.44
Granite gneiss	0.28	0.15
Granite	0.57	0.23
Halite	0.37	0.15
Limestone, Solenhofen	0.55	0.21
Quartzite	0.97	0.42
Shale:		
Siltstone dry	0.44	
Siltstone wet	0.19	

* E is Young's modulus, G is modulus of rigidity. E and G are given in megabars. Note that the values given are for specific tests and indicate only approximately the values for each rock type.

Source: Birch, in Clark (1966).

vary depending on the fabric and structure of the rock and the direction along which it is deformed. Changes in values may result from variations in temperature and confining pressure also.

As an example of a distortion strain, consider the changes that take place in a bar placed under axial tensile stress. The bar elongates and the other two dimensions of the bar are shortened provided the bar is isotropic. The strain in this bar may be referred to in terms of the changes that occur in its dimensions. The longitudinal strain is the ratio of the strained length to the original length; the transverse strain is the ratio of the strained width to the original width. The ratio of the longitudinal to the transverse strain is called *Poisson's ratio* and is used as one of the physical constants for describing the elastic properties of materials.

A mechanical model which corresponds to elastic behavior is a spring (stretched within the yield point).

Viscous Behavior

Sir Isaac Newton formulated the concept of fluid viscosity. Mechanically it can be represented by the behavior of a fluid layer between two rigid plates. A tangential force is applied to the upper plate, causing the plate to move. Because the fluid adheres to both plates the slip must occur in the fluid. The fluid is found to exert an internal frictional resistance, viscosity, to the movement; therefore, a force (a shearing stress) must be continually applied to keep the plate moving. For such fluids the strain is proportional to the stress and to the time it acts, and inversely proportional to the viscosity, η.

$$\varepsilon = \frac{\sigma t}{\eta}$$

Movements within the fluid are represented by laminar flow, or parallel shearing of the fluid on many fine laminae. Newton's law of viscosity states that the shearing stress applied to the plate is equal to the coefficient of viscosity (dynamic viscosity) multiplied by the rate of change of velocity of movement with distance. Another term, kinematic viscosity, is the ratio of the dynamic viscosity to the density of the fluid.

Newtonian fluids are those which follow the law proposed by Newton. The critical aspect of this is that the coefficient of viscosity (dynamic viscosity) is not a function of the velocity gradient or rate of application of the shearing stress. The viscosity is constant for all rates of strain in true Newtonian fluids. The viscosity of many fluids is found to be a function of the rate of application of the shearing stress. These are called nonnewtonian fluids. Most highly viscous materials, e.g., rocks, are nonnewtonian. Variations in viscosity with strain rate are usually attributed to structural changes in the material during flow. Viscosity is particularly sensitive to temperature conditions for both types of fluids. A mechanical model for viscous flow is the dashpot.

Some materials exhibit unusual combinations of properties. Bentonite muds, for example, will flow under very low stress if they are first subjected to a sudden high stress. Otherwise they behave as solids. This type of behavior is called *thixotropy*.

Osborne Reynolds investigated the conditions under which two different flow situations are dynamically similar. He succeeded in showing that the variable's velocity of flow, V; diameter of a tube through which flow occurs, D; density of the fluid, ρ; and coefficient of viscosity, η; are related as follows:

$$\frac{VD}{\eta}\,\rho = \text{a constant called } \textit{Reynolds number}$$

This provided a means of comparing the behavior of different fluids, and Reynolds was able to show that when the Reynolds number of a flow situation reaches a certain value, laminar flow begins to break up into turbulent flow. Reynolds' work was done with straight glass tubes of uniform diameter, and does not include effects of irregular boundary walls.

Combinations of Elastic and Viscous Behavior

Characteristics of the three "ideal" materials here considered, elastic, viscous, and plastic, may be combined in different ways to produce other relatively simple behavioral models. Two of these involve combinations of viscous and elastic behavior—elasticoviscous (Maxwell) and vis-

coelastic (also firmoviscous, Kelvin, Voigt) materials.

The easiest way to envision these two is in terms of their mechanical models (Fig. 2-18). The Maxwell body is represented by a spring and a dashpot connected in series, and the Kelvin body is represented by a spring and dashpot conected in parallel.

A Maxwell elasticoviscous substance (many waxes and pitches display this type of behavior) behaves as an elastic material for instantaneously applied stress, but if the stress is applied and held constant the substance will yield continuously in the manner of a viscous substance after the initial elastic strain. When stress is removed only the elastic component is recoverable. Like viscous substances any differential stress will produce continuous strain as long as it acts. One of the characteristics of such materials is what is called *stress relaxation*. If the material is strained a certain amount by an applied stress, the amount of stress required to sustain the strain will decrease through time. The *relaxation time* is the time required for the stress to reduce to $1/e$ (e is the base of natural logarithms, 2.72) of its original value if

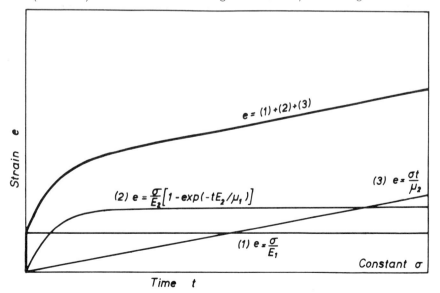

Fig. 2-19 Strain-time curve for a series combination of a spring, dashpot, and Kelvin body. (*From Ramsay, 1967.*)

the strain is held constant. Elastic substances theoretically will hold stresses permanently. The relaxation time is given by η/E, where E is Young's modulus and η is the coefficient of viscosity.

The Kelvin (viscoelastic) substances are essentially solids, but they differ from elastic materials in that the strains are not instantaneous when stress is applied. Some time is required for the maximum strain to occur after a stress is applied. It is found that strain is taken up exponentially, and the time required for the strain to reach $1/e$ of its final value is called the retardation time. Strain also dissipates exponentially when the applied stress is released. The dashpot connected in parallel with the spring in the mechanical model of a Kelvin body acts to dampen the action of the spring.

Ramsay (1967) describes a model that provides the best fits for stress-strain curves derived from experimentally deformed rocks. This model is made by compounding a spring, a Kelvin unit, and a dashpot in series. The strain-time curve (creep curve) for this body (Fig. 2-19) is the sum of the three components.

Plastic Behavior

An ideal plastic body does not yield until a particular load, the yield stress, has been applied. Most materials that approach being plastic behave like elastic substances (called *elastic-plastic*) below the yield point. Beyond the yield point a plastic will strain continuously; it flows, but it differs from viscous fluids which do not have a fundamental strength. Once plastic flow begins, it continues ideally without rupture as long as the yield stress is applied and the strain beyond that at the yield point is permanent. Some materials have a well-defined yield point at which an increase in deformation occurs without an increase in stress. More typically for rocks the stress-strain curve continues to rise beyond the yield point but at a lower slope than is found in the elastic range. Such materials are said to show strain hardening.

Plastic deformation in metals and other crystalline solids is often accompanied by the development of physical discontinuities along which abrupt displacements occur, called *slip lines*. They sometimes appear as orthogonal sets oriented at 45° to the maximum principal stress direction. Continuous internal changes occur during plastic deformation. Work is expended in producing new slip surfaces, in causing disorder in crystal lattices, etc., and this energy cannot be recovered as in elastic material.

St. Venant in 1870 suggested that during flow of a plastic material the principal axes of the strain increments are parallel to the principal axes of the stress system. This fundamental law of plastic behavior has been supplemented by several other generalizations: (1) that the ratios of the incremental changes are directly proportional to the ratios of the magnitudes of the principal stresses, (2) that plastic flow takes place without appreciable volume changes even when strain is great.

A generalized plastic material, also called *plasticoviscous* or *Bingham body,* is represented in Fig. 2-18 by a sliding block, a spring, and a dashpot connected in series. The initial behavior is elastic, but as the level of stress is increased, the yield stress is reached and the material flows like a liquid. After release of applied stress, the elastic component is recovered but strain by flow remains permanent.

REFERENCES

Andrade, E. N. C., 1914: Royal Soc. London Proc., v. A90; also 1911: v. A84.

Brace, W. F., 1961, Mohr construction in the analysis of large geologic strain: Geol. Soc. America Bull., v. 72, p. 1059–1079.

——— 1960, Analysis of a large two dimensional strain in deformed rocks: Internat. Geol. Cong., 21st, Norden, v. 18, p. 261–269.

Carey, S. W., 1953, The rheid concept in geotectonics: Geol. Soc. Australia Jour., v. 1, p. 67–117.

Clark, S. P., Jr., ed., 1966, Handbook of physical constants: Geol. Soc. America Mem. 97, 587 p.

Donath, F. A., 1963, Fundamental problems in dynamic structural geology, *in* Donnelly, T. W., ed., The earth sciences: Problems and progress in current research: Chicago, Univ. of Chicago, p. 83–103.

Handin, J. W., and Hager, R. V., Jr., 1957, Experimental deformation of sedimentary rocks under confining pressure—tests at room temperature on dry samples: Am. Assoc. Petroleum Geologists Bull., v. 41, p. 1–50.

Hubbert, M. K., 1951, Mechanical basis for certain familiar geologic structures: Geol. Soc. America Bull., v. 62, p. 355–372.

Jaeger, J. E., 1936, Elasticity, fracture, and flow: London, Methuen.

——— 1956, Elasticity, fracture and flow with engineering and geological applications: London, Methuen; New York, Wiley.

Kamb, W. B., 1959, Theory of preferred crystal orientation developed by crystallization under stress: Jour. Geology, v. 67.

Love, A. E. H., 1944, A treatise on the mathematical theory of elasticity: New York, Dover.

Mohr, Otto, 1914, Abhandlungen aus dem Gebiete der technischen Mechanik, 2d ed.: Berlin, Ernst.

Nádai, A., 1931, Plasticity: New York, McGraw-Hill.

——— 1950, Theory of flow and fracture of solids, 2d ed.: New York, McGraw-Hill.

Oppel, G., 1961, Photoelastic strain gages: Experimental Mechanics, v. 1, p. 65–73.

Ramsay, J. G., 1967, Folding and fracturing of rocks: New York, McGraw-Hill, 560 p.

Reiner, M., 1943, Ten lectures on theoretical rheology: Rubin Mass., Jerusalem, 33 p.

Roberts, A., 1964, Progress in the application of photoelastic techniques to rock mechanics: Rock Mechanics Symp., 6th, Rolla, Mo., p. 606–648.

Timoshenko, S. P., and Gere, J. M., 1961, Theory of elastic stability, 2d ed.: New York, McGraw-Hill, 541 p.

Turner, F. J., and Weiss, L. E., 1963, Structural analysis of metamorphic tectonites: New York, McGraw-Hill, 560 p.

Varnes, D. J., 1962, Analysis of plastic deformation according to Von Mises' theory, with application to the South Silverton area, San Juan Co., Colo.: U. S. Geol. Survey Prof. Paper 378-B, p. B1–B49.

Voight, Barry, 1967, On photoelastic techniques *in situ* stress and strain movement, and the field geologist: Jour. Geology, v. 75, no. 1, p. 46–58.

Whitten, E. H. Timothy, 1966, Structural geology of folded rocks: Chicago, Rand McNally, 663 p.

Willis, Bailey, 1923, Geologic structures: New York, McGraw-Hill.

3
theory of rock failure— fractures

ROCK FAILURE IN THEORY AND EXPERIMENT

The results of experimental studies of rock failure have proven to be applicable to geologic field studies. A broad range of experimental results is available including the behavior of single crystals and crystalline aggregates. One of the most striking observations from experimental work is the consistency of the relationship between the attitude of zones of fracture and the applied stress direction for deformation of materials while they are brittle. When such materials are compressed, either they fail by development of longitudinal fractures oriented parallel to the principal stress direction or they deform by shearing along planes inclined at angles of 45° or less to the principal stress direction. When such materials are extended they fail either by development of tension fractures normal to the direction of extension or by shearing with fractures oriented so that the direction of extension bisects obtuse angles between fractures (Fig. 3-1). Fractures with these types of angular relationships have been described from field studies.

The question of defining when a rock has failed in an experiment is not difficult when the rock is brittle and the material is deformed by extension. Failure is marked by the sudden formation of fractures, sudden loss of cohesion, and loss of resistance to differential stress. The question is not so easily settled in cases of rocks deformed at high temperatures and under high confining pressures when the behavior is ductile nor in cases of brittle materials when they fail by shear. The fractures formed in a series of experiments with marble and limestone ranging from brittle to ductile behavior are shown in Fig. 3-2. Griggs and Handin (1960) have suggested that all rocks probably will be found to exhibit similar regimes of behavior

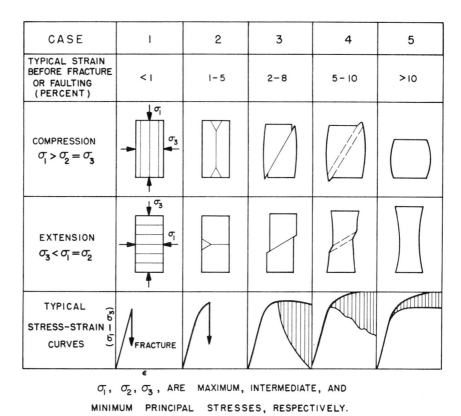

CASE	1	2	3	4	5
TYPICAL STRAIN BEFORE FRACTURE OR FAULTING (PERCENT)	< 1	1-5	2-8	5-10	>10
COMPRESSION $\sigma_1 > \sigma_2 = \sigma_3$					
EXTENSION $\sigma_3 < \sigma_1 = \sigma_2$					
TYPICAL STRESS-STRAIN CURVES					

σ_1, σ_2, σ_3, ARE MAXIMUM, INTERMEDIATE, AND MINIMUM PRINCIPAL STRESSES, RESPECTIVELY.

Fig. 3-1 Schematic representation of the spectrum from brittle fracture to ductile flow, with typical strains before fracture and stress-strain curves for uniaxial compression and extension. The ruled portions of the stress-strain curves indicate the variation within each case and the overlap between cases 3, 4, and 5. (*From Griggs and Handin, 1960.*)

(although the conditions may be quite varied). In general, materials exhibit brittle behavior at low temperatures and confining pressure. These temperatures are below normal room temperature for some materials. As higher temperatures and pressures are reached, however, the materials are able to sustain large permanent deformation—they become ductile. Continuous rehealing without loss of cohesion or release of strain energy is considered to be an important factor in the continuous deformation of most rocks at high temperature and high pressure. In view of the transitional nature of brittle-ductile behavior, we should expect no clear definition

of rock failure. Griggs and Handin (1960, p. 348) propose a threefold classification of fracture and flow as follows:

1. An extension fracture is separation of a body across a surface normal to the direction of least principal stress. There is no offset parallel to the fracture surface. The correlation between extension fractures and the principal stresses follows from the criterion of no offset and involves no additional hypotheses. Separation is parallel to a plane of vanishing shear stress.

The term "fracture" is used here advisedly since the phenomenon described involves total loss of cohesion, separation into two parts, release of

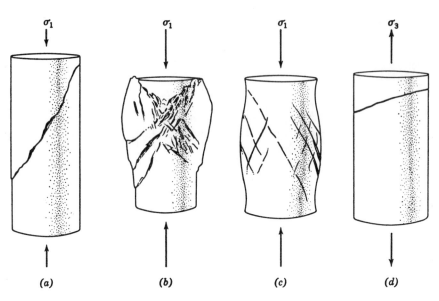

Fig. 3-2 Shear fractures and faults characteristic of failure of dry limestone and marble. (*a*) Marble, brittle failure; 25°C, 35 bars, 1 percent strain. (*b*) Marble, transitional failure; 25°C, 280 bars, 20 percent strain. (*c*) Solenhofen limestone, almost ductile failure; 25°C, 1,000 bars, 11.2 percent strain. (*d*) Solenhofen limestone, ductile behavior followed by rupture; 150°C, 6,500 bars, 9.1 percent strain. (*After Heard and Paterson.*)

stored elastic strain energy, and loss of resistance to differential stress. These characteristics are all associated with "fracture" (or "rupture") in the ordinary sense, so that the definition should be unambiguous.

2. A fault is a localized offset parallel to a more or less plane surface of non-vanishing shear stress. The surface may be inclined at from 45° to a few degrees to the direction of maximum principal (compressive) stress in homogeneous materials. As examples will show, there may or may not be total loss of cohesion, actual separation, release of stored elastic energy, or loss of resistance to differential stress. In other words, the phenomenon need not involve "fracture" in the ordinary sense. To be unequivocal the writers prefer "fault," and their usage of the term implies neither more or less than that of the field geologist.

The name "shear fracture" is used by many metallurgists in reference to fractures parallel to planes of maximum shearing stress, hence only to planes inclined at 45° to the extreme principal stresses. This is a special case of faulting, as is the "shear fracture" of engineering which implies complete loss of cohesion.

3. Uniform flow denotes macroscopically homogeneous deformation. There are three principal flow mechanisms: (1) cataclasis, involving crushing, granulation, and intergranular adjustments for which friction is important, (2) intragranular gliding, involving translation (slip) and twinning for which friction is relatively unimportant, and (3) recrystallization by local melting or solid diffusion, or through the agency of solution. The writers wish to emphasize that these mechanisms are not always distinguishable from one another or from faulting on the basis of the stress-strain relations measured during a short-time triaxial test.

Significantly, it is possible for a material to fault without exhibiting loss of cohesion or fracture in the usual sense of the word. Thus in dealing with the phenomena of rock failure we must cope with a spectrum of behavior that varies with material type, conditions of confining pressure, temperature, strain rate, and type of stress application. This spectrum (Fig. 3-1) is divided here into five cases each for compression and extension. The arbitrary definition of each case is based on percentage of strain (shortening or lengthening of specimen) and the boundaries of these various types of response are not rigid. They are shown overlapping. In general the spectrum represents the transition from brittle to ductile behavior of material; any material, therefore, which is brittle, case 1, under normal conditions may be expected to show behavior typical of higher cases as temperature or confining pressure is increased.

Brittle material deformed by extension deforms first by elastic strain followed by an abrupt failure by fractures oriented normal to the direction of extension. Under compression a brittle material deforms first by elastic strain followed by failure along fractures oriented parallel to the load axis. A ductile material extended undergoes elastic strain followed by plastic deformation accompanied by formation of a neck (narrowing of the specimen) and finally by failure in which a cup and cone structure is formed. Fibrous structure is often found in the break. Under compression, ductile materials undergo plastic deformation, or flow, after elastic strain.

MOHR REPRESENTATION

The Mohr circle method of representing stress is a valuable tool in visualizing the various criteria which have been used to study the theory of failure. Conditions of pure tension, shear, and uniaxial and triaxial compression are shown in Fig. 3-3 on a Mohr diagram. Each of these is defined by the maximum and minimum values of the principal stresses. These stresses are, respectively, a negative value and zero in pure tension; equal negative and positive values for simple shear; zero and a positive value for uniaxial compression; and both positive values for triaxial compression.

CRITERIA OF FAILURE

A number of theories of failure have been formulated which involve the establishment of certain criteria by which the state of failure can be expressed mathematically. None of these theories is completely satisfactory for the purposes of giving a general criterion which can be applied to the failure of all rock types. Some criteria are completely unsuccessful. For example, according to one criterion, failure occurs when the maximum principal stress reaches a certain value regardless of the value of the other principal stresses; the criterion which predicts failure when the elastic strain reaches a certain value also appears faulty (Varnes, 1962). Among the more successful criteria are:

1. Coulomb's criterion (also called Mohr's criterion). Failure is predicted when the shear stress along the planes of potential slip reaches a certain value.
2. Tresca's and Von Mise's (for plain strain) maximum shear-stress criterion. Failure by flow or by rupture occurs when the maximum shear stress reaches a constant value, which is characteristic of the material.
3. Griffith's criterion. Failure is related to the propagation of cracks originating from small flaws, cracks, or foreign matter.

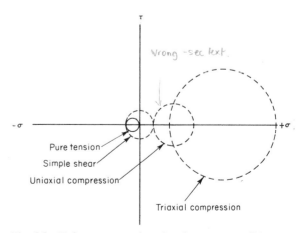

Fig. 3-3 Mohr representation of various stress conditions.

Varnes (1962, p. B-17) points out the difficulty in applying these criteria to geological situations:

It should be emphasized that the laws governing fracture and flow of solids are still imperfectly understood. Internal flaws and duration of stress are but two of many factors that influence fracture, in addition to the overall relations of principal stress. Temperature and chemical action of fluids have potent effects on the strength and on the mechanical type of failure of many geologic materials.

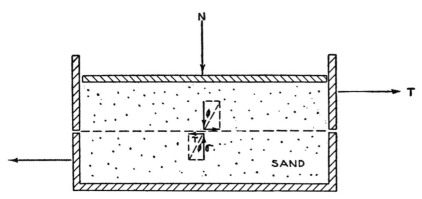

Fig. 3-4   Test box for measuring τ/σ, ratio at which slippage occurs. (*From Hubbert, 1951.*)

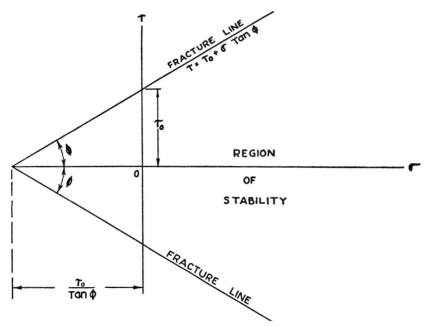

Fig. 3-5   Position of the fracture lines on $\sigma\tau$ diagram for cohesive materials. (*After Hubbert, 1951.*)

COULOMB'S CRITERION OF FAILURE

The way normal and shearing stresses vary with the angle of inclination of an arbitrary plane due to compression of the principal stress direction in a bar was pointed out earlier (Fig. 2-9). From this diagram and from the Mohr representation of stress, we see that shearing stresses reach a maximum on planes inclined at 45° to the direction of the principal stress. Experiments show clearly that when materials fail in shear, the shear plane lies at something less than 45° to the principal stress direction. This difference was attributed by Navier to internal friction and cohesive properties of the material. One method of evaluating the internal friction of sand or soil consists of filling a specially designed container (Fig. 3-4) with sand. The container is constructed so that when the top half of the box is moved, movement within the sand occurs in only one plane. The amount of load N can be varied, and the amount of shearing stress necessary to start movement for each increment of load is determined. The ratio of shearing stress to normal stress is equal to tan ϕ (Fig. 3-4); ϕ is called the *angle of internal friction*. It is about 30 to 35° for sand. The angle ϕ for rocks may be obtained by observing the angle between slip planes in a specimen being deformed in a known stress field.

The French physicist Coulomb recognized the difference between cohesive materials such as rocks and noncohesive materials such as sand and formulated an equation to represent tan ϕ for cohesive materials as follows:

$$\tan \phi = \frac{\tau - \tau_0}{\sigma}$$

cohesive strength

where τ_0 is the cohesive shear stress typical of the material. This equation can be rewritten as follows: $\tau = \tau_0 + \sigma \tan \phi$ and it can be plotted on a diagram of τ against σ, lines of failure for the material with a specified τ_0 and ϕ (Fig. 3-5). The fractures shown in Fig. 3-5 are oriented so that the acute angle of intersection is bisected by the principal stress. The spatial relationship

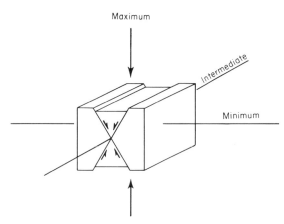

Fig. 3-6 The relationship between principal stress axes and conjugate shear set of fractures or faults.

is shown in three dimensions in Fig. 3-6. The two conjugate shears intersect in the intermediate stress direction.

A plot of Mohr circles showing successive increases in the amount of compression illustrates results of a triaxial test (Fig. 3-7). In these tests the confining pressure is built up to a certain value; then the directed pressure is increased until the maximum shearing stress is obtained and the material fractures. The confining pressure is then increased and the next test run. The line (surface in three dimensions) that is tangent to each of these circles is called the envelope, and it was thought to represent the fracture plane. It does very closely approximate the fracture in soil mechanics test with loose granular material and in some ductile materials.

Mohr found that the angle ϕ does not remain constant for all pressures. It is not wholly a property of the material, but is also a function of the pressure. Thus Mohr envelopes are not necessarily straight lines.

GRIFFITH'S THEORY OF BRITTLE FRACTURE

Griffith (1920, 1924) formulated the theory that fractures in brittle materials (he used glass) are

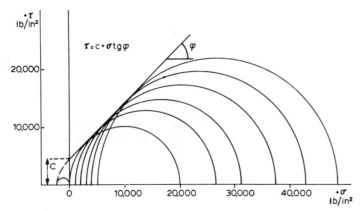

Fig. 3-7 Mohr circles with envelope for Pennant sandstone. (*After Price, 1958.*)

propagated from small randomly oriented cracks in the material. The theory was first proposed for tensile fracture and later extended to failure in compression. These cracks have been thought of as highly eccentric ellipsoids in the mathematical development of the theory. Griffith analyzed the stresses on cracks of different orientations relative to the principal stresses to determine which cracks would be stable and which would be propagated. He found that the stress is increased on one edge of a favorably oriented flaw, causing the fracture to be propagated normal to the tensile stress. The flaws might be pore spaces, grain boundaries, inclusions, etc.

Ode (1960) summaries conclusions from the theory:

1. In pure tension the crack requiring the smallest amount of principal stress for instability is normal to the principal stress direction.
2. In compression the crack leading to instability is oriented at 30° to the direction of principal stress.
3. The envelope of all limiting stress circles for rupture can be computed and has the shape of a parabola (Fig. 3-8). This is significant because the envelopes derived

from tests on specimens of many rocks under hydrostatic pressure are nearly parabolic.

There are a number of drawbacks to the Griffith theory; notably the theory assumes elastic behavior of the material up to the moment of rupture—a condition which is not fulfilled in cases of sand, clay, and other materials under high confining pressure and temperatures.

BRITTLE FRACTURING IN EXPERIMENTS

Experiments with brittle materials have repeatedly shown the development of fractures oriented parallel to the maximum stress direction (direction of the largest compressive load), called *axial fractures*. They are oriented in the plane of the maximum and intermediate stress directions. If compression continues beyond the initial formation of these fractures, zones of fractures develop about 45° to the compressive stress (Fig. 3-10), and this orientation is the one most commonly reported in experiments and from field studies.

One of the notable experiments of Gramberg (1965) involved compression of a cylinder of a single crystal of salt in which the cleavage

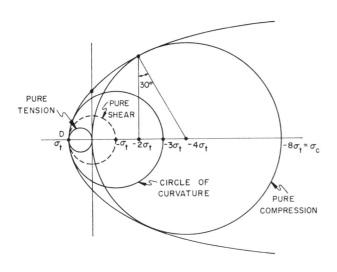

Fig. 3.8 Stress circles showing the ratio between σ_c (compressive strength) and σ_t (for tensile strength) for Griffith's hypothesis, $\sigma_t =$ tensile strength. (*From Ode, 1960.*)

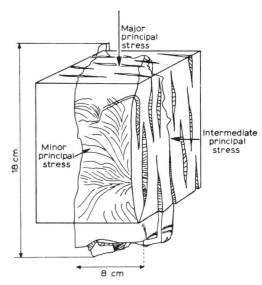

Fig. 3-9 Brittle fracture. (*From Gramberg, 1965.*)

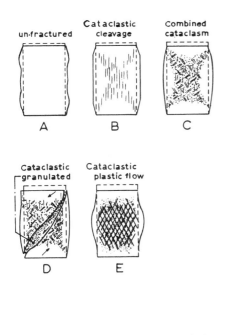

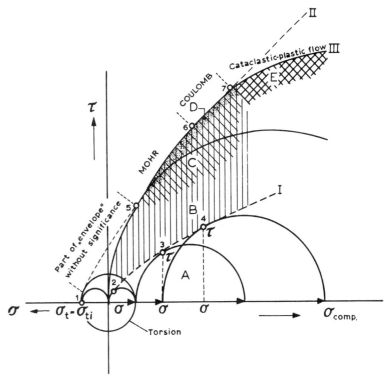

Fig. 3-10 Representation by Mohr circles. Rock material passes through various structural stages when compressively loaded. (*From Gramberg, 1965.*)

planes were oriented at about 36° to the direction of maximum compression. Despite this, a crack which initially developed along a cleavage cut across the cleavages to become oriented parallel to the load axis. Thus this orientation is a highly preferred fracture orientation under these conditions. (This conflicts directly with the Griffith theory of prediction of oblique preferred orientations.) If deformation is carried beyond the stage of initial formation of fractures (Fig. 3-10), the rock becomes increasingly subject to cataclastic deformation. The specimen's shape changes by shortening and bulging, the volume increases, and an oblique shearing off occurs.

A representation of progressive stages in brittle deformation is shown in Fig. 3-10 on a Mohr diagram for compressive loading. The diagram is divided into zones A to E. These zones are: (A) Unfractured material. This is the zone of purely elastic behavior; no structural

changes; boundary I marks initial development of fractures. (B) The zone in which cataclastic fracturing is prominent. The test piece is now inhomogeneous, and lateral expansion occurs. (C) Cataclastic fracturing continues accompanied by development of shearing zones, sliding movements; "cataclastic plastic flow" results in collapse by shear. (D) Collapse by shearing off. (E) Zone of large cataclastic plastic flow. Envelope II is that predicted according to Mohr-Coulomb criteria; envelope III is a branch for large cataclastic plastic flow (Gramberg, 1965).

Shear Failure in Anisotropic Rocks

We have examined experimental results from tests run on specimens selected primarily because they are nearly uniform throughout. Yet large bodies of rock are rarely isotropic. Anisotropic effects are caused by variations in physical properties, composition, or older structures,

No see Price pp 35-36

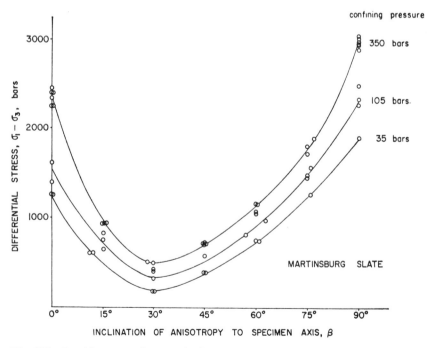

Fig. 3-11 Breaking strength versus inclination of cleavage, Martinsburg slate. (*From Donath, 1961.*)

and it is important that we know how to evaluate the effects of these anisotropies. Donath (1961) has examined some of the effects to be expected in anisotropic rocks. He studied the variation of breaking strength with respect to the angle of inclination of cleavage in Martinsburg slate (Fig. 3-11). The tests were run at room temperature and under low confining pressures such that the rocks exhibited brittle behavior. The breaking strength was least when the cleavage was oriented at about 30° to the differential stress, and the specimens tended to fail along cleavages when cleavages were oriented from 15 to 45° to the differential stress axis, and some effects of cleavage were noticed even at inclinations of 60°. In tests on Longwood shale Donath and Cohen found shear fractures developed at angles of about 30° for nearly all orientations of bedding, despite the distinct bedding of the shale.

OCCURRENCE OF FRACTURES

Fractures are surfaces of secondary origin across which there has been a loss of cohesion. They occur in most igneous, metamorphic, and sedimentary rock bodies, and they are commonly found in unconsolidated sediment. Fractures usually occur as sets of subparallel trend and sometimes have even spacing that break the rock up into blocks; two or more sets are common. Fractures are important as reservoirs for ground water, oil, and gas; they are used in quarrying operations to remove large building stones; they often present structural problems in dam and foundation engineering; and they can provide valuable clues to the deformational history of an area or a structural feature. An understanding of fracturing is especially critical to the study of faults because many faults result from movements along fractures or fracture systems.

No single explanation satisfactorily describes the origin of all fractures; in fact, the origin of many fractures is still unknown. This is especially true of the fracture systems which seem to pervade the Precambrian basement complexes. Fractures are found in undeformed, unconsolidated sediment, in slightly arched coal, in all plutons, and in most extrusive bodies; highly complicated patterns are found in the folded mountain belts and in the Precambrian crystalline complexes. The widespread occurrence of fractures and their presence in all rock types suggests a multiplicity of causal conditions. The origin of fractures in nature must be considered in the light of the particular geological circumstances in which they are found. The fractures which formed in experiments described earlier were the result of stresses applied externally to the specimen. These were imposed on the material, but many fractures must originate in the absence of external stresses. Fractures in undeformed lava flows and in dried lake muds prove this. It is likely that most fractures in dikes, sills, and plutons form as a result of internal stresses set up as a result of cooling and contraction. Fracture sets are usually well developed in flat-lying sedimentary rocks, both consolidated and unconsolidated, that show no sign of strong deformation. These and the beautifully developed cubic fractures so typical of bituminous coal even where it is flat-lying prompt us to look for explanations of these fractures in processes such as consolidation, compaction, and drying—the diagenetic processes. Such fractures may be intrinsic in the materials in which they occur.

Fractures are a guide to the mechanics of deformation only where they have been imposed on the rock during diastrophism. Characteristic relationships between the direction of the deforming stresses and the attitude of the fractures under conditions of compression and extension have been found in experiment, confirmed in theory, and substantiated by numerous field observations.

However, fracture patterns can be complex and can originate in various ways. Some are imposed on the rock by an external stress field of local character such as that associated with a fold or fault; some cannot be related to external stresses, but must arise as a result of internal strains; some are part of regional patterns the origin of which is usually open to debate; some result from superimposed deformation; some are intrinsic in the type of material and the response of that material to stress; others arise from boundary conditions due to local irregularities.

In order to make the most intelligent interpretation of fractures, careful attention must be given to the following features during field study: (1) the pattern of the fracture system, (2) the nature of features on the fracture surfaces, (3) the geometrical relations of the fracture pattern to the structure of the rock mass in which the fractures occur, (4) the physical properties of the rock and other features of the rock which might indicate the conditions under which fracturing took place.

We will hope to find evidence which may help us decide whether the fractures originated through:

Uniextensional strain: Characterized by tension fractures normal to the direction of elongation.

Biextensional strain: Characterized by tension fractures normal to the direction of maximum elongation, and with possible shear frac-

tures oriented so that the obtuse angle between the shears face the direction of maximum elongation.

Nonrotational strain: In which the external forces bear the same relation to the strain throughout the deformation, with two sets of tension and two sets of shear fractures possible. The principal stress direction bisects the two shears; tension fractures are normal to one another and one is normal to the maximum principal stress direction.

Rotational strain: Under the action of a couple, the strain axes rotate with the continued application of the external forces. The possible fracture sets are the same as those for nonrotational strain.

FEATURES ON FRACTURE SURFACES

Woodworth (1896) and Hodgson (1961) have described features on fracture surfaces. Some of the more prominent of those found on fracture surfaces in sandstone are illustrated in Fig. 3-12. The main fracture plane contains raylike ridges which diverge from a central axis to form a larger plumose structure. These plumose features are very similar to fracture surfaces produced by axial loading (Fig. 3-9). Many fractures of this character may form as a result of vertical loading where they are normal to bedding—particularly those in unfolded strata. The rays are the traces of cross fractures oriented in *en échelon* fashion on the main fracture surface.

Slickensides may appear where there has been even slight displacement along fractures. Such striations appear only when the surfaces of the fracture are forced together during slippage; they should not be expected on fractures formed in tension except in cases where the rock mass has been subjected to a second deformation.

Gramberg (1966) concludes that most fractures which do not have slickensided surfaces or show offsets are of tensional origin. A great many fractures show no offset, but fracture sets are frequently too irregular to allow proof of a consistent offset direction.

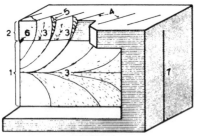

1. MAIN JOINT FACE
2. FRINGE
3. PLUMOSE STRUCTURE
4. F-JOINTS, (B-PLANES)
5. C-FRACTURES, (STRAIGHT MEDIAL)
6. SHOULDER
7. TRACE OF MAIN JOINT FACE

Fig. 3-12 Schematic block diagram showing primary surface structures of a systematic joint. (*From Hodgson, 1961a.*)

DETERMINATION OF THE AGE OF FRACTURES

Dating fractures with precision is very difficult. Even the obvious statement that the fractures in a sedimentary rock are formed after the rock was deposited is made complicated by the observation that fractures in sediment and in sedimentary rocks can be inherited from the underlying "basement" rock, as shown in the Grand Canyon (Fig. 3-31). This is borne out by the similarity of fractures in Precambrian crystalline rocks in the Canadian Shield and in unconsolidated sediment overlying them. The fracture pattern formed under these circumstances may be related to a stress system which acted on the basement before the overlying cover was formed. The phenomena of inherited fractures seems verified although the mechanism is poorly understood.

The observation that fracture orientations in layers of different lithology in a simply deformed stratified sequence are often very different stands in strong contrast to the idea of inherited fracture patterns. It is not valid to assume that fractures of different orientation in such a sequence were formed at different times or under different stress fields.

Open fractures are excellent avenues for the movement of fluids, and veins of calcite, quartz, and epidote are among the most common vein fillings found in fractures. Dikes of all types also usually follow fractures. Dikes and other types of fracture fillings provide the most useful means of dating fractures, or at least making a minimum age determination for the injected fracture set. It is often possible to date pegmatite dikes and veins by radiometric dating methods, and other dikes can be dated by the age of the youngest units intruded, by unconformities that cut the dike, and by other crosscutting relationships. A classic study of differentiation of dikes of different ages has been made in Scotland by Richey (1939). Extensive dike swarms and related intrusions of very different trends are found there. These dike swarms are thought to be related to different regional stress systems that affected the area at different times. The fracture sets may be dated relative to one another by the crosscutting relationships of one set to another. If each set of dikes can then be recognized by its particular petrography, the dikes of each age can be recognized in areas where crosscutting is not found. Printz (1964) made effective use of this technique in a study of Precambrian dikes in the Beartooth Mountains of Montana and Wyoming.

A more tenuous argument about the character of fractures during intrusion can be made on the basis of which fractures are injected. Intrusion should be easier along fractures that are open at the time of intrusion. The opening of one or more sets suggests that the area might have been under tension along lines normal to the open set.

DETERMINING THE FRACTURE PATTERN

Determination of the fracture pattern is the initial problem in most fracture studies. The pattern is known when it is possible to describe the number and orientation of fracture sets of parallel or subparallel trend at a point, and to describe the way that the geometry of the fracture sets varies from place to place over the area or structural feature being studied. Various techniques are used to establish the geographic distribution of the fracture sets. These usually involve determination of the number and orientation of fracture sets within a small area, called a *station,* and a comparison among the various stations. If the local geology is known, stations may be intentionally located on fold axes, fold limbs, or in other positions selected to establish a relationship between the fractures and the structure. When the structure is unknown, stations may be set up on intersection points on an arbitrarily established grid system. Regional patterns are often measured from aerial photographs on which lineaments can be seen.

Various methods of sampling are used in

efforts to determine fracture patterns. If there is but one set of fractures all of which have identical strikes and dips, the task is simple. Usually, however, even when there are only one or two sets there will be slight variations in strike and dip of fractures belonging to a set, and therefore a statistical approach is used (Pincus, 1951). The strike and dip of a large sample (usually 100) of fractures is measured and plotted on a point diagram. The diagram is then contoured (see Appendix B for use of stereographic projection), and the centers of the concentrations are used as the attitudes of the fracture sets.

One of the most difficult problems in the interpretation of the contoured point diagram is to determine which of the concentrations are significant. Sometimes only a few centers of concentration appear, but more often there are several low value maxima. When the number of isolated concentrations is great, some criterion has to be used to separate those which are to be considered significant. The Poisson exponential binomial limit may be used to give an approximation of the probability that various levels of concentration will occur on a point diagram (Pincus, 1951, and Spencer, 1959). A perfectly uniform distribution of 100 measurements would consist of one point in each 1 percent counting area. The Poisson exponential binomial limit gives the probability of finding more than each of the following number of points in any 1 percent area as follows:

Points	Probability
0	1.00
1	0.63
2	0.26
3	0.08
4	0.02
5	0.005
6	0.0006

The chances of having a 4 percent concentration in a random distribution are therefore approximately 1 in 50. The angle between frac-

ture maxima is readily determined from the stereogram. If the fractures are all vertical or if a study is being made of fracture lineaments from aerial photographs, the data may be represented in a rose diagram or a histogram (Fig. 3-13).

Several sets of fractures frequently appear together, and sometimes, especially in areas of multiple deformation, the pattern is extremely complex. It is most helpful in later analysis if some means of differentiating sets in the field can be found. Among useful features are fraction fillings, features on fracture surfaces, and spacing of fractures. In the absence of suitable features to differentiate the various sets, a large random sample must be collected.

FRACTURE PATTERNS ON FOLDS

If fractures do form in response to stress fields then it should follow that folds in layered sedimentary rocks which are deformed by buckling under compression parallel to the layers should be fractured, and the fracture pattern should be related to the direction of the compressive stress. Some of the best examples of this relationship are found on folds formed in ice. The ice layers on lakes are compressed as expansion of the layer takes place; ice in the Ross Ice Shelf area has many beautifully developed doubly plunging folds formed in response to at least local compression of the ice sheet. Common fracture orientations on such folds are (1) a longitudinal fracture which extends along the crest of the anticline and which formed as a result of tension across the crest of the fold, and (2) a set perpendicular to the first, oriented vertically and across the fold axis. The second set may also be due to tensional forces set up along the fold axis due to the plunge of the fold. Two other sets, which cross one another at acute angles that are bisected by lines normal to the fold's axial plane, can best be related to shearing forces. Such shear fractures intersect at angles of about 60° in many rocks.

De Sitter (1964) has illustrated (Fig. 3-14) all

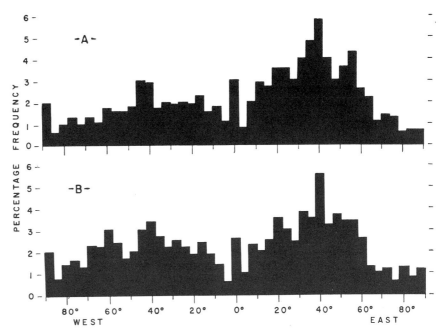

Fig. 3-13 Histograms of lineaments identified as fractures on aerial photographs.

the theoretically possible tension and shear fractures that might be expected on an anticlinal fold. Only a few of these sets are normally encountered in the field, and often fractures on folds are difficult to relate to any of these sets. One reason for this is that many rocks buried at shallow depths are brittle and fracture early in the folding process. Once fractures are formed, movements take place along them, and when blocks bounded by fractures are shifted, stress fields of new orientation can be set up in the block possibly resulting in fractures not directly related to the fold.

Fractures on the Pico Anticline

Bonham's (1957) description of the Pico anticline located in the Ventura basin near Los Angeles, Calif., affords a good example of a study in which microfractures as well as larger fractures have been positively related to the fold on which they occur. The Pico anticline (Fig. 3-15) is a tightly folded anticline, nearly chevronlike in cross section, doubly plunging,

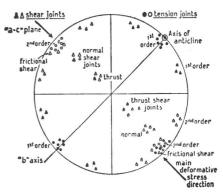

Fig. 3-14 Stereographic representation of possible joints in an anticlinal structure. (*From De Sitter, 1964.*)

and upright. It developed in Tertiary sequences consisting primarily of silty, laminated shale with sandstone interbeds, and lenticular conglomerates. The fold is described as a simple flexure slip fold in which there has been little stretching on flanks or thickening on the axes

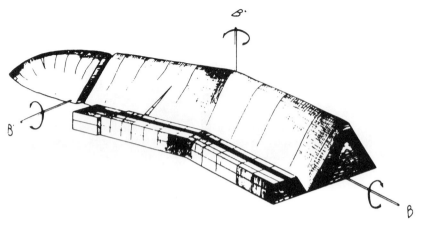

Fig. 3-15 Idealized block diagram of the Pico structure showing three axes of external rotation. (*From Bonham, 1957.*)

in the sandstone beds or conglomerate lenses, but the shales have behaved incompetently and have deformed by thinning on flanks and thickening in fold hinges. External rotation of beds has occurred about three axes shown in Fig. 3-15. These are the axis of the fold, the plunge, and a third located where the trend of the fold changes direction. Fabric directions used in the study are: (*a*) parallel to the fold axes; (*b*) normal to fold axial planes; (*c*) vertical.

Fractures and faults were measured in the study as well as microfractures. One set of the fractures was found to be preferentially oriented normal to the fold axes. This set is vertical in the central part of the fold, but it dips at progressively lower angles where the fold plunges reflecting the rotation of the fold in the area of plunge. These fractures are considered to be tension fractures developed in the *ac* fabric plane, and a result of tension acting normal to the maximum compressive stresses during deformation. Other sets of fractures were found to have orientations parallel to the faults. The faults are transverse, cutting the fold axes at angles of 30 to 40°, and they are oriented symmetrically with the *a* fabric direction. They cause lateral offsets of the bedding, indicating the action of a couple, a shear, along them.

Well-developed systems of microfractures were found in the quartz grains and these were measured using a universal stage and plotted on stereographic projections. Twenty-eight oriented specimens were collected from various places on the fold. Point diagrams produced by plotting the microfractures on each of these generally have one of two arrangements of the maxima or some combination of these two. Many of the plots show a single maximum corresponding to fractures preferentially oriented normal to the fold axes (in the *ac* fabric plane). Where two maxima are found, they correspond to fractures with consistent preference for orientations in two planes bisected by the *ac* fabric plane (Fig. 3-16). As with the tension fractures, the microfractures show a rotation of the sets where the fold plunges.

Ross Ice Shelf

The Ross Ice Shelf is a sheet of floating névé ice covering about 192,000 miles in the Antarctic Ocean. The ice is from 100 to 400 m thick. It is grounded on a number of islands in the sea and at its margins. One such island is Roosevelt Island, located southeast of the area illustrated in Fig. 3-17. The ice flows around the island, and where this constriction occurs the ice sheet is laterally compressed and thrown into a system of folds. These folds are cut by prominent crevasses, most of which are oriented normal to the fold axes (Zumberge and others, 1960).

Fracture patterns in the ice are of special interest because ice is so homogeneous, and because the conditions so closely approximate those of a single layer of brittle material buckled by lateral forces (water below and air above confine the ice layer), producing both fractures and folds.

Study of fold and fracture pattern (Fig. 3-17) will reveal that the structure is not so simple as we might hope to find. The folds are not all parallel and the crevasses have several orientations. Some are normal to the horizontal fold axes, but others cross the axes at angles which deviate from normal by 20° or more, and many of the crevasses have a sigmoidal pattern. The simplest interpretation appears to be that the crevasses initially formed normal to the fold axes and were later modified by movements of the ice sheet. It must be noted that this ice has moved several miles from the place where the folds are presumed to have formed. The movement of the ice is toward the northwest at a

small angle to the trend of the folds. Thus the opening of the crevasses and the development of sinuous traces could be due to differential movement in the ice sheet in the direction of flow.

FRACTURES IN PLUTONS

Intrusions often follow the zones of weakness represented by preexisting fractures, but many fractures are apparently formed as a result of the forceful injection of magma. Within the pluton itself joints appear to arise primarily from cooling and contraction of the magma, from fracturing along compositional layering or the planar flow structure, and as a result of denudation of the pluton and consequent development of sheeting.

Primary Fracture Systems

Hutchinson (1956) recognizes three mutually perpendicular fracture sets which are related to flow structure as in the Enchanted Rock batholith in Texas (Fig. 3-18). Balk (1937) described four sets of fractures (Fig. 3-19) as being of primary origin in plutons, and he contends that all these are related to flow structures. The four

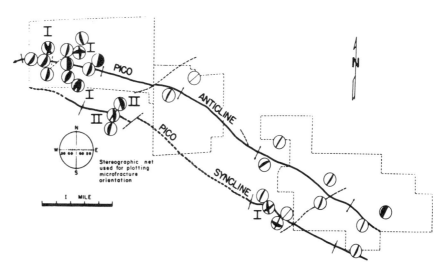

Fig. 3-16 Preferred spatial orientation of microfractures as determined by means of the universal stage. (*From Bonham, 1957.*)

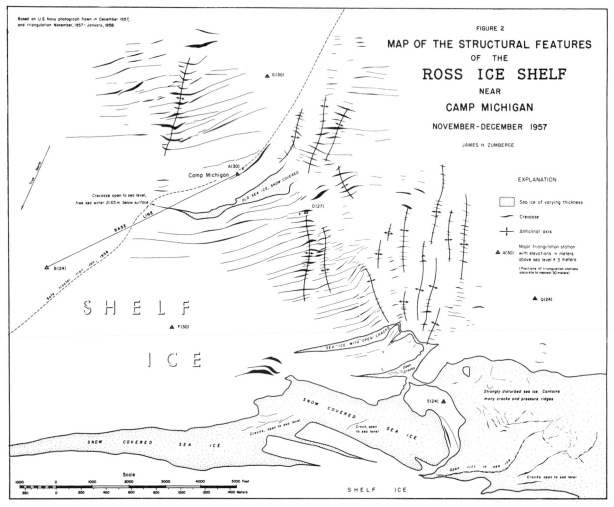

Fig. 3-17 Map of the structural features of the Ross Ice Shelf near Camp Michigan. (*From Zumberge, 1957.*)

types of fractures are cross, longitudinal, diagonal, and primary flat; the first three are named for their relationship to flow lines. The cross fractures are nearly perpendicular to flow lines; they are commonly filled with pegmatite, other hydrothermal deposits, and dikes. They are among the first fractures to form in the cooling magma and sometimes extend well beyond the intrusion's margins. Their origin is described by Balk (1937, p. 31) as follows:

The cross joints appear as a continuation of the viscous elongation, through other forcible means. A viscous east-west flow will be recorded by flow lines in the same direction, but, when this material has consolidated, a lengthening in the same direction will be recorded by a set of joints striking north-south.

Longitudinal fractures follow the physical weakness imparted to the igneous mass by flow structures and may be due to contraction on cooling, but they are not so commonly found as the cross fractures. Diagonal fractures strike across the flow lines at angles of about 45° and usually occur as two intersecting sets most com-

monly interpreted as resulting from shear of the intrusion. Flat-lying fractures, as indicated by flat-lying dikes and vein filling, indicate that a consolidating igneous mass tends to break up

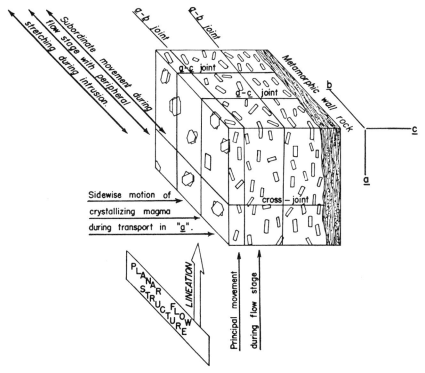

Fig. 3-18 Relationship of primary fractures to primary flow structures. (*From Hutchinson, 1956.*)

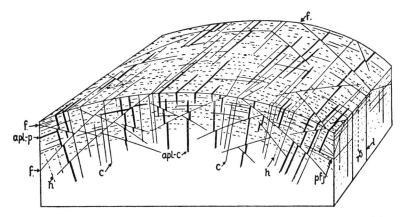

Fig. 3-19 Primary structure elements and directions of parting in the Strehlen Massif. (*Redrawn from H. Cloos by Balk, 1937.*)

into slabs separated by fractures of low dip. In some instances these joints parallel flat-lying flow layers, but in others they do not. Certainly the volume decrease of a cooling igneous intrusion would partially explain this fracture orientation since the heat would tend to be lost most readily upward.

Sheeting

Fractures subparallel to the topography and apparently unrelated to flow or other primary structures have been found in granites in many parts of the world, and these, called sheeting, are extremely useful in many quarries. Sheeting is sometimes referred to as a sort of large-scale exfoliation. Jahns (1943) has described sheeting in New England granites. The sheets are usually more conspicuous parallel to the granite surface near the surface, as on a hill, and they tend to flatten and become more nearly horizontal at depth (Fig. 3-20). The spacing of sheets also shows an increase with depth. Sometimes a single joint can be traced laterally into another, and others die out laterally or end abruptly against older steep fractures. This last relation is important because it is taken to indicate that the sheeting formed later than the steep fractures. The sheeting cuts across flow lines, roof

pendants, xenoliths, and late-stage pegmatites. At Quincy, Mass., sheeting has been reported at depths of 320 ft. Sheeting in modern quarries is often subject to buckling as is seen at the Mount Airy quarry, North Carolina; similar broad, thin slabs break or "pop" up in New England quarries showing that the rock mass is under compressive strain. Jahns (1943) reported that a channel cut in the granite of one New England quarry was suddenly narrowed by about half its width.

Most geologists are inclined to view the origin of sheeting as being due to dilation upon the relief of a primary confining pressure—to which the rock has become adjusted—through removal of superincumbent load. Jahns, 1943.)

Fractures in Dikes, Sills, and Flows

Columnar fractures (joints) of varied polygonal cross section are well-known features of tabular, shallow intrusions and of extrusions. Theoretically these fractures would form perfect hexagons if the cooling were uniform and the cooling rock homogeneous (Fig. 3-23), and fractures in many bodies such as the Devil's Tower, Wyoming, and the Giants Causeway, Wales, come close to outlining hexagonal patterns in sections. The fracture faces of these columns

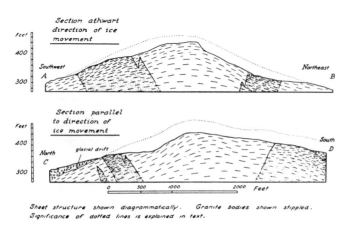

Sheet structure shown diagrammatically. Granite bodies shown stippled. Significance of dotted lines is explained in text.

Fig. 3-20 Cross sections of Kittredge Hill showing relations of rock types, sheet structure, and topography. (*From Jahns, 1943.*)

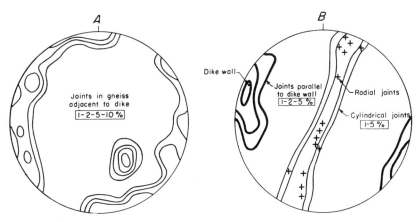

Fig. 3-21 Joint measurements in and adjacent to dike with cylindrical columnar joints, Cloverleaf Lakes area. (*a*) Poles to joints in gneiss adjacent to dike, 100 readings. (*b*) Poles to joints in dike with cylindrical columnar jointing—joints parallel to dike wall, 50 readings; cylindrical columnar joints, 100 readings; radial joints, 15 readings. Diagrams are equal-area projections on the lower hemisphere. (*From Prinz and Bentley, 1964.*)

form approximately normal to the cooling face (and isotherms) of the igneous body; therefore, in a flat-lying sill they are vertical. If the body varies in thickness the fractures fan out. A secondary fracture usually associated with the columnar joints lies in the plane normal to the long axis of the column and is commonly referred to as *sheeting*. These sheets are typically saucer-shaped with the concave side facing upward.

Although the simple pattern described above is common, it is by no means universal and even in bodies which display well-developed columnar joints, the joints may be traced into fractures of much more complex character. Such is the case at the Palisades sill in New Jersey, where concentric cylinder-shaped joints, radiating planar fractures, and curviplanar fractures can all be seen near the top surface of the sill. All of these are approximately normal to the sill surface. Similar cylindrical columnar fractures have been described in much thinner Precambrian dikes in the Beartooth Mountains of Montana (Prinz and Bentley, 1964), as shown in Fig. 3-21. These dikes have three dominant joint sets: one parallel to the dike wall, the

cylindrical set normal to the wall, and a set of radial fractures.

Hill (1965) describes probable modes of development of curviplanar and concentric fractures in a dolerite sill in Tasmania. Some of the fracture patterns found in this study are illustrated in Fig. 3-22. These were found near the base of a sill more than 2,000 ft thick. Hill favors the idea that these patterns formed on the explosive release of stresses accumulated in the central part of the sill during cooling. In a cooling slab the surfaces are in tension as a result of contraction on cooling, and the center is brought under compression (Preston, 1926). As the cooling proceeds, fractures are extended from the margins into the center where the rate of advance becomes very rapid, virtually explosive. Figure 3-23 schematically illustrates the possible origin of the curviplanar fractures.

ANALYSIS OF REGIONAL FRACTURE PATTERNS

A fracture pattern of definite geometry can usually be determined at any sufficiently large rock outcrop. Sometimes the pattern can be re-

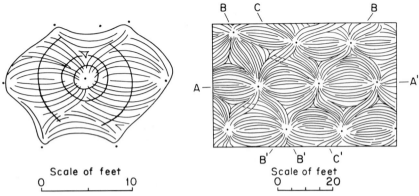

Fig. 3-22 Left: Concentric joints. Innermost ones are always at right angles to curviplanar joints, outer ones less so. Right: Festoon and bow-tie patterns formed by surface traces of curviplanar joints. (*From Hill, 1965.*)

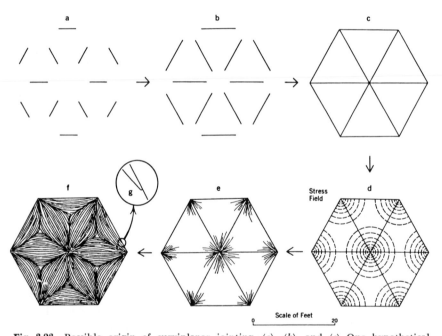

Fig. 3-23 Possible origin of curviplanar jointing. (*a*), (*b*), and (*c*) One hypothetical cross section at three different time intervals, spaced 1 msec apart, depicting the upward propagation of master columnar joints originating below, in the lower columnar zone. These have their leading edge convex-upward. (*d*) An interim period, duration unknown; stress is concentrated along the edges of the triangular prisms (here represented by triangles). (*e*) and (*f*) A hypothetical cross section spaced about 1 msec apart, showing curviplanar fractures beginning at edges of prisms and being propagated with their leading edge concave-upward and developing at right angles to the stress lines of (*d*). (*g*) The right-angle relationship sought, but not found, in the field between master columnar joints (planar joints) and curviplanar joints. (*Note:* Edge is used in this description in two different senses.) (*From Hill, 1965.*)

lated to the structural feature of which the rock is a part in such a way that conclusions regarding the nature of the stress field responsible for the fracturing can be drawn. Interest in determination of regional patterns is partially derived from the hope that similar conclusions can be drawn on a regional basis where the pattern is consistent over a region or where regional components can be recognized. Where regional patterns do exist, it is important that they be identified if an attempt is to be made to relate other fractures to particular structural features. Regional patterns have been identified in many places, but explanations of their origin have not been widely accepted. Some of the more ambitious efforts have sought to establish patterns of worldwide scope. Several attempts have been made to relate most of the major faults and submarine lineaments to global shear patterns; others have concluded that most regional patterns are extensional in origin.

Examples of several types of regional studies have been selected to illustrate variations in regional patterns and in the interpretive use of the data. The fracture patterns in the Appalachian Plateau are regional in nature and largely unrelated to the broad folds on which they occur. A much closer relationship between regional structure and fracture patterns seems to emerge in the Colorado Plateau. Fracture patterns in Oklahoma and in the Basin and Range region have been related to regional stress systems, and the nature of Precambrian fracture patterns and their influence on later events is examined for one of the large Precambrian exposures in the Middle Rocky Mountains.

Appalachian Plateau

Several significant studies have been made of regional fracture patterns in the Appalachian Plateau region (Parker, 1942; Nickelsen and Hough, 1967). The region is particularly suitable for such analysis because fracture patterns are well developed in several rock types, shale, coal, sandstones, of late Paleozoic age which are

widely distributed over a region in which folding dies out as one proceeds from the southeast to the northwest across it. The axial traces of the folds, most of which are broad and open, bend to form a broad arcuate belt in Pennsylvania.

Both Parker and Nickelsen found that fractures have locally consistent patterns for any given rock type, and that regional patterns do exist, but these patterns are not directly related to the folds on which they are so often well developed. Both conclude that the regional patterns predate the folding. Evidence for this is found by Parker in that one fracture set that is parallel to the direction of dip in the southwestern part of the area swings until it is parallel to strike of bedding in the east. Nickelsen found that fractures in coal are completely independent of fold axis trends, that fractures in shale are more consistent regionally than are fold axis orientations, that fractures are rotated near faults, and that a systematic fracture pattern continues west of the folded part of the plateau. The pattern consists of trends of uniform orientation which overlap one another. Although the regional pattern is not related to fold trends, each trend is best developed where it is most nearly perpendicular to fold axes.

The interpretation of the origin of the patterns differs in these two studies. Nickelsen and Hough favor an extensional origin for the fractures on the basis of their open, lensing nature; the character of the surfaces; and the lack of lateral movement. Where complex patterns occur, they are interpreted as an overprinting of systematic and nonsystematic sets (Fig. 3-24).

Parker interpreted the regional pattern as consisting of two sets of shear fractures which intersect at about 19° and one set approximately at right angles to the first two, which is attributed to tension.

A system of fracturing in Carboniferous coal beds in eastern Ohio also shows a regional swing. These fractures form cleats in the coal and are perpendicular to one another and normal to bedding. The trends of the sets swing

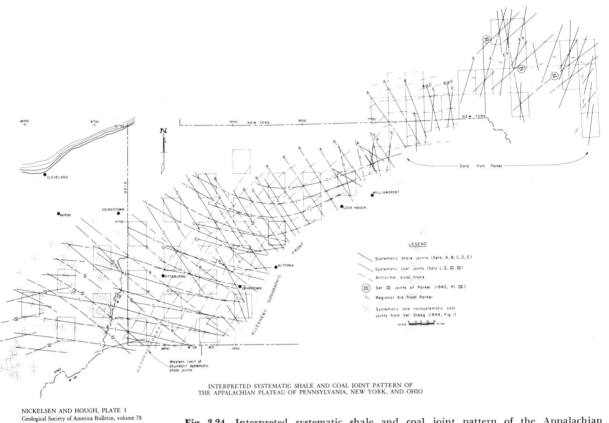

Fig. 3-24 Interpreted systematic shale and coal joint pattern of the Appalachian Plateau of New York, Ohio, and Pennsylvania. (*Redrawn from Nickelsen and Hough, 1967.*)

regionally in an arc convex to the west and following the swing of Appalachian folds (Ver Steeg, 1942). The origin of the cleat is uncertain. It has been interpreted as a shrinkage feature. The rocks in which they occur are little deformed, but the regional swing may be of tectonic origin.

Fracture Systems in Oklahoma

Melton (1929) analyzed the fracture patterns of the central Oklahoma plains and demonstrated their relation to the Ouachita Mountains of southeastern Oklahoma. The Ouachita Mountains consist of a belt of folded and thrust-faulted Paleozoic sedimentary rocks. The front of the zone of intense deformation swings across

southeastern Oklahoma, and the direction of movement was from the southeast toward the west and northwest. Concentric with this belt of strong deformation is an outer belt of broadly folded Paleozoic rocks, and beyond this lie the nearly flat, slightly deformed Paleozoic rocks of the plains. Although the rock units exposed in the plains are very slightly deformed, they are fractured (Fig. 4-57). The *en échelon* fracture pattern is one of the most prominent structural features of this region. The lengths of the lines used to show fracture directions (Fig. 3-25) provide a measure of the percentage of the fractures at a station with the direction shown. A vector scale is provided to use in measuring the lengths of the fracture lines. Where the bedding dips more than 5°, it has been rotated back to a horizontal position and the fractures have been rotated a similar amount before they were plotted. The fracture systems thus indicated are presumably formed before folding. The pattern is one of fanning fractures apparently related to the Ouachita Mountains. Melton concludes that the fractures formed in response to the stress fields developed during the folding and faulting of the Ouachitas, and that the stress system was operating at or later than the youngest fractured rocks, which are Permian in age.

Friedman (1964) has reinterpreted Melton's fracture data and concludes that the data show

four sets of fractures (Fig. 3-26). Two of these sets, *A* and *B*, are approximately at right angles to one another. The other two sets intersect at acute angles, are approximately bisected by set *D*, and probably represent conjugate shears. The entire pattern is not equally developed; the *C* set is the best developed of the sets, and the patterns are slightly rotated with changes in the strike of beds. The conjugate shears are interpreted as having formed in response to horizontally directed maximum principal stresses everywhere normal to the trend of the Ouachita Mountain front (the intermediate stress axis is interpreted as vertical). Set *B* would

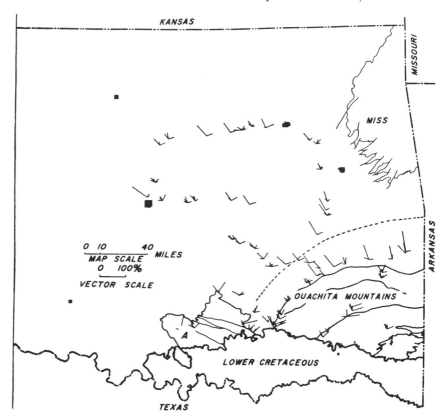

Fig. 3-25 The joint vectors shown in the Central Plains. At all stations where the bedding dips more than 5°, it has been rotated back to the horizontal position around the line of its strike. The joints have been rotated an equal amount in the same direction around the same line. To the extent that the joints were formed before folding and faulting, their original positions have been restored. In the open fold zone the coincidence of these strikes with those of the same joints in the unrotated positions is remarkable. (*From Friedman, 1964, after Melton, 1929.*)

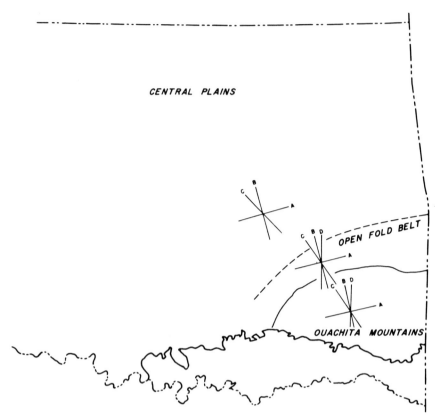

Fig. 3-26 The average fracture patterns in the Central Plains, open fold zone, and Ouachita Mountains. (*From Friedman, 1964.*)

then be a tension set, and set *A* is interpreted as resulting from relaxation of compressive stresses. Because the beds in the plains are nearly flat, the *A* set could not be a tension set developed along a fold crest during compression.

Regional Fault Patterns in the Great Basin

The trends of the faults and edges of block-faulted mountain ranges in the Great basin have been compiled in several studies. Donath (1962) prepared a rose diagram showing the frequency of fault strike directions in a 420-sq-mile area of southern Oregon (Fig. 3-27). Two maxima emerge from this plot, one about N 20° E, the second about N 35° W. Most of the faults repre-

sented in these plots are vertical or very steep. The pattern is interpreted as a set of conjugate shear directions developed in a stress system in which the maximum or principal stress direction is oriented north-south (Fig. 3-28).

Stokes (1964) reports the analysis of fault patterns over an area of 40,000 sq miles in the Great basin. He measured 3,053 faults and analyzed both orientation and aggregate lengths of faults along each direction. The total aggregate length of these faults was 4,130 miles. Rose diagram plots reveal that the maximum number of faults and the greatest aggregate miles of faults fall between N 20° W and N 25° E, with the greatest concentrations between north-south and N 10° W. He noted that the N 50–60° W trend associated with the ancestral Rockies in eastern Utah is weak in the Great basin.

This strong north-south orientation is one that is repeatedly found in structures in the Rocky Mountain region, and it can be related to the conjugate set suggested by Donath (1962). The north-south faults may be explained as having formed in response to extension normal to the direction of the principal stress.

The Colorado Plateau

Aerial photographs (Fig. 3-29) have been used to analyze fracture patterns in the Colorado Plateau. Lineaments from the photographs are shown plotted on a regional map of the area covering parts of four states. The rocks of the

plateau, largely Mesozoic sandstones and shales, have been deformed. Broad basins, elongate domes, block faulting, and various types of flexures are found in the region. Kelley (1960) found great variation in the frequency and orientation of fractures in adjacent beds and in the number of sets present from place to place. Fractures are commonly vertical in the flat-lying beds, but inclined on the monoclinal flexures. Fractures on three of the uplifts in the plateau (Fig. 3-30) show quite different patterns. Two sets are prominent on the Uncompahgre uplift. These are transverse and longitudinal to the uplift and may be explained as having originated from extension of the beds both along and normal to the axis. Other sets are

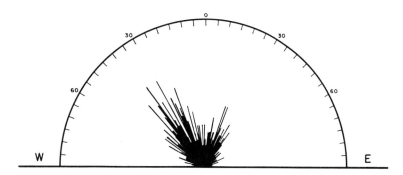

Fig. 3-27 Fault-strike frequency diagrams; 625 faults and fault segments plotted at 1° intervals. Radius of diagram equals 18 faults or fault segments. (*From Donath, 1962.*)

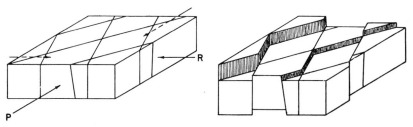

Fig. 3-28 Diagrammatic representation of structural development in the Summer Lake area. North-south maximum principal stress *P* and east-west minimum principal stress *R* produced a system of conjugate strike-slip shears. Redistribution of surface forces caused dip-slip movements and resultant fault blocks. Note the inverse relation shown at the right rear of the block. (*From Donath, 1962.*)

Fig. 3-29   Aerial photograph of fractures in the Colorado Plateau. (*U.S. Geol. Survey.*)

oblique and are presumably shear sets. Sets oblique to the axis are found on the Monument uplift. Here two such sets are evident near the central part of the uplift, while a strongly developed transverse set appears at the north end. The San Rafael swell fractures are interesting in that the density of the fractures is related to the asymmetry of the structure. Longitudinal, transverse, and oblique fractures are all evident.

Fractures in Basement Rocks

Basement rocks in the Grand Canyon show three prominent fracture sets (Hodgson, 1961b) with trends northeast, northwest, and N 70° W (Fig. 3-31). These fractures formed initially in the Precambrian; they contain Precambrian pegmatite dikes. Faults with the same trend became activated during the Laramide deformation, and the same trends have become estab-

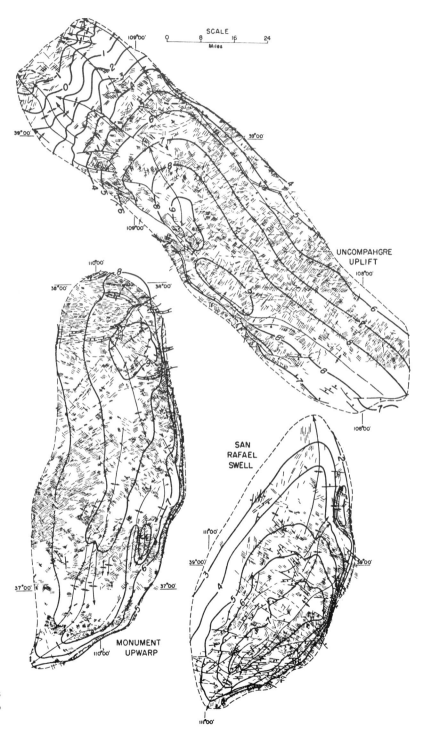

Fig. 3-30 Fracture lineaments on three uplifts in the Colorado Plateau. (*From Kelley, 1960.*)

lished in the overlying sedimentary cover, as can be seen in the exposed layers in the canyon wall (Fig. 3-31). Many fracture directions in the sedimentary layers appear to have been inherited from the basement, and these zones of basement weakness have often had a controlling influence on the development of structural features in the overlying cover when they have been reactivated.

Although fracture directions in the sedimentary cover are often the same as fracture sets in the basement, the Precambrian rocks often have a much more complex pattern consisting of other sets as well (Hoppin and Palmquist, 1965). The fracture patterns are also governed by lithology and often show variation from layer to layer when compositions of layers are different.

Patterns in the Precambrian Basement

The highly elevated blocklike uplifts of the Middle Rocky Mountains have been stripped of their Paleozoic sedimentary veneer in many places, exposing an early Precambrian granitized crystalline basement which typically shows a well-developed system of major fracture zones. Many of the zones are parallel to margins of the uplifts or the axes of major structural features that are dated as being of Laramide age. When it was discovered that these same trends are occupied by dikes of Precambrian age it became apparent that much of the Laramide deformation was controlled by ancient Precambrian zones of weakness.

The regional pattern has been analyzed in the Beartooth Mountains (Spencer, 1959), where 25,000 fractures were measured (100 at each of 250 stations) over an area of 700 sq miles. Many local variations in pattern are found, but when the data are summarized by plotting the concentrations from each station on a point diagram, the concentrations shown in Fig. 3-32 are found. This pattern consists mainly of vertical sets with strong trends of N 45° E, N 45° W,

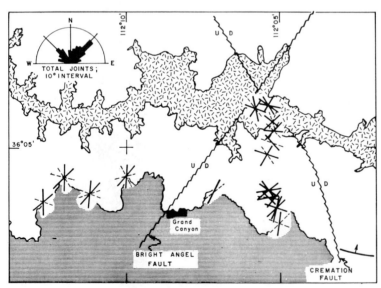

RECONNAISSANCE   JOINT   SURVEY,   BRIGHT   ANGEL   AREA
GRAND CANYON, ARIZONA
Robert A. Hodgson
1964

0   4000'   12,000'

KAIBAB LS. (PERMIAN)   VISHNU SERIES (PRE ϵ)

Fig. 3-31 Map showing joint directions measured in Bright Angel area of Grand Canyon, Ariz. Scale in feet. (*From Hodgson, 1965.*)

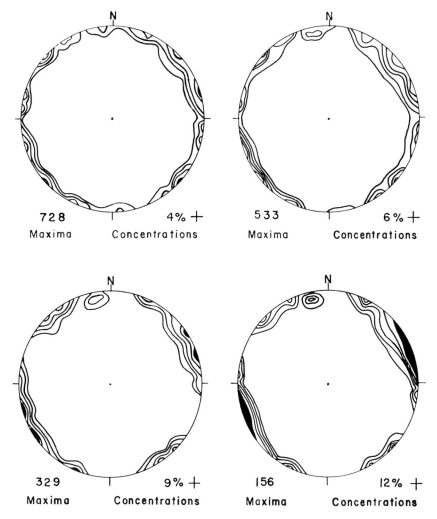

Fig. 3-32 Fracture concentrations from point diagrams of stations on the southwestern slope of the Beartooth uplift. Diagrams were obtained by plotting the concentrations from each point diagram of every station on the southwestern slope of the uplift as points with the coordinates of the center of that concentration on a Schmidt net. This was done for all concentrations of 4 percent plus, 6 percent plus, 9 percent plus, and 12 percent plus. The number of concentrations, maxima, used for each diagram is given. The lowest contour for each diagram is 2 percent, and the contour interval is 1 percent. (*From Spencer, 1959.*)

N 65° W, and N 15° W. In addition, a number of less prominent trends are indicated. The age of the fracture pattern is established because all of these trends are occupied by Precambrian dikes. Moreover, several sets of dikes of different

Precambrian ages occupied these fracture sets at different times, indicating a repeated activation of these zones of weakness. Wise (1964) extended the study to show that the same fracture trends occur in other areas of Precambrian exposure in the Middle Rocky Mountains and that the same regional trends which occur as major fracture zones are found among *microjoints,* defined as four or more macroscopic subparallel fractures spaced closer than 3 mm. A comparison between fracture and dike lineaments from aerial photographs of the Beartooth Range and the measurements on the ground show that the two types of data do yield similar results, but they are by no means identical. A closer parallelism might be expected in regions of less complicated structure.

Patterns of similar orientation are found in the Big Horn Mountains, the Wind River Mountains of Wyoming, and the Madison Mountains of Montana. The patterns are notable for the steepness of the most prominent sets, but the large number of trend directions precludes reaching a conclusive answer to the question of the origin of the fractures.

Complex fracture patterns similar to those in the Beartooth Range are found in the Canadian shield (Mollard, 1957). The fractures are similar in age, in the preponderance of vertical set, in that the patterns consist of paired sets that are nearly perpendicular to one another (Fig. 3-33), and in that shatter zones are common.

Basement Fracture Zones

Basement rock in the Grand Canyon, the Rocky Mountains, the Canadian shield, and other shield areas is usually broken by complex fracture systems. Sometimes fracturing is evident down to the individual feldspar crystal, but we are more aware of the larger fractures seen in outcrops and the fracture zones. Some of these zones are faults or weathered dikes, but in others, called *shatter zones,* faulting is uncertain. They are zones from a few feet to several tens of feet wide, in which the rock is intensively fractured. These zones show up on aerial photographs as strong lineaments and are likely to be of great tectonic importance. The fracture zones typically have the same orientation as a prominent set of fractures. It is likely that these fracture zones localized the basement yield during the Laramide, determining the position of uplifts. These zones also would be the natural lines of weakness for lateral crustal movements along strike slip faults.

The origin of these basement fractures and zones of weakness is not known. They most certainly formed after the cooling of the magmas and after the high grade metamorphism which affected the rocks in which they are developed. Mollard (1957) has pointed out that these strong lineaments also appear in flat-lying Paleozoic sedimentary rocks, and in Pleistocene deposits in the Canadian shield. The surfaces

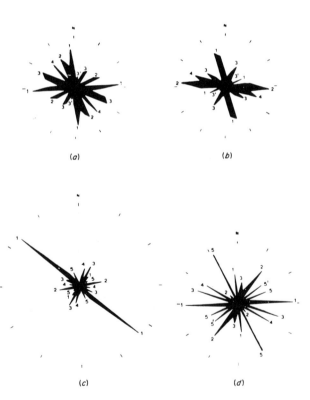

(a)   (b)

(c)   (d)

Fig. 3-33 Rose diagrams showing the directions of lineations, revealed by aerial photographs, southern Saskatchewan. These directions are similar to those of the fracture patterns in the underlying bedrock. Each direction might be accompanied by a usually less pronounced conjugate one, approximately perpendicular to the first. (*After Mollard, 1959.*)

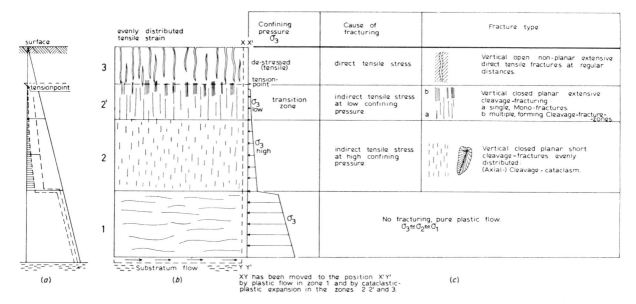

Fig. 3-34 Highly idealized model (II) showing the generation of four types of vertical tension joints in close connection with one another. (*From Gramberg, 1966.*)

on which they appear are as varied as glacial lake beds, alluvial flood plains, muskeg, marshes, and glacial scoured bedrock. Thus the trends are being impressed on unconsolidated materials at present, which gives us cause to wonder if the trends are now being impressed on the new sediment by the same process which caused them initially.

Among the ideas which have been put forward to explain the origin of these fractures are:

1. Earth tides. (These appear too weak to cause fractures initially, but they might be effective in propagating basement fractures upward into the cover).
2. Oscillatory response (perhaps at resonance) to a nonoscillatory force such as earthquakes.
3. Crustal compression at depth.
4. Isostatic adjustments causing extension.
5. Expansion of the earth's interior causing extension in the crust.

Unfortunately, there are no criteria by which

we can conclusively evaluate these various possibilities.

Gramberg (1966) has advanced the idea that most vertical fractures in the crust, without shearing movement in the fracture plane, are caused by tensile stresses; the best explanation is that they begin as a "Griffith crack." Two types of external loading are recognized: (1) direct tensile loading in which the crack forms normal to the tensile load; a single crack is formed leaving an open gap with rough walls; (2) indirect or induced tensile loading in which the fracture plane extends in the direction of the major load axis and normal to the minor load. Closely spaced fractures are formed which cut through mineral grains, pebbles, etc. These fractures, also called *axial cleavage fracturing* by Gramberg, form as short, closed fractures more or less evenly distributed through the rock, as a single closed fracture, or as a zone of closely repeated, closed fractures.

The above tension fractures are generated by some external process, e.g., convection flow in the mantle or expansion of the earth. The crust may be divided into three zones (Fig. 3-34): (1) a zone in which the rock is in a ductile state, purely plastically deformable, (2) rock in a brittle state, so deep that vertical lithological pressure is sufficient to cause indirect tensile fracturing, (3) brittle rock too shallow for the lithological pressure to cause induced fracturing. According to Gramberg's model, most regional fracture patterns, particularly those in basement rocks, form as a result of ductile flow in zone 1 which causes destressing in horizontal directions within zones 2 and 1. Two vertical fracture systems may form at right angles to one another if both the least and the intermediate stress directions are horizontal, and multiple vertical fracture directions may arise from several periods of destressing.

REFERENCES

Appleby, A. N., 1940, Joint patterns in highly folded and crystalline rocks of the New Jersey Highlands: Geol. Soc. America Bull., v. 51, p. 1919.

Balk, Robert, 1937, Structural behavior of igneous rocks: Geol. Soc. America Mem. 5.

Bonham, L. C., 1957, Structural petrology of the Pico anticline: Jour. Sed. Petrology, v. 27.

Boyer, R. E., and others, 1961, Comparison of two joint study methods, applied to the Red Mountain gneiss, Llano County, Texas: Texas Jour. Sci., v. 13.

Brace, W. F., 1960, An extension of the Griffith theory of fracture to rocks: Jour. Geophys. Research, v. 65, no. 10, p. 3477–3480.

Bucher, W. H., 1920–1921, Mechanical interpretation of joints: Jour. Geology, v. 28, p. 207.

Chapman, C. A., and Rioux, R. L., 1958, Statistical study of topography, sheeting and jointing in granite, Acadia National Park, Maine: Am. Jour. Sci., v. 256.

Chiliggar, G., and Richards, C. A., 1954, Use of gash fractures in determining direction and relative amount of movement along faults: Compass, v. 31.

Cleary, J. M., 1958, Hydraulic fracture theory, pts. I and II: Illinois Geol. Survey Circs. 251 and 252.

——— 1959, Hydraulic fracture theory, pt. III—Elastic properties of sandstone: Illinois Geol. Survey Circ. 281, 44 p.

Cloos, Ernst, 1968, Experimental analysis of Gulf Coast fracture patterns: Am. Assoc. Petroleum Geologists Bull., v. 52, no. 3, p. 420–444.

De Sitter, L. U., 1964, Structural geology, 2d ed.: New York, McGraw-Hill, 587 p.

Donath, F. A., 1961, Experimental study of shear failure in anisotropic rocks: Geol. Soc. America Bull., v. 72, no. 6, p. 985–989.

——— 1962, Analysis of basin-range structure, south-central Oregon: Geol. Soc. America Bull., v. 73, p. 1–16.

——— 1963, Strength variation and deformational behavior in anisotropic rock: Internat. Conf. State of Stress in Earth's Crust Proc., Santa Monica, Rand Corp.

Fairhurst, C., ed., 1963, Rock mechanics: New York, Pergamon, 726 p.

Fath, A. E., 1920, The origin of the faults, anticlines and buried "granite ridge" of the northern part of the Mid-continent oil and gas field: U. S. Geol. Survey Prof. Paper 128*A, p. 75–84.

Firman, R. J., 1960, The relationship between joints and fault patterns in the Eskdale granite (Cumberland) and the adjacent Borrowdale volcanic series: Geol. Soc. London Quart. Jour., v. CXVI p. 317–347.

Friedman, Melvin, 1964, Petrofabric techniques for the determination of principal stress directions in rocks, in State of stress in the earth's crust: New York, Elsevier, 1964.

Gramberg, J., 1965, Axial cleavage fracturing, a significant process in mining and geology: Eng. Geol., v. 1, p. 31–72.

——— 1966, A theory on the occurrence of various types of vertical and sub-vertical joints in the earthcrust: Internat. Soc. Rock Mechanics, Cong. Proc., 1st, p. 443–450.

Griffith, A. A., 1920, The phenomena of rupture and flow in solids: Royal Soc. [London] Philos. Trans., ser. A, v. 221, p. 163–198.

——— 1924, The theory of rupture: Proc. Internat. Cong. Appl. Mechanics, 1st, Delft, p. 55–63.

Griggs, D. T., 1954, High pressure phenomena with applications to geophysics, in Ridenour, L. N., ed., Modern physics for the engineer: New York, McGraw-Hill, p. 272–305.

Griggs, D. T., and Handin, John, 1960, Observations on fracture and a hypothesis of earthquakes, in Griggs, D., and Handin, J., eds., Rock deformation—a symposium: Geol. Soc. America Mem. 79, p. 347–373.

Harris, J. F., 1960, Relation of deformational fractures in sedimentary rocks to regional and local structure: Am. Assoc. Petroleum Geologists Bull., v. 44, p. 1853–1873.

Hill, P. A., 1965, Curviplanar (radial, bow-tie, festoon) and concentric jointing in Jurassic Dolerite, Mersey Bluff, Tasmania: Jour. Geology, v. 73, p. 255–271.

Hodgson, R. A., 1961a, Classification of structures of joint surfaces: Am. Jour. Sci., v. 259.

———— 1961b, Regional study of jointing in Comb Ridge–Navajo Mountain area, Arizona and Utah: Am. Assoc. Petroleum Geologists Bull., v. 45, p. 1–39.

———— 1965, Genetic and geometric relations between structures *in* basement and overlying sedimentary rocks, with examples from Colorado Plateau and Wyoming: Am. Assoc. Petroleum Geologists Bull., v. 49, p. 935.

Hoppin, R. A., and Palmquist, J. C., 1965, Basement influence on later deformation: the problem, techniques of investigation, and examples from Bighorn Mountains, Wyoming: Am. Assoc. Petroleum Geologists Bull., v. 49, p. 993–1004.

Hubbert, M. K., 1951, Mechanical basis for certain familiar geologic structures: Geol. Soc. America Bull., v. 62, no. 4, p. 255–372.

Hutchinson, R. M., 1956, Structure and petrology of the enchanted rock batholith, Llano and Gillespie Counties, Texas: Geol. Soc. America Bull., v. 67, p. 763–806.

Jaeger, J. C., 1960, Shear failure of anisotropic rocks: Geol. Mag. [Great Britain], v. 97, p. 65–72.

Jahns, R. H., 1943, Sheet structure in granite: its origin and use as a measure of glacial erosion in New England: Jour. Geology, v. 51, p. 71–98.

Kelley, V. C., 1960, Slips and separations: Geol. Soc. America Bull., v. 71, p. 1545–1546.

Kelley, V. C., and Clinton, N. J., 1960, Fracture systems and tectonic elements of the Colorado Plateau: New Mexico Univ. Pubs. Geology No. 6, 104 p.

Lachenbush, A. H., 1961, Depth and spacing of tension cracks: Jour. Geophys. Research, v. 66.

Lovering, T. S., 1928, The fracturing of incompetent beds: Jour. Geology, v. 36, p. 709–717.

McKinstry, H. E., 1953, Shears of the second order: Am. Jour. Sci., v. 251, no. 6, p. 401–414.

Melton, F. A., 1929, A reconnaissance of the joint systems in the Ouachita Mountains and central plains of Oklahoma: Jour. Geology, v. 37, p. 729–746.

Mollard, J. D., 1959, Aerial mosaics reveal fracture patterns on surface materials in southern Saskatchewan and Manitoba: Oil in Canada, v. 9, no. 40, p. 26–50.

Muehlberger, W. R., 1961, Conjugate joint sets of small dihedral angle: Jour. Geology, v. 69, no. 2, p. 211–219.

Nickelsen, R. P., and Hough, V. N. D., 1967, Jointing in the Appalachian Plateau of Pennsylvania: Geol. Soc. America Bull., v. 78, p. 609–630.

Ode, Helmer, 1960, Faulting as a velocity discontinuity in plastic deformation, *in* Griggs, D. T., and Handin, J., Rock deformation—a symposium: Geol. Soc. America Mem. 79, p. 293–321.

Orowan, E., 1949, Fracture and strength in solids: Repts. Prog. Physics, v. 12, p. 185–232.

———— 1960, Mechanism of seismic faulting, *in* Griggs, D. T., and Handin, J., Rock deformation—a symposium: Geol. Soc. American Mem. 79, p. 323–346.

Parker, J. M., 1942, Regional jointing systematic in slightly deformed sedimentary rocks: Geol. Soc. America Bull., v. 53.

Pincus, H. J., 1951, Statistical methods applied to the study of rock fractures: Geol. Soc. America Bull., v. 62, p. 403–410.

Preston, F. W., 1926, The spalling of bricks: Am. Ceramic Soc. Jour., v. 9, p. 654–658.

Price, N. J., 1958, A study of rock properties in conditions of triaxial stress, *in* Walton, W. H., ed., Mechanical properties of non-metallic brittle materials: London, Butterworth, p. 106–122.

———— 1966, Fault and joint development in brittle and semibrittle rock: New York, Pergamon, 176 p.

Prinz, Martin, and Bentley, R. D., 1964, Cylindrical columnar jointing in dolerite dikes, Beartooth Mountains, Montana–Wyoming: Geol. Soc. America Bull., v. 75, p. 1165–1168.

Richey, J. E., 1939, The dykes of Scotland: Geol. Soc. Edinburgh Trans., v. 13, no. 4, p. 393.

Roberts, J. C., 1961, Feather-fracture, and the mechanics of rock-jointing: Am. Jour. Sci., v. 259, no. 7.

Secor, D. T., Jr., 1965, Role of fluid pressure in jointing: Am. Jour. Sci., v. 263.

Sheldon, P. G., 1912, Some observations and experiments on joint-planes: Jour. Geology, v. 20.

Spencer, E. W., 1959, Fracture patterns in the Beartooth Mountains, Montana and Wyoming: Geol. Soc. America Bull., v. 70, p. 467–508.

Spry, A., 1962, The origin of columnar jointing, particularly in basalt flows: Geol. Soc. Australia Jour., v. 8, p. 191–216.

Stokes, W. L., 1964, Analysis of Eastern Great Basin fault patterns [abs.]: Geol. Soc. America Ann. Mtg. Program, p. 197.

Swanson, C. O., 1927, Notes on stress and strain joints: Jour. Geology, v. 35, p. 193–223.

Turner, F. J., and Weiss, L. E., 1963, Structural analysis of metamorphic tectonites: New York, McGraw-Hill, 560 p.

Ver Steeg, K., 1942, Jointing in the central coal beds of Ohio: Econ. Geology, v. 37.

Vinogradov, S. D., 1960, On the distribution of the number of fractures in dependence of the energy liberated by the destruction of rocks: Izvestiya, Geophys. Ser., Trans. 1959, no. 12, p. 1292–1293.

Wager, L. R., 1931, Jointing in the Great Scar limestone of Craven and its relation to the tectonics of the area: Geol. Soc. London Quart. Jour., v. 87, p. 392–420.

Wallace, R. E., 1951, Geometry of shearing stress and relation for faulting: Jour. Geology, v. 59, no. 2, p. 118–130.

Wilson, C. W., Jr., 1934, A study of jointing in the Five Springs Creek area, east of Kane, Wyoming: Jour. Geology, v. 42, p. 489–522.

Wilson, G., 1960, Tectonics of the Great Ice Chasm, etc.: Geol. Assoc. Proc., v. 71, p. 130.

Wilson, J. Tuzo, 1954, A physical explanation of graben and zwischengebirge: Am. Geophys. Union Trans., v. 35, no. 2, p. 386.

Wise, D. U., 1964, Microjointing in basement, Middle Rocky Mountains of Montana and Wyoming: Geol. Soc. America Bull., v. 75, p. 287–306.

Woodworth, J. B., 1896, Fracture system of joints: Soc. Natural History Boston, v. 27.

Zumberge, J. H., 1960, Geologic studies of the Ross Ice Shelf, Antarctica: Rept. Internat. Geol. Cong. XXI Sess., Norway, p. 60–67.

Zumberge, J. H., and others, 1960, Deformation of the Ross Ice Shelf near the Bay of Whales, Antarctica: Intern. Geophys. Year Glaciological Rept. Ser., no. 3.

4

faults

INTRODUCTION TO THE GLOSSARY OF
FAULT NOMENCLATURE

A fault is a break or zone in crustal rocks parallel to which there has been displacement. Such breaks are often evident at the ground surface where the *fault trace* may be represented by an escarpment or made evident by displaced surface features. Faults occur in a broad range of structural situations varying from minor faults associated with flexural folds to major fault zones which form borders for large mountain ranges and others which are major zones of weakness in the earth's crust. Some of these faults can be traced to depths of thousands of feet, and their presence to depths as great as 700 km is inferred from the depth of the deep focus earthquakes which are thought to result from movements along faults.

The fault plane may be a smooth, a finely striated, or a slickensided surface, but more commonly it is a zone ranging from several feet to several hundred feet in width in which the rock has been brecciated or mylonitized. In many instances the fault zone is composed of a number of subparallel faults, *synthetic faults*. In these the bedding may be systematically displaced as in a step fault pattern or the sections of rock caught between faults may be folded and rotated forming a chaotic structural pattern.

Fault nomenclature which follows in glossary and illustrated form is involved because the number of variables is great. The fault attitude, the attitude of the faulted beds relative to the fault, and the amount, direction, and type of movement between the blocks may all vary. The movement may be such that adjacent points are displaced by translation, by rotation, or by both.

In the study of a fault such problems as determining the amount and direction of actual displacement are encountered, or it may be necessary to locate the position of some displaced unit. This must normally be accomplished through the use of distances between portions of displaced beds on

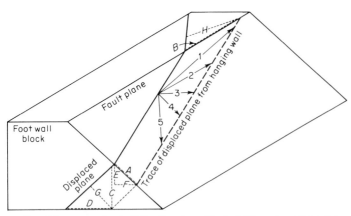

The strike-separation is *B*, the dip-separation is *A*. Other separations are:
   C Vertical
   D Horizontal
   E Vertical component of dip
   F Horizontal component of dip
   G Stratigraphic
   H Normal horizontal

Only the dip separation *A* and the strike separation *B* are used to classify a fault.
   Some possible net-slips are shown by 1 through 5. Notice that (1) has a relative upward component of the hanging wall and that (5) has a lateral component of actual relative displacement.

Fig. 4-1   Diagram of left-lateral fault showing separations and slips. (*Redrawn from M. L. Hill, 1947.*)

opposite sides of the fault (separations of beds across the fault). Separations may be observed from a geologic map or from subsurface data, and they provide the basis for Hill's (1947, 1959) fault classification. The various types of separations include horizontal separation of two beds along some particular direction (along the strike of the fault in the case of strike separation), the amount of separation in some particular vertical line, separation down the dip of the fault, separation obliquely in the fault, or stratigraphic separation (the thickness of beds omitted between units adjacent on opposite sides of the fault) (Fig. 4-1). Separations shown in Fig. 4-1 include:

   A = dip separation
   B = strike separation
   C = vertical separation
   D = horizontal separation (in dip plane)
   E = vertical component of dip separation
   F = horizontal component of dip separation

   G = stratigraphic or perpendicular separation
   H = normal horizontal separation

Only the dip separation *A* and the strike separation *B* are used to classify a fault. Some possible net slips are shown by 1 to 5. Notice that 1 has a relative upward component of the hanging wall and that 5 has a right-lateral component of actual relative displacement.

Slip

Another class of terms is related to the actual relative displacements of formerly adjacent points on opposite sides of the fault, called *slip*. It is possible to determine net slip or actual relative displacement if two such adjacent points can be located. This is possible if some elements of a linear character were offset by the fault. Crowell (1959) points out some linear features which may be used:

   1. Lines formed by intersection of two planes such as the line of intersection of two

dikes, a dike with a bed, two veins, etc.

2. Lines formed by the trace of one plane on another:
   a. Trace of a bed below or above an unconformity against the unconformity
   b. Any older structure terminating against an unconformity or older fault (faults, dikes, sills, veins, sheets, fold axial surfaces, etc.)
3. Linear geological features:
   a. Buried river channels, shoestring sand, attenuated sand lines
   b. Volcanic necks, ore shoots, etc.
   c. Recent physiographic features along recent faults
4. Stratigraphic lines:
   a. Pinch-out line
   b. Lines formed by facies changes
   c. Shoreline, basin marginal features
5. Constructed lines:
   a. Isopach lines
   b. Lithofacie lines
   c. Axial and crestal lines

It is essential to keep the distinction between the concepts of slip and separation clearly in mind. The separation of marker horizons along the fault or down its dip are often known. The actual movements which produced a given separation are rarely known because many different movement patterns can produce the same separations. Usually the data available to solve a fault problem are derived from a geologic map or from a well. These readily yield information about separations and rarely about slip.

FAULT NOMENCLATURE*

I. General Terms

Fault: A fracture or fracture zone along which there has been displacement of the two sides relative to one another parallel to the fracture. The displacement may be a few inches or many miles. (Reid, 1913, A. G. I. Glossary.)

Reid's definition is adequate to explain faulting in brittle materials, but displacements in plastic materials are not always accompanied by loss of cohesion. A more general definition of

* Definitions taken from Am. Geol. Inst., © 1960, Glossary of geology and related sciences, and are indicated by (A. G. I. Glossary).

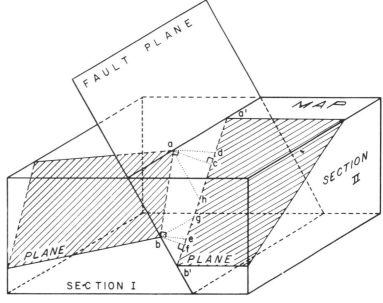

Fig. 4-2 Isometric block diagram showing several kinds of separation. Reference bedding plane, cut by fault, has different strike and dip on the two sides of fault. Front surface of block diagram is perpendicular to fault strike line. aa' = strike separation on map level (horizontal surface of block diagram); bb' = dip separation on section I; ah = dip separation through a ($ah \neq bb'$); bg = strike separation through b and g ($bg \neq aa'$); ac, ad, be, bf = separations perpendicular to one trace of bedding on fault, but not perpendicular to the other. (*From Crowell, 1959.*)

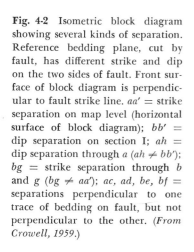

a fault would be: a zone across which there has been displacement of the two sides relative to one another parallel to the zone.

Fault block: A mass bounded on at least two opposite sides by faults; it may be elevated or depressed relative to the adjoining region, or it may be elevated relative to the region on one side and depressed relative to that on the other. (Reid and others, 1913, A. G. I. Glossary.)

Fault fold: A fold accompanied by steep faults that are parallel to the fold and are contemporaneous with the folding. Originally described from Saxony in Germany. (Hills, J. M., 1953, A. G. I. Glossary.)

Hanging wall: The mass of rock above a fault plane, vein, lode, or bed of ore. (Structural Committee, A. G. I. Glossary.)

Footwall: The mass of rock beneath a fault plane, vein, lode, or bed of ore. (Structural Committee, A. G. I. Glossary.)

Fault plane: A fault surface.

Fault scarp: "The cliff formed by a fault. Most fault scarps have been modified by erosion since the faulting." (U. S. Geol. Survey Bull. 611, p. 200, A. G. I. Glossary.)

Fault zone: A fault, instead of being a single clean fracture, may be a zone hundreds or thousands of feet wide; the fault zone consists of numerous interlacing small faults or a confused zone of gouge, breccia, or mylonite. (Billings, 1954, A. G. I. Glossary.)

Shear zone: In geology, a zone in which shearing has occurred on a large scale, so that the rock is crushed and brecciated. (La Forge, A. G. I. Glossary.)

Fault trace (syn.: *fault outcrop, fault line*): The intersection of a fault surface with the surface of the earth or with any artificial surface of reference. (Lindgren, 1933, A. G. I. Glossary.)

Hade: The angle of inclination of a vein, fault, or lode measured from the vertical.

Translational movement: Refers to movement along faults. All straight lines on opposite sides of the fault and outside the dislocated zone that were parallel before faulting are parallel after faulting. (Reid, 1913, A. G. I. Glossary.)

Rotational movement. Refers to movement on faults. Blocks rotate relative to one another about an axis perpendicular to the fault. Some straight lines on opposite sides of the zone and outside the dislocated zone, parallel before the displacement, are no longer parallel after it. (Reid, 1913, A. G. I. Glossary.)

II. Features of Fault Zones

Fault breccia (syn.: *crush breccia, fault gouge*): The assembly of broken fragments frequently found along faults. (Lindgren, 1933, A. G. I. Glossary.)

Mylonite: A fine-grained, laminated rock formed by extreme microbrecciation and milling of rocks during movement on fault surfaces. Metamorphism is dominantly cataclastic with little or no growth of new crystals.

Slickensides: Polished and striated (scratched) surface that results from friction along a fault plane. (Billings, 1954, A. G. I. Glossary.)

III. Apparent Relative Movements

Separation: Indicates the distance between any two parts of an index plane (bed, vein, etc.) disrupted by a fault measured in some specified direction. Horizontal separation is separation measured in any indicated horizontal direction; vertical separation is measured along a vertical line; stratigraphic separation is measured perpendicular to the bedding planes. (Billings, 1954, A. G. I. Glossary.)

Stratigraphic separation: Stratigraphic throw. The stratigraphic thickness that separates two beds brought into contact at a fault. (Billings, 1954, A. G. I. Glossary.)

Strike separation: In faulting, the distance on a map between the two parts of an index plane (bed, vein, dike, etc.) where they are in contact with the fault and measured parallel to the fault. (Reid, 1913, A. G. I. Glossary.)

Right (syn.: *right-lateral, right-handed, dextral*): Horizontal separation along a fault such that an observer walking along an index plane (bed, dike, vein, etc.) must, upon crossing the fault, turn to the right to find the index plane on the opposite side of the fault. The actual movement along the fault can be a strike-slip movement, a dip-slip movement, or a diagonal-slip movement. (Structural Committee, A. G. I. Glossary.)

Boyer and Muehlberger (1960) have suggested that the suffix *-lateral* be reserved for separation-based terms and *-handed* for slip-based terms.

Left (syn.: *left-lateral, left-handed, sinistral*): Horizontal separation along a fault such that an observer walking along an index plane (bed, dike, vein, etc.) must, upon crossing the fault, turn to the left to find the index plane on the opposite side of the fault. The actual movement along the fault can be a strike-slip movement, a dip-slip movement, or a diagonal-slip movement. (Billings, 1954, A. G. I. Glossary.)

Dip separation: In faulting, the distance between two parts of a disrupted index plane (bed, dike, vein, etc.) measured in the fault plane parallel to its dip. (Billings, 1954, A. G. I. Glossary.)

Offset (syn.: *normal horizontal separation*): Normal horizontal separation. Determined from outcrop of the index plane at the surface of the ground. In faulting, the *Horizontal separation,* q.v., can be measured parallel to the strike of the fault. Offset is the component of this horizontal separation that is measured perpendicular to the strike of the disrupted index plane (bed, dike, vein, etc.). (Reid, 1913, A. G. I. Glossary.)

Gap: In faulting, the *Horizontal separation,* q.v., can be measured parallel to the strike of the fault. Gap is the component of this separation that is measured parallel to the strike of the disrupted index plane (bed, dike, vein, etc.). Overlap is defined in the same way; however, gap is used when it is possible to walk at right angles to the strike of the disrupted index plane and miss it completely. Overlap is used when, under similar conditions, one would cross the index plane twice in certain places. (Reid, 1913, A. G. I. Glossary.)

Overlap: See *Gap.*

IV. Actual Relative Movements

Slip: The relative displacement of formerly adjacent points on opposite sides of the fault, measured in the fault surface. (Lindgren, 1915, A. G. I. Glossary.)

Shift: (1) The maximum relative displacement of points on opposite sides of the fault and far enough from it to be outside the dislocated zone. (Lindgren, 1915, A. G. I. Glossary.) (2) Displacement on opposite sides of fault measured outside the zone of dislocation. Whereas the net shift along a fault might be 1,000 ft, because of drag the net slip along the fault might be much less. (Reid, 1913, A. G. I. Glossary.)

Net slip (syn.: *displacement*): The total slip along a fault; the distance measured on the fault surface between two formerly adjacent points situated on opposite walls of the fault. It is the shortest distance measured in the fault plane between the two formerly adjacent points. (Reid, 1913, A. G. I. Glossary.)

Strike slip: The component of the slip parallel to the fault strike, or the projection of the net slip on a horizontal line in the fault surface. (Lindgren, 1915, A. G. I. Glossary.)

Right (syn.: *dextral strike slip, right-lateral slip*).

Left (syn.: *sinistral strike slip, left-lateral slip*).

Dip slip: The component of the slip parallel to the fault dip, or its projection on a line in the fault surface perpendicular to the fault strike. (Lindgren, 1933, A. G. I. Glossary.)

Oblique slip: A fault in which the net slip lies between the direction of dip and the direction of strike. (Lindgren, 1933, A. G. I. Glossary.)

Throw (syn.: *vertical slip*): (1) The amount of vertical displacement occasioned by a fault. (Page, David, 1859, A. G. I. Glossary.) (2) More generally, the vertical component of the net slip.

Heave: In faulting, the horizontal component of the dip separation; that is, the apparent horizontal component of displacement of a disrupted index plane on a vertical cross section, the strike of which is perpendicular to the strike of the fault. (Structural Committee, A. G. I.

Glossary.) (*Note:* The term is frequently applied to the horizontal component of the net slip. In such cases the meaning is ambiguous.)

Trace slip: Component of net slip parallel to the trace of an index plane (vein, bedding, etc.) on plane of the fault. (Reid, 1913, A. G. I. Glossary.)

Trace-slip fault: A fault on which the net slip is parallel to the trace of a bed (or some other index plane) on the fault. (Reid, 1913, A. G. I. Glossary.)

Perpendicular slip: The component of the net slip measured perpendicular to the trace on the fault of the disrupted index plane (bed, dike, vein, etc.) in the fault plane. (Reid, 1913, A. G. I. Glossary.)

Horizontal slip: In faulting, the horizontal component of the net slip. (Gill, 1941, A. G. I. Glossary.)

Horizontal dip slip: The horizontal component of the dip slip. (Gill, 1941, A. G. I. Glossary.)

FAULT CLASSIFICATIONS

Normal (syn.: *gravity*): A fault at which the hanging wall has been depressed, relative to the footwall. (Lindgren, 1933, A. G. I. Glossary.)

Reverse: A fault along which the hanging wall has been raised, relative to the footwall. (Lindgren, 1933, A. G. I. Glossary.)

Thrust: A reverse fault that is characterized by a low angle of inclination with reference to a horizontal plane.

Hill (1947, 1959) has suggested that a distinction should be drawn between normal, reverse, thrust, right-lateral, and left-lateral faults that are recognized by separations and those that are recognized by slips (e.g., normal-separation fault; normal-slip fault). In cases of oblique slip or where both strike and dip separations are found, a combined term could be used such as reverse-left-lateral-slip fault.

Overthrust: (1) A thrust fault with low dip and large net slip, generally measured in miles. (2) A thrust fault in which the hanging wall was

the active element; contrasted with underthrust, but it is usually impossible to tell which was actively moved. (3) The process of thrusting the hanging wall (relatively) over the footwall.

Upthrust: A high-angle gravity or thrust fault in which the relatively upthrown side was the active (moving) element. This is usually impossible to determine. (Billings, 1954, A. G. I. Glossary.)

Underthrust: A thrust fault in which the footwall was the active element. In most instances, it is impossible to tell which element was active. (Billings, 1954, A. G. I. Glossary.)

Gravity-glide fault: A fault produced by the sliding of rock masses or strata downslope from an uplifted area. Nappes, recumbent folds, or low-angle overthrust faults may be associated with gravity gliding.

I. Based on Net Slip

Strike-slip fault (syn.: *wrench, transcurrent*): A fault in which the net slip is practically in the direction of the fault strike. (Lindgren, 1933, A. G. I. Glossary.)

Dip-slip fault (could include normal, reverse, and thrust faults): A fault in which the net slip is practically in the line of the fault dip. (Lindgren, 1933, A. G. I. Glossary.)

Oblique-slip fault (could include normal, reverse, and thrust faults): A fault in which the net slip lies between the direction of dip and the direction of strike. (Lindgren, 1933, A. G. I. Glossary.)

Megashear: A strike-slip fault whose horizontal displacement significantly exceeds the thickness of the crust. (Carey, 1958, A. G. I. Glossary.)

II. Based on Relation of Fault to Adjacent Strata

Bedding fault: A fault that is parallel to the bedding. (Reid, 1913, A. G. I. Glossary.)

Dip fault: A fault that strikes approximately perpendicular to the strike of the bedding or cleavage. (Billings, 1954, A. G. I. Glossary.)

Strike fault: A fault whose strike is parallel

to the strike of the strata. (Lindgren, 1933, A. G. I. Glossary.)

Oblique fault: A fault whose strike is oblique to the strike of the strata. (Lindgren, 1933, A. G. I. Glossary.)

Longitudinal fault: A fault whose strike is parallel with the general structure. (Lindgren, 1933, A. G. I. Glossary.)

Tear fault (syn.: *transverse fault*, Geikie): A strike-slip fault that trends transverse to the strike of the deformed rocks. (Hills, J. M., 1953, A. G. I. Glossary.)

III. Based on Fault Pattern

En échelon: Parallel structural features that are offset as are the edges of shingles on a roof when viewed from the side. (Structural Committee, A. G. I. Glossary.)

Parallel faults: A group of faults having essentially the same dip and strike. (Power, A. G. I. Glossary.)

Peripheral faults: Faults along the periphery of a geologically elevated or depressed region. (Reid, 1913, A. G. I. Glossary.)

Radial faults: A group of faults that, on a map, radiate from a common center. (Billings, 1954, A. G. I. Glossary.)

Step faults: "A series of parallel faults, which all incline in the same direction, gives rise to a gigantic staircase; hence these are called step faults. Each step is a fault block and its top may be horizontal or tilted." (Scott, 1922, A. G. I. Glossary.)

Antithetic faults (anton.: *synthetic faults*): Faults that dip in the opposite direction from that in which the associated sediments dip. (Cloos, H., 1936, A. G. I. Glossary.)

Synthetic faults: Subsidiary faults parallel to the master fault. (Cloos, H., 1936, A. G. I. Glossary.)

Fenster (syn.: *window*): An exposure of the rock beneath a thrust sheet or recumbent fold produced where erosion has locally truncated the overlying rock units. The exposure is completely surrounded by units on the thrust sheet in a perfectly developed fenster.

Klippe: An erosional remnant of a thrust sheet, nappe, or recumbent fold.

Graben: An elongate fault block, usually a depression, bounded on two or more sides by normal or vertical faults and formed by the downthrow of the central block relative to the adjacent blocks.

Horst: An elongate fault block, usually high, bounded on two or more sides by normal faults and formed by the upthrow of the central block relative to the adjacent blocks.

ANALYSIS OF FAULT AND FRACTURE ORIENTATIONS

The three principal stress directions near the surface of the earth tend to have strong preferred orientations because of the nature of the surface boundary. "There can be no pressure or tension perpendicular to the surface, and no shearing force parallel to it, in its immediate vicinity." Thus Anderson (1951) argues that the normal to the ground surface will tend to be one of the three principal stress directions except in "Alpine"-type topography. He assumes this is true for depths at which most faulting occurs. With this assumption three general cases of stress distribution are most likely (Fig. 4-3):

1. Maximum and intermediate principal stress are both horizontal—thrust faults
2. Maximum stress is vertical—normal faults
3. Maximum and least principal stress directions are horizontal—wrench faults

The conditions for development of normal and reverse faults are shown as they might be analyzed by means of Mohr analysis (Fig. 4-4). In reverse faulting the least principal stress (vertical) remains constant while the horizontal stress is increased, represented by increasing sizes of circles. This continues within the region of stability until the circle becomes tangent with the line of fracture. This occurs when

$$2\alpha = (90° + \phi)$$

$$\alpha = 45° + \frac{\phi}{2}$$

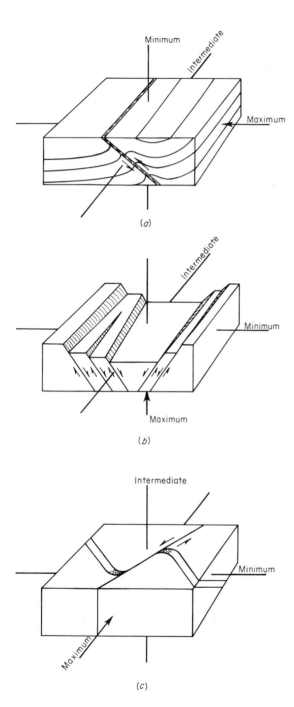

(a)

(b)

(c)

Fig. 4-3 Relationships between principal stresses and common fault orientations, for thrust, normal, and transcurrent faults. (*After Anderson, 1951.*)

However, as we saw in the preceding chapter the observed angle between shears is almost always less than 90°. For normal faulting the least principal stress is horizontal while the maximum stress direction is vertical. If normal faults do form under conditions of tension, then the least stress becomes smaller while the maximum stress remains constant. This continues until the circle again becomes tangent to the fracture line.

STRESS DISTRIBUTION AND FAULTING

Hafner (1951) has analyzed a number of stress systems caused by various types of boundary forces which might be expected within the

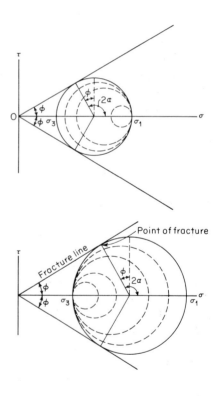

Fig. 4-4 Normal (top) and reverse (bottom) conditions. The minimum stress decreases in normal faulting; the maximum stress increases in reverse faulting. (*From Hubbert, 1951.*)

earth. Although the theoretical treatment is too advanced to present here, the conclusions regarding the stress fields are highly significant because the locations of fault surfaces most likely to be associated with these various stress conditions are indicated. Three conditions are analyzed:

1. Horizontal compression with constant vertical and lateral gradients (Fig. 4-5). These diagrams are drawn in the xy plane so that lines on the drawings represent planes extending perpendicular to the page. The diagrams are of arbitrary length and depth, but the top of the diagrams is taken as the ground surface. Figure 4-5a depicts

shearing and normal stresses acting on the boundaries of the block. These include a rock pressure that is a function of depth, indicated by ay where y is depth and a equals density times the gravitational constant; a vertically directed pressure σ_y shown as constant across the base of the block; a horizontally directed stress σ_x which is defined in this case as being constant from the top to the bottom of the block. In addition to these there are shearing stresses acting on the faces of the block. These are necessary to fulfill the requirement for equilibrium (nonrotation) for the block. The trajectories of maximum and minimum principal pressure are cal-

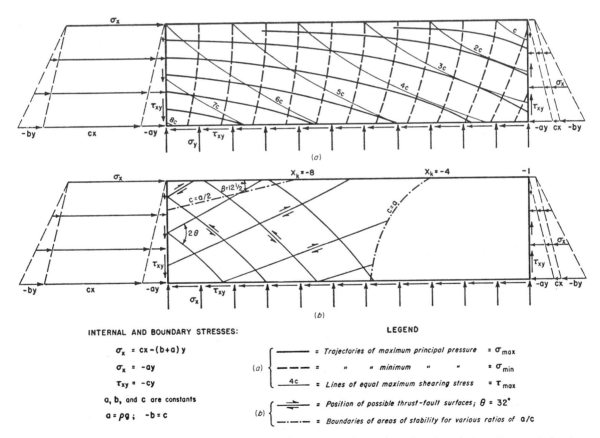

INTERNAL AND BOUNDARY STRESSES:

$$\sigma_x = cx - (b+a)y$$
$$\sigma_x = -ay$$
$$\tau_{xy} = -cy$$

a, b, and c are constants

$a = \rho g$; $-b = c$

LEGEND

(a)
- —————— = Trajectories of maximum principal pressure = σ_{max}
- — — — — = " " minimum " " = σ_{min}
- ——$4c$—— = Lines of equal maximum shearing stress = τ_{max}

(b)
- ⇉ = Position of possible thrust-fault surfaces; $\theta = 32°$
- —·—·—·— = Boundaries of areas of stability for various ratios of a/c

Fig. 4-5 Stress system with superimposed horizontal pressure with constant lateral and vertical gradient, and showing lines of maximum shearing stress. (*From Hafner, 1951.*)

culated on the basis of stress theory (Hafner, 1951); c is a constant. Since a wide range of values is possible in nature, only a few selected ones are used. Those selected are ratios of c/a thus expressing the lateral gradient of the superposed horizontal stress in terms of a fraction of the vertical pressure gradient. Figure 4-5b shows areas of stability for the assumed ratio of a/c and potential fault planes. The position of the fault plane is determined by drawing it so that it crosses each maximum principal pressure contour at an angle of about 32°, selected as the angle of fracture.

The striking conclusion from this diagram is that the potential fault planes are curved surfaces showing a tendency in this case to flatten at depth. Other potential fault planes for different types of stress systems are shown in the following examples. Perhaps the main value in these lies in the light they throw on the potential variations of natural faults at depth, and the implications of stress conditions that may be inferred from fault patterns and attitudes. This first example is highly suggestive of the low-angle thrust faults of the folded mountain belts which have curved surfaces.

2. Horizontal compression with exponential lateral attenuation yields potential faults as illustrated in Fig. 4-6. The increase of hydrostatic pressure with depth is taken into consideration, but is not depicted in this figure. Note that the zone of potential faulting is now narrow and nearly vertical, and that the potential fault system in the shallow parts of the block is similar to that in the first case. Horizontal thrust faults are also possible in this system.

3. Sinusoidal vertical and shearing forces act

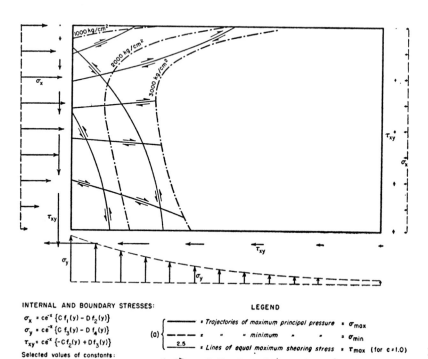

INTERNAL AND BOUNDARY STRESSES:

$\sigma_x = ce^{-x}\{C\,f_1(y) - D\,f_2(y)\}$

$\sigma_y = ce^{-x}\{C\,f_3(y) - D\,f_4(y)\}$

$\tau_{xy} = ce^{-x}\{-C\,f_2(y) + D\,f_3(y)\}$

Selected values of constants:

$C = -1.0$

$D = +2.0$

c from 1000 kg/cm² to 3000 kg/cm²

LEGEND

(a) {
—————— = Trajectories of maximum principal pressure = σ_{max}

----- = " " " minimum " " = σ_{min}

2.5 = Lines of equal maximum shearing stress = τ_{max} (for $c = 1.0$)
}

(b) {
⇌ = Position of potential fault surfaces; $\theta = 30°$

—·—·— = Boundaries of areas of stability for various values of c
}

Fig. 4-6 Superimposed horizontal stress decreasing exponentially in horizontal direction. *(From Hafner, 1951.)*

on the bottom of the block in the third case (Fig. 4-7). This case is pertinent to two general geological conditions, one involving vertical uplift and the second involving such frictional drag as is presumed to exist in convection current hypotheses. The potential fault surfaces and regions of stability are shown for two relative values of the constants A and B. It is of interest geologically to note that these stress systems predict the possible existence of normal faults that vary in dip at depth and low-angle normal faults. Both of these conditions have been observed in nature. It is also possible to have potential fault surfaces which are thrust faults at the surface but change to normal faults at depth. Note that this analysis predicts zones of faulting above and below zones of stability.

Sanford (1959) describes a method of theoretical analysis of fault structures which is similar to that of Hafner. Sanford's method is based on the distribution of vertical displacements along the base of a homogeneous elastic layer. Block faulting of sedimentary layers above a rigid basement can be represented best by specifying displacements which can often be determined in the field, whereas the magnitude and distribution of stress along the base of the layer cannot. In simple examples of this type of structure, adjacent blocks of basement rock are moved uniformly up or down with respect to one another.

The method is based on the theory of elasticity. Assumptions are: (1) that displacements and strains are small; (2) that the material undergoing deformation must be perfectly elastic, homogeneous, and isotropic. Application of the theory is greatly simplified if the lower boundary of a layer undergoes displacements in the x and y directions only and if these displacements are identical for all cross sections along the z axis. The problem is essentially reduced to a two-dimensional analysis, and it is applicable if a single cross section of a structure can be selected

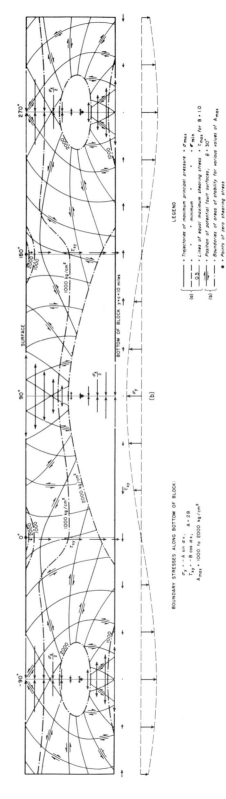

Fig. 4-7 Supplementary stress system consisting of variable vertical and shearing stress along bottom of block. (*From Hafner, 1951.*)

as approximating the structure for a long distance. The derivation of the theory which involves partial differential equations (see Sanford, 1959) is omitted here. The internal stress distribution of a deformed elastic layer is portrayed by stress trajectories whose directions can be calculated by using

$$\tan 2\beta = \frac{2\tau_{xy}}{\sigma_x - \sigma_y}$$

where β is the angle between the positive x axis and the principal stress measured in the direction of the positive y axis. Stress trajectories can be constructed graphically on the basis of β values computed for grid points within the layer. The distribution of displacement in a deformed layer can be portrayed by a field of displacement vectors. The orientation and length

of each vector indicate the direction and magnitude of the net displacement at the point from which the vector originates. The only factors which influence the orientations and relative magnitudes of the displacement vectors are the shape of the layer and Poisson's ratio. Stress distributions and displacement fields of different examples can be computed and compared if each numerical example sustains an amount of applied displacement which is just necessary to initiate fracture at some point within the layer. In this study the Mohr fracture criterion is used to determine the amount of displacement which is necessary to initiate fracture at each point. The point requiring the least displacement to originate fracture is taken as the point of fracture.

Several hypothetical cases are examined by

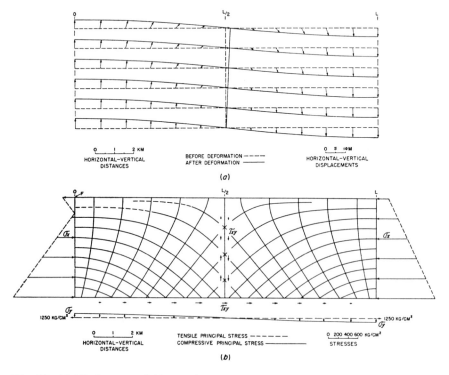

Fig. 4-8 (a) Displacement field and (b) stress distribution, calculated for an elastic layer 5 km thick and 15.7 km long which undergoes half a wavelength of sinusoidal vertical displacement. (*From Sanford, 1959.*)

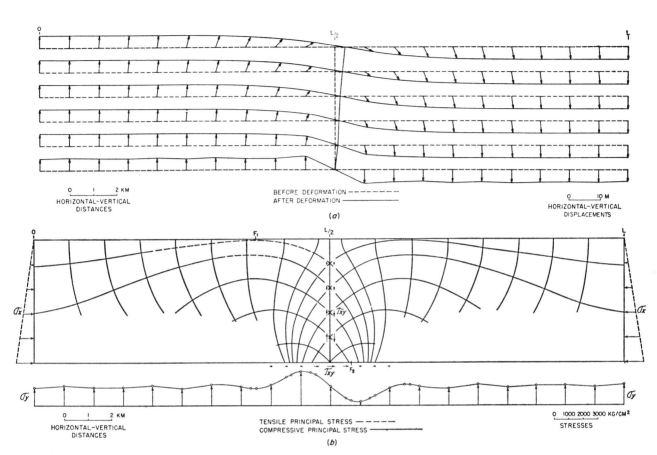

Fig. 4-9 (a) Displacement field and (b) stress distribution, calculated for an elastic layer the lower boundary of which undergoes a steplike displacement. (*From Sanford, 1959.*)

Sanford, including (1) a vertical displacement applied in a sinusoidal waveform to the bottom of the section; (2) a vertical steplike displacement; (3) the lower boundary undergoing sinusoidal vertical and horizontal displacements (Figs. 4-8 and 4-9).

Analysis of a Low-angle Thrust— the Williams Range Thrust

The Williams Range thrust is a major east-dipping fault located in Middle Park, Colo. (Fig. 4-10). Howard (1966) has synthesized the regional geology and made an analysis of this fault based on theory developed by Sanford

(1959). It is possible to see a cross section of the fault in places because of the high relief, and data on its elevation and dip and on the rotation of strata above the fault all show that the fault has a curved surface. It is assumed in this analysis (1) that the stress within the body is describable by methods of the theory of elasticity; (2) that the faults and stress are related by the Mohr criterion of failure; (3) that faulting does not affect the orientation of the principal stresses at the time of faulting; and (4) that faulting tends to increase the magnitude of stress near the tip of the fault and decrease them after faulting occurs.

The upper and lower boundaries of the area

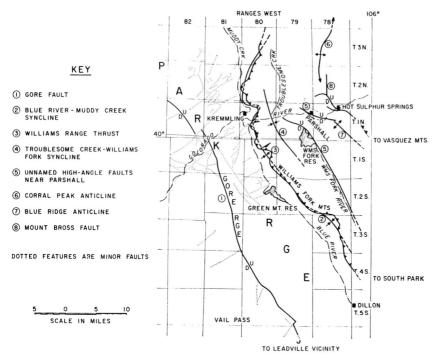

Fig. 4-10   Regional structure map of Williams Range thrust. (*From Howard, 1966.*)

were set as nearly as possible to approximate the air-earth interface at the time of fault initiation (which now lies at approximately 11,000 ft) and the horizon where a system of geologically practicable stresses and displacements could be reasonably imposed (selected as the Precambrian to Jurassic unconformity). A simplified and idealized cross section (Fig. 4-11) showing the Williams thrust and the major normal fault east of it were constructed on the basis of cross sections across the range. The stress system which was found to come closest to explaining the observed features of this structure consists of the sum of two of the systems studied by Sanford: (1) a system characterized by a cosine displacement plus a step displacement of the lower boundary. The boundary stress arrangement calculated to prevail at the time of fault initiation and the possible fault orientations for

these particular boundary conditions and displacement fields are illustrated in Fig. 4-11. This system of stresses does lead to a distribution of stress trajectories which can account for the shape and sense of movement of the upthrust in the center of the body. In summary, once the displacement field is specified as based on field observations, the system of stresses necessary to cause those displacements can be calculated. When the stresses at some place within the body fulfill the Mohr criteria for failure, faulting starts.

It is possible to estimate the potential for faulting of various parts of the body from values of stress calculated for grid points within the body. Potential for faulting is a comparison of the proximity of a Mohr circle for stress to the failure line. If the radius of the circle just touches the failure line, the value of the poten-

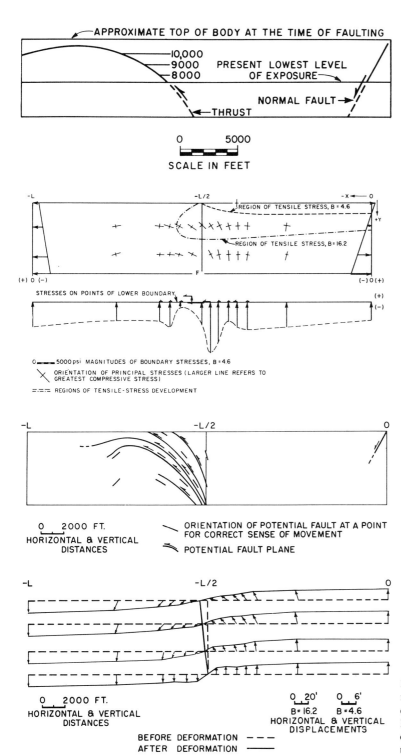

APPROXIMATE TOP OF BODY AT THE TIME OF FAULTING

—10,000
—9000   PRESENT LOWEST LEVEL
—8000   OF EXPOSURE—

NORMAL FAULT→

←THRUST

0   5000
SCALE IN FEET

-L   -L/2   -X←   0
                                    REGION OF TENSILE STRESS, B = 4.6
                                                              +Y
REGION OF TENSILE STRESS, B = 16.2

F
(+) 0 (−)   (−) 0 (+)

STRESSES ON POINTS OF LOWER BOUNDARY   (+)
                                                  (−)

0 ▬▬ 5000 psi MAGNITUDES OF BOUNDARY STRESSES, B = 4.6
       ORIENTATION OF PRINCIPAL STRESSES (LARGER LINE REFERS TO
       GREATEST COMPRESSIVE STRESS)
= ·= ·= REGIONS OF TENSILE-STRESS DEVELOPMENT

-L   -L/2   0

0   2000 FT.   ╲ ORIENTATION OF POTENTIAL FAULT AT A POINT
HORIZONTAL & VERTICAL   FOR CORRECT SENSE OF MOVEMENT
DISTANCES   ╲═ POTENTIAL FAULT PLANE

-L   -L/2   0

0   2000 FT.   0 20'   0 6'
HORIZONTAL & VERTICAL   B = 16.2 B = 4.6
DISTANCES   HORIZONTAL & VERTICAL
                                  DISPLACEMENTS

BEFORE DEFORMATION − − −
AFTER DEFORMATION ———

Fig. 4-11 Idealized cross section of the region, top; boundary stresses and orientation of principal stresses which will lead to the potential fault planes, middle; and the displacement field, bottom. (*Redrawn from Howard, 1966.*)

tial for faulting becomes 100. Note that the term B appears in the diagram of principal stress orientations. This term is called the displacement factor; it has the dimensions of length, and its magnitude governs the actual distance any point will be displaced by elastic deformation. Failure first occurs within the body when this factor equals 4.6 ft, and the faults predicted are the thrust faults shown in Fig. 4-11. If B is increased to a value of 16.2, however, the orientation of the principal stress is quite different, and the field that shows the potential for faulting favors the development of the normal fault shown in the idealized cross section. Thus both major faults can be explained if the assumptions first stated are accepted as valid.

DEPTH OF FAULTING

Faults do extend to the ground surface, but their extension in depth is a more difficult matter. It has long been recognized that at some level in the earth's interior the rocks would lose their capacity to support large-scale shear and would undergo flow instead. The results of seismological studies indicate focal depths for deep earthquakes at 700 km, which has come to be recognized as the limiting depth for faults, but experimental work now appears to indicate that this conclusion cannot be correct. The reason for associating earthquakes with faulting is based on the nature of seismic waves. They appear to be set up by shear offsets which are propagated at the elastic wave velocity. According to the most widely accepted view, elastic strain is built up across the fault plane until it is released by a slip and elastic rebound.

Griggs and Handin (1960) point out that the confining pressure at 700 km is on the order of 250,000 bars and temperatures are high; it would therefore be reasonable to expect the shear strength of rocks at that depth to be low— on the order of 10 to 100 bars. Thus it might be argued that the fracture theory of generating earthquakes at 700 km would require a shear

strength for the rock at that depth about 10,000 times greater than the expected strength. All rocks except quartzite exhibit uniform flow or "faults" without a sudden release of elastic energy at 5,000 bars and 500°C. In view of this result, even much shallower earthquakes could not be generated by ordinary fracturing. Indeed, Orowan (1960) estimates that the limiting depth for earthquakes caused by shear failure is 5 to 10 km. Thus the development of faults through brittle-shear failure is limited to the upper part of the earth's crust.

Several alternative hypotheses have been advanced to explain generation of earthquakes at moderate and great depths. Griggs (1954) suggests that deep-focus earthquakes are generated by shear melting. According to this hypothesis, melting is initiated at a flaw in the mantle (suggested flaws include fluid-filled cavities or relatively weak, tabular mineral grains) and as a result of shear stresses the flaw is deformed, enlarged, and propagated with seismic velocity. Thus a rapid shear displacement occurs which sets up seismic waves.

Orowan (1960) proposed that these earthquakes are due to instability of plastic deformation (creep). He argues that if creep produces structural changes which accelerate creep then the deformation is gradually concentrated into thin layers in which very high rates of flow are developed. If the process proceeds fast enough, shear melting may occur.

Other suggestions have been advanced, including phase changes of a solid nature; however, this suggestion is not favored because such a change would presumably involve only a change in volume and would not produce shear waves unless the change occurred at explosive rates. The idea of shear melting provides an explanation for the coincidence in time and space of earthquake and volcanic belts around the Pacific. In the past the explanation most often offered for this coincidence has been that magma is generated by faulting as a result of heat which in turn is generated by friction along the fault. As with so many questions involving the earth's interior, it is difficult to formulate geological criteria by which the various hypotheses may be judged.

THRUST FAULTS

Low-angle thrust faults are one of the most prominent characteristics of the young folded mountain belts throughout the world. Displacements of several miles are often proved, and in some instances evidence supports tectonic transport of large rock masses for 20 or more miles.

Low-angle thrusts are found most frequently in the thick accumulations of sedimentary rocks in deformed geosynclinal belts. Some details of these belts in the Appalachians and Alps are cited later. Some common features of thrust faults are illustrated in Fig. 4-12. The leading edge, the fault trace, is actively rising more rapidly than it is being removed by erosion in this example, but as the faulting continues, fans of sediment derived from the thrust are spread in front of and covered by the advancing overthrust plate to become mixed with the fault breccia. Longwell (1949) describes such a situation in the northern Muddy Mountains of Nevada. Drag of the beds above and below the fault zone and the development of secondary faults subparallel to the main thrust are commonly encountered. Thrust fault zones may be either extremely complex zones or simple relatively smooth surfaces.

The degree of complexity is related to such factors as the behavior of the rock which is a function of lithology, temperature, strain rate, confining pressure (depth), and the amount of pore pressure developed in water contained in the rock. Extremes are found in the Appalachians, where breccias hundreds of feet thick occur along outcrops of bedding thrusts in the Elbrook formation of Cambrian age. The Elbrook is heterogenous, lithologically consisting of dolomites which behaved as brittle materials (these are shattered, filled with veins) and shales which were much more ductile during the thrusting. Where thrusts have passed through

thick sections of shale the thrust plane may be very difficult to distinguish from bedding or cleavage. Alternatively, the fault appears as a thick zone of closely spaced shears forming a shaly cleavage in the fault. A third type of fault zone in which limestones or thick sections of interbedded shales and limestone occur is characterized by highly complex folding rather than by brecciation or movement on closely spaced faults.

Thrust faults may consist of breccia-free zones where the rock on either side has been highly ductile or where friction along the fault has been very low. If the thrust is deep, there is a large component of lithostatic pressure normal to the fault plane. This pressure may be sufficient to promote ductile behavior and may inhibit the development of breccia, which is accompanied by an increase in volume. Friction may be reduced by the presence of zones of high pore pressure (water) such as might be expected where a claystone caps a porous sandstone.

It is not usually easy to determine the dip of a fault where it crops out because of the complications of the fault zone, because folding and subsidiary faults often accompany a major fault, and because these zones are usually susceptible to erosion. In regions of high relief, a low-angle fault may be recognized by the deflection of the fault trace in the topography. The fault trace, like a dipping contact, will have a V shape in stream valleys; or in cases of extremely low dips, parts of the thrust mass may become isolated as klippes (most frequently older rocks thrust

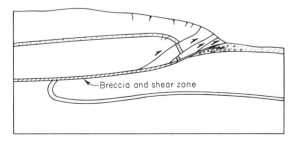

Fig. 4-12 Features associated with thrust faults. (*From Hans Cloos, 1936.*)

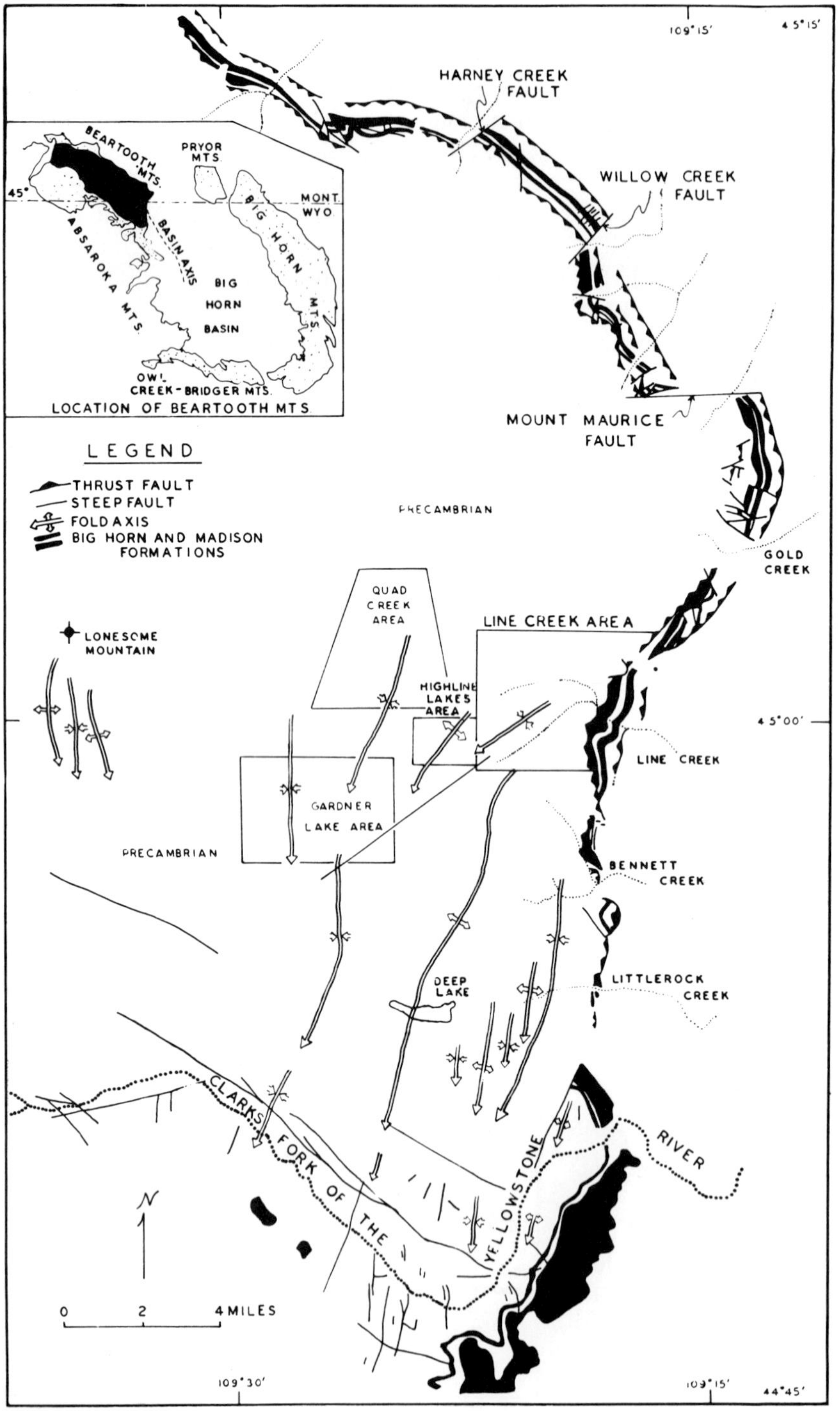

Fig. 4-13 Thrust faults and structure at the northeast corner of the Beartooth Mountains, Mont. (*From Casella, 1964.*)

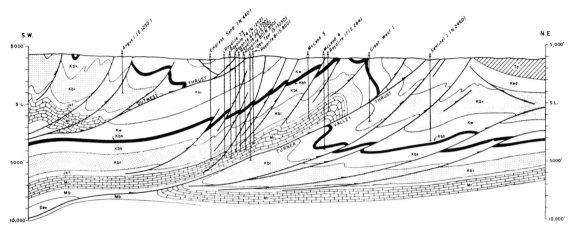

Fig. 4-14 Cross section across the central sector of the Turner Valley. Two large thrust faults and a number of smaller thrusts are shown. *(From Fox, 1959.)*

onto younger rocks). Three principal types of structures are responsible for bringing isolated masses of rocks of older age onto younger strata. These are thrusting followed by erosion and the development of klippes, folding resulting in formation of nappes, and mass movement or gravitational sliding. These are not always easily differentiated. There are a number of instances in which gravity sliding can be demonstrated, but the evaluation of the role of gravity in most low-angle faulting is very difficult and particularly in mountain belts which have experienced post-thrust folding, tilting, or warping.

Structural Patterns along Thrust Faults

Certain characteristic patterns are associated with each major type of fault. Some of the patterns are similar but generally they are quite distinct. Multiple subparallel faults are characteristic of thrusts. A single fault trace may be followed into numerous branches some of which may rejoin the master fault, whereas others die out in folds, along bedding, or at transverse faults. This branching is evident both on maps of fault zones and in cross sections (Figs. 4-14 and 4-15). Slices are formed along faults in this fashion.

Smaller faults, called *tear faults*, of vertical

orientation and transverse to the major thrust are found where one part of the thrust sheet has moved farther than another. An excellent example of this is found at the northeastern corner of the Beartooth Mountains, Mont. (Fig. 4-13). The Paleozoic sedimentary section stands nearly vertical. We can envision the formation of the tears in the sedimentary rocks as this mountain front was rotated to a vertical position during uplift and thrusting. Some portions of the front are thrust nearly a mile farther than other parts across the tears. In this case the orientation of the tears is governed by the orientation of ancient fractures in the Precambrian rocks. Tears oriented normal to the thrust and in positions which might be explained in terms of shear failure (two conjugate sets at ±30° to the direction of transport of the thrust) of the overthrust plate are commonly found.

Thrusting is described as imbricate when a number of subparallel thrusts are found in a belt (Figs. 4-14 and 4-15). Slice after slice of the same bed may be stacked on top of one another in such zones.

Folding usually accompanies thrusting particularly if the section has a varied lithology. Some folding can certainly be attributed to drag

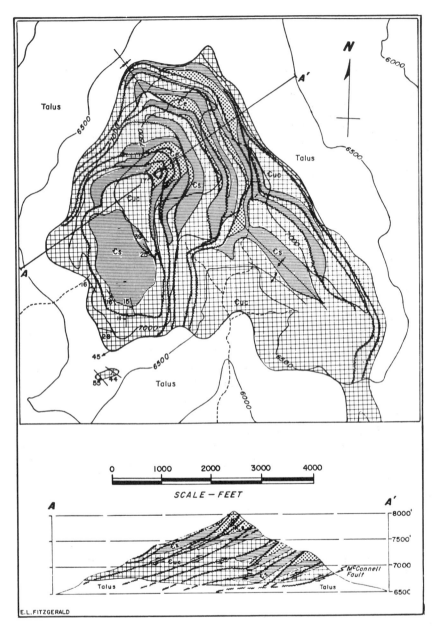

Fig. 4-15 Map and structure section *A–A'* through Black Rock Mountain. (*From Fitzgerald, 1962.*)

along the fault zone, but it is often difficult to determine whether folding preceded or followed faulting or both. One common interpretation is that folding proceeds from open, to asymmetrical, to overturned folding, with a fault forming on the overturned limb and being drawn out into a thrust fault. Not all thrusts fit this picture. Thrusts cut both the forelimb (the overturned limb) and the back limb in Turner Valley oil field (Fig. 4-14). Many geologists prefer the view that the fault forms first, often as a shear across competent strata, following bedding in incompetent beds, and that the fold forms as movement proceeds along the fault.

EXAMPLES OF MAJOR THRUSTS

Laramide Thrust Belts

A major zone of thrusts formed during the Laramide orogeny (Cretaceous to Eocene) in the Rocky Mountain region. This belt is well preserved along the eastern side of the Canadian Rockies and into northern Montana, where continuity is lost; it appears again along the Idaho-Wyoming boundary, but it is not so well preserved farther south. The belt is developed in a portion of the geosyncline in which thick sediment accumulated during the Paleozoic, and the sediment thickness seems to have been a critical determinant of deformational pattern. East of this geosyncline, the area of Paleozoic shelf sedimentation in Montana, Wyoming, Utah, and Colorado yielded to Laramide stresses by block faulting. Asymmetrical folds and imbricate thrust faults characterize the thrust belt. The nature of the belt is shown for a small area where the McConnell thrust sheet is exposed (Figs. 4-16 and 4-17). Middle Cambrian units are brought into juxtaposition with Upper Cretaceous rocks by this thrust; lateral

movement amounts to at least several miles. The thrusts are folded in places, but there is no positive proof of the age of this. Such folding is frequently interpreted as having formed in late stages of the thrusting. Douglas (1958) suggests that folding in the McConnell thrust

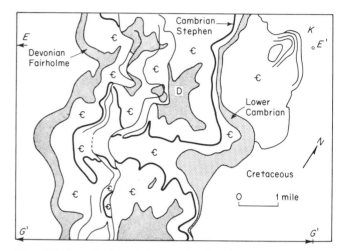

Fig. 4-16 Simplified geologic map showing thrust faults and several marker horizons in Ghost River area, Alberta. (See sections in Fig. 4-17.) (*From Fitzgerald, 1962.*)

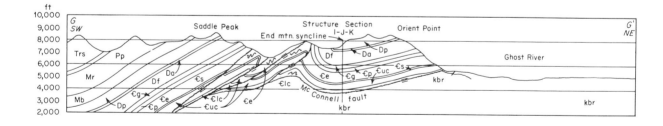

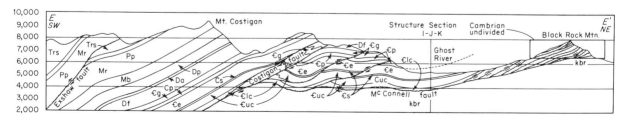

Fig. 4-17 Cross sections across the Rocky Mountain front in the Ghost River area of Alberta. Vertical and horizontal scales are the same. (*Redrawn from Fitzgerald, 1962.*)

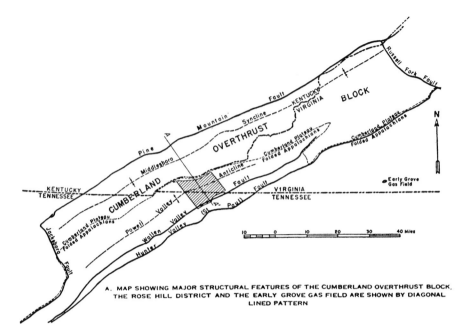

A. MAP SHOWING MAJOR STRUCTURAL FEATURES OF THE CUMBERLAND OVERTHRUST BLOCK.
THE ROSE HILL DISTRICT AND THE EARLY GROVE GAS FIELD ARE SHOWN BY DIAGONAL
LINED PATTERN

Fig. 4-18 Pine Mountain overthrust. (Figure continued on opposite page.) (*From Miller and Fuller, 1954.*)

has been caused by development of subsidiary thrusts located under the McConnell thrust and terminated against it. As movements on both faults continued, the wedge between the two thickened, forcing the McConnell thrust to become bent upward.

Minor subsidiary thrust faults associated with the larger faults are attributed to a reorientation of stresses along the major early-formed thrust, giving rise to second-order shear structures (Anderson, 1951; McKinstry, 1953). Why these zones are localized as they are is not clearly understood.

The Cumberland Overthrust

The Cumberland overthrust block is one of the unique structural features of the Appalachians. It consists of a huge plate, approximately 125 miles long, which has been thrust an estimated 6 miles to the northwest along a thrust fault that is nearly flat-lying under most of the block. The structure of this plate is known through both surface mapping and subsurface information

obtained by drilling in several small oil and gas fields in the area (Miller and Fuller, 1954). The block is located northwest of the belt of folds and faults in eastern Tennessee. The outcrop of the Pine Mountain fault, which defines the leading edge of the thrust block, is the westernmost major fault in the region; it lines up approximately with the long thrust on the west limb of the Sequatchie anticline of Alabama and Tennessee.

The Pine Mountain overthrust fault brings Devonian and Mississippian shales in fault contact with Pennsylvanian units. The block is bounded on the north by the Russell fault and on the south by the Jacksboro fault, both of which become part of northeast-southwest-trending faults in the strongly folded and faulted belt to the east (Fig. 4-18). The western portion of the overthrust block is a broad open syncline, and the central portion is the Powell Valley anticline. In the axis of this anticline the Pine Mountain overthrust comes to the surface. Erosion along the crest of the anticline has exposed

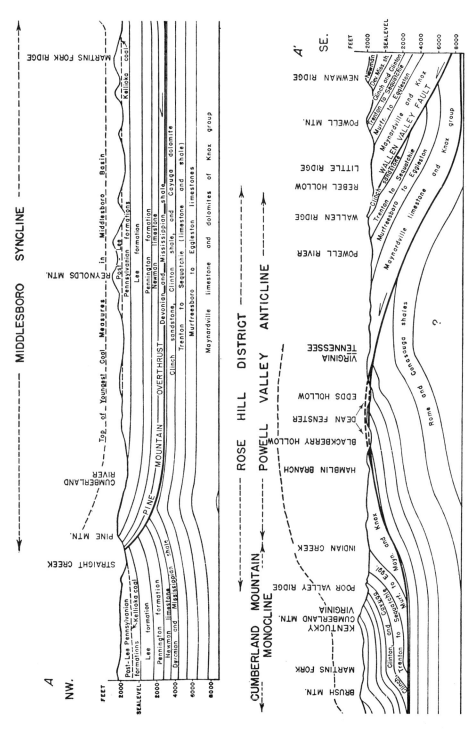

B. GEOLOGIC SECTION THROUGH THE CUMBERLAND OVERTHRUST BLOCK ALONG THE LINE A-A' OF PLATE A. LENGTH OF SECTION, 27 MILES. DISPLACEMENT ON PINE MOUNTAIN FAULT, 5.8 MILES

Fig. 4-18 (*Continued.*)

the units under the thrust, forming several fensters. These fensters provide an exceptional opportunity to study the character of the thrust zone. In the detailed map of the edge of the Dean fenster (Fig. 4-19) the faults are actually fault zones in which slices of the units over and underlying the fault zone have become folded and displaced.

Under much of the Cumberland fault block, the Pine Mountain thrust is known or assumed to be a bedding fault. In the Middleboro syncline, the fault is parallel to bedding and is located in shales of Devonian and Mississippian

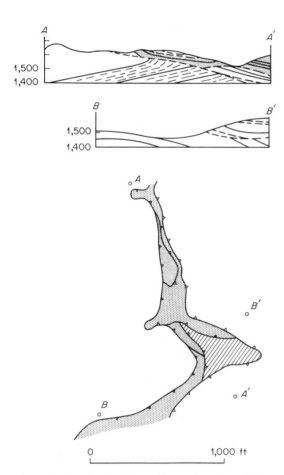

Fig. 4-19 Detail of a thrust slice at the edge of the Dean Fenster Pine Mountain overthrust, Virginia, Kentucky, and Tennessee. (*After Miller and Fuller, 1954.*)

age. In this area the units beneath the fault are Silurian and no great stratigraphic separation is apparent in wells, but the character of the fault is clear in the Powell Valley anticline where wells penetrate the Rome formation and the Maynardville limestone (Cambrian) above Silurian units (Fig. 4-18).

Several important conclusions regarding the character of the deformation seem warranted in this area:

1. The thrust faulting on the Pine Mountain fault took place in Pennsylvanian or post-Pennsylvanian time.
2. Over a considerable portion of the area of the thrust plate the main fault is parallel to bedding in shale sequences (Devonian shale in the west, Cambrian Rome shale in the east).
3. The main thrust fault broke across units of limestone and dolostone on the southeast flank of the Powell Valley anticline and continued as a bedding fault in higher shale units until it broke up again in the section at the western edge of the fault block.
4. The direction of transport was from southeast to northwest.
5. Folds and flexures affect the units above and below the fault and the fault plane. The question of whether these folds took place before, during, or after the thrusting remains unanswered. Harris and Zietz (1962) conclude that the folds developed contemporaneously with the faulting. In this interpretation a fold involving basement rocks plays an important role in the development. Evidence for this basement fold is based in part on a number of magnetic profiles. The evolution of this structure is described by Harris and Zietz as follows:

Major folding that apparently involved the basement initiated development of the Cumberland overthrust block near Ewing, Virginia.

The Pine Mountain fault later developed as a bedding-plane thrust in the incompetent Rome Formation in the western part of the area and at the base of the Maynardville Limestone in the eastern part of the area. As the fault began to grow it was deflected upward by the south limb of the primary fold from the Rome and Maynardville across several thousand feet of beds to the Chattanooga Shale. Rocks stripped from the primary fold and moved toward the northwest formed the Powell Valley anticline by duplication of beds. Frictional drag on the fault caused the north limb of the nearly rootless Powell Valley anticline to fold into the Cumberland Mountain monocline. During the final phase of the orogeny the thrust plates locked in the eastern part of the area; this initiated arching of the Pine Mountain fault upward about 5,000 feet from its original position. In the western part of the area the plates did not lock, and movement continued, skewing the axis of the Powell Valley anticline northward about 1.5 miles. Displacement in the eastern part of the area is about 4 miles and in the western part about 5.6 miles.

Analysis of the structure suggests that the initial dip of the Pine Mountain fault, which in the main is a bedding-plane thrust, was predetermined by the attitude of the country rock in which the fault developed. Size and shape of major folds in the moving plate were influenced by the initial fold, the stratigraphic position of the fault, the amount of displacement and frictional resistance, root structures in the stationary block, and folding in the later stage of deformation.

The Heart Mountain Thrust

For many years structural geologists were perplexed by the structural situation at Heart Mountain, Wyo. Heart Mountain is a block nearly 5 miles across composed of Paleozoic rocks [Bighorn dolomite (Ordovician) to Madison limestone (Mississippian)]. These strata are nearly flat-lying at Heart Mountain, but they rest on Eocene strata. It has been understood for many years that this must be some type of thrust, but the Heart Mountain is situated more than 12 miles from the nearest large out-

crops of Paleozoic units, and there is no evidence of large-scale folding or forceful thrusting there, along the edge of the Absaroka Mountains. Furthermore the ground slope is very low from Heart Mountain to the Absaroka Mountains (Fig. 4-20). Pierce (1957, 1963b) has found that there are nearly 50 such fault blocks (klippes) spread out over an area that is about 30 miles wide and 60 miles long. By tracing the fault carefully around each of these blocks, he was able to show that while the fault surface is close to the ground surface at Heart Mountain, it cuts stratigraphically upward in a central area, and that it is a bedding fault just beneath the Bighorn dolomite near the edge of the Absaroka Mountains (Fig. 4-20). To explain these observations, Pierce suggests that the Heart Mountain thrust originated as a detachment thrust or bedding fault and that movements occurred as a result of gravitational sliding.

Summary

King (1960) summarizes the general features of the mode of occurrence of low-angle thrust faults as follows:

1. Low-angle thrust faults did not originate from low-dipping shear planes which cut indiscriminately through heterogeneous rocks. They followed zones of weakness in the incompetent strata, and shifted abruptly from one zone to the next along diagonal shears in the intervening more competent strata. [Fig. 4-21.]

2. The low-angle thrust faults cited, and probably many others, did not originate late in the orogenic cycle in strata already deformed, but earlier, when the strata were little deformed. The thrust sheets moved as broad plates and were not much folded, except where they were warped over the flats and pitches of the fault surface beneath. The overridden rocks were more folded, but probably mainly as a result of frictional drag of the thrust sheet above. Part of the forward movement of the overriding rocks probably resulted from shortening of the overridden rocks by this folding. . . .

3. If a low-angle thrust fault developed in de-

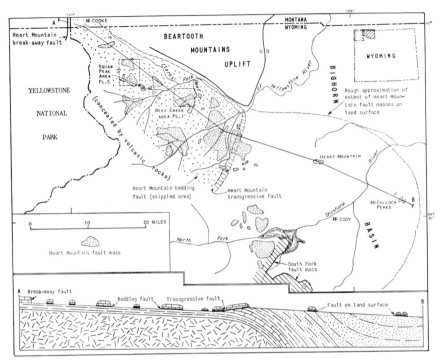

Fig. 4-20 Distribution of Heart Mountain fault masses and cross section showing four types of faults constituting the Heart Mountain detachment fault, northwestern Wyoming. *(From Pierce, 1963.)*

formed rocks of varying competence its initial rupture could not have been a smoothly-dipping shear plane. Rupture would have been along bodies of incompetent rock, or along zones of weakness already existing. As a simple example, if a thick unit of competent rocks were down-folded into a syncline, the base of the unit in the syncline would not be truncated by the fault, but it would follow the next layer of downfolded in-competent rocks beneath. The resulting fault surface would be complex and its form would be un-predictable.

4. Thrusting of older rocks over younger is char-acteristic of most of the exposed thrust faults in the Appalachian and Rocky Mountain regions, but in recent decades many thrust faults along which younger rocks override older have been dis-covered in the eastern part of the Great Basin. Along the Pine Mountain fault, older rocks are thrust over younger along the pitches, younger rocks over older along the flats. Both relations are thus normal and expectable along low-angle thrust faults, but occur in different parts of the same fault.

5. Low-angle thrust faults have finite breadth, and end both rearward and forward. Rearward ends of low-angle thrust faults are seldom avail-able for examination, even in such ideal examples as the Pine Mountain and Johnnie-Wheeler Pass faults, but Nolan's suggestion is plausible that the faults die out rearward by decrease in contrasts between the deformation of the overriding and overridden blocks. Forward, a low-angle thrust fault ascends on a succession of pitches and the highest pitch will bring it to the surface, over which the forward edge of its thrust sheet will ad-vance along an "erosion thrust" (Hayes, 1891, p. 149–150). These forward edges have long since been carried away by erosion in the Appalachian and Rocky Mountain regions, but they seem to be preserved along many of the thrust faults of the southern Great Basin.

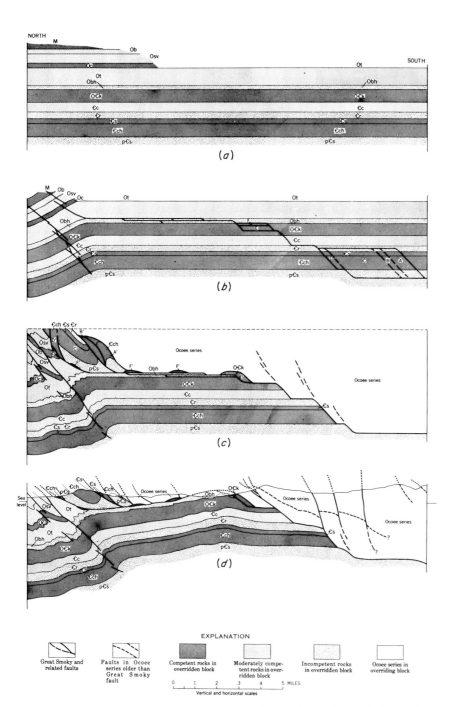

Fig. 4-21 Development of thrust faults along the northwest front of the Smoky Mountains. (*From King, 1964.*)

6. Low-angle thrust faults likewise have finite length. Thrust sheets have limits of strength, depending on the materials which compose them, beyond which they cannot move as a single mass. Low-angle thrust faults must end laterally, either along transverse faults with strike-slip displacement, or by loss of displacement along the thrust itself.

Criteria for Underthrusting

Thrust faults are usually recognized and identified from field exposures in which it can be shown that older rocks rest with fault contact on younger rocks; however, this relation is no part of the definition of thrust fault, and a number of thrusts are known in which younger rocks are faulted onto older rocks. In either case it is often impossible to establish which was the active block or whether both moved. Most thrusts are interpreted as overthrust in which the upper plate moved up and over the lower block. This interpretation is favored on mechanical grounds because there is a free surface

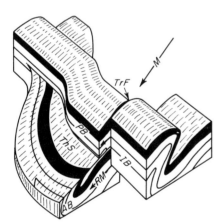

Fig. 4-22 Underthrust fault passing into overturned fold at one end and broken by tear fault at the other end. *M* = direction of movement of underthrust fault block; *RM* = relative movement of hanging and footwalls of thrust fault along tear fault, shown by length and direction of arrows; *TrF* = tear fault; *ThS* = surface of footwall of thrust fault; *IB* = inactive block of tear fault or region of less intense deformation; *PB* = passive or hanging wall block of underthrust fault; *AB* = active or footwall block of underthrust fault. (*From Lovering, 1932.*)

above. The upper fault plate can move upward into an area of less pressure. Underthrusting occurs when the lower plate is moved down and under the upper plate. For this to happen the progressively greater friction due to the weight of the upper plate must be overcome as movement proceeds to progressively greater depths. Despite this problem, underthrusts have been proposed to explain certain field relations. One such condition arises where thrust faults dip toward intrusions which are apparently unfaulted. The intrusions are envisioned as stationary features which have acted as buttresses to movement along the fault.

Although the distinction between overthrust and underthrust may not generally be possible, it is possible where the thrust breaks from an overturned fold in a zone of tear faulting. The criteria are described as following (Lovering, 1932):

> The active wall in a tear fault is the wall next to the region of more intense deformation; the passive wall is the wall on the side next to the region of less intense deformation. If the active wall of a tear fault has moved in the direction that the hanging wall of the thrust has apparently moved it indicates an overthrust fault; on the other hand, if the active wall of the tear fault has moved in an opposite direction, e.g., in the direction that the foot wall of the thrust fault has apparently moved, it indicates an underthrust fault. [Fig. 4-22.]

This criterion has been used to interpret thrusting along the eastern edge of the Colorado Front Range.

MECHANICAL CONSIDERATIONS IN THRUST FAULTING*

Thrust faults are one of the most prominent features of the orogenic belts. Some thrusts have been traced for distances measured in hundreds of miles; the amount of displacement is often a

_____
* See Hubbert and Rubey (1959).

few miles, and in some instances displacements of as much as 50 miles have been postulated. The dips of the thrusts are usually steep where the fault outcrops, but they flatten at depth and many are thought to become bedding thrusts with flat or very low dips. Most of what is known about thrusts is derived from study of the leading edge of the fault. The character of the back edge is generally unknown; the fault is presumed to pass back into folds, to die out along a bedding surface, to pass into basement rocks where it disappears, or to come back to the surface and disappear into the air as in a klippe or nappe structure. Suggestions for mechanisms to move thrust plates include: (1) gravity sliding of the thrust sheet down an inclined surface and (2) lateral compression resulting in movement of the thrust plate up the inclined fault plane or horizontally along the fault. These two differ notably in that the force in gravity sliding is a body force while the force in lateral compression is a directed push. Either of these models is capable of rather simple representation by the inclined-plane problem of physics, and provided some reasonably accurate determinations can be made regarding the size of the thrust sheet, the angle of dip of the fault, and the coefficient of friction of the material, it is possible to reach some interesting conclusions regarding such questions as:

1. The angle of dip of a fault necessary to allow gravity sliding
2. The force necessary to push a thrust plate of given size horizontally or up an inclined fault
3. The strength required for materials in the plate in order for the thrust plate to move as a plate and not fail by crushing

The force required to move the block by a push from the rear is that necessary to overcome the frictional resistance between the thrust plate and the underlying rock.

F = force required to move the block
a, b, c = lengths of the sides of the block

W = weight of the block (product of the density and volume)
e = coefficient of frictional resistance

Therefore

$$F = We = a \cdot b \cdot c \cdot \rho e$$

The dimensions of many thrust plates can be closely approximated and the density of the rock is easily determined. Unfortunately, very little is known directly about the coefficient of frictional resistance. As early as 1909 Smoluchowski assumed a coefficient of friction, using that of iron on iron, and calculated the force necessary to push a thrust plate along a horizontal surface. The force would act as a pressure applied across one end of the block. The pressure across the back of the block may be expressed as

$$\frac{\text{Force}}{\text{Area}} = \text{density} \times \text{coefficient of friction}$$
$$\times \text{length of block}$$

He found that the strength of the rock in the plate would have to be such that it would be able to support a column of granite 15 miles high (the crushing strength of granite is such that it will support a column 2 miles high) if the thrust sheet were 100 miles long. Clearly, thrust faulting along horizontal or up-inclined planes would be unlikely unless the assumptions made are in error. Smoluchowski concluded that thrusts must occur down inclined planes or that the coefficient of friction must be much less than that assumed. More recently Hubbert and Rubey (1959) reexamined the question of the maximum possible length for a thrust block, using Mohr's stress analysis methods and known crushing strengths for rock; they reached the conclusion that the maximum possible length for a thrust block pushed on a *horizontal* surface would be less than 30 km. Blocks 1 km thick and 8 km long, and blocks 5 km thick and 8.4 km long could be thrust according to the assumptions made. Note particularly that one assumption is that the fault is horizontal.

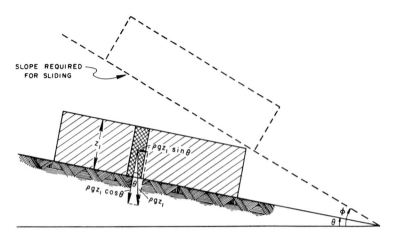

Fig. 4-23 Gravitational sliding of a subaerial block, top. Normal and shear stresses on base of block inclined at angle θ, and angle ϕ required for sliding. (*From Hubbert and Rubey, 1959.*)

If the movement of the block is by means of gravity sliding, the strength of the material in the thrust plate ceases to be of critical importance, but the coefficient of friction continues to present a problem. The forces acting on a block on an inclined plane (Fig. 4-23) (where ρ = density; g = gravity force; z_1 = height of a cross-sectional segment of the block of unit area) include:

1. The weight of the block acting along a vertical line and equal to $\rho g z_1$.
2. A component of the above force acts down the inclined plane with a magnitude that is a function of the slope of the plane and is equal to $\tau = \rho g z_1 \sin \theta$.
3. A component of the weight acts down and normal to the plane. This force is counterbalanced by the force the plane exerts on the block in the opposite direction. This counterbalanced force is equal to: $\sigma = \rho g z_1 \cos \theta$.
4. Frictional resistance of the plane-block contact zone.

If the angle ϕ is the angle of inclination of the plane at which the block begins to slide, $\tan \phi = \tau / \sigma$ (Fig. 4-23). For sliding, θ must equal ϕ. A similar condition was found earlier to apply to the angle of internal friction of sand.

The angle was found to be on the order of 30°, an approximate value for many rocks. Thus for a mass of rock to shear off down slope under the force of gravity a slope on the order of 30° would be required. It seems highly improbable that any major thrust fault developed on a slope of that magnitude, and in the case of some of the best-documented gravity faults, it is improbable that the angle of inclination exceeded a few degrees.

Frictional drag between the thrust sheet and the underlying rock must be greatly reduced by some means in order for either of the suggested models to work satisfactorily. It has long been recognized that many major thrusts are bedding-plane thrusts situated in rocks composed of clay, shale, gypsum, or similar incompetent materials, and various means of lubricating the fault surface have been sought. Probably the most popular one in recent years is the buoyancy effect of high pressures in fluids held within pores of the rock, as described by Hubbert and Rubey (1959). Hydrostatic pressure increases with depth in a column of water, in the ocean, and in porous rocks near the ground surface, but abnormally high pore pressures have been encountered in some wells. The pore pressures in some cases come close to equaling the pressure due to the weight of the overlying water-saturated rock (Fig. 4-24). The water is in essence supporting a large part of the weight of the overlying rock in such a zone of high pore pressure. The significance of this in terms of the models just considered is that the shear stress needed to slide the block depends only on that part of the pressure that is supported by the rock. As the pore pressure goes up, the shear stress required to move the block is decreased. The consequences of this are that frictional drag along a potential fault can be greatly reduced in the case of the first model and that the angle of slope required for gravitational sliding in the second case is greatly reduced.

Values calculated for the maximum length of a thrust caused by pushing across a horizontal plane reach 127 km (if the thrust plate is 8 km thick and 0.9 of overburden pressure is supported by pore pressure). The graph in Fig. 4-25 shows the calculated values of the width of plates which can be pushed downslope in terms of the ratio of pore pressure to overburden and angle of slope for a given plate thickness.

High pore pressures are known in many of the world's deep sedimentary basins and geosynclines such as the Gulf Coast of Texas and Louisiana, and East Pakistan; and such abnormal pressures are found in regions that are now tectonically active such as California, Trinidad, Burma, and Pakistan. The most likely mechanism for creation of the high pore pressures is found in compaction of sedimentary rocks which contain interbedded clays that have very low permeability and produce a self-sealing mechanism as compaction starts.

HIGH-ANGLE FAULTS

Normal faults are found in more diverse geologic settings than low-angle thrust faults. They, like the thrusts, occur in folded mountain belts, but they usually are found to have formed at a later stage in the deformation than the folding and thrusting. One exception to this is the normal faulting which develops along the lead-

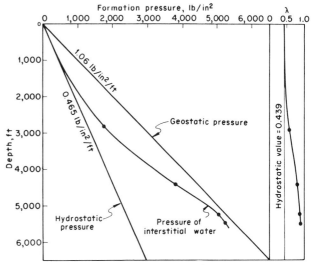

Fig. 4-24 Variation of pressure, and of corresponding values of A, with depth in Khaur field, Pakistan. (*From Keep and Ward, 1934.*)

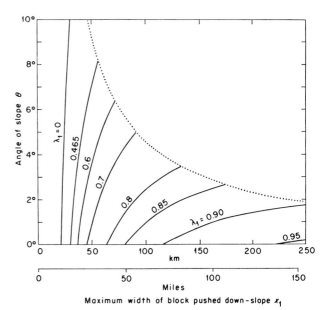

Fig. 4-25 Width of plate, x_1, that can be pushed downslope, for various values of slope angle θ, and fluid pressure-overburden ratio λ_1. Thickness of plate constant at 6 km. Dotted line drawn at difference in elevation of 8 km between front and rear edge of plate. (*From Rubey and Hubbert, 1959.*)

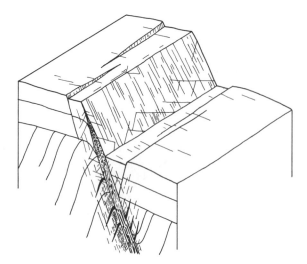

Fig. 4-26 Features commonly associated with normal faults. (*From Cloos, 1936.*)

ing edge of some thrusts. Graben and horst structures are bounded by normal faults along their margins. Grabens particularly occur in a wide range of geologic habitats. Grabens and basins bounded on one side by normal faults occur in the Appalachian Mountains, the Triassic basins. These normal fault structures formed after the Appalachian orogeny, and though they retain the northeast trend of most other Appalachian structures, they cut across the well-defined boundary between the Valley and Ridge (folded sedimentary units) and Piedmont (metamorphic) provinces. In the Cordilleran geosynclinal region grabens and horsts are common in the Basin and Range province, where they formed after the orogeny, and many of these faults have remained active until recent time. The Basin and Range normal faulting can be traced into the Columbia River plateau region where faults displace the Tertiary lava flows. As in the Appalachians, these faults follow the regional trend of the orogenic belt.

Normal faults also occur outside orogenic belts as in the more or less east-west-trending Kentucky River, Rough Creek, and Genevieve fault zones which cut across parts of the Appa-

lachian Plateau, the Cincinnati arch, the Illinois basin, and the Ozark dome. These normal fault zones appear unrelated to the large-scale structures on which they occur. Among the best-known grabens of the world are the Rhine graben, the Ottawa Bonnechere, and the East African rift system. A major system of normal faults marks the edge of the Gulf Coastal Plain. Complex systems of normal faults are found over salt domes, on some folds, and near the surface of the ground along what appear to be deep-seated faults. They occur in cryptovolcanic structures and extend along the crest of the midocean ridges.

Some Characteristics of Normal Fault Zones

Most normal faults dip at steep angles (45 to 90°), and as a consequence the fault traces tend to be straight and are little deviated through topography. While the normal fault may consist of a number of parallel faults, highly deformed and folded units, intense brecciation, and slivers of displaced rock units are not so common as in thrust-fault zones. Usually a major fault zone is found to have one or more parallel faults arranged in a step pattern (Fig. 4-26). Drag features and slickensides are often present. Among the fracture systems present, one is parallel to the normal fault and a second set has similar strike but opposite dip. Often there is displacement on this second set of fractures, called *antithetic faults*. Because normal faults tend to be steep, the scarps produced by them are subject to mass movement, or slumping, particularly along fractures. A third set of fractures, shown in Fig. 4-26, is vertical and normal to the fault strike. The distortion of layering where cut by normal faults may be caused by drag of the layering along the fault as a result of frictional forces set up in the fault zone, but frequently the "drag" on the downthrown side of the fault appears to be in the wrong direction. It is called *reverse drag* or *downbending*, but it is not a true drag process at all. Such bending is encountered in subsurface studies in the Gulf Coastal Plain, and it is seen exposed in the Colorado Plateau. Down-bending along some of the faults in the Grand Canyon has proceeded far enough to produce bedding dips of 26° toward the fault on the downthrown side (Hamblin, 1965). In places the downbending can be seen to pass into anti-thetic fault systems, and where relief is great enough the downbending is found to be related to normal faults which decrease in dip with depth. A similar relation is found in the Gulf Coast subsurface. One of the effects of this flattening of the dip at depth is to cause the two blocks to be pulled apart as well as to be dis-placed vertically. This in turn induces the ma-terial on the downthrown block to move laterally toward the fault plane to fill the gap. This movement may take the form of downbending, slumping, or the development of subsidiary fault systems (Fig. 4-27).

Normal Faults over Salt Domes

Fault patterns over salt domes in the American Gulf Coast are particularly interesting and in-structive because they occur in an environment where the processes causing them to form are still active, and because they can be studied on structures known in detail from subsurface data.

The salt domes have moved up through a thick pile of unconsolidated and semiconsolidated sedimentary rocks. Throughout the Gulf Coast region there is little or no evidence of any hori-zontal compression (i.e., there are no folds or thrust faults that can be related to horizontal compression). Thus the faults over the domes must be related to the vertically directed move-ment of the oval-topped salt plugs. The effect of this movement is to produce a dome in the overlying layered rock. As the doming con-tinues, the layer is stretched and eventually fails by fracturing and faulting. When a homogene-ous brittle material such as glass is deformed over a hemisphere, two systems of fractures usually occur—a radial set and a concentric set. Salt deformation, however, differs in that the material is layered, often inhomogeneous, and the surface of the salt plug is not hemispherical; yet, both of these sets of fractures and faults are sometimes encountered, especially the radial sets (Fig. 4-28). By far the most persistent fault pattern over salt domes is that of a compound graben. There is usually a major graben which splits at one or both ends, and step faults occur along most of the major faults. A less promi-nent set of normal faults perpendicular in trend

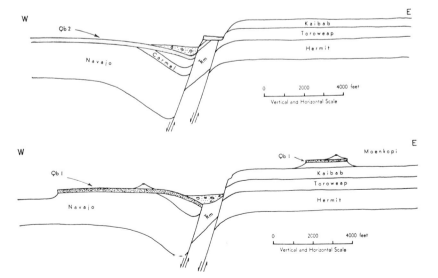

Fig. 4-27 Sections across the Hurricane fault along the Virgin River just north of Hurricane, Utah (top), and 8 miles south of Hurricane, Utah (bottom), showing re-verse drag flexure. Qb = Quaternary basalt. (*From Hamblin, 1965.*)

LOCATION: Southeast corner of Wood County, Texas,
approximately 17 miles northeast of Tyler, Texas.
DATA LEADING TO DISCOVERY: Surface geologic,
reflection seismograph and core drill surveys.
DISCOVERY DATE: December, 1940.
NATURE OF TRAP: Complexly-faulted convex trap
formed by deep-seated salt dome, with approximately
1,200 feet of uplift on producing sand.
PRINCIPAL RESERVOIR: Arenaceous; blanket-sand
of Woodbine (Gulfian Series). Gas and oil originally
entrapped between −4,541 and −3,490 feet, at actual
depths of 4,400 feet, more or less.
APPROXIMATE PRODUCTIVE AREA: 9,400 acres.

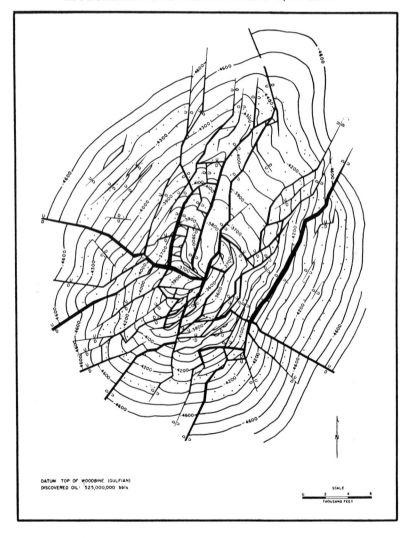

DATUM TOP OF WOODBINE (GULFIAN)
DISCOVERED OIL: 525,000,000 bbls

SCALE
0   2   4
THOUSAND FEET

Fig. 4-28 Fault pattern over the Hawkins field salt dome, Wood County, Tex.
(*From Wendlandt, 1951.*)

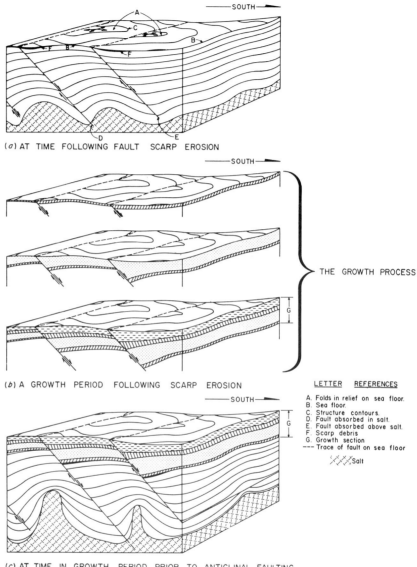

(a) AT TIME FOLLOWING FAULT SCARP EROSION

THE GROWTH PROCESS

(b) A GROWTH PERIOD FOLLOWING SCARP EROSION

LETTER REFERENCES

A. Folds in relief on sea floor.
B. Sea floor.
C. Structure contours.
D. Fault absorbed in salt.
E. Fault absorbed above salt.
F. Scarp debris
G. Growth section
--- Trace of fault on sea floor

Salt

Fig. 4-29 Development of growth-fault structures. (*From Ocamb, 1961.*)

(c) AT TIME IN GROWTH PERIOD PRIOR TO ANTICLINAL FAULTING.

to the main graben frequently intersects the main faults.

Thus it is evident in the case of salt domes that normal faults occur in such a way as to allow extension in the faulted layers over the dome. The radial pattern, the main graben, the step faults, and the normal faults perpendicular to the main faults all allow this extension.

Growth Faults

Subsurface studies in the Gulf Coastal Plain have revealed a number of normal faults which have continued to undergo movement over a period of time during deposition of the faulted units. These faults (Fig. 4-29) dip toward the center of the basins around which they occur. Typically the displaced units are thicker on the

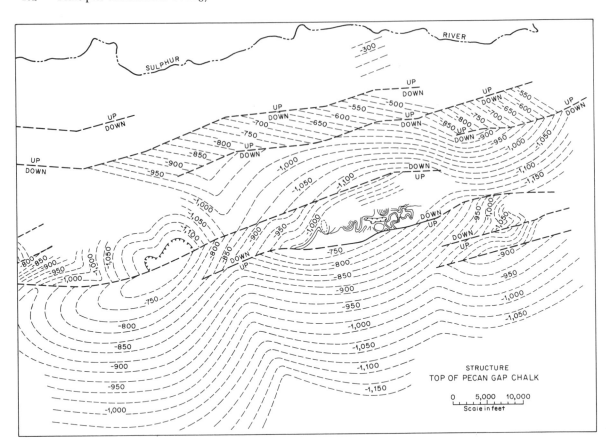

Fig. 4-30 Structure contour map of fault zone in Hopkins County, Tex. (*After Hager and Burnett, 1960.*)

downthrown side as illustrated. This proves that the faults were active during deposition. Reverse drag is found on the downthrown side of some of these faults. Reversal in dip of the units due to sag or slumpage is possible only if the two blocks separated by the fault are tending to pull apart.

Mexia-Talco Fault Line

The Tectonic Map of the United States shows a series of major zones of normal faults in the Gulf Coastal Plain. The westernmost and northernmost of these—the Balcones and Mexia-Talco fault zones and their eastern continuations, the Picken Gilbertown fault zones—form a crescent-shaped zone of normal faults which

rims part of the Gulf Coast geosyncline. These zones are grabens and step faults, but farther south more roughly concentric belts of normal faults occur which are steplike with the downthrown side toward the gulf in almost every instance. Many of these faults exhibit the growth characteristics previously described. Their position between the more stable continental interior and the subsiding geosyncline suggest that they originate as a result of stretching of the strata as the geosyncline subsides. Along the edges of the Coastal Plain, complementary faults have formed, with the central blocks relatively depressed to form grabens. The character of the structure along a portion of this zone in Hopkins County, Tex., is illustrated in Fig. 4-30.

Normal Faults on Folds

Thrust faults associated with folds generally trend parallel to the fold axes and cut across the limbs as a forelimb or more rarely a back-limb thrust. These thrusts may in turn be broken by tears. Normal faults on folds occur in longitudinal, transverse, and oblique positions.

The Elk basin oil field of Wyoming (Fig. 4-31) provides a good example of transverse faulting, and there is also one longitudinal fault shown. The structure is that of a faulted, doubly plunging anticline. Extension of the units of rocks in a doubly plunging structure are mainly in two directions, one over the fold crest and the other along the axis. The orientation of the faults makes this explanation of their origin seem plausible, for they are oriented so as to allow extension in these two directions. Drilling on this structure has shown that the faults become steeper with depth.

RIFT SYSTEMS OF EAST AFRICA

A complex system of faults has been mapped and intensively studied in the region of East Africa around Lake Victoria. This system is traced into the junction of the Gulf of Aden and the Red Sea (Fig. 4-32) along which similar faults have been mapped and inferred from the topography. The Gulf of Aden is now linked with submarine topography of the Indian Ocean (Fig. 4-38), and the fault system at the north end of the Red Sea continues into the Dead Sea rift. The fault system thus defined extends from Lebanon to the Zambeze River of South Africa, a distance more than one-sixth the circumference of the earth. Over a large portion of this region, Precambrian rocks of the shield are covered to shallow depths by Cenozoic volcanics and other sedimentary deposits.

The valleys of East Africa which comprise part of this system (Fig. 4-32) extend from the southern end of the Red Sea as the Abyssinian rift to Lake Victoria where the central Tanganyika Plateau is largely surrounded by rift valleys which join at the southern end and continue south. Local variations in structure over such a vast region must certainly be expected, but remarkable similarity is found. The rift valleys separating the high plateaus have very steep borders; some are precipitous drops of several thousand feet, and they have been interpreted as fault scarps of relatively recent age by all who have studied them. The edges of these valleys, like the faults along the edge of the Red Sea, can be broken into straight line segments which form a zigzag pattern (Fig. 4-33). Similar patterns are found along the border of the Rhine graben, the Appalachian

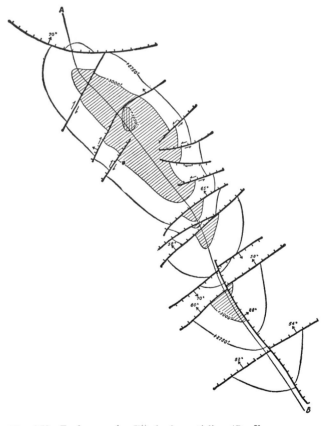

Fig. 4-31 Faults on the Elk basin anticline (*By Korn, after Bartram, 1929.*)

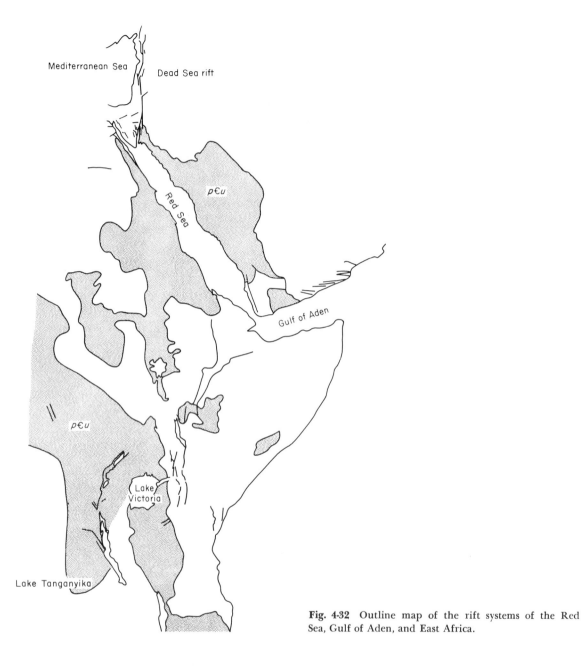

Fig. 4-32 Outline map of the rift systems of the Red Sea, Gulf of Aden, and East Africa.

grabens, and grabens of the Basin and Range region.

Cenozoic volcanic activity is associated with the system as a whole. Some of the highest volcanos in Africa, Kilimanjaro, Kenya, and Elgon, are located along but outside the rifts. Many smaller volcanos occur in and along the rifts, but the arrangement of the volcanic centers is not systematic and the activity does not coincide exactly with the faulting. Both normal and reverse faults are known along the edges of the rifts and they both strike parallel to the rift. Regionally, the structure is that of a broad low dome; folding is not commonly associated with the sediments in the rift valleys or the adjacent bordering plateaus, but folds are known in the Tertiary deposits of the Dead Sea rift and the Albert rift. That the rock units involved are capable of folding is shown north of the rift system, where the same units are folded; the trend of these folds is transverse to the overall trend of the rift system, and the two seem unrelated. Negative-gravity anomalies lie over the rift valleys, indicating a mass deficiency at depth but also raising the question of why an upward adjustment has not occurred over the long time the rifts have been forming.

Locally the margins of the rifts are uplifted quite high. The Ruwenzori Mountains form an anomalous area. These mountains, composed of Precambrian rocks, stand in the Albert rift valley and rise to elevations of over 6,000 ft. Most of the valleys are floored by Tertiary sediments or volcanics.

Hypotheses on the Formation of the Rift System

Willis (1936) outlined the historical development of thought regarding the origin of the East African rift valleys. De Lapparent offered one of the first theories as follows (1898):

> East Africa is a great, super-elevated arch (voussoir), whose axis, directed from north to south, has been appreciably bent and which is flanked on the sides by two ridges, more abrupt and more localized, or at least by two violent folds, whose axes, by their subsidence, have each one given rise to a graben or trough. In this manner, there has well occurred the collapse of a zone, but only there where the earlier elevation had been exceptional.

This view was amplified in 1914 by the German geologist Abendanon:

> The increase of dimension in consequence of the anticlinal stretching is made evident in the

most convincing manner by the numerous graben or depressions, which constitute an eastern and a western fosse. . . . Throughout the length of the *GrossFalte* we observe as direct and indirect effects of the extension (Distraktion) in the anticlinal zone the occurrence of seismotectonic and volcanic phenomena, the latter more than 1000 km from the coast.

A second hypothesis, that the rifts resulted from thrusting, has been upheld by a number

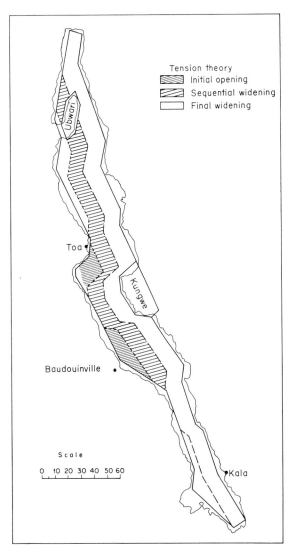

Fig. 4-33 Lake Tanganyika; diagram illustrating parting by tension. (*From Willis, 1936.*)

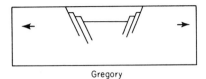

Gregory

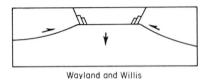

Wayland and Willis

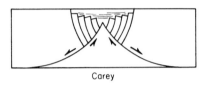

Carey

Fig. 4-34 Cross sections showing three interpretations of the rift valley origin by simple extension, thrusting, and extension along faults which start as vertical tension fractures and pass downward into shears, shown in a later stage of development after secondary faults have formed.

of geologists who have quoted evidence such as that of Uhlig (1909) to support the views that the down-dropped valley centers are actually forceably depressed by overriding thrust sheets. These points of evidence include:

(1) In certain districts of the southern part of the Great Rift Valley, where great vertical displacements have been produced, volcanic eruptions, such as would presumably occur along tension faults, are lacking; (2) the observation that ancient mica schist overlies relatively very young lavas east of the great escarpment on the western side of Lake Natron in the Great Rift Valley indicates an overthrust of 2 and ½ km; (3) the notable elevation of the plateau between the Great Rift Valley and the Indian Ocean appears to be of the nature of uparching due to horizontal pressure; (4) the elevated margins of the rift valleys suggest uparching along their trends in a manner consistent with the hypothesis of overthrusting.

Willis (1936) regarded the thrust faults as defining wedges of the crust (Fig. 4-34) and explained the steep valley walls as slumping of the edges of the thrusts.

Gregory (1920) concluded from his studies of the rift system that the faults are very steep, vertical or normal faults and explained the origin this way:

The evidence seems clear that the Red Sea trough was formed by earth-movements at successive dates, beginning not later than the Oligocene and continuing until quite recent times.

The history of the Rift Valley in British East Africa is dependent in the main on the volcanic history of the country; the two are connected, as the subsidence of the earth blocks doubtless forced up the lavas along the fractures.

The first stage in the formation of the Rift Valley was the uplift of a long, low arch with the axis trending north and south. . . .

The second stage was the cracking of the sides of the arch as the lateral pressure was reduced, and the top sank as the keystone of an arch sinks if the end supports give way. The sinking of the keystones of the East African arch into the plastic material below forced some of it up the adjacent cracks, through which it was discharged in volcanic eruptions.

The subsidence of the Arabian Sea and the outflow of the vast quantities of lava left the East African arch insufficiently supported and the top of it sank between parallel fractures. This subsidence happened along the first of the Rift Valley faults.

Krenkle (1922) stated the case against thrusting:

The tectonic setting of the East African fault zones, whether considered in detail or as a whole, admits of only one explanation: they are zones of tearing apart of the crust, produced by a directed tension. Only as tension phenomena can the wealth of observed structural facts and changes be brought into orderly relations. Accompanying these deep-seated developments as inevitable accompaniments are disturbances of gravity, earthquakes, and volcanic activity. Forces that produce partings (disjunctive forces) alone produce structures like the rift valleys with their series of splits, that extending to great depths converge downward and are unequally filled with light-weight superficial rocks. The separation is, however, most evident in those gaping rifts whose depths are filled with water. The action of compressive forces is nowhere recognizable. Overthrusts of significant displacement toward the axes of splitting are everywhere lacking.

The tearing apart has resulted in a certain areal expansion of the central African landmass, which

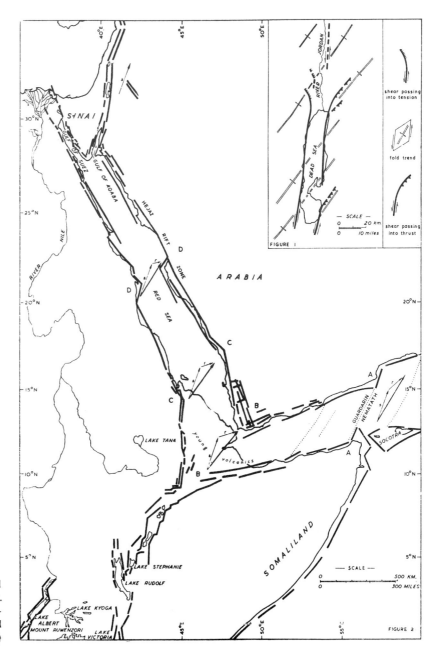

Fig. 4-35 (1) The structural trends in the Dead Sea rift. (*After Lees, 1954.*) (2) Relations of Red Sea and Dead Sea rifts. (*From Carey, 1958.*)

has been most strongly affected. Any estimate of the amount can only be tentative, presenting only a rough approximate value. . . . Nevertheless the attempt must be made in order to obtain some idea of the magnitude of the expansion. Several estimates for the Tanganyika graben result, for example, in a parting coefficient (Lockerungsko-effizient) for its marginal blocks of at least 5 percent. The parting is, therefore, quite considerable. To the end that it may occur, we must assume powerful tensile stresses, which must accumulate in order that they may ultimately be released by the sudden, energetic development of the faulting.

Thus we see that both compression with thrusting and extension over the region have been called on to explain the fault system. Most geologists have been convinced of the extensional origin, viewing the valleys as grabens or complexes of graben and horst structures.

Consideration must also be given to the Dead Sea area, in which Lees (1954) and Quennell (1957) have described folds and thrusts related to the rift system. Both have explained the structures in terms of sinistral simple shear along the Dead Sea valley accompanied by some extension normal to the valley. Major struc-

tural elements and their interpretation by Lees are depicted in Fig. 4-35. The sides of the rift, interpreted as shears, east of the valley pass northward into thrusts; those on the west pass into tensional features; folds are viewed as related to a rotational couple. Carey (1958) has reconciled this interpretation of the Dead Sea rift with the extensional origin of the Red Sea and Gulf of Aden by viewing the origin of the entire system as a result of rotation of East Africa away from Arabia, with the direction and amount of movement indicated by arrows in Fig. 4-35. Thus at the narrow north end of the Red Sea the movement is left-lateral. The dotted lines in the figure are submarine ridges interpreted as marking the trace of the movement.

Red Sea Area

The rift valley from the midocean ridge in the Indian Ocean has been traced into the Gulf of Aden. The rifts are comparable in width and depth, as shown in cross section in Fig. 4-36. The Abyssinian rift is part of the East African rift system, and the straight borders of the Red Sea and Gulf of Aden have long been inter-

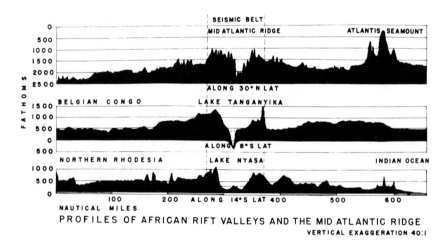

PROFILES OF AFRICAN RIFT VALLEYS AND THE MID ATLANTIC RIDGE
VERTICAL EXAGGERATION 40:1

Fig. 4-36 The mid-Atlantic ridge and the East African rift valleys. The mid-Atlantic ridge and the East African rifted plateau, each lying along a continuous epicenter belt, are nearly identical in morphology and, presumably, in structure and origin. (*From Heezen and Ewing, 1961.*)

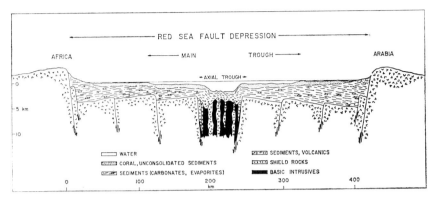

Fig. 4-37 Structural section of the northern part of the Red Sea inferred from geophysical data. (*From Drake and Girdler, 1964.*)

preted as similar rift features. Recent geophysical studies have shown the submarine topography to consist of an inner rift valley within the larger depressions (Fig. 4-37) of the Red Sea. A similar central zone in the Gulf of Aden (Fig. 4-38) is marked by a system of scarps, presumably fault scarps, of northeastern trend (Laughton, 1966) along which the central zone is offset. Earthquake epicenters fall along the inner valley of the Gulf of Aden, but a number of those in the Red Sea lie along the western edge of the sea as well as in the center. Seismic refraction studies made in the Red Sea indicate that high-density materials, probably basic intrusives, lie at a shallower depth under the central portion of the rift and that normal granitic rocks lie to either side. Gravity and magnetic anomalies also are found along this central zone, particularly at the south end of the Red Sea. These geophysical results are interpreted as signifying a compound rift valley with step-fault blocks and an axial trough caused by tension which has allowed intrusion of basic materials along the central zone.

GRABEN EXPERIMENT OF HANS CLOOS

Hans Cloos (1936) successfully produced many structural details of graben structures in wet clay. Possibly part of the success of these experi-

ments lies in the fact that the wet clay came close to having properly scaled-down properties. One of these experiments consisted of stretching a large sheet of the wet clay on a table designed so that it could be extended. Thus in this experiment the clay was brought under tension and it failed by the development of graben structure. A system of step faults formed on either side of the graben, the main faults trending perpendicular to the direction of extension. Note the closely spaced fractures, or antithetic faults, dipping into the major fault. Similar faults, or fractures, occur along the edges of some grabens. The initial angle of dip of the fault agreed closely with that predicted for this particular orientation of the principal stresses. Since the base was rigid in this experiment, the development of the graben structure took place without vertical uplift; however, graben and horst structures have been developed experimentally (Sanford, 1959) in layered materials warped upward over an anticlinal uplift. In both cases the layers in which the faulting occurred were being extended laterally.

FAULTS IN SAND

A number of experimenters have used sand to investigate the development of fracture and fault patterns. Sand offers several advantages to

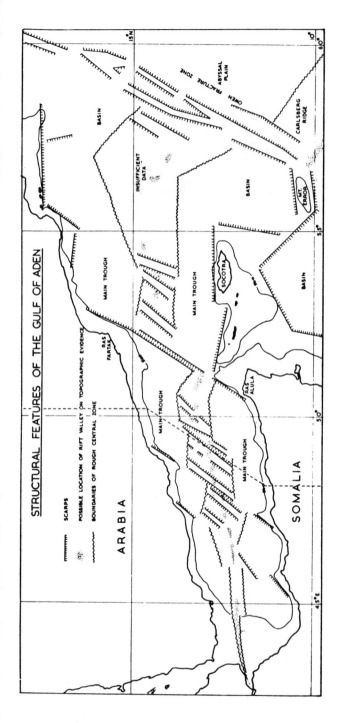

Fig. 4-38 Structural features of the Gulf of Aden. (*From Laughton, 1966.*)

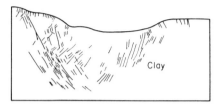

Fig. 4-39 Cloos graben experiment. (Faults traced from a photograph.)

experimenters. It will not adhere to the sides of the confining box (usually glass), and thus the problems of boundary affects are lessened. Furthermore, a great deal is known about the properties of sand through studies of soil mechanics. Notable mathematical analyses combined with experiments have been carried out by Hubbert (1937, 1951) and Sanford (1959). The experiments of the two differed in that Hubbert used a movable rigid partition placed in a sandbox with fixed side boundaries, and produced normal and thrust faults (Fig. 4-40) by moving the partition horizontally; while Sanford employed a flexible floor, and produced faults by vertical rather than horizontal applied stresses.

Sanford analyzed two types of vertical uplift: one consisting of a sinusoidal vertical displacement and the second a steplike uplift of a portion of the basement. The effect of the first type of experiment was the creation of an anticlinal uplift with graben and horst structures developed across the top of the structure as the upper layers began to extend over the fold top, and fractures formed tapering downward. Curved faults were produced in the second type of experiment (Fig. 4-41). At depth these faults are vertical but as they rise up in the section they become high-angle, then lower-dipping, reverse faults. These reverse faults are due to horizontally directed stresses but they arose from vertical movements—not horizontal compression. Note also the normal faults developed above and behind the reverse faults (Fig. 4-41). In this experiment, as in Hubbert's experiments, the faults are curved as predicted by theoretical stress analysis discussed at the beginning of this chapter. A constant angular relationship is maintained between the maximum compressive principal stresses and the line of failure.

The question of the suitability of sand as a material to model rock structures may be answered in terms of the properties of rock and sand. We still have little quantitative knowledge about the strength of large masses of rock.

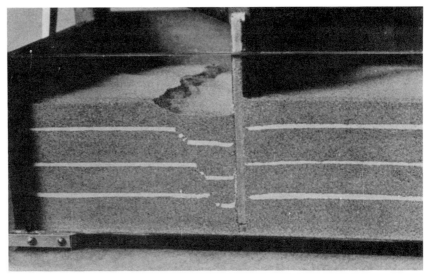

(a)

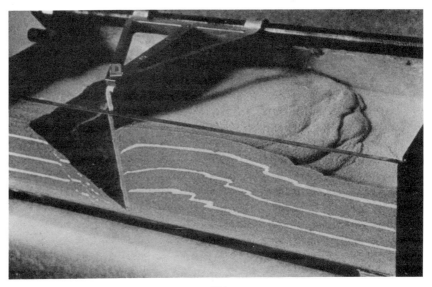

(b)

Fig. 4–40 Faults produced in sand (a) by extension and (b) by compression (*From Hubbert, 1951.*)

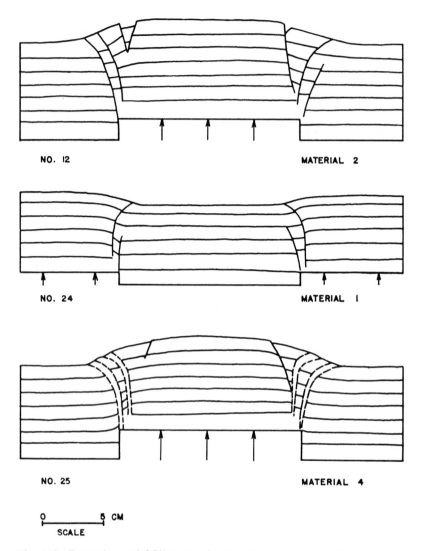

NO. 12   MATERIAL 2

NO. 24   MATERIAL 1

NO. 25   MATERIAL 4

0   5 CM
SCALE

Fig. 4-41 Fracturing and folding experiments. *(From Sanford, 1959.)*

Sanford points out that most rock masses at shallow depths are broken by fractures and therefore the strength is determined in part by the degree of jointing. In highly fractured rock the mass behaves as though it has little cohesive strength; sand, of course, has no cohesive strength. Thus it seems reasonable for sand and rock to behave very similarly when the relationship between the joint bounded blocks and the layer of rock is similar to that between the sand grain and the layer of sand. It is further known that the angle of internal friction of sand is close to that of most sedimentary rocks.

FAULTS WITH LARGE HORIZONTAL DISPLACEMENTS

A third major group of faults is those which have a large component of strike separation. Included in this category are some of the largest of all faults known on the continents, and there is strong evidence for their existence in the ocean basins as well. They have been called *rifts,* but this term is not good because it is also associated with graben structures such as the East African rift system, and the two are very different types of faults. The term *strike slip* is also used, although the amount of slip is usually debatable. The term *transverse* applies where the fault cuts local structures, but these faults often parallel regional trends of the deformed belts in which they are usually located. More recently the term *wrench fault* has come into widespread use. Anderson (1951) recognized wrench faults as one of the three general fault classes (Fig. 4-3) formed as a result of failure in pure shear followed by faulting movement along one of a conjugate set of fractures. It seems probable that some of these faults are not the result of pure shear. For this reason and because the larger faults such as the San Andreas almost certainly cut through all or a large part of the thickness of the crust, Carey (1958) proposed the term *megashear* for them. Among the major faults that fall into this category are the San Andreas fault of California, the Great Glen fault of Scotland, the Alpine fault of New Zea-

land, the Oca fault of Venezuela, and possibly the Brevard fault of the Appalachians.

A number of these faults have undergone movements in the Pleistocene; as a result, the displacements they have caused in recent alluvial fans, in other unconsolidated sediments, and in stream patterns are readily apparent. These displacements do support the idea of strike-slip movement with subordinate vertical movement, as is indicated by matching structures, strand lines, and plutons cut and displaced by the faults. The dip of these faults is poorly known, but their straight-line fault traces indicate vertical or at least steep dips. Only rarely can dips of major transcurrent faults be determined to substantial depth, but some of the transcurrent faults in the Kaikoura Ranges of New Zealand are well exposed and have dips which vary both in amount (through about 100°) and in direction. Tectonic depressions and upbulges also characterize some of these faults, as seen along the Hope fault (Fig. 4-42). Movements have taken place along the Hope fault during the Pleistocene, and the depressions are expressed by modern topographic features. The origin of the depressions is thought to be related to *en échelon* offsets in the fault

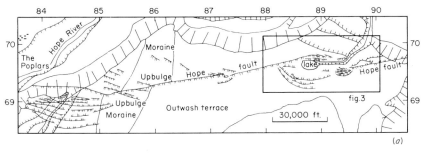

(a)

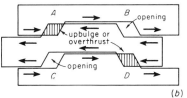

(b)

Fig. 4-42 (a) Map of the lower Hope Valley showing fluvial terraces (single tick marks) and fault or slump scarps (double tick marks); (b) diagrammatic plan view of openings and upbulges or overthrusts formed between echelon segments of a right-lateral and a left-lateral fault. (*From Clayton, 1966.*)

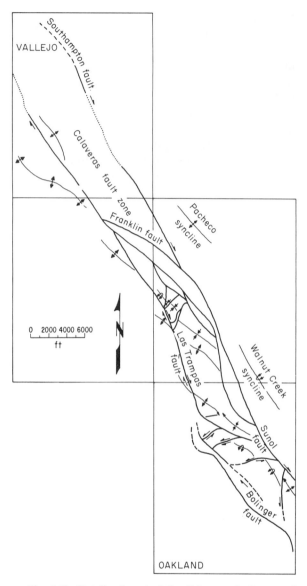

Fig. 4-43 Details of part of the Calaveras fault zone of California. (*Adapted from Saul, 1967.*)

an upbulge with associated minor thrust faulting will form if the offset is in the opposite direction (Clayton, 1966).

Details of the Calaveras fault zone of California, located east of the San Andreas, point up some of the features commonly found along major transcurrent faults. The zone appears to be bounded by faults on either side, and within the zone, faults split and rejoin to create a pattern that resembles the slices along thrust faults. Folds are well developed within the fault zone, and they tend to have a consistent orientation relative to the direction of movement on the bounding faults on either side. Note also the transcurrent faults which cut across from one bounding fault to the other.

California Fault System—the San Andreas

Despite many years of intensive investigation the structure and origin of the fault system of California is still subject to debate. The large components of the system (Fig. 4-44) consist of a number of active faults notably including the San Andreas and Garlock faults. The northwest-trending system of faults is subparallel to the San Andreas; the pattern is characterized by bifurcation and rejoining of the faults and in places by *en échelon* arrangements. The Garlock fault system of east-northeast trend intersects and crosses the San Andreas trends which deviate westward.

Many of these faults have been active in recent times, and a strong strike-slip component of movement is evident where roads, fences, streams, and alluvial fans of unconsolidated sediment are crossed; however, vertical movements are recorded as well. The faults form troughs like plowed furrows with low earth ridges on either side where there is no vertical movement. Features known as *sag ponds* form in the depressions along the fault. The central zone is one of intense shearing: the rock is brecciated and mylonitized. The movement inferred on the San Andreas and many of the subparallel faults is right-lateral, and movement on the Garlock is left-lateral.

trace. The depression is formed where the offset occurs as the strike-slip movement continues. Note that the depression will form when one particular combination of offset direction and sense of strike-slip movement occurs, while

Displacement

A considerable literature, reviewed by Crowell (1962), has been assembled concerning the amount of displacement which has taken place on the San Andreas fault. The region is one of Cenozoic crustal deformation, and stratigraphic and structural relationships are complex. Sedimentary basins adjacent to and between faults have formed while the fault system has been active. Accumulations of sediment, in excess of 50,000 ft in places, have been deposited as the sea invaded and retreated from the region. The usual methods of estimating displacements by determination of separation of marker beds of known attitude is difficult to apply here because the marker beds have been subject to continued

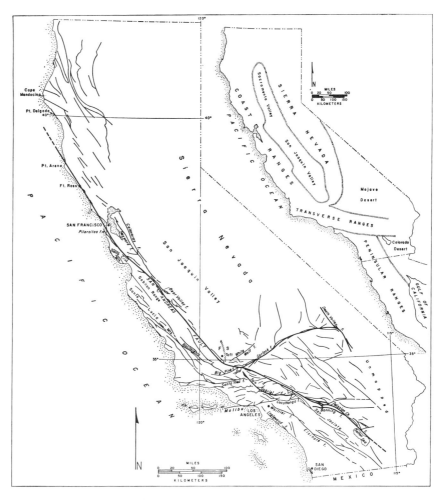

Fig. 4-44 Generalized fault map of coastal and southern California, compiled and edited from selected data in Jenkins (1943), Jahns (1954), Irwin (1960), and Dibblee (1960). Nearby Taft buried contact is between Franciscan (F) and Sierran (S) rocks. Principal physiographic provinces at upper right. (*From Crowell, 1962.*)

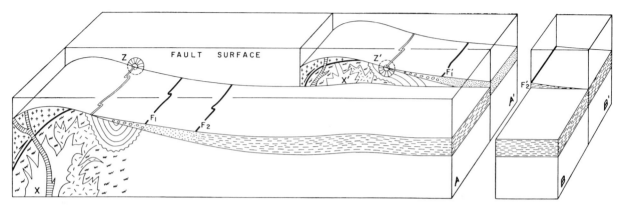

Fig. 4-45 Regional trace slip and use of displaced geological "lines" to find strike slip. (*From Crowell, 1962.*)

deformation after the initial faulting. Examples of the types of offset geological lines used to determine displacement are schematically illustrated in Fig. 4-45. When linear features offset by a fault can be defined and found, they are much more reliable guides to displacement than is the separation of a planar surface (folded or not). Various workers have used: (1) offset of terrain, (2) offset dikes (Fig. 4-46), (3) offset metamorphic and igneous bodies, (4) offset of the contact between continental and marine sedimentary facies of a particular age. Crowell (1962) concludes that the best evidence supports the idea of a right-lateral movement of between 160 and 175 miles on the San Andreas since early Miocene. A separation of 220 to 320 miles since the Cretaceous is possible, although the evidence is "of a different order of acceptability." Accepting the first figures, the *average* rate of movement is 0.4 in. per year or 1 m per century.

Although the idea that most of the faults in this region are major strike-slip faults is widely accepted, there is convincing evidence of local vertical movements of great magnitude, and some geologists prefer to interpret the faults in terms of predominantly dip-slip movement.

Basins along the faults and dip-slip movements

Deep Cenozoic sedimentary basins and Precambrian basement rocks occur along the faults, the first appearing to have risen and the second to have subsided during the faulting. The nature of the problem in fault interpretation may be illustrated by the case of the San Gabriel fault (Fig. 4-47). The fault has been interpreted as a strike-slip fault with 20 miles of displacement (Crowell, 1952) and as a dip-slip fault with 5,000+ ft of displacement (Paschall and Off, 1961) in the eastern Ventura basin area of southern California. Evidence for the strike-slip movement is based on offset of an anorthosite-bearing conglomerate of upper Miocene age now directly across the fault from the gneiss-bearing sedimentary breccia (Violin breccia), also upper Miocene in age. A possible source of the anorthosite is an anorthosite mass 20 miles southeast in the San Gabriel Mountains. The Violin breccia is possibly derived from the breccia across the fault. Paschall and Off point out that sources for the gneiss conglomerate can be found directly across the fault in a narrow outcrop belt of gneiss along the fault, and they argue that the anorthosite could have been de-

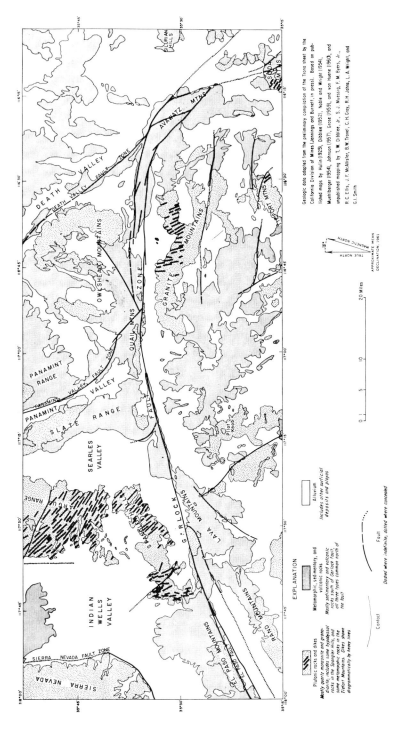

Fig. 4-46 Generalized geologic map of areas along east half of Garlock fault. Map shows relative positions and trends of known major dike swarms, and location of plutonic rocks known to be free of similar dikes. *(From Smith, 1962.)*

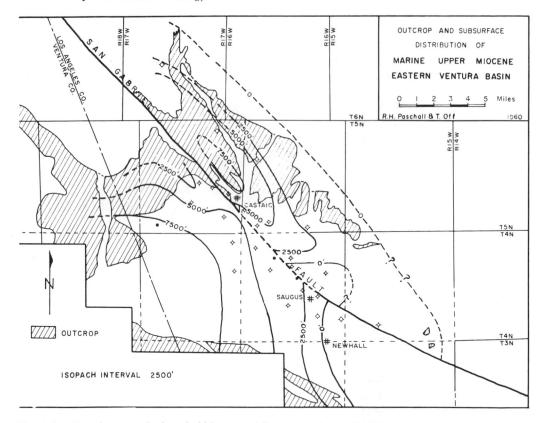

Fig. 4-47 Map shows contiguity of thick upper Miocene marine sedimentary sequences on either side of San Gabriel fault. Left-lateral separation of basin deeps is probably a consequence of erosion and not of movement on fault. (*From Paschall and Off, 1961.*)

rived from anorthosite bodies now buried across the fault. In addition they note that there is uniform regional dip across the fault; that some of the Miocene sedimentary units interfinger (change facies) across the fault; that isopachs of upper Miocene (Fig. 4-47) show adjacent deep basins across the fault; and that no truncated remnant can be found displaced 20 miles. The alternative proposed to strike-slip movement is that movements across the fault have been predominantly vertical with reversal in the sense of movement.

Folds associated with the San Andreas

Numerous folds, thrusts, and other faults are associated with the major fault belts. Some of these folds (Fig. 4-48) are oriented in sub-

parallel fashion as shown, intersecting the major fault at acute angles.

The Great Glen Fault

The Great Glen fault extends in a nearly straight northeast-trending line for 130 miles across the Scottish Highlands (Fig. 4-49). It parallels the regional trend of Caledonian structures. To the north it passes out to sea, where it may continue as a fracture in the floor of the North Sea. Southeast it disappears under Mesozoic and Tertiary rocks at the Island of Mull. As early as 1841 this long topographic depression was related to faulting. Miller (1841) in Kennedy (1946) referred to it as "a foot-track, hollowed by the frequent tread of earthquakes, to make the course in which they journeyed," but it was 1861 when Murchison and Geikie determined that it had undergone displacement. Earthquakes still occur along the fault. Most of these quakes have been minor shocks, but a few major shocks, including a particularly severe one at Inverness in 1901, have occurred in the zone. Up until the time of W. Q. Kennedy's work (1946) most geologists considered the Great Glen fault to be a normal fault.

The fault zone is a belt of crushed, sheared, and mylonitized rock, up to a mile wide, that is covered by numerous lakes and weathered, surficial material. It can be seen, where the zone itself is exposed, that the country rock in it has been converted to a cataclastic schist and that the zone is a complex of numerous vertical faults. In places pegmatites have developed in the crushed rocks. Subsidiary vertical fractures and faults branch out of the zone and run parallel to it. Recognition of the Great Glen fault as a wrench fault depends on establishing the sense of the displacement. W. Q. Kennedy (1946) summarized the evidence for lateral slip as follows:

(1) The dislocation possesses physical characters unlike those of most normal faults but similar to the great strike slip shears of the California Coast Range.

(2) It belongs to the same system as the Strathconon, Ericht-Laidon and Loch Tay faults, all of which have proved lateral displacements of up to 5 miles.

(3) It displaces the great belt of regional injection which affects the Moine Schists of the northern and Grampian Highlands, the nature and amount of the displacement being consistent with lateral shift but not with vertical downthrow.

(4) It similarly displaces the metamorphic zones of the Highlands in an equally significant manner.

(5) It truncates the Strontian Granite, the southern portion of which, according to the detailed structural evidence, is missing. The missing portion, moreover, can be identified in the Foyers mass which outcrops on the other side of the fault-line some 65 miles to the north-east and is similarly truncated by the fault. These two major

Caledonian intrusions consist of identical rock types and are structurally homologous.

(6) Finally, the occurrence of Lewisian and Torridonian rocks in Islay and Colonsay and the presence of the Moine Thrust-plane in the former

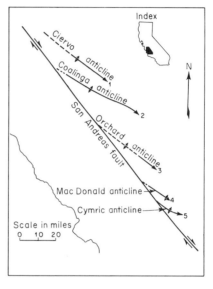

Fig. 4-48 Drag folds along San Andreas fault, California. (*From Moody and Hill, 1956.*)

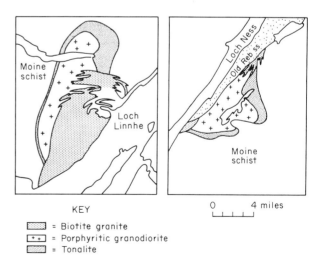

Fig. 4-49 Maps showing similarities between the Strontian (left) and Foyers (right) granites. (*After Kennedy, 1946.*)

island are more readily explained on the assumption of a lateral rather than a vertical displacement along the fault.

As W. Q. Kennedy points out, these lines of evidence are not equally valid. The first two provide indirect evidence as does the character of the fault line, which does not have the zigzag pattern of most long normal faults. It does possess a wide zone of sheared rock, suggesting that the two sides of the fault were under great pressure during movement. Other faults in Scotland belonging to the same system as the Great Glen fault possess the following characteristics:

1. They form marked linear depressions owing to the intense crushing within their shatter belts and the abnormal widths of these zones.
2. As a class they tend to be notably straight.
3. They displace the metamorphic zones of the Highlands.
4. They frequently show evidence of lateral movement such as horizontal slickensides and torsion of the strata toward the fault plane.
5. a. Individual members are demonstrably wrench faults with proved horizontal displacements of up to approximately 5 miles.
   b. The Ericht-Laidon fault, which intersects the Moor of Rannoch and Strath Ossian granites, shifts the vertical margins of these masses for a distance of from 4 to 5 miles, the direction of movement being southwestward on the northwest side.
   c. The Loch Tay fault displaces the axes of folds and the metamorphic zonal boundaries southwestward on its northern side for a distance of 4 miles.

The direct evidence of the nature of the Great Glen fault is found in the displacements of geologic features such as the Strontian granite (Fig. 4-49) and Highland metamorphic zones.

The Strontian granite and the Foyers granite are petrographically very similar, and the two intrusions possess several structural peculiarities which make it probable that they were originally part of the same mass. In both bodies the central core of porphyritic granodiorite is bordered by tonalite. Along the northeast side of each there is a sheet complex of granite that cuts the tonalite. Finally the general shape and size of the two are indicative of their probable former connection.

In conclusion, evidence indicates that the Great Glen fault is a wrench fault with about 65 miles of left-lateral displacement on it. Most of the movement was accomplished before the end of the Paleozoic, but it is still seismically active.

Alpine Fault of New Zealand

Movement along a system of northeast-trending faults has been one of the dominate elements of late Tertiary and Recent diastrophism in New Zealand. The longest of these, called the *Alpine fault*, has been traced from Milford Sound to Cook Strait on the South Island, as shown in Fig. 4-50 (Wellman and Willett, 1942). Its continuation on the North Island is uncertain, but a number of faults of parallel trend do cross the central portion of the North Island.

The Alpine fault is evidenced by scarps, sudden changes in elevation across the fault amounting to thousands of feet in places. In addition, river courses are offset so that the west side is displaced to the northeast; Pleistocene river gravels are cut and offset by the fault; a zone of crushed and mylonitized rock reaches a width of a mile in places; and Pleistocene deposits are found tilted in a few places.

There is relatively little evidence to pin down the attitude of the fault. In such a zone of major faulting it is difficult to say whether a given exposed fault is "the" fault or a minor part of the larger structure. Judging from the long, nearly straight character of the fault zone, it should be a high-angle fault, and this is con-

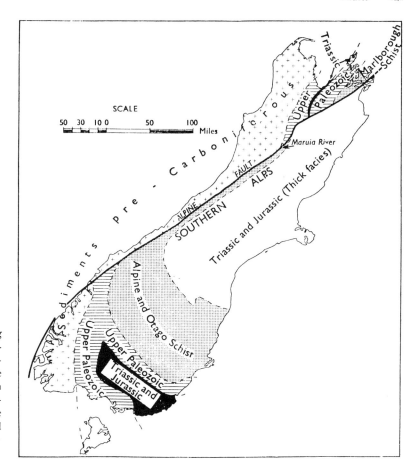

Fig. 4-50 Sketch map showing the Alpine fault and pre-Cretaceous rocks of South Island, reproduced from Wellman (1952). The 300-mile lateral shift is based on the correspondence of regional sequences on opposite sides of the Alpine fault in the north and south of the island. (*From Suggate, 1963*.)

firmed by a few locally exposed faults within the zone.

The type of movement is reported by Wellman (1954) to be transcurrent with the west side moving northeast by an estimated 300 miles. On a fault of this magnitude it is not surprising to find many local variations in structure. Differences in elevation of topography across the fault indicate that the eastern side is elevated relative to the western side, and it has been suggested that the fault is a thrust fault, at least locally. The strongest evidence for the transcurrent nature of the fault is found in the displacement of rock masses. Note, for example, the displacement of the upper Paleozoic in Fig. 4-50. If the suggested 300-mile displacement is reversed and the rock masses restored

to their original position, a good alignment of rock types and structure is effected.

Displaced Pleistocene terraces indicate that activity on the fault has continued until very recently. Curiously, however, earthquake epicenters do not line up clearly along the fault. When the movements started is open to speculation, but much of the movement has been assigned to late Tertiary. It is possibly related to the Pliocene Kaikoura orogeny, to which Tertiary folds and faults in New Zealand are clearly related.

Extension of the Alpine fault to the southwest from Milford Sound has been suggested on the basis of submarine topography. The extension would coincide with the eastern edge of the Fiordland trough and farther southwest with a

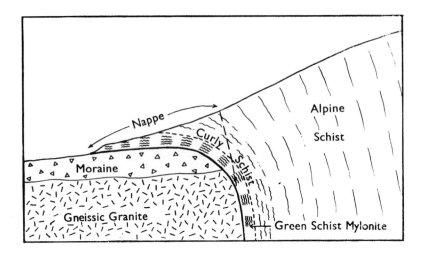

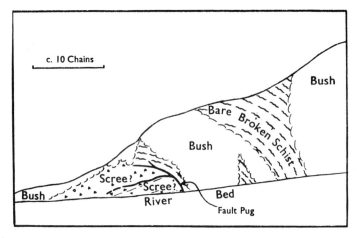

Fig. 4-51 Superficial overthrusting at the Alpine fault. Top: Diagrammatic representation by Wellman (1955). Bottom: Section exposed at Gaunt Creek, Waitangitaona River, South Westland, from a sketch by Suggate. (*Note:* To match the top diagram, the bottom sketch is shown in mirror image of the actual exposure on the southwest bank.) (*From Suggate, 1963.*)

steep change in gradient west of Puysegur bank. If this is topographic expression of the fault, then the fault is vertical or nearly so and has about 13,000 ft of relief across it (Brodie, 1964). Extension of the fault to the northeast is supported by the presence on the North Island, New Zealand, of numerous faults of similar trend; however, identification of the Alpine fault on the North Island is uncertain, and it is not possible to demonstrate transcurrent movements of comparable magnitude. This may be due in part to the fact that the structural trends of folds in the north are parallel to the fault trend, or to extensive covers of recent volcanics. Much farther to the northeast, the

Kermadec and Tonga trenches lie roughly on trend with the fault.

The Alpine fault is a relatively narrow zone in the south, but a system of subparallel faults branching off it appear toward the north. These faults are associated with folds that are, in their relation to the faults, somewhat similar to those described in California.

The attitude of these faults ranges from vertical to dips of as little as 40°, and locally the stratigraphic throw across them is many thousands of feet. It would be incorrect, therefore, to think of these fault systems in simple terms of blocks slipping along smooth vertical breaks. Some of the faults seem instead to vary both in direction and amount of dip while retaining an essentially straight strike. The Mesozoic basement has been elevated in places along the fault, while Cenozoic basins have formed in other places.

Vertical Displacement Along Strike-slip Faults

The topographic relief across major strike-slip faults is often great. The New Zealand Alps rise to 12,000 ft east of the Alpine fault; deep sedimentary basins have formed adjacent to the San Andreas; and dip-slip components are common along many recent faults showing predominantly strike-slip movement. A 40-cm vertical movement accompanied a horizontal movement of several meters during the Tango and Idu earthquakes in Japan (Chinnery, 1961). The presence of demonstrable dip-slip movements and the ambiguities so often present in estimates of strike-slip displacements have led to considerable debate regarding the nature of these faults. If strike-slip faults die out, vertical displacements must accompany the horizontal movements.

An interesting approach to the problem has been made by Chinnery (1961, 1965) and Press (1965). Mathematical analyses of effects of transcurrent faulting on the ground surface have been based on the elastic dislocation theory of Staketee. Assumptions are that the fault is vertical; that movement is strike-slip; that the crust behaves as a semi-infinite elastic solid; that the ground surface is horizontal; and that displacement is constant over the fault surface and falls to zero in a very short distance from the edge of the fault. Results are essentially the same if it is assumed that displacement dies exponentially at the edge of the fault. The vertical displacements predicted near a fault in which the depth of the fault is one-twentieth of the length are shown in Fig. 4-52. Solid lines represent uplift; dashed lines are depressions. The contours are in units of 10^{-4} times the amount of the displacement. If vertical movements can be accumulated over a long time interval in this way, great vertical displace-

ments can result (Fig. 4-53). This is highly significant because the major strike-slip faults are so very long and the horizontal displacements estimated are very great. The theory would predict scissorlike displacements along the fault, and could account for large regional vertical movements near the faults and smaller regional movements hundreds of miles away.

SOME MECHANICAL CONSIDERATIONS IN STRIKE-SLIP FAULTING

Moody and Hill (1956) extended Anderson's ideas concerning fault orientations as they apply to wrench faults, to explain the origin of structures associated with strike-slip faults.

Assuming that the principal stress direction is north-south, a set of conjugate shears (first-order shears) may form when the rock fails (Fig. 4-54). These are oriented at angles of about 30° to the principal stress. Once the first shears form, local stress conditions are reoriented (this is attributed to body forces developed as a result of movement on the fault), and a second set of shears becomes possible. It follows that a third-order set of shears could develop along the second-order structures; fourth-order features would parallel preexisting lower-order structures. A total of eight shear directions and three directions of compression is postulated. This theory is applied to many of the large strike-slip faults, and indeed many of the small faults and folds, as in Fig. 4-48, are aligned as predicted by the theory. It is difficult to test the theory adequately because the predicted directions of shear and folding are so numerous. They box the compass so completely that almost any fold or fault lies close to one or the other of the predicted directions. This theory is used by Moody and Hill to show how many of the world's faults and related folds can be related to a north-south compression. The validity of this extension of the theory is questionable. In order to relate some major faults to the north-south compression, the faults must be considered as second- or third-order

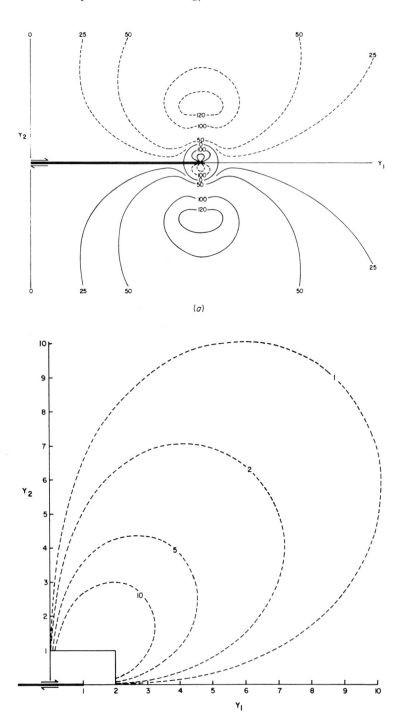

Fig. 4-52 The vertical displacements for a fault with $D = 0.1L$ (depth $= \frac{1}{20}$ of total length): (a) in the region close to the fault (only one-half the fault length is shown) and (b) at larger distances from the fault (axes are marked in units of L). Contour values are in units of $10^{-4}U$, where U is the net displacement of the two sides of the fault. Solid lines represent uplift, dashed lines represent downthrow. (*From Chinnery, 1965.*)

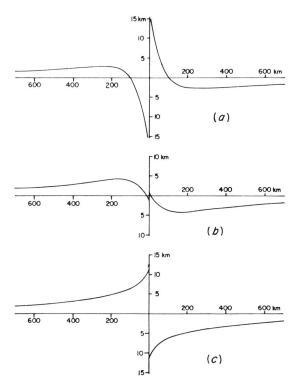

Fig. 4-53 Vertical displacements in the plane $y_1 = L$ for a hypothetical fault of length 2,000 km, depth 100 km, and displacement 200 km: (a) at the ground surface, (b) halfway down the fault, and (c) at the lower edge of the fault. (*Chinnery, 1965.*)

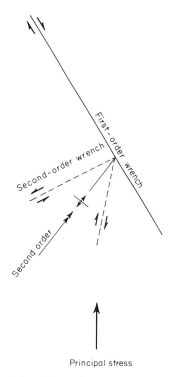

Fig. 4-54 Orientations of second-order shears. (*After Moody and Hill, 1956.*)

features in the absence of known first-order features (Maxwell and Wise, 1958).

Structures the size of the faults discussed here might best be considered to result from simple shear with a rotational couple rather than from pure shear. These faults must extend very deep, possibly through the entire crust, and though the rock may behave as a brittle substance near the surface, it must behave as a plastic at depth due to lithostatic pressure and elevated temperatures. Thus it is not valid to consider the crust as a homogeneous layer of material. The orientation of the folds and subsidiary faults associated with the major strike-slip faults can be equally as well explained in terms of simple shear. The fault is a zone of concentrated shear, but the couple acts over a broader zone, causing the material in this zone to be strained. If the strain is simple shear completely across this zone, then it is characterized by parallel slip planes, but if any compressional component acts across the zone Z, then some shortening X across the zone will tend to occur producing a strain rhomb, as shown in Fig. 4-55, with potential fold orientation F, shear fractures S, and tensional fracture T. It is suggested that the conditions at depth in the zone of plastic flow are like those shown in the lower part of the diagram, while surface conditions are like those shown at the top.

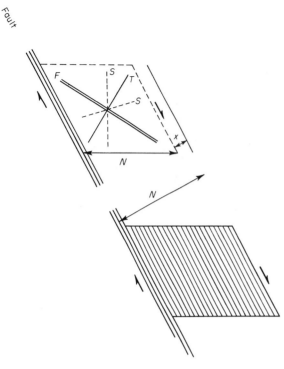

Fig. 4-55 Simple shear (bottom) and a rotational couple (top) with the predicted fold orientation *F*, tension fracture *T*, and shears *S*.

STRUCTURES OVER DEEP-SEATED TRANSCURRENT FAULTS

Many of the *en échelon* fold and fault systems found in sedimentary rocks have been interpreted in terms of strike-slip movements on deep-seated transcurrent faults (also called *megashears, geofractures,* or *shatter zones*) which presumably extend deep into if not through the crust. Some of the zones which have been suggested as deep-seated faults of this nature are illustrated in Fig. 14-4.

The *en échelon* belts of faults and folds in sedimentary units in Oklahoma and in the Nye-Bowler and Lake basin fault zones of Montana have been interpreted as resulting from movements on deep faults that do not break directly through the sedimentary veneer. A mechanism

for the development of such features can be envisioned as follows: Assume that a strike-slip movement occurs in the basement, but that it does not break directly through the covering sedimentary units. As lateral movements take place in the basement, the overlying sediments are subjected to drag effects. At some distance to either side of the fault the sediment moves passively with the basement. The material near the fault zone is subjected to a rotational couple which has the effect of extending the material in one direction, possibly inducing extension fractures, and of shortening the material at right angles to the extension, causing folds, domes, or doubly plunging anticlines. An original circular area of sediment over the fault will be distorted into an elliptical-shaped area (Fig. 4-56) in response to the rotational couple. The sedimentary veneer fails in response to the extension by the development of normal faults oriented with their strike direction normal to the direction of elongation. Gravity is, of course, an important vertically oriented force which acts during the development of the faults.

EN ÉCHELON FAULT PATTERNS

The origin of the belts of *en échelon* fractures and faults in Oklahoma has been much debated. Melton (1929) points out the close parallelism of the *en échelon* fractures with the northwest-trending regional fracture direction. He also emphasized that these belts are almost exactly aligned with the regional strike of bedding and that they may well be strongly aligned because these faults show up best in certain beds.

Another persisting explanation for these faults and fractures, however, is that advanced by Fath (1921) in which the *en échelon* pattern is explained as having originated over north-northeast-trending transcurrent faults located in the Precambrian crystalline basement. Because of strike-slip displacement along the concealed master faults, fractures were developed in the overlying Pennsylvanian strata as a result of extension of those strata over the zone of movement (Fig. 4-57).

The Nye-Bowler lineament of Montana is depicted by means of a structure contour map (Fig. 4-58). The lineament consists of a large number of domes, doubly plunging anticlines, and half domes. All of the faults are normal; presumably most of them are the result of ex-tension parallel to the long axes of the elongate domes and anticlines. A few of the faults, however, are longitudinal to the main lineament. These may be explained as resulting from the folding of the brittle sandstones with development of extension faults across the crest of the structures. This lineament and the parallel Lake basin *en échelon* fault zone north of it have been widely interpreted as arising from

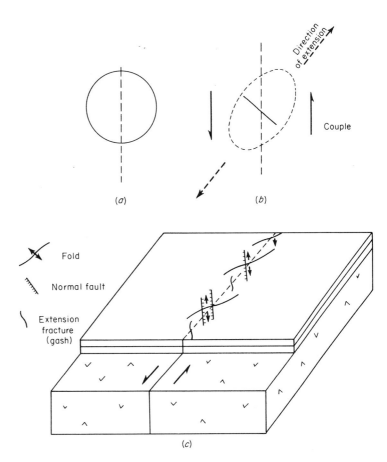

(a)

(b)

(c)

Fig. 4-56 (*a*) Diagrammatic illustration showing an imaginary circular area of sediment over a deep-seated strike-slip fault; (*b*) the same area distorted as a result of movement on the fault; (*c*) the associated structural features.

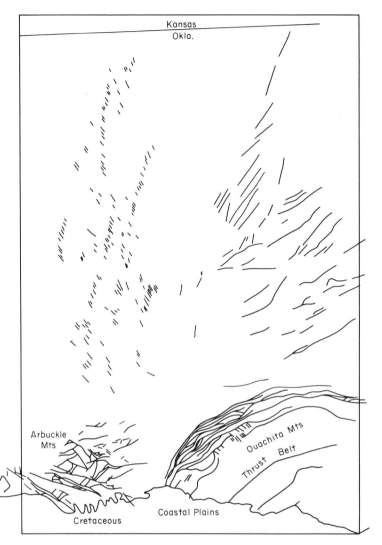

Fig. 4-57 Fault map of eastern Oklahoma showing the thrust belts of the Ouachita Mountains and the *en échelon* fault zones developed in Pennsylvania units. The fault pattern in eastern Oklahoma involves Mississippi units. (*From the State Geologic Map of Oklahoma.*)

movements on left-lateral transcurrent basement faults. The lineaments parallel one of the main fracture directions in the basement of the region. An alternative which has been offered is that the zones arise from torsional deformation due to differential uplift in the region. This would be analogous to deformation obtained by twisting two ends of a slab in opposite directions.

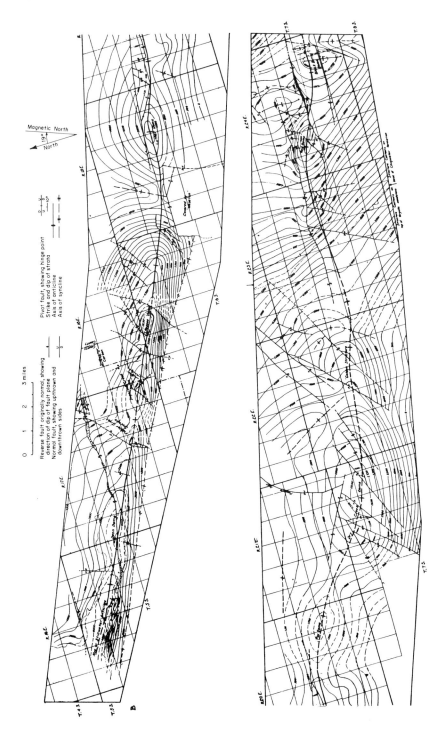

Fig. 4-58 Structure contour map of the Nye-Bowler lineament. Contours on top of the Virgelle member of the Eagle sandstone. Contour interval is 250 ft. (*From Wilson, 1936.*)

REFERENCES

Abendanon, E. C., 1914, Die grossfalten der Erd-rende: Leiden.

Anderson, E. M., 1951, The dynamics of faulting, 2d ed.: Edinburgh, Oliver & Boyd.

Barber, A. J., 1965, The history of the Moine thrust zone, Lochcarron and Lochalsh, Scotland: Geol. Soc. America Proc., v. 76, p. 215–243.

Bartram, J. G., 1929, Elk basin oil and gas field, Park County, Wyoming, and Carbon County, Montana, *in* Structure of typical American oil fields—a symposium, v. II: Am. Assoc. Petroleum Geologists, Tulsa, Okla., p. 577–588.

Berg, R. R., 1962, Mountain flank thrusting in Rocky Mountain Foreland, Wyoming and Colorado: Am. Assoc. Petroleum Geologists Bull., v. 46, p. 2019–2032.

Billings, M. P., 1954, Structural geology, 2d ed.: Englewood Cliffs, N.J., Prentice-Hall.

Birch, Francis, and others, 1961, Role of fluid pressure in overthrusting: Geol. Soc. America Bull., v. 72.

Boyer, R. E., and Muehlberger, W. R., 1960, Separation versus slip: Amer. Assoc. Petroleum Geologists Bull., v. 44, no. 12, p. 1938–1939 (Geological Notes).

Brodie, J. W., 1964, Bathymetry of the New Zealand Region: New Zealand Oceanographic Inst. Mem. 11, Wellington.

Carey, S. W., 1958, The tectonic approach to continental drift, *in* Continental drift—a symposium: Geol. Dept. Univ. of Tasmania, p. 177–355.

Carlisle, Donald, 1965, Sliding friction and overthrust faulting: Jour. Geology, v. 73, p. 271–292.

Carver, R. E., 1968, Differential compaction as a cause of regional contemporaneous faults: Am. Assoc. Petroleum Geologists Bull., v. 52, no. 3.

Casella, C. J., 1964, Geologic evolution of the Beartooth Mountains, Montana and Wyoming, pt. 4, Relationship between Precambrian and Laramide structures in the Line Creek area: Geol. Soc. America Bull., v. 75, p. 969–986.

Chinnery, M. A., 1961, The deformation of the ground around surface faults: Seismol. Soc. America Bull., v. 51, p. 355–372.

——— 1965, The vertical displacements associated with transcurrent faulting: Jour. Geophys. Research, v. 70, no. 18, p. 4627–4632.

Clark, S. K., 1943, Classification of faults: Am. Assoc. Petroleum Geologists Bull., v. 27, p. 1245–1265.

Clayton, Lee, 1966, Tectonic depressions along the Hope fault, a transcurrent fault in North Canterbury, New Zealand: New Zealand Jour. Geol. Geophys., v. 9, nos. 1 and 2, p. 95–104.

Cloos, Ernst, 1932, Structural survey of the granodiorite south of Mariposa, Calif.: Am. Jour. Sci., v. 23, p. 289–304.

——— 1934, The Loon Lake pluton, Bancroft area, Ontario, Canada: Jour. Geology, v. 42, no. 4, p. 393–399.

——— 1968, Experimental analysis of Gulf Coast fracture patterns: Am. Assoc. Petroleum Geologists Bull., v. 52, no. 3.

Cloos, Ernst, and Hershey, H. G., 1936, Structural age determination of Piedmont intrusions in Maryland: [U. S.] Natl. Acad. Sci. Proc., v. 22, p. 71–80.

Cloos, Hans, 1936, Einfuhrung in die Geologie: Berlin, Gebruder Borntraeger.

Crowell, J. C., 1952, Probable large lateral displacement on San Gabriel fault southern California: Am. Assoc. Petroleum Geologists Bull., v. 36, p. 2026–2035.

——— 1959, Problems of fault nomenclature: Am. Assoc. Petroleum Geologists Bull., v. 43, p. 2653–2675.

——— 1962, Displacement along the San Andreas fault, California: Geol. Soc. America Spec. Paper 71.

De Lapparent, A., 1898, Soulèvements et affaissements: Revue des Questions Scientific, v. 14.

De Sitter, L. U., 1954, Gravitational gliding tectonics—an essay in comparative structural geology: Am. Jour. Sci., v. 252, p. 321–344.

Dibblee, T. W., Jr., 1960, Geology of the Rogers Lake and Kramer quadrangles, California: U. S. Geol. Survey Bull., 1089-B, 139 p.

Donath, F. A., and Kuo, J. T., 1962, Seismic-refraction study of block-faulting, South-central Oregon: Geol. Soc. America Bull., v. 73, p. 429–434.

Douglas, R. J. W., 1958, Mount Head Map-area, Alberta: Geol. Survey Canada Mem. 291.

Drake, C. L., and Girdler, R. W., 1964, A geophysical study of the Red Sea: Geophys. Jour. Royal Astronomical Soc., v. 8, no. 5, p. 473–495.

Fath, A. E., 1921, The origin of faults, anticlines, and buried "granite ridge" for the northern part of the mid-continent oil and gas field: U. S. Geol. Survey Prof. Paper 128, p. 75–84.

Fitzgerald, E. L., 1962, Structure of the McConnell thrust sheet in the Ghost River area, Alberta:

Alberta Soc. Petroleum Geologists Jour., v. 10, p. 553–574.

Fox, P. P., 1959, Geology of Furnas Dam, Minas Gerais, Brazil: Geol. Soc. America Bull., v. 70, p. 1605.

Fuller, R. E., and Waters, A. C., 1929, The nature and origin of the horst and graben structure of southern Oregon: Jour. Geology, v. 37, p. 204–238.

Gill, J. E., 1941, Fault nomenclature: Royal Soc. Canada Trans., ser. 3, v. 35, sec. 4, p. 71–85.

Gramberg, J., 1966, Axial cleavage fracturing, a significant process in mining and geology: Eng. Geology, v. 1, p. 31–72.

Gregory, J. W., 1920, The African rift valleys: Geog. Jour., v. 56.

Griggs, D. T., and Handin, John, 1960, Observations on fracture and a hypothesis of earthquakes, in Griggs, D. T., and Handin, John, eds., Rock deformation—a symposium: Geol. Soc. America Mem. 79, p. 347–373.

Hafner, W., 1951, Stress distributions and faulting: Geol. Soc. America Bull., v. 62, no. 4, p. 373–398.

Hager, D. S., and Burnett, C. M., 1960, Mexia-Talco fault line in Hopkins and Delta Counties, Texas: Am. Assoc. Petroleum Geologists Bull., v. 44, p. 316–356.

Hamblin, W. K., 1965, Origin of "reverse drag" on the downthrown side of normal faults: Geol. Soc. America Bull., v. 76, p. 1145–1164.

Hardin, F. R., and Hardin, G. C., Jr., 1961, Contemporaneous normal faults of the Gulf Coast and their relation to flexures: Am. Assoc. Petroleum Geologists Bull., v. 45, p. 238–248.

Harris, L. D., and Zietz, Isidor, 1962, Development of Cumberland overthrust block in vicinity of Chestnut Ridge fenster in SW Va.: Am. Assoc. Petroleum Geologists Bull., v. 46, p. 2148–2160.

Hayes, C. W., 1891, The overthrust faults of the southern Appalachians: Geol. Soc. America Bull., v. 2, p. 141–154.

Heezen, B. C., and Ewing, M., 1961, The mid-oceanic ridge and its extension through the Arctic basin, in Geology of the Arctic: Toronto, Univ. of Toronto, p. 622–642.

Hill, M. L., 1947, Classification of faults: Am. Assoc. Petroleum Geologists Bull., v. 31, p. 1669–1673.

——— 1959, Dual classification of faults: Am. Assoc. Petroleum Geologists Bull., v. 43, p. 217–222.

Hills, J. M., 1953, Subsurface logging methods: Petroleo Interamericano, v. 11, p. 38–39.

Howard, J. H., 1966, Structural development of the Williams Range thrust, Colorado: Geol. Soc. America Bull., v. 77, p. 1247–1264.

Hubbert, M. K., 1937, Theory of scale models as applied to the study of geologic structures: Geol. Soc. America Bull., v. 48, p. 1459–1519.

——— 1951, Mechanical basis for certain familiar geologic structures: Geol. Soc. America Bull., v. 62, p. 355–372.

Hubbert, M. K., and Rubey, W. W., 1959, Role of fluid pressure in mechanics of overthrust faulting. I. Mechanics of fluid-filled porous solids and its application to overthrust faulting: Geol. Soc. America Bull., v. 70, no. 2, p. 115–166.

Irwin, W. P., 1960, Geologic reconnaissance of the northern coast ranges and Klamath Mts., California, with a summary of the mineral resources: California Div. of Mines Bull. 179, 80 p.

Jahns, R. H., ed., 1954, Geology of Southern California: California Dept. Natl. Reserves, Div. Mines Bull., 170.

——— 1958, The geologic framework of So. Calif., in Higgins, J. W., ed., A guide to the geology and oil fields of the Los Angeles and Ventura regions: Am. Assoc. Petroleum Geologists, 204 p.

Jenkins, O. P., 1943, Introduction to Cretaceous California: Am. Assoc. Petroleum Geologists Bull., v. 27, p. 249–261.

Keep, C. E., and Ward, H. L., 1934, Drilling against high rock pressures with particular reference to operations conducted in the Khaur field, Punjab: Inst. Petrol. Technologists Jour. (London), v. 20, p. 990–1013.

Kelley, V. C., and Clinton, N. J., 1955, Fracture system and tectonic elements of the Colorado Plateau: Albuquerque, Univ. New Mexico Pub. in Geology, no. 6.

Kennedy, G. C., 1959, The origin of continents, mountain ranges, and ocean basins: Am. Sci., v. 47, p. 491–504.

Kennedy, W. Q., 1946, The Great Glen fault: Quart. Jour. Geol. Soc. London, v. 102, p. 41–76.

King, P. B., 1960, The anatomy and habitat of low angle thrust faults: Am. Jour. Sci., v. 258-A, p. 115–125.

——— 1964, Geology of the central Great Smoky Mountains, Tenn.: U. S. Geol. Survey Prof. Paper 349-C, p. 1–148.

Krenkel, E., 1922, Die bruchzonen Ostafrikas: Berlin.

Laubschen, H. P., and others, 1960, Role of fluid pressure in mechanics of overthrust faulting: Geol. Soc. America Bull., v. 71, p. 611–628.

Laughton, A. S., 1966, The Gulf of Aden, in relation to the Red Sea and the Afar depression of Ethiopia, in The world rift system: Geol. Survey of Canada Paper 66–14, p. 78–95.

Lees, G. M., 1954, The geological evidence of the nature of the ocean floor: Roy. Soc. London Proc., v. 22, p. 400–402.

Lensen, G. J., 1958, A method of graben and horst formation: Jour. Geology, v. 66, p. 579–587.

Lillie, A. R., and Gunn, B. M., 1963, Steeply plunging folds in the Sealy Range, southern Alps: New Zealand Jour. Geol. and Geophys., v. 7, p. 403–423.

Lindgren, Waldemar, 1915, The igneous geology of the Cordilleras and its problems, in Problems of American geology: New Haven, Conn., p. 234–286.

——— 1933, Mineral deposits, 4th ed.: New York, McGraw-Hill.

Longwell, C. R., 1949, Structure of the Northern Muddy Mountain area, Nevada: Geol. Soc. America Bull., v. 60, p. 923–968.

——— 1951, Thrust faulting—what does it mean?: N.Y. Acad. Sci. Trans., ser. 2, v. 14, p. 2–5.

Lovering, T. S., 1932, Field evidence to distinguish overthrusting from underthrusting: Jour. Geology, v. 40, p. 651–663.

Maxwell, J. C., 1959, Turbidity, tectonic and gravity transport, northern Apennine Mountains, Italy: Am. Assoc. Petroleum Geologists Bull., v. 43, p. 2701–2719.

Maxwell, J. C., and Wise, D. U., 1958, Wrench-fault tectonics—a discussion: Geol. Soc. America Bull., v. 69, p. 927–928.

McKinstry, H. E., 1953, Shears of the second order: Am. Jour. Sci., v. 251, no. 6, p. 401–414.

Melton, F. A., 1929, A reconnaisance of the joint systems in the Ouachita Mts. and central plains of Oklahoma: Jour. Geology, v. 37, p. 729–746.

Miller, R. L., and Fuller, J. D., 1954, Geology and oil resources of the Rose Hill district—the fenster area of the Cumberland overthrust block—Lee County, Virginia: Va. Geol. Survey Bull., v. 71, 383 p.

Moody, J. D., and Hill, M. J., 1956, Wrench fault tectonics: Geol. Soc. America Bull., v. 67, p. 1207–1246.

Moore, Walter, 1961, Role of fluid pressure in overthrusting: Geol. Soc. America Bull., v. 72, notes.

Morgan, P. G., 1908, Geology of the Mikonni subdivision, North Westland: New Zealand Geol. Survey Bull., v. 60.

Murray, G. E., 1967, Salt structures of Gulf of Mexico basin—a review: Am. Assoc. Petroleum Geologists Bull., v. 50, p. 440.

Ocamb, R. D., 1961, Growth faults of South Louisiana: Gulf Coast Assoc. of Geol. Socs. Trans., v. XI, p. 139–175.

Odé, Helmer, 1960, Faulting as a velocity discontinuity in plastic deformation: Geol. Soc. America Mem. 79, p. 293–323.

Orowan, E., 1960, Mechanism of seismic faulting, in Griggs, D. T., and Handin, John, eds., Rock deformation—a symposium: Geol. Soc. America Mem. 79, p. 323–346.

Paschall, R. H., and Off, Theodore, 1961, Dip-slip versus strike-slip movement on San Gabriel fault, Southern California: Am. Assoc. Petroleum Geologists Bull., v. 45, p. 1941–1956.

Pierce, W. G., 1957, Heart Mountain and South Fork detachment thrust of Wyoming: Am. Assoc. Petroleum Geologists Bull., v. 41, p. 591–626.

——— 1963a, Cathedral Cliffs formation, the early acid breccia unit of Northwestern Wyoming: Geol. Soc. America Bull., v. 74, p. 9–22.

——— 1963b, Reef Creek detachment fault, Northwestern Wyoming: Geol. Soc. America Bull., v. 74, p. 1225–1236.

Platt, L. B., 1962, Fluid pressure in thrust faulting—a corollary: Am. Jour. Sci., v. 260, no. 2.

Press, F., 1965, Displacements, strains, and tilts at teleseismic distances: Jour. Geophys. Research, v. 70, p. 2395–2412.

Price, N. J., 1966, Fault and joint development in brittle and semi-brittle rock: New York, Pergamon, 176 p.

Prucha, J. J., and others, 1965, Basement-controlled deformation in Wyoming Province of Rocky Mountains Foreland: Am. Assoc. Petroleum Geologists Bull., v. 49, p. 966–992.

Quennell, A. M., 1957, The structural and geomorphic evolution of the Dead Sea rift: Geol. Soc. London Proc., no. 1544, p. 14–20.

Raleigh, C. B., 1963, Effect of the toe in the mechanics of overthrust faulting: Geol. Soc. America Bull., v. 74, no. 7.

Reid, H. F., and others, 1913, Report on nomenclature of faults: Geol. Soc. America Bull., v. 24, p. 163–186.

Rubey, W. W., and Hubbert, M. K., 1959, Role of fluid pressure in mechanics of overthrust faulting: Geol. Soc. America Bull., v. 70, p. 167–206

Sanford, A. R., 1959, Analytical and experimental study of simple geologic structures: Geol. Soc. America Bull., v. 70, p. 19–52.

Saul, R. B., 1967, The Calaveras fault zone: Mineral Inf. Service, v. 20, no. 3.

Savage, J. C., and Hastie, L. M., 1966, Surface deformation associated with dip-slip faulting: Jour. Geophys. Research, v. 71, no. 20, p. 4897–4904.

Shand, S. J., 1936, Rift valley impressions: Geol. Mag. [Great Britain], v. 123.

Shawe, D. R., 1965, Strike-slip control of basin and range structure indicated by historical faults in western Nevada: Geol. Soc. America Bull., v. 76, p. 1361–1378.

Shelton, J. W., 1968, Role of contemporaneous faulting during basinal subsidence: Am. Assoc. Petroleum Geologists Bull., v. 52, no. 3.

Shouldice, J. R., 1963, Gravity slide faulting on Bowes dome, Bearpaw Mountain area, Montana: Am. Assoc. Petroleum Geologists Bull., v. 47, p. 1943–1951.

Sinoluchowski, M., 1909, Folding of the earth's surface in formation of mountain chains: Acad. Sci. Craiovie Bull., v. 6, p. 3–20.

Small, W. M., 1959, Thrust faults and ruptured folds in Roumanian oil fields: Am. Assoc. Petroleum Geologists Bull., v. 43, p. 455–472.

Smith, G. I., 1962, Large lateral displacement on Garlock fault, California, as measured from offset dike swarm: Am. Assoc. Petroleum Geologists Bull., v. 46, p. 85–104.

Suggate, R. P., 1963, The Alpine fault: Roy. Soc. New Zealand Geol. Trans., v. 2, p. 105–129.

Tanner, W. F., 1962, Surface structural patterns obtained from strike-slip models: Jour. Geology, v. 70, p. 101–107.

Thom, W. T., Jr., 1955, Wedge uplifts and their tectonic significance: Geol. Soc. America Spec. Paper 62, p. 369–376.

Thompson, G. H., 1959, Gravity measurements between Hazen and Austin, Nevada—a study of basin-range structure: Jour. Geophys. Research, v. 64, p. 217–229.

Uhlig, Johannes, 1909, Untersuchung einiger Gesteine aus dem mordostlichsten Labrador: Ver Erdk Dresden, v. 8, p. 230–236.

Wellman, H. W., 1954, Active transcurrent faulting in New Zealand: Geol. Soc. America Bull., v. 65, p. 1322.

———— 1955, New Zealand Quaternary tectonics: Geol. Rundschau, v. 43, p. 248–257.

———— 1956, Structural outline of New Zealand: New Zealand Dept. Sci. Indus. Research Bull., v. 121, p. 1–36.

Wellman, H. W., and Willett, R. W., 1942, The geology of the West Coast from Albert Head to Milford Sound, pt. I: Royal Soc. New Zealand Trans., v. 71, p. 282–306.

Wendlandt, E. A., 1951, Hawkins field, Wood County, Texas: Austin, Univ. of Texas Pub. No. 5116, p. 153–158.

Whitten, C. A., 1957, Geodetic measurements in the Dixie Valley area [Nevada]: Seismol. Soc. America Bull., v. 47, p. 321–325.

Willis, Bailey, 1936, East-African plateaus and rift valleys: Carnegie Inst. Washington Pub. 470.

Wilson, C. W., Jr., 1936, Geology of Nye-Bowler lineament, Stillwater & Carbon Cos., Montana: Am. Assoc. Petroleum Geologists Bull., v. 20, p. 1161–1168.

Wise, D. U., 1963, An outrageous hypothesis for the tectonic pattern of the North America Cordillera: Geol. Soc. America Bull., v. 74, p. 357–362.

5
behavior of materials

GLOSSARY FOR ROCK DEFORMATION*

Affine deformation: Deformation that takes place in such a way that lines and planes that existed before deformation are transformed into new lines and planes, but these are not curved in the process.

Brittle behavior: When a material fractures early in the history of the stress-strain curve (total strain before fracturing less than 5 percent). (Handin, 1966.)

Creep: The slow permanent and continuous deformation of a material under a constant load over a long period of time. (Nádai, 1950.)

Creep recovery: Occurs when a viscoelastic material is strained for a long period of time after which the stress is removed, part of the creep strain will disappear or be recovered.

Dilation: A change in volume but not in shape.

Ductile materials: Materials which can undergo very extensive plastic deformation before failing by rupture. (Turner and Verhoogen.) Handin (1966) uses total strain before fracture to approximate brittle-ductile behavior. A strain of 5 to 8 percent is considered moderately ductile, and over 10 percent is ductile.

Elastic aftereffect (syn.: *elastic afterworking*): A recovery effect in some materials, which undergo instantaneous elastic strain plus creep after being loaded for a time then recover the elastic strain immediately on unloading, and slowly recover some of the creep deformation.

Elastic limit: The stress at which a deviation from the straight-line relation on a stress-strain plot occurs. (Hooke's law does not apply strictly beyond this limit.)

---

* Definitions taken from Am. Geol. Inst., © 1960, Glossary of geology and related sciences, and are indicated by (A. G. I. Glossary).

Elastic Moduli

Elastic modulus: Ratio of stress to the corresponding strain. Includes Young's modulus, shear modulus, and the bulk modulus.

Bulk modulus (syn.: *volume elasticity, incompressibility modulus*): The bulk modulus B is the ratio of the increase in hydrostatic pressure P to the corresponding fractional decrease in volume $(-\Delta V/V_0)$.

$$B = \frac{P}{-\Delta V/V_0}$$

Compressibility: The reciprocal of the bulk modulus. It is defined as the fractional change in volume per unit increase in confining pressure.

Shear modulus (syn.: *modulus of rigidity, torsion modulus*): The ratio of a shearing stress to the corresponding shearing strain.

Young's modulus: The ratio of a tensile stress to the corresponding tensile strain. If a tensile force F applied across a cross-sectional area A produces a change in length ΔL in a bar of original length L, Young's modulus is given by

$$Y = \frac{F/A}{\Delta L/L}$$

Poissons ratio: The ratio of the transverse contraction per unit dimension of a bar of uniform cross section to its elongation per unit length, when subjected to a tensile stress.

$$\sigma = -\frac{\Delta W/W_0}{\Delta L/L_0}$$

where σ = Poissons ratio
W = transverse dimensions
L = length
The value is less than 0.5.

Flow

Flow: Any deformation, not instantly recoverable, that occurs without permanent loss of cohesion. (Handin and Hager, 1957.)

Gliding flow: The type of solid flow which takes place by the combined mechanisms of translation and twin gliding.

Pseudoviscous flow: Load recrystallization.

The type of solid flow which takes place under a strain and a stress too low to produce gliding flow, producing instead intergranular movement and dimensional orientation for the most part.

Competent: Applied to a bed or group of beds which, during folding, is able to lift not only its own weight but that of the overlying beds without appreciable internal flowage. (Willis.)

Incompetent: Applied to a bed that is relatively weak and thus cannot transmit pressure for any distance. (Structural Committee, A. G. I. Glossary.)

Slip: Macroscopically discontinuous flow characterized by displacement on subparallel surfaces that pervade a rock. (Donath, 1963.)

Ideal Rheologic Substances

Elasticoviscous substance (syn.: *Maxwell liquid, elasticoviscous solid*): In the ideal case, a substance which when stressed undergoes an instantaneous elastic strain that is followed by viscous behavior if the stress is continued.

Firmoviscous substance (syn.: *Kelvin body*): A substance which has characteristics of viscous and elastic substances. Unlike elasticoviscous bodies in which elastic response to stress is instantaneous, firmoviscous substances require some time to react to the applied stress.

Elastic substance (syn.: *Hookian solid*): A substance which behaves exactly as described by Hooke's law. Within the elastic limit, strain in the material is directly proportional to the applied stress.

Pure viscous substance (syn.: *Newtonian fluid*): A fluid characterized by purely viscous behavior such that the fluid deforms continuously and in a linear manner under any applied force. Most real liquids are not quite true Newtonian fluids because they do not behave in a purely linear manner.

Plastic substance (syn.: *St. Venant body*): The ideal plastic material is one which deforms continuously when it is stressed above a certain critical yield stress.

Plasticoviscous substance (syn.: *Bingham body, viscoplastic material*): A material exhibiting a combination of the properties of plastic and viscous materials; a dense suspension of solid particles in a viscous fluid such that a stress must reach a certain finite or yield value before viscous flow can start. (Bingham.)

Isotropic substance (anton.: *anisotropic*): A material which has uniform mechanical properties in all directions in space.

Luder's lines: Very fine lines which appear on the surface of polished metals stressed in tension just at the moment when the yield point is reached. (Nádai, 1950.)

Relaxation: The phenomenon in which, if a spring is held in a stretched position for a sufficiently long time at high temperature, the force exerted by the spring will gradually start to diminish and may disappear entirely. (Nádai, 1950.)

Rheology: The science treating of the deformation and flow of matter. More specifically, it deals with the flow and permanent deformation of materials.

Rheid: Body of rock showing flow structure. (Carey, 1953, A. G. I. Glossary.)

Rheid folding: Folding accompanied by slippage along planes at an angle to the bedding or earlier developed foliation. (Weiss, 1959, A. G. I. Glossary.)

Rheidity: Capacity of material to flow within the earth. (Scheidegger, 1958, A. G. I. Glossary.)

Strain

Strain: Any change occurring in the dimensions or shape of a body when forces are applied to it.

Elastic strain: Strain which is instantaneously reversible, as when a body returns completely to its original unstrained state when the deforming stress is released.

Plastic strain: The permanent strain or deformation developed in a material stressed beyond its elastic limit.

Strain ellipsoid: (1) In elastic theory, a sphere under homogeneous strain is transformed into an ellipsoid with this property; the ratio of the length of a line, which has given direction in the strained state, to the length of the corresponding line in the unstrained state, is proportional to the center radius vector of the surface drawn in the given direction. (Love, A. G. I. Glossary.) (2) The ellipsoid whose half-axes are the principal strains. (Structural Committee, A. G. I. Glossary.)

Principal directions of strain: The three mutually perpendicular axes of the strain ellipsoid which correspond to the directions of greatest, intermediate, and least strain. The axes are generally designated *A, B,* and *C* when *A* is the axis of maximum elongation and $A > B > C$.

Strain hardening (syn.: *work hardening, cold working*): A force-induced change in molecular structure of a crystalline material caused by bending or distortion and resulting in an increased resistance to further deformation.

Dilation: A strain in which the change is purely one of volume.

Pure extension or compression: The phenomenon in which all points are displaced parallel to one coordinate axis. (Nádai, 1950.)

Pure rotation: Rotation of a rigid body.

Pure shear: A combination of pure extension in one coordinate direction and pure compression in another coordinate direction. (Nádai, 1950.)

Pure strain: Any general strain that lacks a rotational component.

Simple shear: Shear that takes place when all points are displaced parallel to one coordinate axis by an amount proportional to the displacement parallel to another coordinate axis. (Nádai 1950.)

Strength

Strength of a material (described qualitatively as *resistance to failure*): The force per unit area necessary to cause rupture at normal temperature and pressure conditions over a short period of time (crushing strength).

Fundamental strength: The stress a material is able to withstand, regardless of time, under any given set of conditions (temperature, pressure, solutions, etc.) without deforming continuously.

Ultimate strength: The highest stress a material attains on the stress-strain curve.

Cohesion: The maximum load a material can take impulsively (meaning that the load is applied so fast that no nonelastic deformation occurs) without rupture. (Carey.)

Practical strength: The maximum strength which may be sustained by a material within a definite time limit and within a specified sensitivity of measurement. (Carey.)

Stress

Stress: (1) Force per unit area, found by dividing the total force by the area over which the force is applied. (2) The intensity at a point in a body of the internal forces or components of force which act on a given plane through the point. As used in product specifications, stress is calculated on the basis of the original dimensions of the cross section of the specimen. (After Am. Soc. Testing Materials, A. G. I. Glossary.)

Normal stress (syn.: *normal traction*): That part or component of a stress which acts perpendicular to a given surface.

Shear stress (syn.: *shear deviator*): That part or component of a stress which acts tangentially to a given surface.

Yield point: A stress at which a body of a given material stressed in tension begins to stretch permanently.

Surface force (syn.: *surface traction, external, impressed force*): A force which acts across an external surface of a body as a result of action and reaction between the body and another body with which it is in contact. (Turner and Weiss, 1963.)

Tectonite: (1) Any rock that owes its fabric to the summation of indirectly interrelated componental movements of the fabric elements, provided these movements take place in such a way that the spatial continuity of the rock is not impaired. (Knopf 1938.) (2) A deformed rock the fabric of which is due to the systematic

movement of the individual components under a common external force.

Viscosity: A measure of the resistance of a fluid to flow. It may be thought of as the internal friction of a fluid. The coefficient of viscosity of a fluid, η, can be measured by use of Stoke's law or with various types of viscosimeters.

PHYSICAL CHARACTER OF EARTH MATERIALS

The diversity of materials in the earth's crust should be sufficiently apparent to any student of geology to make him expect to find significant differences in the behavior of rock materials under stress. What may not be so evident is the way the behavior of any rock type changes under changing temperature and confining pressure conditions such as those arising from depth of burial in the earth. In ancient folded mountain belts, we often encounter flowage structures in gneissic rocks which behave as brittle elastic material under surface conditions. Obviously the material has either been greatly altered or its behavior under conditions at depth is vastly different from that at the surface. Judging from the fabric of the rock, the unusual folds are usually formed during metamorphism.

An attempt to classify all crustal materials according to differences in physical properties would necessarily require a great many categories because of the involvement of different chemical compositions, as expressed physically in different atomic arrangement, as well as variations in the relations of individual crystals or fragments to the whole rock. But some broad categories may be listed as follows:

1. Fragmental materials (coarse)—sandstones, siltstones, clastics in general
   a. Cemented (quartzite)
   b. Uncemented (loose sediment)
2. Colloidal materials—notably clay, silica gel, and oozes

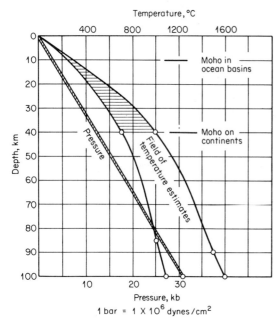

Fig. 5-1 Temperature and confining pressure variation with depth in the crust and upper mantle. (*After Gutenberg, 1951.*)

3. Crystalline aggregates—basalt, marble, and granite
4. Amorphous materials—natural glass

Each of these classes of material presents certain unique characteristics that are important factors governing its behavior when stressed. For example, in fragmental materials the size, sorting, packing, sphericity, and presence of cementing material, as well as its composition and bond to the fragments, are all important considerations, as is the composition of the fragmental material itself.

It is also important to consider the degree of isotropy of all the above categories. Some plutonic rocks may be essentially isotropic for large volumes of material in that the size and composition of crystals and their fabric may be reasonably uniform, but in most fragmental materials and often in crystalline aggregates there is layering and the layers have different physical properties.

Experimental work has been done to examine the behavior of some materials when subjected to various temperatures and confining pressures. Tests have been made particularly on certain types of materials:

Metals (for engineering purposes)
Single crystals (notably calcite and quartz)
Crystalline aggregates (particularly limestone and marble, and a few igneous rocks)

We are far from having comprehensive data, but the work accomplished so far is impressive and instructive.

At the onset it is important to stop thinking in terms of rigid models such as three distinct "states" of matter (solid, liquid, gas). These models are satisfactory to classify the behavior of most materials under normal conditions, but they are of little use in thinking about rock behavior, and they fail to account for transitional phases. Temperature is the basis for making our usual distinction among solids, liquids, and gases, but consider the behavior of silly putty. This material shatters if hit with a sudden and forceful impact, but it will flow through cloth if given time, and it will bounce like a rubber ball. Clearly this behavior is that of a brittle solid elastic under one condition, but fluid under another.

The rate of application of the deforming stress is certainly one of the conditions which affect a material's behavior, along with temperature and confining pressure. In the following discussion experiments carried out under specific confining pressures and temperatures are described. Figure 5-1 shows estimates of the variation of these two variables in the crust and outer mantle.

METHODS OF EXPERIMENTAL DEFORMATION

The techniques used to deform crystals and rocks are continually being refined and improved, and although design features are not our primary concern, it is important to understand something of the degree of control and care with which the experimental tests are conducted.

The pioneer in experiments on rock deformation was Sir James Hall whose work marked the start of what has become a highly sophisticated and significant study in geology. In the early 1900s Frank Adams performed a number of highly significant experiments with equipment that was very simple in design compared with that of modern investigators, Fig. 5-2. The arrangement used by Adams consisted essentially of a nickel-steel cylinder with a 2-cm-diameter bore in the center and thicker walls at the ends. The specimen was cut to fit the bore or embedded in some other material. Pistons were inserted and the loaded "bomb" put in a press. Adams also devised a means of heating the bomb. In the experiments pressure was applied to the pistons. The sides to the cylinder acted to confine the specimen laterally. The thickness of the walls in the section of the cylinder adjacent to the specimen was varied to produce varying confining pressures. Great care was exercised in grinding and fitting the specimens. This arrangement was versatile in that it allowed variation of temperature, confining pressure, directed stress, and presence of fluids, and the results were good. The main disadvantages came about through boundary conditions arising from the contact of the specimen with the walls of the enclosing cylinder, and temperature and confining pressure control were both uncertain. These problems have been largely overcome in modern equipment such as that illustrated in breakaway view (Fig. 5-2). The sample, still very small, is surrounded by a fluid in which carefully measured confining pressure is built up. The specimen does not touch the walls of the "bomb" and temperature is much more readily controlled and measured. The equipment shown is for studies in axial compression; other types of machines are in use for applying torsion and tension to specimens under precisely controlled conditions.

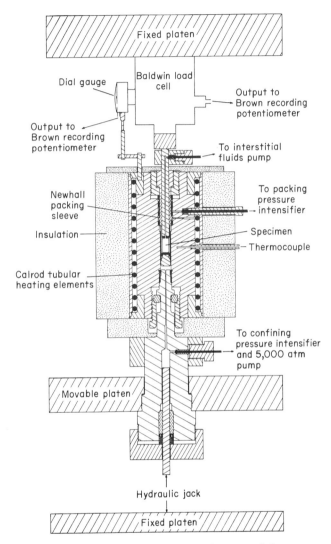

Fig. 5-2 Upper cylinder is heated by the external furnace. Force on upper piston and piston displacement are measured by load cell and dial gauge, respectively. Stress-strain curves are derived from these measurements. (*From Griggs, Turner, and Heard, 1960.*)

DEFORMATION OF SINGLE CRYSTALS

Deformation of crystals is very closely dependent on the atomic configuration of the crystal

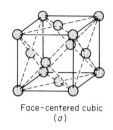

Face-centered cubic
(a)

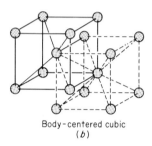

Body-centered cubic
(b)

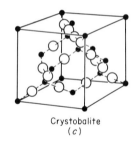

Crystobalite
(c)

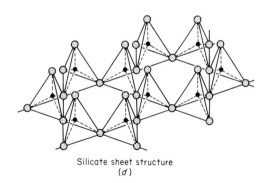

Silicate sheet structure
(d)

Fig. 5-3 Common atomic arrangements in minerals.

structure and the strength of bonds holding atoms together. The student should already be somewhat familiar with crystal structures such as the cubic structure of halite and the silica-oxygen tetrahedra which are important components of the silicates. A few of the atomic arrangements found in minerals are illustrated in Fig. 5-3.

Designation of Planes in Crystals

A system of symbols called *Miller indices* is used in crystallography to designate the position of planes in a crystal. These indices are related to what is known as a *unit cell*—the smallest arrangement of atoms which, if repeated in space, can be used to reproduce the larger crystals. The unit cell of a cubic crystal is a convenient example. Three mutually perpendicular lines form the corner of the cube. These axes may be called the x, y, and z axes. The unit cell may be thought of as having sides of unit length. The orientation of a plane is indicated by noting how far along the axes the plane intersects each axis. By convention the distance on each axis is indicated in a certain order—x first, y second, z third. Consider a plane that is in the plane of the y and z axes. That plane does not cut those axes at all. But it cuts the x axis at a unit or some multiple of the unit cell length. Thus this plane is designated (100). The three planes that define the sides of the cube are thus (100), (010), and (001).

A plane which is parallel to one axis but cuts the other two at unit cell distances becomes (011), (110), or (101). A plane which cuts all three unit cell axes at a unit distance becomes (111).

It should also be noted that we have so far considered only those planes lying in one direction from the point of origin, but the planes could lie in any direction. Thus negative signs are used to designate the other direction. The negative sign is placed over the index number to which it applies.

It is possible for planes to intersect the axis

at less than unit distance and these are indicated by the reciprocal of the fraction of the distance. Thus (112) intersects the x axis at 1, the y axis at 1, and the z axis at one-half the unit distance. It should be evident that the (222) plane has the same orientation in space as the (111) plane, and by convention the unit system is used since there is no real point of origin from which the system applies.

In crystallography the x, y, and z axes are the a, b, and c crystallographic axes.

For minerals belonging to systems with four crystallographic axes (i.e., calcite, quartz) a similar system of notation is used but with four rather then three digits.

One very useful way to visualize the planes in a crystal is by means of the stereographic projection on which the pole to a plane is drawn as a point, as illustrated for calcite in Fig. 5-4.

Zone notation [ ] is widely used in structural petrology to describe the direction of lineations such as fold axes, intersection of planes, etc. A *zone* is defined as a set of faces with mutually parallel intersections. The direction of the line of intersection, called the *zone axis*, may be determined by considering that the line passes through the origin of the crystallographic axes. Another point on the line has coordinates $[x, y, z]$ relative to the crystallographic axes where x, y, and z are multiples of the axial units a, b, and c.

Translation Gliding

The arrangement of atoms in each of the models of compounds illustrated in Fig. 5-3 is different, but in almost all the models the density of atoms is greater in certain planes through the crystal than in others. This is particularly clear in the case of metals in which the atoms are all the same size and each is surrounded by 12 others in a close-packed structure. In three dimensions metal consists of sheets of atoms; each atom in any of these sheets has six atoms of the same sheet touching it. Atoms in the

sheet above or below are situated so that they are centered over the spaces between atoms in the sheet below and above. This structure is illustrated in a two-dimensional sketch in Fig. 5-5, with lines representing the planes of greatest density of atoms. If this crystal is subjected to stress in either compression or tension, the crystal will tend to deform by slip along these planes. This is seen in the experimental deformation of single crystals of metal. In the cases illustrated the sides of the crystal are unrestricted so the slip planes go completely across the crystal and are expressed by changes in shape of the outer boundary of the crystal (Fig. 5-6). Slip of this nature is called *translational gliding* (referred to as *plastic flow* in metallurgy), and such a slip occurs when the energy supplied through shearing stress along a potential slip plane is great enough to lift the

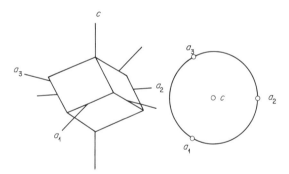

Fig. 5-4 Schematic of calcite crystal showing crystallographic axes and stereographic projection of axes with c axis vertical.

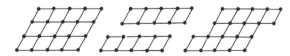

Fig. 5-5 Atom centers before, during, and after slip in a perfect, close-packed crystal.

Fig. 5-6 Slip in a single crystal of metal. The sides of the crystal were not confined during the extension.

atoms in one plane out of their position in the spaces they occupy in the next lower sheet. The translation may result in movements of the sheets amounting to one or more interatomic distances. In a material such as the metal crystal consider, a large number of closely spaced parallel slips is likely to occur (Fig. 5-7).

A number of potential planes of translation gliding occurs in some crystals. For example, the planes containing high densities of atoms in a cubic crystal are illustrated in Fig. 5-8. The density of atoms is not uniform in all these planes, and for this reason the tendency for a slip to occur in all directions is not equal. In some crystals not only the plane but the direction of movement within that plane and the relative sense of movement are restricted by crystal structure. If a given crystal contains a number of planes of potential slip, then the slip is most likely to occur on the planes which are oriented relative to the stress field in such a way that the shearing stress components on them are highest. (The variation of shearing stress on planes inclined at different angles to the principal stress direction was discussed under the section on stress concepts.)

What is known as *bend gliding* is a type of translation gliding in which the gliding planes undergo elastic deformation before the slip occurs. This occurs when the axis of loading is either parallel or perpendicular to the glide surface.

Defects

Translation gliding has been successfully studied by means of deforming bubble rafts, large float-

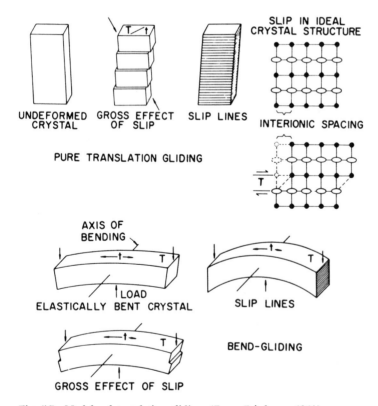

Fig. 5-7 Models of translation gliding. *(From Friedman, 1964.)*

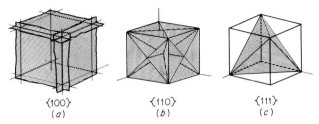

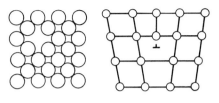

Fig. 5-8 Planes of possible slip in a cubic crystal. (a) Three {100} planes; (b) six {110} planes; (c) four {111} planes. Planes with higher indices are not shown.

Fig. 5-9 Examples of crystal defects. A line defect due to an extra row of atoms (right) and a point defect due to a missing atom (left).

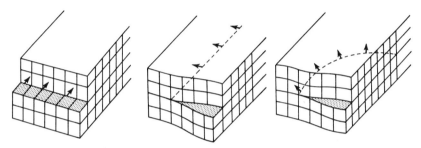

Fig. 5-10 Shear dislocations by edge dislocation (left), screw dislocations (center), and loop with edge and shear components (right).

ing rafts of similar-size bubbles. The surface tension approximates atomic bonds. Gliding often takes place by movements in planes which contain defects in crystal structure. Many types of defects occur in crystals. In fact, perfect crystals are rare. Defects may arise from the presence of a partially complete plane of atoms in the structure which produces a linear defect along the edge of the extra plane of atoms. Point defects (Fig. 5-9) occur where an atom is missing or where extra atoms or atoms of a different size occur in the crystal.

Gliding may consist of a simple shift of a whole plane of atoms over those below, but it is much more common in the bubble raft experiments for a dislocation to "run" along the slip plane. Run occurs so that only a few of the bonds need to be broken at a time. Sheets of marbles are often used to visualize movements in gliding. Marbles in the upper sheet initially

located in spaces between marbles in the lower sheet must be forced to rise up and over the top of a stable position. Bubble rafts differ in that the bubble is not rigid; shapes can therefore be deformed and thus the movements can take place as a progressive process. These dislocations may occur in several ways (Fig. 5-10).

Twin Gliding

The second important gliding mechanism is that accomplished through twinning. The crystal structure of the mineral becomes essentially reversed on opposite sides of the twinning plane. The significant difference between translation gliding and twinning is found in the sense and amount of movement. All the layers of atoms between glide planes are displaced by the same amount in simple translation gliding. In twin gliding each layer of atoms above the twin plane is displaced more than the one below (Fig. 5-11). In most minerals which show twin gliding the crystal is divided by twin gliding planes into a number of parallel lamellae.

Inferring Stress Direction from Glide Systems

Gliding by translation or twinning occurs when the shearing stress directed parallel to the glide plane and in the right direction within that plane exceeds some critical value. This is most likely to happen when the component of shearing stress on the plane is a maximum. Friedman (1964) has outlined the stress conditions which are most favorable to gliding as follows (Fig. 5-12):

1. The intermediate stress direction lies parallel to the potential glide plane, and perpendicular to the gliding direction.

2. The maximum stress direction is inclined 45° to the potential glide plane and is oriented in such a way as to produce the correct sense of shear on the glide plane.
3. The minimum stress direction is oriented at 45° to the glide plane and in the plane containing the maximum stress direction.

The idea that mineral and rock fabric can be directly related to stress conditions accompanying the formation of the fabric has been the basis for much work in petrofabrics. The study of gliding in crystalline aggregates has shown promise of being one of the most fruitful approaches to the problem of determining stress conditions. In dealing with an aggregate it is necessary to deal with the fabric statistically. This is generally done by use of the stereo-

TWIN GLIDING

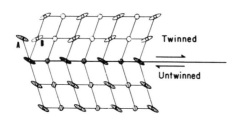

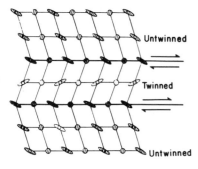

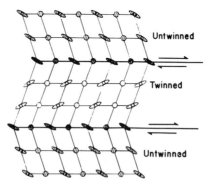

Fig. 5-11 Diagrammatic illustration of twin gliding and the development of a twin lamella. The movement along any one ionic layer (gliding plane) is a fixed fraction of the unit interionic distance, e.g., ion at A moves to B. As a result, a symmetrical relationship exists across the twin plane. A twin lamella is formed if twinned material is bounded on both sides by untwinned structure. *(From Friedman, 1964.)*

graphic projection to plot poles to twin planes and other fabric elements.

Although many crystals exhibit both translation gliding and twinning, only a few common rock-forming minerals display the properties. Of these calcite and dolomite have been studied most thoroughly; however, gliding systems have been compiled for a large number of other crystals (Clark, 1966).

Kink Bands

A type of failure phenomenon known as kinking was first recognized in studies of deformation of single crystals of metal. In the case of the single copper crystal the edges of the crystal were shown unrestrained (Fig. 5-6), and glide surfaces crossed the entire crystal. In most experimentally and naturally deformed crystals the boundaries are restrained by adjacent crystals or by the specimen jacket. The gliding surfaces in such cases often show abrupt changes in orientation. *Kink bands* are deformation bands bounded by surfaces which cut across the active glide planes (Turner and others, 1954). During deformation the material within the band is rotated relative to that outside the band, which may remain relatively undeformed. Rotation within the band is initially about an axis that lies in the glide plane and normal to the glide direction. As deformation proceeds, the material outside the band is rotated (externally) in the opposite direction from the internal sense of rotation along the glide surfaces (Fig. 5-13), in which several different forms of kink banding are illustrated. It is possible to calculate the local strain from these rotations (Turner, 1962; Borg and Handin, 1966).

$$S = \cot \alpha + \cot \beta$$

where S is the shear strain and α and β are the angles between the gliding plane and the boundary measured within the band and outside the band, respectively.

Kinking is found in many types of crystals but it is particularly well displayed in single crystals of mica and in rocks with a high per-

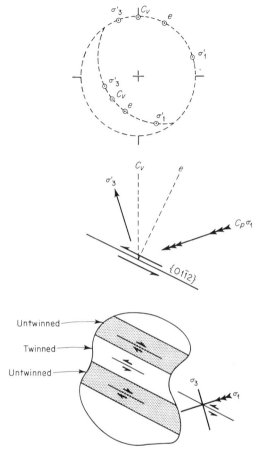

Fig. 5-12 Relations between principal stress directions and twin gliding showing maximum compressive stress σ_1' and maximum extension σ_3' axes oriented to produce glide on e. Section is normal to e plane and contains glide direction and optic axis, C_v. A section through a twinned calcite crystal is shown below. (*After Friedman, 1963.*)

centage of micaceous minerals such as slate, phyllite, schist, and gneiss.

Kink bands in biotite

The behavior of single crystals of biotite and crystalline aggregates containing large percentages of mica has been reviewed by Borg and Handin (1966). When the orientation of the

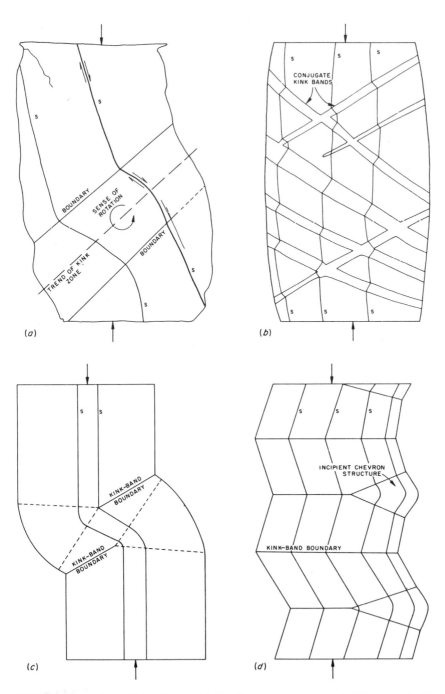

Fig. 5-13 Examples of kink bands. (*a*) Fordham gneiss shortened 10.3 percent; (*b*) phyllite shortened 13 percent (*from Paterson and Weiss, 1962*); (*c*) single crystal of zinc (*after Orowan, 1942*); (*d*) single crystal of cyanite (*from Mugge, 1898*). (*From Borg and Handin, 1966.*)

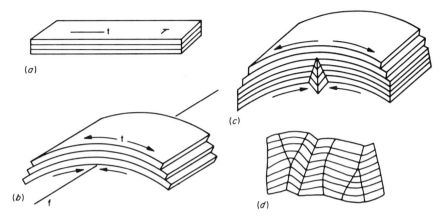

Fig. 5-14 Sketch showing the development of kink bands by the mechanism of bending gliding. (*a*) Undistorted crystal; (*b*) crystal bent by "two-sided" gliding, parallel to *t*; (*c*) initial stage kinking, chevron structure; (*d*) complex kinking as seen in a section normal to *f*. *T* = gliding plane, *t* = gliding line, *f* = axis of rotation or bending. (*After Mugge, 1898; from Borg and Handin, 1966.*)

foliation, *s,* is inclined at low angles to the principal stress direction, kinking is likely because the basal translation glide plane {001} is suitably oriented for bend gliding. The way bend gliding may lead to kinking is shown in Fig. 5-14. However, when the *s* surfaces are nearly normal to the principal stress direction, failure by faulting rather than kinking is favored. A single crystal of biotite cut normal to the {001} plane and shortened 29 percent at 5 kbars confining pressure and 500°C (simulating conditions at a depth of 11 miles) showed the following features:

1. Prominent bending and kinking of {001} are best developed at the ends of the specimen (most other minerals show greatest deformation in the central section).
2. Wedge-shaped kink bands are most common.
3. Sharper boundaries are associated with larger rotations. Some rotations reach as much as 40 to 60°.
4. Kink-band boundaries are not offset.
5. No preference in sense of external rotation of {001} in different bands was found; both

directions of rotation occur along the same glide surfaces. Gliding in two directions is indicated by the bending (Fig. 5-14).

The kinking of biotite in polycrystalline aggregates has been found to provide an indication of the principal stress direction. Griggs, Turner, and Heard (1960) found that kink bands were concentrated nearly normal to the axis of compression (σ_1) and were best developed in grains whose *c* axes were steeply inclined to σ_1. Borg and Handin (1966) have confirmed this in specimens of biotite gneiss. The biotites are most frequently kinked when *s* (foliation) is nearly parallel to σ_1.

Deformation of Calcite*

Calcite exhibits gliding of both twin and translational character, and deformation of calcite and aggregates of calcite crystals have been extensively studied (Turner et al., 1954; Bell, 1941; see additional references in Friedman, 1964). Some of the most significant glide planes in calcite crystals are shown plotted on a stereo-

* Refer to Turner, Griggs, and Heard (1954) for further details.

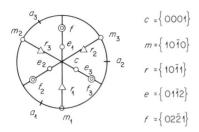

$c = \{0001\}$

$m = \{10\bar{1}0\}$

$r = \{10\bar{1}1\}$

$e = \{01\bar{1}2\}$

$f = \{02\bar{2}1\}$

Fig. 5-15 Crystallographic planes in a calcite crystal. The *c* axis is vertical, *a* axes are horizontal. (*After Turner, Griggs, and Heard, 1954.*)

graphic projection in Fig. 5-15. The *c* axis is shown vertical and the three *a* axes are horizontal in this illustration. Single crystals of calcite were deformed in the experiments by Turner, Griggs, and Heard (1954) at temperatures of 20, 150, 300, and 700°C; under confining pressures in the range of 5,000 to 10,000 atm; with shortenings or extensions of 2 to 20 percent; and with a range of crystallographic orientations. A variety of effects, including formation of slip lamellae, partings, kink bands, and deformation bands, was found in the deformed crystals, but the dominant mechanism of deformation throughout the range of temperatures tested was by twin gliding on the

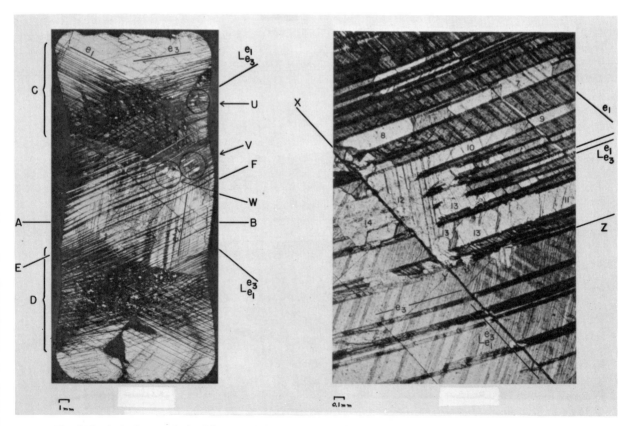

Fig. 5-16 A single crystal of calcite extended 20 percent parallel to the *c* axis at 25°C, 5 kbars; annealed at 800°C for half an hour. Note enlarged section at right showing effects of annealing recrystallization. (*From Griggs, Paterson, Heard, and Turner, 1960.*)

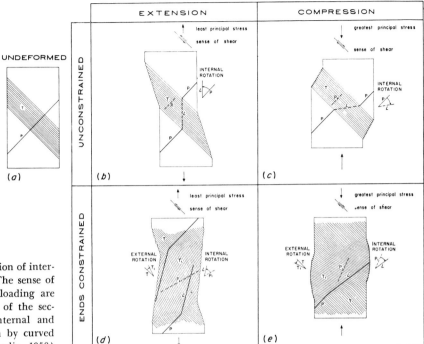

Fig. 5-17 Schematic illustration of internal and external rotations. The sense of shear and the direction of loading are indicated by arrows at ends of the sections. Direction senses of internal and external rotations are shown by curved arrows. (*From Higgs and Handin, 1958.*)

plane designated as e $\{01\bar{1}2\}$. This occurred whenever the orientation of the crystal was favorable for movement on this plane, and in the lower temperature range, $20°C$, calcite was found to be much stronger when the crystal was unfavorably oriented for this gliding to occur; at higher temperatures the difference disappeared.

In summary, gliding systems were recognized on the following planes:

$\{01\bar{1}2\} = e$ twin gliding   (1)

$\{10\bar{1}1\} = r$ translation gliding (all temperatures)   (2)

$\{02\bar{2}1\} = f$ translation gliding (low temperatures)   (3)

Several of these are indicated on the photograph of a calcite crystal extended parallel to the c axis (Fig. 5-16).

Another important discovery in this study was that the twin lamellae are rotated in a systematic way in deformed crystals and that

the rotations are related to the directions of stress application. There is both external and internal rotation, but they are in opposite directions (Fig. 5-17).

Deformation of Quartz

The behavior of quartz is highly significant because it is one of the most common rockforming minerals. The three-dimensional network of silicon-oxygen tetrahedron which comprises the basic atomic structure of quartz should be familiar (Berry and Mason, 1959). Unlike some of the other crystals we have considered, quartz lacks the closely spaced planar arrangements of atoms which make translation and twin gliding so common in other crystals, and for many years efforts to produce plastic deformation of quartz experimentally failed. Yet, quartz is found naturally deformed in a number of different ways. One of the indications of this is the strain evidenced when quartz is viewed in polarized light as the plane of

Fig. 5-18 Photomicrograph (bright-field illumination) of a set of several parallel northeast-trending kink bands. Bands containing abundant fractures at high angles to their boundaries are relatively less deformed. Lamellae are faintly visible in the clear, more highly deformed bands. Scale line beneath photo represents 0.1 mm. (*From Christie, Griggs, and Carter, 1964.*)

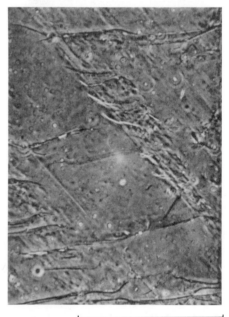

Fig. 5-19 Slip bands seen on the polished surface (top) and deformation lamellae (bottom) of a quartz crystal compressed (normal to r) top to bottom, at 500° C, 20 kbars confining pressure, shortening about 1 percent. East-west cracks formed on unloading. (*From Christie, Griggs, and Carter, 1964.*)

polarization is changed. If the quartz is undeformed the transmitted light becomes extinguished throughout the crystal at the same time as the crystal is rotated. But if the quartz is deformed the extinction undulates as the crystal is rotated. The margins of quartz grains are found granulated in some specimens; quartz is commonly fractured in strongly deformed rocks; and deformation lamellae are also visible with the petrographic microscope in some deformed rocks.

Although the crystal structure of quartz does not contain the strong alignments of planes of such atoms as calcite, metals, or even some other silicate minerals, there is a prominent sheeting of SiO$_4$ tetrahedra of wide spacing and weak bonding parallel to the unit rhombohedron and a less prominent one parallel to the basal plane (Griggs and Bell, 1938). Experimental results by Carter, Christie, and Griggs (1964) have confirmed this earlier prediction. In these studies, carried out under high confining pressures (20 kbars) and high temperatures (500°C), zones of undulatory extinction formed subparallel to the *c* crystallographic axis of the quartz, and deformation lamellae formed in three orientations. The most common orientation was basal, parallel to the *a* axes; there was a weaker orientation at angles of 20 to 60° to the base and a third subparallel to *c*. The lamellae subparallel to *c* were found to originate by movement on {0001}, and these were accompanied by the development of kinks in the slip planes. Slip on basal planes was common among those grains, oriented in such a way that the base was a plane of high shearing stress in experiments with aggregates of quartz grains. Causes of lamellae on the other directions seem less certain.

The deformation lamellae, slip bands, and kink bands are well shown at high magnifications in deformed quartz (Figs. 5-18 to 5-20). Optical studies of the basal lamellae indicate sharp boundaries and a thickness of 0.2 μ.

Kink bands in the deformed quartz are oriented in such a way as to suggest that they are induced by movements parallel to the basal slip planes, and the density of deformation lamellae is often much greater on one side of a kink than on the other.

DEFORMATION OF CRYSTALLINE AGGREGATES

Having examined some of the mechanisms of single-crystal deformations, we should now examine the characteristics of crystalline aggregates which approximate much more closely the natural occurrence of crustal materials. One of the principal differences in single-crystal and aggregate deformation is the role played by the grain or individual crystal boundaries. In

(a)   (b)

Fig. 5-20 Quartz crystals compressed perpendicular to (01$\bar{1}$1). Compression direction *P* and orientation of the crystals are shown beneath the photographs. The large horizontal cracks are extension fractures produced on unloading the samples. Width of the specimens is approximately 3 mm. (a) Deformed at 400°C and 23 kbars confining pressure; sample was shortened 10 percent. Broad northwest trending bands are zones of undulatory extinction produced by bending the structure. (b) Deformed at 750°C and 22 kbars confining pressure; sample was shortened 15 percent. Deformation bands oriented subparallel to the *c* axis pervade the sample. (*From Carter, Christie, and Griggs, 1964.*)

marbles and in most intrusive igneous rocks the boundaries are distinct and form a mosaic pattern separating domains in which the atomic configuration is different. Even in monomineralic rocks the crystallographic axes are likely to be oriented in different directions—some favorable for one or another of the glide systems, others not. Clastic rocks are different in that the grain boundaries are more prominent unless the rock is tightly cemented. Although some attention will be given to this particular problem of the boundaries, greater emphasis is laid on the behavior, the stress-strain relations, of rocks under various conditions of temperature and confining pressure. These data are summarized for a number of common rocks in a plot of temperature versus compressive strength (Fig. 5-21).

Some of the most significant results of studies of rock deformation are available in a memoir on rock deformation (Griggs and Handin, 1960). Knowledge of the subject and the data available have become too vast to be treated in their entirety here, but some significant examples will serve to bring out the more important results.

The usual procedure in designing an experiment is to control all variables except one and observe the effects of changing that variable. The main variables in rock deformation experiments are:

1. Rock type
2. Confining pressure
3. Temperature
4. Amount of directed stress and manner of its application
5. Effects of solutions
6. Time
7. Rate of strain

Of these, the time factor is the most difficult to treat experimentally, for experiments are of short durations while rocks are deformed naturally over periods of perhaps millions of years.

Deformation of Slate by Kinking

Kinking similar to that described earlier in single crystals of biotite occurs in slate, phyllite, and other metamorphic rocks with highly developed schistosity. Experimental studies with slates and phyllites have recently (Paterson and Weiss, 1962; Borg and Handin, 1966) clarified the mechanisms involved in this type of deformation. Kinks, *chevron-type folds* or *knicks* as they are sometimes called, are found to form when slate or phyllite is compressed parallel or subparallel to the cleavage or foliation; such folds do not appear when the angle between the foliation and direction of compression is 45° or greater. The development of a kink in a slate shortened 27 percent by compression parallel to cleavage starts with external rotation of s (also the initial glide plane) through about 90°. At this position the resolved shear stress becomes zero on the initial glide planes and a new set of glide planes s^1 develops. After this, rota-

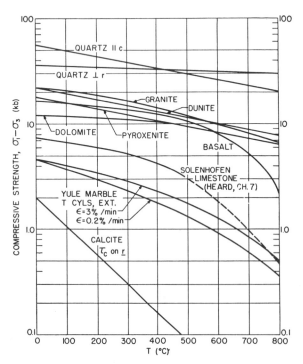

Fig. 5-21 Strength of rocks and minerals at 5 kbars. (*From Griggs and Handin, 1960.*)

tion of s^1 starts (s is rotated also by slip on s^1 but in the opposite direction), and ultimately the two are oriented in the same direction; finally, faulting occurs. Bend gliding is favored as a mechanism for kinking in slate (Borg and Handin, 1966), but the band boundaries tend to form at 45° or less to σ_1 and s (in biotite single crystals they were nearly normal to σ_1 and the slip plane). Thus kinks in slates should serve as a clue to principal stress directions. Even if they are at a 45° angle to the principal stress, that direction can be identified by the sense of external rotation of s.

Deformation of Marble and Limestone

The deformation of aggregates of calcite crystals has been studied extensively (Griggs and Miller, 1951; Griggs and Handin, 1960; Heard, 1960) with specimens taken from the Yule marble and the Solenhofen limestone. The results are most conveniently shown in graphs such as those showing plots of strain versus differential stress under various temperatures, confining pressures, and manner of deformation (Figs. 5-22 to 5-25).

Increasing confining pressure on limestone has the following effects under both extension and compression:

1. Raises the differential stress it will sustain before rupture.
2. Raises the differential stress required to produce a given amount of strain.
3. Increases the amount of strain which takes place before rupture. In most of the experiments rupture took place before the specimen was strained more than 10 percent, but at very high confining pressures, rupture had not taken place as the experiment ended.

Increasing temperature on limestone has these effects in both extension and compression:

1. Increases the amount of strain at a given differential stress.

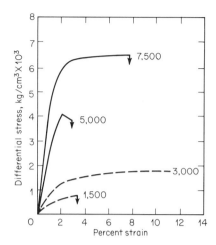

Fig. 5-22 Extension stress-strain curves for Solenhofen limestone at various confining pressures. Solid lines are for test run at 25°C; dashed lines are for test run at 600°C. (*From Heard, 1960.*)

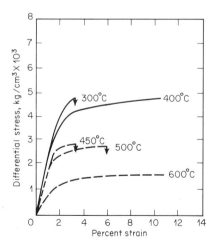

Fig. 5-23. Extension stress-strain curves for Solenhofen limestone at various temperatures and confining pressures. Solid lines are for test run at 5,000 atm confining pressure; dashed lines are for test run at 3,000 atm confining pressure. (*From Heard, 1960.*)

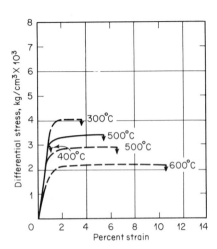

Fig. 5-24 Compression stress-strain curves for Solenhofen limestone at various temperatures and confining pressures. Solid lines were run at 1 atm confining pressure; dashed lines were run at 400 atm confining pressure. (*After Heard, 1960.*)

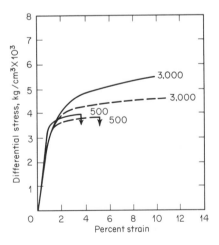

Fig. 5-25 Compression stress-strain curves for Solenhofen limestone for various confining pressures. Solid line is for test run at 300 °C; dashed line is for test run at 400 °C. (*From Heard, 1960.*)

2. Increases the amount of strain before rupture.

3. Decreases the maximum amount of differential stress the specimen would stand before rupture.

The qualitative effects of increasing temperature and confining pressure are the same for extension and compression. The limestone's behavior changes from that of a brittle material to that of a ductile material as temperature and confining pressures are increased. Heard (1960) has plotted the transition from brittle to ductile behavior as a function of confining pressure and temperature (Fig. 5-26). When this is done the difference in behavior of the limestone in extension and compression becomes clear. Much higher confining pressures are required to obtain ductile behavior of materials deformed by extension. The difference in behavior of limestone deformed by extension and compression can also be seen by comparing the stress-strain curves (Figs. 5-22 to 5-25). Note the lower differential stresses required in extension to produce any given amount of strain.

The effects of having solutions in pore spaces of experimentally deformed sedimentary rocks have been examined by Handin and others (1963). Tests were run on shale, mudstone, and sandstone as well as on dolomite and limestone. In these tests the pore pressure of the interstitial fluids was maintained at a constant value, and the fluids were inert chemically. The tests showed that the ultimate strength and ductility of the rocks were dependent on the difference in the pore pressure and the confining pressure in rocks with sufficient permeability to ensure that the interstitial fluids were distributed throughout the rock. We will examine later the effects of fluids in promoting recrystallization.

Cataclastic Deformation

Experimental deformation of sandstone

Sandstone differs from marble and limestone not only in that most sandstone is composed of

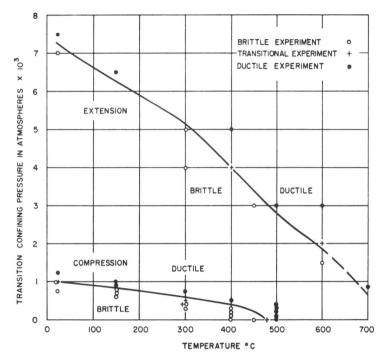

Fig. 5-26 Brittle-ductile transitions in compression and extension as a function of confining pressure and temperature. (*From Heard, 1960.*)

quartz, which is not so prone to gliding mechanisms as calcite, but also in the physically different nature of the individual grain boundaries. Compare Figs. 5-27 and 5-28. Two studies will serve the purpose of illustrating some important characteristics of sandstone deformations.

The St. Peter sandstone is noted for its well-sorted even texture, and it has been selected for the experimental work by Borg and others (1960) described below. The sand grains are initially unfractured, few grains show strain effects such as undulating extinction, and few grains show slip lamellae. Results of experiments involving various confining pressures, extension, and compression for several sizes of disaggregated dry sand are illustrated in Fig. 5-29. The shape of these curves shows a pronounced difference from those of single crystals or limestone. This is related to the fact that the rock is not cemented, so that grain boundary movements take place much more readily. The results of the experiments may be summarized as follows:

1. Fracturing is the dominant process of deformation.
2. Fracture patterns reflect the symmetry of the deformation when the differential stress is applied. The fractures are oriented at small angles to the principal stress direction, probably shears, when the specimens are compressed. Most fractures are normal to the axis of extension, and are presumably tension fractures, when the specimens are extended.
3. Grains show a tendency to be rotated in extension test. The grains are normally

Fig. 5-27 Yule marble extended at 600° C, 3 kbars. Note partial twinned grains in less deformed regions, completely twinned in necks. (*From Griggs, Paterson, and Heard, 1960.*)

slightly elongated, and the long axis tends to become rotated until it parallels the direction of greatest extension.

4. No evidence of deformation lamellae or undulatory extinction was found.

5. The quartz grains tend to become oriented so that the optic axes assume a preferred alignment relative to the applied stress.

The deformation of the sand in these experiments is dominantly through cataclastic flow. Because the sand was dry no recrystallization effects occurred. It is remarkable that the fracturing shows a preferred orientation related to the applied stress system, because in sand the grains are in contact with other grains only at

point contacts, producing a complex system of stress application which one might expect to produce a more random fracture pattern. We may think of a cataclastic flow as consisting of:

1. Fracturing by shear and tension
2. Rotation of grains
3. Eventual fragmentation of the grains

Friedman (1963) examined deformed calcite-cemented sandstone and found that the various components deformed by mechanisms that are the same as those in monomineralic aggregates. Thus calcite deformed primarily by twin gliding on *e*, and quartz, feldspar, and garnet grains deformed primarily by fracturing. Both the

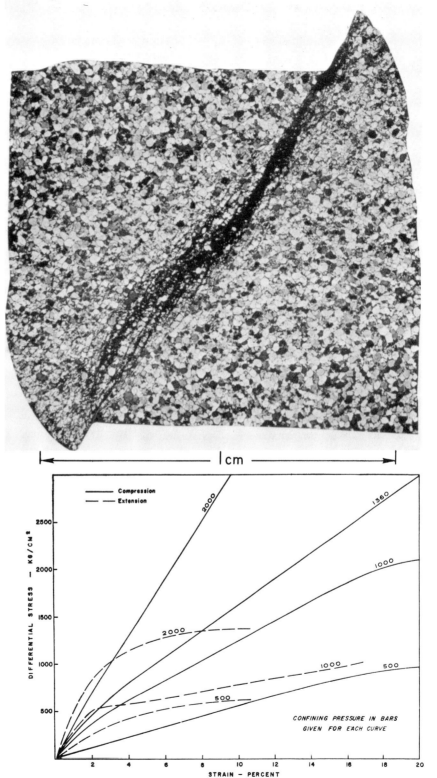

Fig. 5-28 St. Peter sand specimen shortened 40 percent at 5,000 bars confining pressure, 1,000 bars interstitial water pressure, 500°C. Note lack of grain breakage except in gouge zone along thrust fault. (*From Griggs and Handin, 1960.*)

Fig. 5-29 Stress-strain curves for dry, disaggregated St. Peter sand (250 to 300 μ) deformed in compression and extension under different confining pressures. (*From Borg and others, 1960.*)

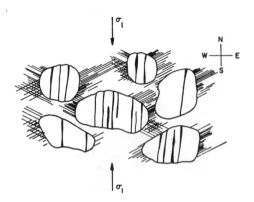

Fig. 5-30 Sketch of fractured detrital grains and twin lamellae in calcite crystal. Twin lamellae are best developed on east and west sides of fractured grains and tend to die out into the interstices. Few lamellae are developed north and south of grains. (*After Friedman, 1963.*)

fractures and the twin lamellae are directly related to orientations of the principal stresses (Fig. 5-30).

While fracturing is extremely important in dry test of sandstone, Handin and others (1963) have shown that grain breakage becomes progressively less important as pore pressure is increased. High pore pressure reduces internal friction.

Deformation of Igneous and Metamorphic Rocks

Borg and Handin (1966) have summarized the behavior of 18 basement-type (igneous and metamorphic) rocks (Table 5-1), deformed in triaxial compression test at a strain rate of 1 percent per minute under temperature and confining pressure conditions which should simulate a shallow depth of 15,000 ft (1 kbar pressure and 150°C) and great depth of about 11 miles (5 kbar and 500°C). The 11-mile depth would approximate the bottom of a geosynclinal accumulation such as those of the North American geosynclines.

Under shallow conditions the behavior of the rocks was brittle, largely elastic, before failure by shear fracturing. Only schist faulted under

these conditions without loss of cohesion. Schist was also the weakest of these rocks with ultimate compressive strength of 2 kbars, compared with granite at 3.3 kbars and granodiorite at 8.2 kbars. The stronger rocks contained higher proportions of quartz and feldspar. Fine-grained rhyolite was found to be twice as strong as coarse-grained granite. The shear fractures formed at angles of 21 to 33° to the maximum principal compression.

The high temperature and pressure conditions resulted in a variety of modes of deformation (Fig. 5-31). The nonmicaceous anisotropic rocks (amphibolite and peridotite) are brittle. The foliated rocks containing 10 percent or less mica, granite gneiss, are brittle or transitional. Of the richly micaceous rocks, only schist is ductile in all orientations. Slate is ductile only when the cleavage is inclined at high angles to the maximum principal compression. Shortening in the brittle rocks (Fig. 5-31) is due to offset along one or two faults. The fault is sharp, often granulated, and generally cuts through grains. The transitional rocks deform by multiple faulting in a broad zone with numerous

Table 5-1 Behavior of Rocks and Strength When Compressed at 5 kbars Confining Pressure, 500°C

State	Rock type	Strength, kbars
Brittle	Diabase	5.5
	Diorite	7.1
	Granite	8.3
	Rhyolite	10.5
	Amphibolite (normal to *s*)	11.4
	Biotite gneiss (normal to *s*)	11.3
	Granite gneiss (normal to *s*)	11.5
	Migmatite (normal to *s*)	9.9
	Peridotite (normal to *s*)	4.0
Transitional	Gabbro	8.2
	Pyroxenite	6.4
	Fordham gneiss (parallel to *s*)	8.8
	Migmatite (parallel to *s*)	6.7
Ductile	Fordham gneiss (normal to *s*)	4.3
	Slate (parallel to *s*)	6.3
	Schist (normal to *s*)	6.1

Source: After Borg and Handin (1966).

conjugate faults. Shear tends to be distributed, and there is some intracrystalline flow of mica and enstatite (a pyroxene), individual grains of which may be kinked. Ductile behavior is characterized by intragranular flow in kink bands due to bend gliding in mica plus intergranular shear along *s* surfaces of highly oriented micaceous grains. Faulting occurs only after large permanent strains.

EFFECTS OF PORE PRESSURE

Most sediments are deposited in water; water thus becomes trapped in intergranular pore spaces and is absorbed in colloids in the case of clay. Some of this water is forced out during compaction and cementation, but much of it remains. Water or other fluids may be present in pore spaces in igneous and metamorphic rocks as well. This water promotes recrystallization, and it affects the mode of deformation of the rock in which it is trapped. The pressure in the pore water, called *pore pressure,* may become very great, even equal to the confining pressure. Pore pressure will be considered in relation to faulting and sedimentary structures later. Here we will examine its effect in experimental deformation of sediments as revealed in the work of Handin and others (1963) and Robinson (1959).

Handin and others (1963) subjected Berea sandstone, Marianna limestone, Repetto silt-

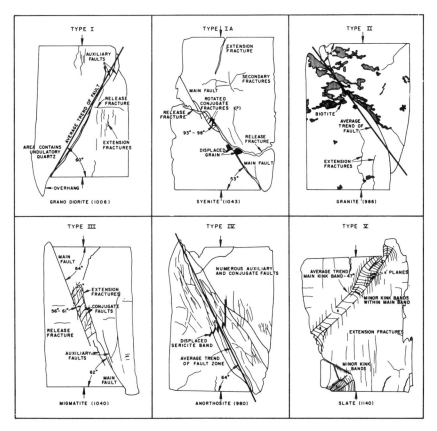

Fig. 5-31 Sketches of cross sections of representative specimens illustrating arbitrary deformational categories and subsidiary features. (*From Borg and Handin, 1966.*)

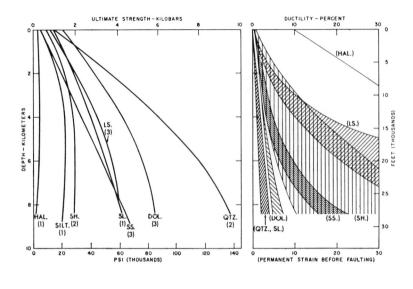

Fig. 5-32 Ultimate compressive strengths and ductilities of dry rocks as functions of depth. Effects of confining (overburden) pressure and temperature (30°C/km) included. (*From Handin and others, 1963*.)

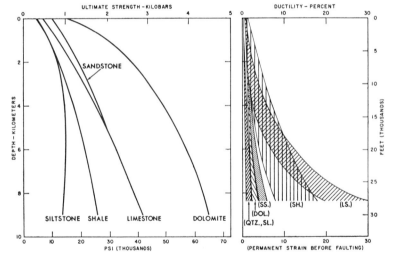

Fig. 5-33 Ultimate compressive strengths and ductilities of water-saturated rocks as functions of depth. Effects of confining (overburden) pressure, temperature (30°C/km), and "normal" formation (pore) pressure included. (*From Handin and others, 1963*.)

stone, Muddy shale, and Hasmark dolomite to triaxial compression tests in which the external confining pressures and internal pore pressures were applied and measured independently. Interstitial water pressure was maintained constant throughout the test, and porosity changes were determined as a function of the amount of shortening. Both the ultimate strength and the ductility (Figs. 5-32 and 5-33) were found to be a function of the effective confining pressure, the difference between the external and internal pore pressures. This is shown on the stress-

strain curves in Fig. 5-34. This relation holds when the pore fluid is chemically inert, when the permeability is sufficient to ensure pervasion and uniform pressure distribution, and when the configuration of the pore space is such that the interstitial hydrostatic pressure is transmitted fully throughout the solid framework of the specimen. These conditions were not met for shale or dolomite, nor would they hold for Solenhofen limestone, marble, or most other metamorphic or igneous rocks.

When the effective pressure is relatively high,

on the order of 1 kbar, the amount of porosity decreases with progressive amounts of permanent strain. When the effective pressure is intermediate, about 500 bars, the porosity remains essentially constant for compressions resulting in shortenings of about 20 percent. At low pressures, about 200 bars, the rocks become dilatant. In the case of sandstone the grain breakage becomes progressively less important as pore pressure is increased until the deformation becomes entirely intergranular and shortening leads to increased void volume. Permanent shortening of porous sediments and sedimentary rocks is accompanied by a reduction of porosity whenever the ratio of pore pressure to confining pressure is on the order of 0.6 or less. At ratios of 0.6 to 0.8 the pore volume remains essentially constant, and above 0.8 the porosity increases and the rock becomes dilatant.

It is found that the pore pressure effects can be explained satisfactorily on the basis of the Coulomb criterion of failure. The high pore pressure reduces internal friction although it does not modify the coefficient of internal friction. The rocks become relatively brittle, and brittle fracture and faulting are favored. The interstitial water does not have a pronounced effect on the angle of internal friction. Thus fault and fracture angles in most rocks should be inclined about 25 to 35° to the maximum principal stress direction.

It is notable that whenever the pore pressure in a formation is normal, that is, when it is equivalent to the hydrostatic head of a column of water equal in height to the depth of the formation, it is possible to predict the strength and ductility of the sediment by use of the curves in Figs. 5-32 and 5-33. Abnormally high pore pressures result, however, when there are impervious beds in the sequence which prevent the free movement of the pore water out of the formation.

Robinson (1959) studied failure characteristics of limestone, sandstone, and shale under varying confining and pore pressures in experiments designed to show the effects of pore pres-

sure on the yield strength of each rock type. Yield strength, the stress at which an increase in strain is not accompanied by an increase in applied stress, was found to increase as the pore pressure decreases for any constant confining pressure. The yield points in a series of experiments on Indiana limestone at increasing pore pressures and with constant confining pressure (Fig. 5-35) are marked by letters a to e. Note that peaks appear at a to d on these plots.

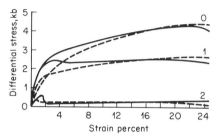

Fig. 5-34 Stress-strain curves for Berea sandstone (solid line) and Marianna limestone (dashed line) at different pore water pressures (kilobars) given for each curve. All tests were run at 2 kbars confining pressure, 24°C temperature, and in compression. (*After Handin and others, 1963.*)

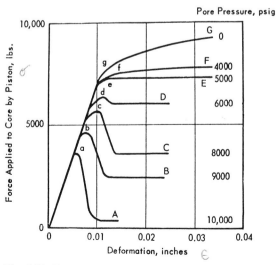

Fig. 5-35 Force deformation curves for Indiana limestone at a confining pressure of 10,000 psig. (*From Robinson, 1959.*)

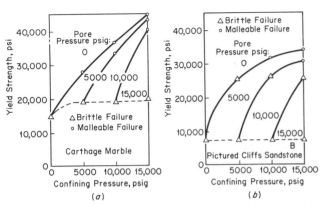

Fig. 5-36 Effects of confining pressure on the yield strength of (a) limestone and (b) sandstone. (*From Robinson, 1959.*)

Robinson refers to these as *strain-softened effects (trixotrophy)*. A clear load maximum appears. Strain hardening is quite common in which, after an initial yielding, the material becomes "hardened" and on reapplication of load the yield stress is found to be higher. In strain softening the material must become softened or loosened at the yield stress. The effect of pore pressure on yield strength of limestone is also clearly shown in Fig. 5-36 for several different values of confining pressure. In each case the yield strength is lowered as pore pressure increases.

Failure curves for sandstone (Fig. 5-36) differ from those of limestone in three ways: (1) the yield strength of sandstone increases more rapidly with increased differential pressure between confining and pore pressure; (2) higher differential pressure is required before the sandstone fails ductilely; (3) as long as pore and confining pressures are equal, the magnitude of the pressures has no effect on rock strength.

Data on shale are similar to data on limestone and sandstone. This particular shale has a low yield strength at zero differential pressure, but strength increases rapidly as the differential is applied.

THE ROLE OF RECRYSTALLIZATION IN ROCK DEFORMATION

Recrystallization is one of the main processes by which sedimentary rocks become metamorphosed. Sometimes this recrystallization occurs under conditions of directed stress, and at other times directed stress appears to be absent. That these two conditions exist is shown geologically by the presence of undeformed as well as deformed fossils in metamorphic rocks. Were it not for the little-deformed fossils, some metamorphic rocks might be thought to have undergone much greater strain. For example, little-deformed recrystallized invertebrate fossils are found in the Bündner Schïefer formation, an Upper Jurassic schist, in Germany. Some of the best examples of fossils in metamorphic rocks were reviewed by Bucher (1953).

That recrystallization can occur without deformation is also indicated by undeformed crinoid stems in coarse limestones. The finer-grained original limestone is transformed into a coarsely crystalline limestone or marble. In such cases there is gradual replacement without mechanical flowage. However, recrystallization also occurs in rocks that are being deformed, and a considerable body of experimental information is now available which bears on these effects and processes.

Two types of experimental work bear directly on the role of recrystallization in deformed rocks. The first type is recrystallization which takes place during deformation, usually referred to as *syntectonic recrystallization,* and the second type is recrystallization of materials that have first been strained and then heated while recrystallization takes place, called *annealing recrystallization.* Below certain critical temperatures most materials will not anneal.

It has been demonstrated in experiments with quartz (Carter, Christie, and Griggs, 1964) and with calcite (Griggs, Paterson, Heard, and Turner in Griggs and Handin, 1960) that a highly preferred mineral orientation develops in syntectonic recrystallization. Griggs found that recrystallization reached a maximum at 600°C in a marble deformed at a strain rate of 3 percent per minute. At lower rates of strain, lower temperatures were required to produce a maximum recrystallization. (Recrystallization started at 300°C, 5-kbar pressure.) In these tests the *c* crystallographic axis of recrystallized grains was found to be parallel to the maximum principal compressive stress. Water and carbon dioxide had no apparent effects. Recrystallization was found to occur both within crystals—intragranular recrystallization—and between grains along grain boundaries—intergranular recrystallization. Only a few nuclei were found to grow within grains, the recrys-

tallized portion having irregular boundaries with the host, but the *c* axis in the recrystallized portion is oriented at a different angle than the host. Intergranular recrystallization was most pronounced in the portions of the specimens which were greatly elongated (Fig. 5-37). The new crystals grow from nuclei along grain boundaries. Again the *c* axes cluster at high angles to the extension.

Syntectonic recrystallization of quartz is found to be somewhat similar to that of calcite. Carter, Christie, and Griggs (1964) found the first indications of changes in boundaries of quartz grains at 1000°C, at which point serrate edges appeared on the grain boundaries. As

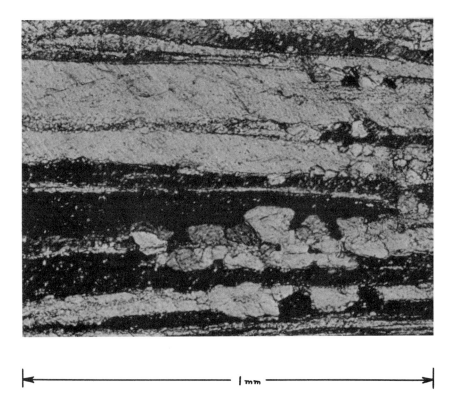

|←—————————————— 1 mm ——————————————→|

Fig. 5-37 Effects of recrystallization in Yule marble deformed at 600°C, 3 kbars, dry. The new grains are developing in clusters along margins of extended grains. (*From Griggs, Paterson, and Heard, 1960.*)

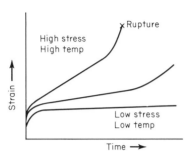

Fig. 5-38   Generalized   strain-time curves.

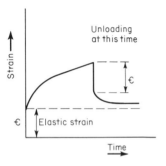

Fig. 5-39 Strain-time curve with elastic and creep deformation showing afterworking effects. (*After Nádai, 1950.*)

new grains crystallized they were restricted to regions near boundaries of deformation bands and grain boundaries. At a later stage in recrystallization, original grains are completely replaced by aggregates of new grains, and the new grains show strong preferred orientations. Larger grain sizes appear to result when recrystallization takes place in the presence of water. The resulting textures of some of the syntectonically recrystallized quartzites are remarkably similar to quartzites found in nature.

Studies of annealing recrystallization of calcite crystals and aggregates (Griggs, Paterson, Heard, and Turner in Griggs and Handin, 1960) indicate that the critical temperature for

recrystallization of Yule marble is 500°C. The recrystallized specimens have textures like those of granoblastic or porphyroblastic metamorphic rocks, and the new crystals lack preferred orientations. One exception to this occurred with a specimen of marble which was first powdered and then recrystallized. In this case the axis of greatest elastic modulus (called the *Cu axis*) of the crystals was found parallel to the axis of compression.

RECRYSTALLIZATION AND THERMODYNAMICS

Recrystallization, which is temperature-sensitive, is essentially a process of solution and redeposition or solid diffusion that occurs below the melting point. One approach to the study of recrystallization in deformed solids is found in the theory of thermodynamics (see Kamb, 1961; Verhoogen, 1951). Unfortunately, conflicting predictions of mineral orientations to be expected in minerals recrystallized under stress have been reached by various proponents of the thermodynamic approach. A comparison of two such studies may be found in Friedman (1964).

TIME FACTOR IN ROCK DEFORMATIONS—CREEP

Evaluation of the effects of time in rock deformation is of critical importance. Short-duration experiments are valuable in helping us understand rock fabric and mechanisms by which it is created, but we must also be aware of the effects of stresses applied over long periods of time. Most experiments last no more than a few days, but rocks being slowly lowered in a geosyncline are subjected to gradually increasing confining pressure, and the geological evidence indicates that long periods of time, measured in millions of years, are involved in orogeny. The effects of long-term stress have been sufficiently evaluated by experiment to give us some notion of the factors involved.

Creep rate (the ratio of strain to time during steady deformation) for metals is an important factor in determining a metal's useful life. Creep effects in rocks are similar, and they are schematically illustrated in Fig. 5-38. The material undergoes an elastic strain initially, followed by a period of adjustment along grain boundaries and within crystals which constitutes a plastic strain. This is followed by a long period of slowly but steadily increasing strain. The third stage is one of accelerated strain rate which continues until rupture occurs. Thus three stages of creep are recognized:

1. Transient—creep in the initial stages of deformation
2. Steady state—occurs when strain rate becomes steady
3. Accelerating—final stage before rupture as strain rate increases rapidly

The creep rate is highly sensitive to temperature, and much higher creep rates are observed at high temperatures.

When the load stress is removed from a metal that has been stressed long enough to show creep, a partial recovery takes place. The elastic strain is recovered and a part of the creep strain is recovered (Fig. 5-39).

Creep in alabaster and limestone has been studied by Griggs (1939), Griggs and others (1954), and Robertson (1960). The results of the two of Griggs' experiments are shown in Figs. 5-40 and 5-41. The first of these shows that alabaster behaves as a brittle material in a rapid test at room temperature, but when subjected to confining pressure and stresses it creeps. Samples were also tested in a dilute solution of HCl, and under these conditions the creep strength of the alabaster was greatly reduced.

Robertson (1960) examined creep phenomena in Solenhofen limestone and concluded that:

1. Creep rate is decreased by increasing hydrostatic pressure.
2. Highly fractured specimens displayed creep

behavior that is very similar to that of unfractured specimens. He suggests that fracturing may be one of the mechanisms of creep and that these fractures are healed because the specimens recover partially on unloading.

Data are also available on the creep of igneous rocks, granodiorite, and gabbro (Lomnitz, 1956) deformed in a torsion apparatus with low stress levels applied at room temperature, atmospheric pressure, and for a period of one week. The rocks were found to creep, and examination of thin sections before and after showed no change in texture. The behavior suggests that steady-state creep might eventually be reached for rocks subjected to only very small

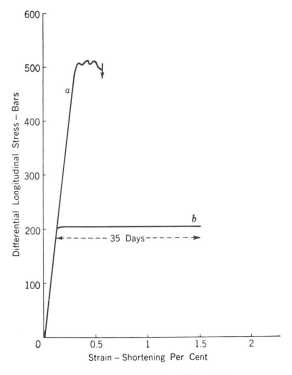

Fig. 5-40 Stress-strain curves for Ohio alabaster. $a =$ normal rapid compressive test; $b =$ test loaded at 205 bars in water (creep). (*From Griggs, 1939.*)

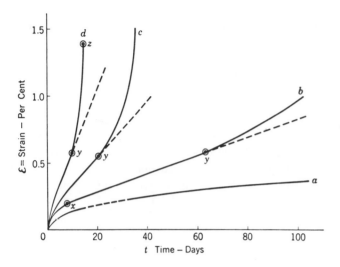

Fig. 5-41 Creep curves for alabaster in water at room temperature and pressure. Steady-state secondary creep rate is projected beyond y as broken lines. Longitudinal differential stresses: $a = 103$ bars; $b = 150$ bars; $c = 205$ bars; $d = 250$ bars; rupture at z. (*After Griggs, 1939.*)

stresses, and this would be of great importance in interpretation of creep in the crust.

Mechanisms of creep presumably include a wide range of possibilities such as the gliding mechanisms, fracturing, recrystallization, and adjustments along grain boundaries. The relative importance of these is not clearly understood, although it is clear that fracture phenomena do become important in the last stages of accelerating creep.

Various mathematical expressions have been applied to creep. A particularly significant one is that proposed by Griggs (1939):

$$\varepsilon(t) = a + b \log t + ct$$

where $\varepsilon(t) =$ creep strain
a, b, and $c =$ constants
$t =$ time

The term ct is called *pseudoviscous flow* and is obviously important in long-period creep.

EFFECT OF STRAIN RATE ON DEFORMATION MARBLE

One of the problems in extrapolating from experiments to nature is that the rate of straining in experiments must generally be of short duration, particularly when high temperatures and confining pressures are involved. In most in-

stances deformation in nature is a long-term phenomenon with very low strain rates. To investigate the effects of strain rate changes, Heard (1963) designed a series of experiments using Yule marble deformed in equipment capable of holding 500°C temperatures, 5-kbar confining pressure, and strain rates of 0.4 to 3.10^{-8} sec^{-1}. Samples were cut parallel, at 45°, and normal to foliation, and samples were deformed 10 percent.

The results of these experiments are summarized here. For specimens extended normal to foliation, the effects of changing strain rate from 10^{-1} to 10^{-8} sec^{-1} were as follows:

1. At 25°C the change has little effect on character of stress-strain curve.
2. At 300°C all stress-strain curves are lowered. (Less stress is required to produce a given amount of strain.) Strain hardening, which requires an additional increment of stress for each increment of permanent strain, seems less important at low strain rates. Strength is lowered 25 percent as strain rate is varied from 10^{-1} to 10^{-8} sec^{-1}.
3. At 400°C the above trends continue. Strain hardening disappears near strain rates of 10^{-5} sec^{-1}, giving nearly steady-state flow at all lower strain rates. Strength is low-

ered 50 percent as strain rate is varied from 10^{-1} to 10^{-8} sec^{-1}.

4. At 500°C the above trends continue. Strength is lowered 75 percent as strain rate is changed from one extreme to the other.

Similar results were obtained for less extensive tests on samples cut at 45° and parallel to foliation. Steady-state flow is approximated at 10^{-7} sec^{-1} at 300°C and at 10^{-4} sec^{-1} at 400°C.

The results of these experiments can be described by equations which agree closely with a model of steady-state flow proposed by Eyring. This model is "based on a diffusion mechanism to explain creep behavior in metals at high temperature where the activation energies for creep are equal to those for self-diffusion. They suggest a mass transport in the slip plane in the slip direction, the velocity of which is governed by the rate of movement of dislocations by crystal imperfections in the plane along that direction." (Heard, 1963.)

The implication of these experiments for deformation in nature lies in extrapolating the strain rate to very low rates. Assuming a rate on the order of 3.10^{-14} sec^{-1} for geologic deformation of the Yule marble, the strength would vary from 70 to 500 bars (at 300°C) depending on the orientation of the stress with regard to the fabric. At 500°C the strength would be on the order of 10^{-3} bars. Steady-state flow would begin at 200°C.

A second important result of these experiments is that "syntectonic" recrystallization was well developed at 400°C with 10^{-7} sec^{-1} strain rate. Previously this effect was found at temperatures over 600°C at strain rates of 10^{-3} sec^{-1}. It appears probable that recrystallization of marble might be important at 200°C temperature and strain rates of 10^{-14} sec^{-1}.

BEHAVIOR OF A GENERAL KIND OF BODY

Models of a number of ideal kinds of bodies, elastic, plastic, viscous, etc., were discussed in the preceding chapter. Andrade (1914) describes a model for the behavior of a general kind of body which behaves with components of elastic, plastic, and viscous properties. The components of the total strain are:

1. A purely elastic component conforming closely to Hooke's law
2. A time-dependent nonelastic nonrecoverable component (referred to as *plasticity*)
3. An elastic and viscous afterworking and "transient creep," which diminish with time, with or without some finite permanent strain or "set," and with or without some "work hardening"
4. A viscous component by which the strain increases at a slow but steady rate, so that this part of the strain is directly proportional to the duration of the loading

Total strain = elastic component + plastic component + transient creep + viscous strain

$$\varepsilon = \frac{\sigma}{\mu} + f(\sigma) + \beta t^{\frac{1}{3}} + \frac{\sigma t}{\eta}$$

where s = shear strain
σ = shear stress
μ = rigidity
β = a constant
η = coefficient of viscosity

A mechanical model of this general body would consist of a spring, a dashpot, and a block on an inclined plane connected in series.

THE RHEID CONCEPT

The great importance of the time factor in the behavior of rock being deformed is pointed out by Carey (1954), who has developed Andrade's model as it applies to the earth. In geotectonic phenomena the duration of loading is generally very long—so long, in fact, that the transient creep and viscous strain (steady creep), both of which are time-dependent, become the dominant processes of deformation. For short times the transient creep may be larger than the viscous strain because of the large coefficient of viscosity of rocks, but for longer times the viscous strain becomes the main component.

The viscosity, η, of rocks is very poorly known, but experimental evidence suggests that it contains components of boundary layer flow (similar to Newtonian viscosity) and movements such as intralattice slip, which are stress-dependent. Thus it is called *pseudoviscosity,* and the magnitude of η is found to vary with the stress applied, according to the expression $\eta = e^{-A\sigma}$, where A = a constant; and with temperature according to $\eta = e^{B/KT}$, where B — activation energy, K = Boltzmann's constant, T = absolute temperature.

Rheidity of a material is defined by the amount of time required for the viscous strain component to become 1,000 times as great as the elastic strain component. This is equal to $\eta/\mu \times 10^3$ sec. (The term η/μ is Maxwell's relaxation time.) This time is arbitrarily adopted as the threshold of wholly fluid behavior. "A *Rheid* is a substance whose temperature is below the melting point, and whose deformation by viscous flow during the time of the experiment is at least three orders of magnitude greater than the elastic deformation under the given conditions." (Carey, 1954.) The approximate rheidities of some common earth materials are:

Ice	2 weeks
Rock salt	10^6–10^8 sec (10 years)
Gypsum	1 year
Serpentine	10,000 years

APPLICATION OF EXPERIMENTAL RESULTS

Great progress has been made in the fields of experimental and theoretical structural geology in the last decade. Already the results of these studies are being applied in the interpretation of the structural features found in the field, but this phase of structural geology is only in its early stages. Experiments can be run under carefully controlled conditions, and simplifying assumptions can be made in theoretical analysis, but the range of conditions and the large number of variables in natural situations make the application of theory and experiment difficult and often problematical.

The terms *competent* and *incompetent* are deeply ingrained in the literature of structural geology. Competence was used by Willis (1923, p. 149) as follows:

> In order that any stratum shall be competent it should possess certain inherent characteristics in a degree superior to that in which they are possessed by other strata. These qualities are (*a*) strength to resist shear; (*b*) capacity to heal fractures; (*c*) inflexibility. On the other hand, the conditions which favor incompetence of strata in folding are (*a*) lack of coherent strength; (*b*) lack of cementing quality; (*c*) flexibility. . . . Weak beds are often incompetent to lift any appreciable part of the confining pressures. They perforce move passively. Strong beds, on the other hand, are competent to move the passive beds and carry up the weight of overlying strata.

The terms competent and incompetent are still in wide use, but they are gradually being replaced by more precisely defined terms such as *ductility,* which is defined as the total percent deformation of a rock under given conditions before fracture.

Much of this chapter has been devoted to showing how the behavior of selected rocks has been studied, to outlining the way in which the variables encountered in nature influence the behavior of these rocks, and to pointing out some of the textural and structural features which may be expected to be associated with certain conditions. We have seen that quantitative values can be set to describe the behavior of rocks, and a few examples are given. A more complete listing of such values as compressive breaking strength, tensile strength, tensile and shearing strength under high hydrostatic pressures, and other data related to the ductility of rocks may be found in Clark (1966).

REFERENCES

Adams, F. D., and Nicholson, J. T., 1901, An experimental investigation into the flow of marble: Royal Soc. [London] Philos. Trans., v. 195, p. 363–401.

Andrade, E. N. C., 1914: Royal Soc. London Proc., v. A90.

Bailey, S. W., and others, 1958, Plastic deformation of quartz in nature: Geol. Soc. Am. Bull., v. 69, p. 1443–1466.

Bell, J. F., 1941, Morphology of mechanical twinning in crystals: Am. Mineralogist, v. 26, p. 247–261.

Berry, L. G., and Mason, B., 1959, Mineralogy: San Francisco, Freeman.

Borg, Iris, and Handin, John, 1966, Experimental deformation of crystalline rocks: Tectonophysics, v. 3, no. 4, Spec. Issue: New York, Elsevier.

Borg, Iris, and Maxwell, J. C., 1956, Interpretation of fabrics of experimentally deformed sands: Am. Jour. Sci., v. 254, no. 2.

Borg, Iris, and others, 1960, Experimental deformation of St. Peter sand: A study of cataclastic flow, in Griggs, D. T., and Handin, John, eds., Rock deformation—a symposium: Geol. Soc. America Mem. 79, p. 133–191.

Borg, Iris, and Turner, F. J., 1953, Deformation of Yule marble: pt. VI, Identity and significance of deformation lamellae and partings in calcite grains: Geol. Soc. America Bull., v. 64, p. 1343–1352.

Bucher, W. H., 1953, Fossils in metamorphic rocks: Geol. Soc. America Bull., v. 64, p. 274–300.

Carey, S. W., 1954, The rheid concept in geotectonics: Geol. Soc. Australia Jour., v. 1.

Carter, N. L., Christie, John, and Griggs, D. T., 1964, Experimental deformation and recrystallization of quartz: Jour. Geology, v. 72, p. 687–733.

Carter, N. L., and others, 1961, Experimentally produced deformation lamellae and other structures in quartz sand: Jour. Geophys. Research, v. 66, p. 2518–2519.

Christie, John, and Raleigh, C. B., 1959, The origin of deformation lamellae in quartz: Am. Jour. Sci., v. 257, no. 6.

Christie, John, Griggs, D. T., and Carter, N. L., 1964, Experimental evidence of basal slip in quartz: Jour. Geology, v. 72, p. 734–756.

Clark, S. P., Jr., ed., 1966, Handbook of physical constants: Geol. Soc. America Mem. 97, 587 p.

Crampton, C. B., 1958, Muscovite, biotite, and quartz fabric reorientation: Jour. Geology, v. 66, no. 1.

Friedman, Melvin, 1963, Petrofabric analysis of experimentally deformed calcite-cemented sandstones: Jour. Geology, v. 71, p. 12–37.

———— 1964, Petrofabric technique for the determination of principal stress directions in rocks, in Judd, W. R., State of stress in the earth's crust: New York, Elsevier.

Goranoon, R. W., 1940, Flow in stressed solids—an interpretation: Geol. Soc. America Bull., v. 51, p. 1023–1034.

Griggs, D. T., 1936, Deformation of rocks under high confining pressures: Jour. Geology, v. 44, p. 541–577.

———— 1938, Deformation of single slate crystals under high confining pressures: Am. Mineralogist, v. 23, p. 28–33.

———— 1939, Creep of rocks: Jour. Geology, v. 47, p. 255.

———— 1940, Experimental flow of rocks under conditions favoring recrystallization: Geol. Soc. America Bull., v. 51, p. 1001–1022.

———— 1942, Strength and plasticity. Handbook of physical constants: Geol. Soc. America Spec. Paper no. 36, p. 107–130.

Griggs, D. T., and Bell, J. A., 1938, Experiments bearing on the orientation of quartz in deformed rocks: Geol. Soc. America Bull., v. 49, p. 1723–1746.

Griggs, D. T., and Handin, John, eds., 1960, Rock deformation—a symposium: Geol. Soc. America Mem. 79, 382 p.

Griggs, D. T., and Miller, W. B., 1951, Compression and extension experiments on dry Yule marble at 10,000 atmospheres confining pressure, room temperature, pt. 1, in Deformation of Yule marble [Colo.]: Geol. Soc. America Bull., v. 62, p. 853–862.

Griggs, D. T., and others, 1951, Effects at 150°C, pt. 4, in Deformation of Yule marble [Colo.]: Geol. Soc. America Bull., v. 62, p. 1385–1405.

———— 1954, Deformation of rocks at 500°C, 5000 atmospheres pressure: Geol. Soc. Amercia Bull., v. 65, p. 1258.

Griggs, D. T., Paterson, M. S., Heard, H. C., and Turner, F. J., 1960, Annealing recrystallization in calcite crystals and aggregates, in Griggs, D. T., and Handin, J., Rock deformation—a symposium: Geol. Soc. America Mem. 79, p. 21–39.

Griggs, D. T., Turner, F. J. and Heard, H. C., 1960, Deformation of rocks at 500°C to 800°C, *in* Griggs, D. T., and Handin, John, eds., 1960, Rock deformation—a symposium: Geol. Soc. America Mem. 79, p. 39–104.

Gutenberg, Beno, 1951, Internal constitution of the earth, 2d ed.: New York, Dover.

Hahn, S. J., Ree, Taikyue, and Eyring, H., 1967, Mechanism for the plastic deformation of Yule marble: Geol. Soc. America Bull., v. 78, p. 773–782.

Handin, John, and Hager, R. V., Jr., 1957, Experimental deformation of sedimentary rocks under confining pressure: Tests at room temperature on dry samples: Am. Assoc. Petroleum Geologists Bull., v. 41, p. 1–50.

———— 1958, Experimental deformation of sedimentary rocks under confining pressure: Tests at high temperature: Am. Assoc. Petroleum Geologists Bull., v. 42, p. 2892–2934.

Handin, John, and others, 1963, Experimental deformation of sedimentary rocks under confining pressure: Pore pressure tests: Am. Assoc. Petroleum Geologists Bull., v. 47, p. 717–755.

Hansen, Edward, and Borg, I. Y., 1962, The dynamic significance of deformation lamellae in quartz of a calcite-cemented sandstone: Am. Jour. Sci., v. 260, no. 5.

Heard, Hugh, 1960, Transition from brittle fracture to ductile flow in Solenhofen limestones as a function of temperature, confining pressure, and interstitial fluid pressure, *in* Griggs, D. T., and Handin, John, eds., Rock deformation—a symposium: Geol. Soc. America Mem. 79.

———— 1963, Effect of large changes in strain rate in the experimental deformation of Yule marble: Jour. Geology, v. 71, p. 162–195.

Higgs, D. V., and Handin, John, 1959, Experimental deformation of dolomite single crystals: Geol. Soc. America Bull., v. 70, no. 3, p. 245–277.

Kamb, W. B., 1961, The thermodynamic theory of nonhydrostatically stressed solids: Jour. Geophys. Research, v. 66, p. 259–271.

Knopf, E. B., and Ingerson, E., 1938, Structural petrology: Geol. Soc. America Mem. 6.

Lomnitz, C., 1956, Creep measurement in igneous rocks: Jour. Geology, v. 64, p. 473–479.

Mügge, O., 1898, Über Translationen und verwandte Erscheinungen in Krystallen, Neues Jahrb. Mineralogie, Geologie u. Paläontologie Abh. B, v. 1, p. 71–75.

Nádai, A., 1950, Theory of flow and fracture of solids, vol. 1, 2d ed.: New York, McGraw-Hill, 567 p.

Orowan, E., 1942, A type of plastic deformation new in metals: Nature, v. 149, p. 643–644.

———— 1952, Creep in metallic and non-metallic materials: Proc. 1st Natl. Cong. Appl. Mech., ASME, p. 453–472.

Paterson, M. S., 1958, The experimental deformation and faulting in Wombeyan marble: Geol. Soc. America Bull., v. 69, p. 465–476.

Paterson, M. S., and Weiss, L. E., 1961, Symmetry concepts in the structural analysis of deformed rocks: Geol. Soc. America Bull., v. 72, p. 841–882.

Robertson, E. C., 1955, Experimental study of the strength of rocks: Geol. Soc. America Bull., v. 66, p. 1275–1314.

———— 1960, Creep of Solenhofen limestone under moderate hydrostatic pressure, *in* Griggs, D. T., and Handin, John, eds., Rock deformation—a symposium: Geol. Soc. America Mem. 79.

Robinson, L. H., Jr., 1959, The effect of pore and confining pressure on the failure process in sedimentary rock: Colorado School Mines Quart., v. 54, no. 3, p. 177–199.

Turner, F. J., 1962, Rotation of the crystal lattice in kink bands, deformation bands, and twin lamellae of strained crystals: Natl. Acad. Sci. Proc., v. 48, no. 6, p. 955–963.

Turner, F. J., Griggs, D. T., and Heard, Hugh, 1954, Experimental deformation of calcite crystals: Geol. Soc. America Bull., v. 65, p. 883–934.

Turner, F. J., and Verhoogen, John, 1960, Igneous and metamorphic petrology, 2d ed.: New York, McGraw-Hill.

Van Vlack, L. H., 1964, Elements of materials science: Cambridge, Mass., Addison-Wesley.

Verhoogen, Jean, 1951, The chemical potential of a stressed solid: Am. Geophys. Union Trans., v. 32, p. 41–43.

Willis, Bailey, 1923, Geologic structures: New York, McGraw-Hill.

6
folds and folding

STRUCTURAL NOTATIONS

The description of many features of deformed rocks is simplified by the use of notations which indicate the orientation of the feature and its relation to other parts of the structure. Use of notations is particularly widespread in discussions of the structure of metamorphic rocks and in analyses of rock fabric, but it has also been used when several generations of structures are superimposed in sedimentary rocks. In general the notations can be applied to any linear or planar structures. Unfortunately, some of the notations have been used in more than one way. Ideally they should be applied in a purely descriptive manner, but at times certain lines and planes have been widely thought to bear definite relations to the movements which took place during deformation and the notations have therefore been used to indicate the movement picture. Cloos (1946) outlines the history of the usage of various types of notations. The notations proposed by Sander (1926, 1930) are among the most commonly used ones.

Sander's Notations

1. *s surface.* A planar structure (any plane of mechanical inhomogeneity). The term is used in a purely descriptive, nongenetic way. It may be applied to bedding, the individual layers in a cross-bedded deposit, foliation, schistosity, banding, cleavages, joints, etc. When more than one planar structure exists in the field of study, the various *s* surfaces may be designated $s_1, s_2, s_3, \ldots, s_n$.

2. *Coordinate axes b, a, c.* Three mutually perpendicular axes defined as follows:

   b = the direction of orientation of the most prominent fold axes.

   a = the direction perpendicular to b and lying in the plane of movement, the direction of tectonic transport. In cases of schistosity it lies in the plane of the schistosity. The direction may be visualized in terms of the direction of maximum expansion in a block of clay compressed in a vise. Note the restrictions recommended by Turner and Weiss later in this section.

c = the direction perpendicular to the ab plane.

3. B. Used to designate a fold axis actually measured on the fold where it can be positively identified: $B = b$.

4. β. Used to designate a line constructed by the intersection of two planes. For example, in the case of cylindrical folding the lines formed by the intersection of planes tangent to bedding are parallel to the fold axis. The tangent planes would, of course, correspond to strike and dip measurements on the fold limbs.

5. π. Used to designate the pole to a π circle as plotted on a stereographic projection.

6. π *circle*. A circle or arc defined on the stereographic projection by the plot of a number of poles. The poles to a large number of bedding-plane measurements on a folded bed define great circles in cylindrical-type folding or small circles in conical folding.

7. *Lineations*. Sander originally used b to designate lineations. Many lineations do form parallel to fold axes, and it was on account of this very common occurrence that use of b as a lineation was originally proposed, but because many other lineations are not parallel to b, as previously described, it seems advisable to follow Cloos's suggestion and designate lineations by L. When more than one lineation is present, the lineations become L_1, L_2, L_3, etc. Linear features arise in a variety of ways. Flow in igneous rocks commonly gives rise to lineations parallel or perpendicular to flow direction. Flow axes are lineations, and where many small folds with parallel axes are formed the lineation is quite prominent. The intersection of bedding with cleavage, foliation, or joints, or more generally the intersection of any two s surfaces, produces a lineation. Slick-

ensides, oriented elongate minerals, **and** smeared-out crystals also form lineations.

Turner and Weiss Usage

The rules set forth by Turner and Weiss (1963) for the application of the notations a, b, and c deserve special attention. The notations a, b, and c are three orthogonal fabric axes which can be selected only in a fabric that is at least in part homogeneous. As a purely descriptive notation they are used according to the following rules:

1. In a fabric dominated by a prominent planar structure S, S = the ab plane, and any regular lineation in S is called b.

2. In fabrics with two or more intersecting planar structures such that they intersect in a common axis, the most prominent planar structure is called ab and the axis of intersection is b.

3. In fabrics with two or more intersecting planar structures that do not intersect in a common axis, the most prominent planar structure is called ab and the intersection with the second most prominent planar structure is called b.

4. In fabrics dominated by a strong lineation, that lineation is called b.

Unhappily even this use of notation involves a subjective element, as when the observer must decide which of two planar elements is the most prominent.

Turner and Weiss have restricted the use of axes a, b, and c to describe the kinematic (or movement picture) axes to fabrics having monoclinic symmetry and expressible in terms of gliding upon a prominent structural discontinuity such as a set of foliations or cleavages. In such cases,

a = glide direction
b = normal to a and lies in the glide plane
c = normal to the ab plane
ab = glide plane
ac = deformation plane

Axes of the Strain Ellipsoid

A, *B*, and *C* are conventionally used as symbols to designate the maximum (longest), intermediate, and least axes of strain of the strain ellipsoid. The strain ellipsoid is most easily envisioned as the form taken by a reference sphere embedded in the rock as a result of the strain. Oolites closely approximate such reference spheres.

SYMMETRY

The symmetry of rock fabrics and structural forms can be described in terms analogous to those used to classify mineral forms, for example:

Isotropic symmetry: Fabric elements are aligned in a random fashion.

Axial symmetry: Elongate minerals are aligned as in a flow pattern.

Orthorhombic symmetry: The fabric can be divided so that there are three mutually perpendicular planes of symmetry.

Monoclinic symmetry: The fabric has only one plane of symmetry.

Triclinic symmetry: The fabric has no plane of symmetry.

FOLD NOMENCLATURE*†

Definitions of terms most frequently used to describe folds are cited here along with some genetic terms. Many of the terms will be discussed at greater length in following sections.

I. Parts of a Fold

Fold: A deformation of a preexisting surface rock to a continuous curved surface that is convex in a single sense. (Carey, 1962.)

Curvature: A measure of the degree of bending of a line or surface. Curvature of a portion of a line is defined by the radius of a circle which would coincide with that portion of the line. Any point on an *s* surface has a curvature which is defined by a maximum and a minimum radius of curvature. The two are equal in the case of spheres, and both are infinite for planes.

Hinge (syn.: *hinge line, fold hinge; axis* or *fold axis* is often used in this sense, see below): A continuous line on a folded *s* surface connecting points of maximum curvature (minimum radius of curvature). The amount of curvature may vary along the hinge.

Profile plane (syn.: *normal cross section*): A cross section of a fold drawn normal to the hinge (McIntyre, 1950). If the curvature is constant near the hinge, the hinge may be defined as "the locus of mid-points of the arcs of constant curvature in an infinite number of profile-planes." (Turner and Weiss, 1963.)

Limb: The portion of a folded *s* surface located between two adjacent hinges. If the two limbs are not of equal length they may be called the *short limb* and the *long limb*. (White and Jahns, 1950.)

Apex: [syn.: *vertex* (Clifford and others, 1957); *apical region* (Stone and Lambert, 1956)]: The point representing the hinge in any cross section.

---

* This is not a comprehensive glossary of fold nomenclature. It does not include all terms which have been applied to folds and folding, nor does it give all the various uses which have been made of individual terms. No new terms are introduced, but a selection from existing terms and usage has been made. A discussion of usages is given by Fleuty (1964). The following terms not included here are defined by Fleuty: apical region; apical plane; axial direction; axial plane separation; appressed fold; bottoming fold; close fold; concertina fold; convolute fold; dependent fold; dihedral angle; flowage fold; facing; inconstant fold; independent fold; joint drag; knee fold; *M, W, S, Z* folds; polyclinal; parasitic; ped fold; tight; topping fold, undulations; unsymmetrical; vertical fold; vergence; vertex; warps. Other rarely used terms which have been omitted include: brachyanticline; brachysyncline; carinate fold; crumpling; dejective folding; downfold; drapefold; ejective folding; flank; fold bundle; posthumous folding; and sigmoidal fold.

† Definitions are taken from Am. Geol. Inst., © 1960, Glossary of geology and related sciences, and are indicated by (A. G. I. Glossary).

Axial surface [syn.: *apical plane* (Hills, 1953); also called *axial plane* although it is rarely plane]: The locus of the hinges of all beds (*s* surfaces) forming the fold (Clark and McIntyre, 1951). *Axial plane* is used in several somewhat different ways, including "a plane that intersects the crest or trough in such a manner that the limbs or sides of the fold are more or less symmetrically arranged with reference to it." (Leith, 1913.)

Axial trace: The line formed by the intersection of the axial surface with any other surface or plane (commonly the ground).

Axis: Multiple definitions are in use. (1) Used in the same sense as *hinge*. (2) The line of intersection of the axial surface and any bed or *s* surface. (Billings, 1954, A. G. I. Glossary.) (3) The nearest approximation to the line which, moved parallel to itself, generates the folded surface .(McIntyre, 1950).

Crest: The highest point in a given *s* surface on an anticline in a given cross section.

Crest line: The line connecting the highest points in an infinite number of cross sections.

Trough: The lowest point in a cross section.

Trough line: A line connecting the lowest points in an infinite number of cross sections of a syncline.

Crestal surface: A plane formed by joining the crests of all beds in an anticline.

Trough surface: A plane formed by joining the crests of all beds in a syncline.

Core: The inner part of a fold; the part located nearest to the axial surface.

Envelope: The outer part of a fold; the part located farthest from the axial surface.

II Fold Dimensions

Wavelength: The distance between two adjacent anticlinal or synclinal axes measured normal to those axes. (See Mathews, 1958, for discussion of problems of asymmetrical folds.)

Height: The vertical distance between the crest and the trough of a single marker horizon or an *s* surface.

Interlimb angle: The minimum angle between the limbs as measured in the profile plane. (Dahlstrom, 1954.)

III Shape of a Fold in Profile Plane (Right Normal Cross Section)

A. Symmetry

Asymmetrical: A fold in which the limbs are not symmetrically disposed about the axial surface. (Stoces and White, 1935.)

Symmetrical: A fold in which the limbs are symmetrically disposed about the axial surface. (Stoces and White, 1935.) A *symmetrical* fold is a plane fold whose profile is bilaterally symmetrical across the axial plane; other folds are asymmetrical. (Turner and Weiss, 1963.)

B. Attitude of axial surface

Upright fold: A fold with a vertical (or near-vertical) axial plane surface. (Structural Committee, A. G. I. Glossary.)

Inclined fold: A fold with axial surface dips of less than 80°. (Nevin, 1949, A. G. I. Glossary.)

Overturned fold [syn.: *overfold, overthrown fold, inverted fold* (obs.)]: A fold in which the beds on one limb are overturned, that is, have been rotated through more than 90° so that they are inverted. (Billings, 1954, A. G. I. Glossary.)

Reclined fold: A fold with axial dip of between 10 and 80° and a hinge which has a pitch of more than 80° on the axial plane (surface). (Fleuty, 1964.)

Recumbent fold: A fold in which the axial surface is more or less horizontal.

C. Divergence of limbs

Usage has varied considerably. The terms *gentle, broad, open, close, closed, tight,* and *isoclinal* have all been used to describe various interlimb angles. (Fleuty, 1964.)

Isoclinal: A fold the limbs of which have parallel dips; may be an anticline or a syncline. The interlimb angle equals zero.

D. Fold shape

Antiform (syn.: *arch*): When beds are arched so as to incline away from each other, they form an antiform. (Bailey and McCallien, 1937, in Fleuty, 1964.) (This definition was originally the meaning of anticline.)

Anticline: A fold with older rocks in its core. (Bailey and McCallien, 1937, in Fleuty, 1964.)

Synform: A fold in rocks in which the strata dip inward from both sides toward the axis.

Syncline: A fold with younger rocks in its core. (Bailey and McCallien, 1937, in Fleuty, 1964.)

Neutral fold: A fold with horizontal axial surface.

Box: A fold in which the broad, flat top of an anticline (or the broad, flat bottom of a syncline) is bordered on either side by steeply dipping limbs. (Hills, 1953, A. G. I. Glossary.)

Chevron (syn.: *zigzag, kink fold, accordion*): Angular folds with plane or nearly plane limbs. When distinctions among these terms are made, chevron folds have limbs of approximately equal length, alternate limbs parallel; zigzag folds have limbs of unequal length; kink folds are very small.

Fan: An anticlinal fold in which the two limbs dip toward one another, or a syncline in which the two limbs dip away from one another. (Billings, 1954, A. G. I. Glossary.)

Conjugate folds: Sets of paired, reversed folds whose axial planes are inclined toward one another. (Ramsay, 1962b.)

Curvilinear: Consisting of, or bounded by, curved lines; as, a curvilinear angle. Fold hinges are described as curvilinear or rounded, meaning that they are connected by a surface with nearly constant radius of curvature. (Fleuty, 1964.)

Angular (syn.: *sharp, acute*): Having an angle or angles; forming an angle; sharp-cornered. Fold hinges are angular when the limbs are plane.

Cylindrical fold: A fold the poles of whose bedding planes when plotted on a stereogram lie close to a great circle. (McIntyre, 1950, A. G. I. Glossary.)

Conical fold: A conical surface is a surface generated by a straight line that always passes through a fixed point and always touches a fixed curve. (Stockwell, 1950.)

Irregular fold: A polyclinal fold characterized by irregularity of axial plane(s) and discontinuities and rapid variation in the thickness of bands (Fleuty, 1964). This term was proposed as a replacement for such terms as *flow fold, wild fold, turbulent flow fold.*

Paraboloidal fold: A fold with parabolic profile and hinge or approximately these shapes. (Carey, 1962.)

Parallel fold (syn.: *concentric*): A fold in which each bed maintains the same thickness (assuming it was initially of uniform thickness) throughout all parts of the fold. Structural Committee, A. G. I. Glossary.)

Similar fold: A type of folding in which each successively lower bed shows the same geometrical form as the bed above. The thickness of beds measured parallel to the axial surface is constant.

E. Flexures

Homoclines: "A general name for any block of bedded rocks all dipping in the same direction. It may be a monocline, an isocline, a tilted fault block, or one limb of an anticline or syncline. The field data in hand are often insufficient to show which of these categories is represented . . . the only ascertained element being a dip persisting in one direction." (Daly, 1915, A. G. I. Glossary.)

Monocline: (1) Beds inclined in a single direction. (Chamberlin and Salisbury, 1927.) (2) A steplike bend in otherwise horizontal or gently dipping beds. (Lahee, 1952.)

Structural terrace: Where dipping strata locally assume a horizontal attitude. (Billings, 1954, A. G. I. Glossary.)

IV. Change of Shape of Fold with Depth

Disharmonic: A fold in which abrupt changes in geometric relations occur in passing from one bed to another, especially where alternations of plastic and rigid beds occur. (Hills, 1953, A. G. I. Glossary.)

V. Terms Based on Map and Profile Shape

Dome (structural): A roughly symmetrical upfold, the beds dipping in all directions, more or less equally, from a point. (Nevins, 1936, A. G. I. Glossary.)

Basin (structural): A depressed area with the strata dipping inward. (Emmons, 1863, A. G. I. Glossary.)

Sag: (1) A broad gentle shallow basin, e.g., the Michigan and Illinois basins (Bucher, 1933) . (2) Downwarping of beds near a fault that is opposite of that of frictional drag. (Structural Committee, A. G. I. Glossary.)

Swell: (1) A low dome or quaquaversal anticline of considerable areal extent. (La Forge, 1920, A. G. I. Glossary.) (2) An essentially equidimensional uplift without connotation of size or origin. (Bucher, 1933.)

Closure: In an anticline, a dome, or a swell, the vertical height between the highest point on a given *s* surface and the lowest horizontal plane which gives a closed trace for that *s* surface.

VI. Relations Among Folds

Cross folds (syn.: *transverse folds, oblique folds*): Informally used for folds with axial surface or axial directions, or both, at a high angle to the direction of comparable structures related to the main regional folds. (Fleuty, 1964.)

Congruous folds: Folds which conform with each other in attitude of axial surface and hinge, or vary systematically in attitudes of these structures as an original geometrical feature of the fold system. (Fleuty, 1964.)

Incongruous folds: Folds which do not conform with each other in the ways mentioned above. (Fleuty, 1964.)

Superposed folds (syn.: *refolded fold*): Folds formed in a rock that has been previously folded.

VII. Genetic Classification of Fold Types

Flow fold: A fold formed by rock flowage in which the rocks behave as fluids.

Shear fold (syn.: *slip fold*): A fold formed as a result of the minute displacement of beds along closely spaced fractures or cleavage planes. (Billings, 1954, A. G. I. Glossary.)

Flexural folds: Where flow or slip is restricted by layer boundaries, the layering exercises an active control on the deformation, and the resulting folds represent a true bending of layers. (Donath and Parker, 1963.)

Flexural flow

Flexural slip

Passive folds: Where flow or slip crosses the layer boundaries, the layering exercises little or no control on the deformation (the layering is passive), and layer boundaries (interfaces) serve merely as markers, parts of which are displaced relative to other parts to produce an apparent bending. (Donath and Parker, 1963.)

Passive flow

Passive slip

Quasi-flexural: A gradational class of folding, particularly characteristic in rocks of moderate to high ductility, in which individual layers within a folded sequence are flexed in response to passive behavior in the associated rocks. (Donath and Parker, 1963.)

Supratenuous: (1) A fold in which the beds thicken toward the syncline because the basin subsided during sedimentation. (After Nevin, 1931, A. G. I. Glossary.) (2) A fold which shows a thinning of the formations upward above the crest of the fold. (Hills, 1953, A. G. I. Glossary.)

Drag: Minor folds that form in an incompetent bed when the competent beds on either side of it move in such a way as to subject it to a couple; the acute angle between the main bedding and the axial planes of the drag folds indicates the direction of the shear. (Billings, 1954, A. G. I. Glossary.)

Rheid folding: Flow folding in which the rocks have remained solid or crystalline, but have deformed as fluids because the duration of the loading was much longer than the relevant deformation time constant (i.e., the rheidity). (Carey, 1954.)

Diapiric fold: A piercement structure in which a fold formed in a highly mobile material breaks through, or pierces, less mobile layers.

VIII. Fold Systems and Features of Folded Systems

Fold system: A group of folds which occur together.

Fold generation: A group of cognate folds. (Turner and Weiss, 1963.)

Geanticline: A broad uplift, generally referring to the land mass from which sediments in a geosyncline are derived. (Structural Committee, A. G. I. Glossary.)

Geosyncline: "A surface of regional extent subsiding through a long time while contained sedimentary and volcanic rocks are accumulating; great thickness of these rocks are almost invariably the evidence of the subsidence, but not a necessary requisite. Geosynclines are prevalently linear, but non-linear depressions can have properties that are essentially geosynclinal." (Kay, 1951.)

Culmination: A portion of a fold system, generally more or less at right angles to the folds, away from which the folds plunge. (Structural Committee, A. G. I. Glossary.)

Salient: That part of an orogenic belt that is convex toward the foreland, i.e., is concave toward the orogenic belt. (Billings, 1954, A. G. I. Glossary.)

Recess: The part of an orogenic belt where the axial traces of the folds are concave toward the outer part of the belt. (Billings, 1954, A. G. I. Glossary.)

En échelon folds: Parallel structural features that are offset as are the edges of shingles on a roof when viewed from the side. (Structural Committee, A. G. I. Glossary.)

Anticlinorium (syn.: *geanticline*): A series of anticlines and synclines so arranged structurally that together they form a general arch or anticline. (Dana, 1873, A. G. I. Glossary.)

Synclinorium: A compound syncline; a closely folded belt, the broad general structure of which is synclinal. (Structural Committee, A. G. I. Glossary.)

Orocline: A fold where the deformed unit is the orogen itself. (Carey, 1955.)

IX. Nappe Structures

Nappe: A sheetlike mass of rock transported laterally for great distances by recumbent folding and/or thrusting. (*Note:* Usage of the term is highly varied, see text.)

Allochthonous: A term originated by Gumbel and applied to rocks of which the dominant constituents have not been formed *in situ.* (Holmes, 1920, A. G. I. Glossary.) The term is applied to rock masses which have moved considerably from their point of origin.

Autochthon: In Alpine geology, a succession of beds that have been moved comparatively little from their original site of formation, although they may be intensely folded and faulted. (Heritsch, 1929.)

Para-autochthonous: In Alpine geology, a term applied to folds and nappe structures which can be connected by their facies and tectonic features with the *Autochthon,* q. v. (Heritsch, 1929.)

Root: (1) The core of a geanticline within a geosyncline, which, after the forward drive of the geosynclinal sediments, became the recumbent fold or nappe (Heritsch, 1929). (2) The back-remaining, steep part of a nappe. (Heritsch, 1923.)

Digitations: A subsidiary recumbent anticline emanating from a much larger recumbent anticline. Where several such smaller folds are associated, they resemble the fingers of a hand. (Billings, 1954, A. G. I. Glossary.)

INTRODUCTION

The term *fold* is applied to a curve or bend developed in a preexisting *s* surface, most fre-

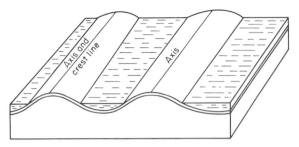

Fig. 6-1 Open, symmetrical, horizontal cylindrical folds.

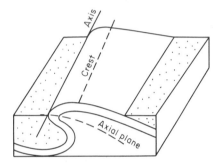

Fig. 6-2 Asymmetrical, overturned anticline.

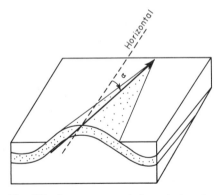

Fig. 6-3 Open, symmetrical, conical anticline (α = plunge).

quently stratification. A single fold is convex in a single sense, but usually several folds occur together. According to this definition a fold is a secondary structure; however, some folds form contemporaneously with the creation of s surfaces, as in the case of the development of new layers in a sedimentary basin which is not subsiding uniformly or which is being deformed by lateral shortening.

The regularity and geometric symmetry of the arch of Kuh-i-Deh Galleh of southwest Persia prompted Busk (1929) to call it a monument to law and order in tectonic process. To the extent that law and order do prevail, we should be able to describe folds precisely, analyze their behavior, and reasonably explain their mode of origin. Folds and flexures in crustal rocks are known on every scale from microscopic to the great basins and geosynclinal belts. They are among the most fascinating and highly varied structures with which we deal. They form under a wide range of physical conditions, in all types of rocks, and as a result of numerous applied stress conditions. Some, like the Kuh-i-Deh Galleh arch, can be readily described by simple geometrical techniques; others defy description by analogy to regular geometric forms.

Attention is directed in this chapter to folds which range from a few miles in length, macroscopic size, to those of hand-specimen size, mesoscopic folds. Examples of larger fold systems, orogenic belts such as the Alps and Appalachians, are described later in a consideration of regional geology and geotectonics.

DESCRIBING FOLDS

Many folds can be described in terms of relatively simple geometrical models, and much fold terminology is based on this principle, but folds and folding processes often appear deceptively simple when in fact the shape is complex and the mode of origin uncertain.

Three types of folds are commonly recognized in the various classifications: (1) Folds in layered sequences which appear to result from flexure of the pile. (2) Folds which appear to result from movements on parallel or subparallel slip planes which cut across the compositional layering. They may appear as discrete fractures a few millimeters to as much as a centimeter apart, but at other times the slips may penetrate the whole rock so completely that individual slip surfaces are not discrete features.

This second fold type is often thought of as a special case of laminar flow. (3) Folds formed by flowage, but lacking the strongly aligned characteristic of laminar flow. Each of these three types may occur alone or in combination with the other types, particularly where the folded pile consists of lithologies which have strongly contrasting physical properties. Fold forms may also be complicated by later modification of initial forms either as the folding process proceeds or when a second generation of folds is superimposed on earlier structures.

Cylindrical folds provide the simplest model of fold shape, and will serve to demonstrate the application of certain nomenclature. In a system of cylindrical folds each fold has the form of a half cylinder. The succession of anticlines and synclines (Fig. 6-1) has a sinusoidal waveform in cross-sectional view, and each fold in the system can be bisected by an imaginary plane surface, the axial surface, into two symmetrical halves. The intersection of the axial surface with the bedding defines a line, called the *axis* or *hinge* (see the glossary on fold nomenclature at the end of this chapter for an alternate definition of axis).

Depending on the orientation of the fold system in space, the axis may or may not coincide with the line drawn along the highest portion of the fold, the *crest line*. Other parts of the fold system include the limbs and trough. In our example of a cylindrical fold the axis was taken as being horizontal, but in nature folds die out laterally. The cylindrical fold may plunge, or the fold may change shape and die out as a conical fold (Fig 6-3).

Occasionally, folds can be studied in three dimensions. One such possibility is in hand specimens, and another is large structures in oil fields, where there is enough subsurface data to outline the fold form in detail (Fig. 6-4) (see Appendix A on structure contour maps). Most large folds, however, are known mainly through their surface expression on a geologic map (Fig. 6-5), through cross section as seen in surface road cuts and valley walls, or through sub-surface sections prepared from seismic profiles or a line of wells. A cross section taken at right angles to a fold's axis provides a standard method for comparing and describing folds. In such sections thicknesses of rock units are normally true thickness, and dips of bedding surfaces are usually true dips. For these reasons many of the adjectives used to describe folds are based on the fold's shape and attitude in cross section (refer to Fig. 6-6 and the glossary on page 173 for definition of unfamiliar terms):

1. On the basis of the symmetry of the fold relative to the axial surface, the fold is *symmetrical* or *asymmetrical*.
2. On the basis of the inclination of the axial surface, the fold is *upright, overturned,* or *recumbent*.
3. On the basis of the divergence of the limbs, the fold is *open, closed,* or *isoclinal*.
4. On the basis of the shape of the fold and the directions of inclination of the limbs, the fold is *angular* or *curvilinear* and may be called an *anticline (antiform),* a *syncline (synform),* a *box,* a *chevron,* a *fan fold,* or a *flexure*.
5. In the case of flexures, the name is determined on the basis of the relation of the inclination of the flexure to the inclination of the rock unit in which the flexure occurs as *homocline, monocline,* or *structural terrace*.

The cross-sectional view of a fold also makes it possible to compare the shape of the fold in depth and on this basis the fold is classed as *disharmonic, parallel,* or *similar*.

Map Patterns of Folds

Based on the shape of the structure on a geologic map, it may be classed as a *dome, basin, flexure, sag, swell* or one of the elongate fold types. Often the appearance of a fold in cross section can be deduced from a geologic map of the fold. For example, the direction and amount of dip of the fold limbs can be inferred

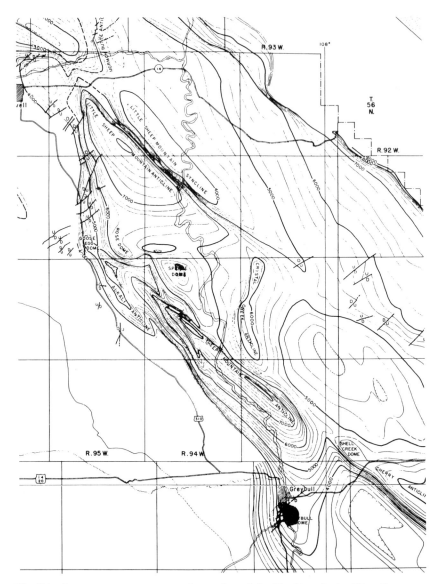

Fig. 6-4 A structure contour map of a portion of the Big Horn basin, Wyo. Contours are drawn on the top of the Frontier formation; contour interval 200 ft. (*From Pierce and others, 1947.*)

from the V-shaped outcrop patterns where streams cross contacts, or dips can be estimated from the width of outcrop on either side of the fold axis, and on most modern geologic maps strike and dip symbols are used. From these various indications the fold symmetry, the attitude of the axial surface, the divergence of limbs, and the fold shape may be inferred. The map provides the additional information necessary to describe the fold's lateral shape and dimensions and its relationship to other folds.

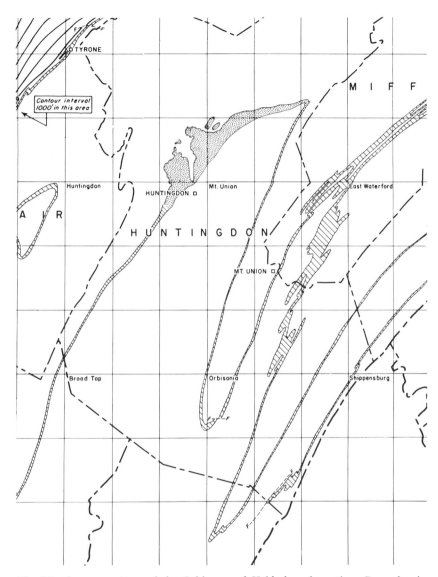

Fig. 6-5 Outcrop pattern of the Oriskany and Helderberg formations, Pennsylvania. *(From Cate and others, 1961.)*

Patterns of Fold Systems

Folds frequently occur in systems in which a large number of folds, usually alternating anticlines and synclines, are arranged in a definite pattern. Very long folds, arranged in parallel or subparallel alignment and forming narrow but very long belts that are often sinuous in map view, commonly occur in orogenic belts. In detail the folds of the belt may have an *en échelon* pattern; however, such a pattern is also found outside orogenic belts.

When a number of folds plunge in the same area along a fold belt, that area represents a transverse zone of low amplitude in the belt

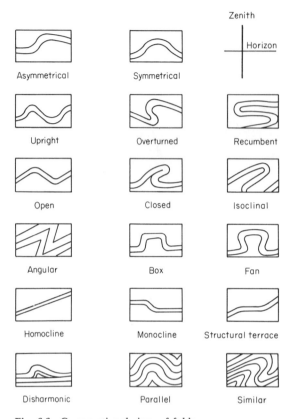

Fig. 6-6 Cross-sectional views of folds.

and is called a *depression*. Similarly, areas of high amplitude are known as *culminations*. Fold belts usually are sinuous, and some have pronounced bends where the front of the folded belt lies beyond or behind the general margin of the belt. The concave portions are called *recesses* and the convex protrusions are known as *salients*.

CLUES TO THE ORIGIN OF FOLDS

Folds are found in all rock types ranging from unconsolidated sediment to high-grade metamorphic rock. All rocks yield by folding under normal conditions either within or on the earth, but the range of conditions and modes of occurrence are great. We may wonder whether

we should approach folding processes from the point of view of folds generated in each rock type. Should we treat surficial folds in unconsolidated sediment separately from folds generated in gneisses. If we do, the number of different divisions required is as great as the number of different modes of occurrence of folds. The movements and strains which accompany the development of folds are very similar in folds obviously formed under quite different geological circumstances. Moreover, certain fold geometries are repeatedly found in folds formed under different conditions. This suggests that while many different modes of occurrence may be found, the mechanisms of folding are more limited in number. From the preceding discussions of the nature of materials, it is reasonable to expect that processes of yield in materials of very different physical properties may be similar. Flow phenomena, for example, may occur in all rocks, although the time or conditions necessary for a given amount of flow may differ greatly.

Experiments in which folds are artificially formed provide one of the few ways of actually observing the formation of fold patterns, and there is always the question of how faithfully the experiment duplicates natural conditions of fold formation in the earth. What we normally see is the result of the folding process, the resultant strain in the rock. We cannot directly observe the way stresses were applied, and often the conditions under which folding took place can only be inferred and approximated.

Among the features of folds which we can observe, describe, and analyze besides the scale and shape of the folds are:

The types and thicknesses of the rocks involved in the fold
    Structures developed within the rock layers
    Changes of the fold form with depth
    Changes between adjacent layers in a deformed sequence

From these we can obtain some insight into the mechanisms of fold formation. Listed below are a number of structural features and characteristics of folds which are related to the folding process. Not all of these features are found in every fold, and in fact, some are mutually exclusive. By carefully noting which features occur together, it is possible to formulate classifications of folds and to gain some understanding of the folding process.

1. *Thickness of beds involved in folding.* Thickness is a valuable clue to the nature of the movements within the unit during folding. Thickness measured normal to contacts remains essentially constant in some folds. In other folds, layers are greatly thickened in the hinge areas of the folds and thinned on the limbs. There are at least two ways in which this can happen. Material from within the unit can become reorganized through lateral movements so that material migrates from the limbs toward the hinges. The effect may also be caused by extending the fold by movements in a series of parallel planes (Fig. 6-7). These planes commonly are parallel to the axial plane, but they need not necessarily be. When this type of extension takes place, the thickness of the unit measured parallel to the plane of movement may be uniform despite the great change in thicknesses measured perpendicular to bedding surfaces. The thickness appears greatest where the planes of slippage are nearly perpendicular as they cut across the beds.

2. *Slippage in folding.* Slip along essentially parallel planes can be identified in many folds. The two common orientations of such slippages are parallel to the bedding surfaces (Fig. 5-14*b*) and parallel to the axial surface; however, slips are also found at other angles. In some folds these surfaces are widely enough spaced and have undergone so much movement that they can be identified megascopically, in which case they are likely to

cause offsets in bedding surfaces if the slips are oriented so that they cross the bedding. In other instances the slips are so small that they can be detected only in thin section. In detail, whether viewed through a microscope or by the unaided eye, slight changes in orientation of the material between slips, called *microlithons* by De Sitter (1954), are usually evidenced.

3. *Deformed primary features of the sediments.* If any feature of known primary shape can be identified in a deformed sequence, then a comparison can be drawn between the original and the deformed shape of the feature. Particularly

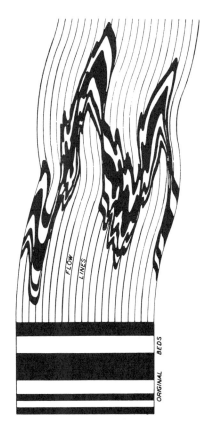

Fig. 6-7 Similar folding. (*From Carey, 1962.*)

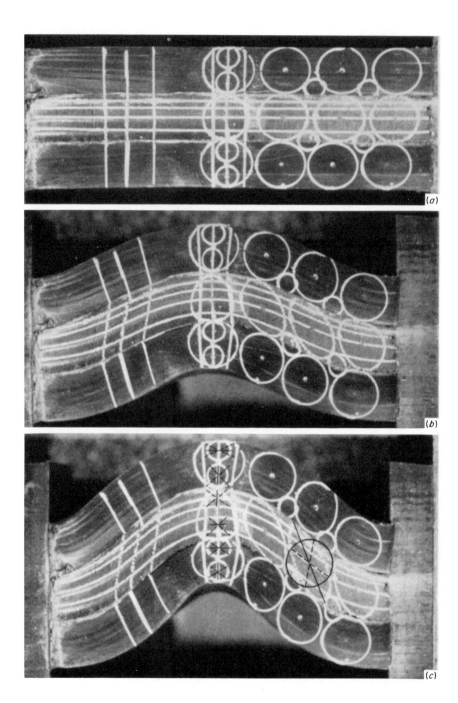

Fig. 6-8 A layer of soft rubber flanked by two layers of stiffer rubber about 12 mm thick. (*a*), (*b*), and (*c*) represent increasing amount of buckling. Stippled black lines indicate finite maximum shear directions; full black lines are parallel to finite maximum extensive strain. Black circle on flank of (*c*) is identical in size to the original unstrained circular markers. Lines between intersections of this circle with the strained ellipse that has the same center are almost parallel to the two directions of finite maximum shearing strain. (*From Ramberg, 1963*.)

important in this regard are fossils, oolites, and some primary features. Valuable references to the application of this principle will be found for deformed oolites in the work of Ernst Cloos (1947), for deformed fossils in Bucher (1953), and for deformed primary structures (Fig. 6-9) in Ramsey (1961). These and other similar studies confirm that several different types of movement are involved in folds. Two principal types seem to emerge. (a) These small features are extended approximately in the plane of the axial surface of the fold in which they occur, as at the South Mountain fold, Maryland (Ernst Cloos, 1947), shown in Fig. 6-10. (b) The changes of shape are not uniform from bottom to top of the folded layer in which they occur. In the upper portions of such a unit the extension is greatest in the plane of the bedding. At some level, called a *neutral surface,* within this type of fold the shapes may show no distortion but at a lower level the greatest extension is approximately in the plane of the axial surface. In this case it seems reasonable to explain the first type of folding as resulting from actual extension taking place within the axial surface. In the second case the variation of the sense of the distortion indicates a change from extension across the hinge on the upper portion of the unit to a *neutral surface* at some level and then to compression along the lower portion of the unit over the hinge (Fig. 6-8).

4. *Slickensides.* The striations and smeared crystals which form slickensides indicate movement between the planes on which they lie; their orientation marks the direction of that movement, and their presence suggests that the surfaces on which they are located were active as boundaries during the folding. Slickensides usually occur either on the bedding surfaces or on fractures cutting across

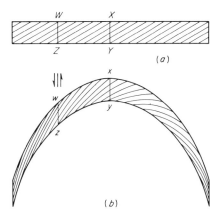

Fig. 6-9 Effects of shear folding upon the inclination of cross bedding. (a) The original orientation of the bedding with uniformly inclined foreset bedding at an angle of 30° to the regional bedding. (b) The effects of shear folding. (*From Ramsay, 1961.*)

bedding. Slickensides on the bedding and oriented in a plane that is perpendicular to the fold axis suggest movement such as might be expected in a flexed pile of layers.

5. *Saddle reef.* This name is applied to an ore deposit formed between bedding surfaces in anticlines where folding has been flexural in character. The shape of the saddle reef (Fig. 6-11) indicates that the rock units on either side moved relative to one another, so that the upper unit folded around a smaller radius of curvature than the lower one, allowing a space to form between the layers. This separation between layers could be progressively filled as the folding proceeded or a void might exist for a time. In either case, however, the beds involved are active in determining the fold form, and they must maintain sufficient strength (competence or rigidity) to support part of the weight over the saddle reef.

6. *Detachment surfaces or décollement.* In the cross section of those folds in which

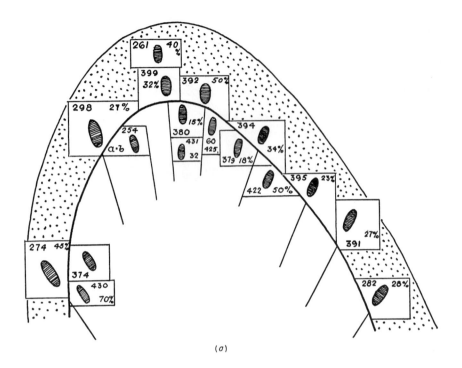

(a)

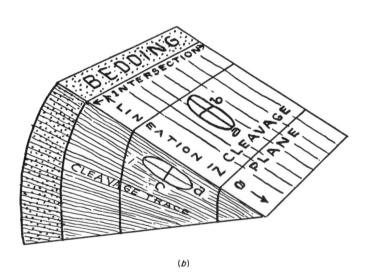

(b)

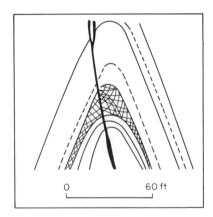

Fig. 6-10 (*a*) Cross section through a fold showing fanning slip surfaces (cleavage) and deformed oolites, South Mountain, Md. (*b*) Deformation plan in South Mountain. Axial portion of overturned fold showing mutual relations of bedding, cleavage, ooid extension, and lineation. (*From Cloos, 1947.*)

Fig. 6-11 Saddle reef, Deborah mine, Bendigo, Australia. (*After Stillwell, 1953.*)

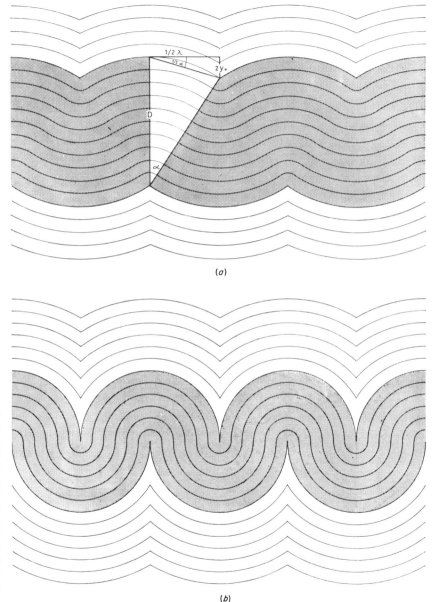

Fig. 6-12 Ideal concentric folds consisting of circular arcs. D is the maximum thickness of the portion of the complex which consists of ideal concentric folds not affected by shortening and thickening of the layers. All layers within the region D have identical length of arc along a complete run from crest to crest. D increases with increasing wavelength if the amplitude y_0 remains constant, but decreases with increasing y_0 if λ remains constant. Compare (a) and (b). (*From Ramberg, 1963b.*)

(Fig. 6-12) the thickness of the units, measured as nearly perpendicular to bedding surfaces as possible, remains essentially uniform with depth, the shape of bedding surfaces changes at successively greater depths in the structure. A method for constructing such parallel folds is described in Appendix A. One of the consequences of this change in the shape of the structure with depth is that at a certain depth the folding dies out. Parallel folds or folds approximating this

Fig. 6-13 Décollement in disharmonic folds of the Besa River formation, British Columbia. (*Photo courtesy of E. L. Fitzgerald.*)

geometry are encountered in nature, and almost always the folding dies out at depth and is underlain by relatively undeformed units. The top surface of the undeformed portion of the section is usually a plane of detachment above which folding has taken place, with the result that material from the bed directly above the detachment has moved into the anticlines and away from the synclines (Fig. 6-13). *Décollements* of this type are known in the Jura Mountains (Chap. 12), in the Rockies (Chap. 14), and in the foreland fold belts of many of the world's young folded mountains. Usually the detachment takes place in an incompetent rock type such as salt, shale, mudstone, gypsum or in one of the less consolidated members of the sequence.

The geometry of the situation described above is sufficient evidence to rule out local vertical movements from below the undeformed layers as the cause of folding, and it supports strongly the view of deformation caused by shallow, lateral stresses.

7. *Change in structure with depth.* In folds which show evidence of extension over the hinge, there may be marked change in the structure of beds lower in the sequence, in tighter portions of the fold. Just as the upper surface of such a bed may have been extended, the lower surface may show features arising from compression, from forcing material together in the hinge zone. This portion of such a fold is especially prone to complicated structure if a competent unit, one which has tended to maintain its coherence through the deformation, is underlain by incompetent units, or especially thin bedded units of alternating lithology. In this case small thrust faults and complicated folding, as a result of the movement of material toward the hinge of the larger fold, may be apparent (Fig. 6-48).

8. *Wedging* (Ernst Cloos, 1964) *of beds on*

the limbs and in the hinge of folds. This condition (Fig. 6-14) arises through failure of a bed along a fracture surface, followed by displacements such that part of a unit is forced along its former lateral continuation. This is most commonly found in sequences composed of beds of alternating competence such as sandstones or quartzites interbedded with shale. This feature clearly indicates that the sense of movement in the portion of the fold on which it is found is parallel to the bedding surfaces.

9. *Drag.* When lithologies of varying physical character are interbedded, large-scale folds are frequently accompanied by smaller folds developed within the less competent layers as a result of drag produced by relative movements of one competent layer relative to the adjacent layer (Fig. 6-15). Such drag folds can be generated when large massive layers slide over weaker units down slopes, as found in some types of mass movement. They occur in folds where the layers are flexed so that couples are set up between layers (Fig. 6-16). This situation is characterized by certain geometrical features which are most useful in field work. The drags are asymmetrical toward the fold hinges on either side of the fold, and the axial planes of the drags are inclined toward the hinges of the major fold. Thus an outcrop may suffice to reveal the direction and approximate attitude of the major fold axial surface.

Caution must be exercised in the application of the above concept because reverse drag is also possible. The drags may be reversed, for example (Fig. 6-17), if the core of an anticline is moving upward relative to adjacent synclines. This type of drag is found most frequently in salt structures, where very plastic cores of domes or anticlines are involved, and it is also likely under metamorphic con-

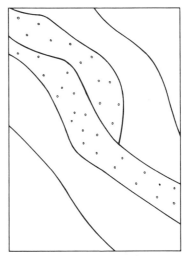

Fig. 6-14 Wedging traced from photograph of Harpers formation, Blue Ridge, Va.

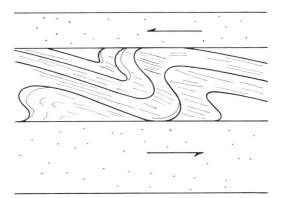

Fig. 6-15 Relationship between drag-type folds and the couple which produces them.

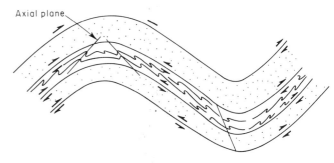

Fig. 6-16 Drag folds in concentrically folded sequence.

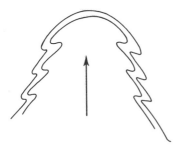

Fig. 6-17 Reverse drag schematic.

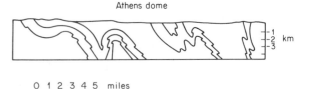

Athens dome

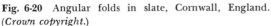

0 1 2 3 4 5 miles

Fig. 6-18 Reverse drag. Simplified from a cross section across the Connecticut Valley synclinorium on the Geologic Map of Vermont, 1961. (*After Doll and others, 1961.*)

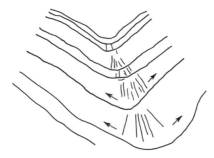

Fig. 6-19 Fractures in the hinge of a folded sequence of sandstones. Traced from a photograph; arrows indicate extension in hinge.

Fig. 6-20 Angular folds in slate, Cornwall, England. (*Crown copyright.*)

ditions (Fig. 6-18), where plasticity is apt to be more pronounced with depth, or where a clay or shale breaks upward and is injected through more brittle layers.

10. *Fractures along the hinge oriented approximately parallel to the hinge.* Such fractures are frequently found in the more brittle members of the folded sequence. These fractures may completely penetrate a unit, or they may be confined to the outer portion as shown in Fig. 6-19. These fracture sets may have a wedge-shaped fracture filling. The orientation and shape of the fracture is indicative of extension in the hinge, with extension taking place as shown by the arrows and causing failure through tension fracturing. Another common characteristic of such fracture sets is their fan-shaped pattern.

11. *Angular folds.* A single fracture may form along the axial surface of angular folds, a special type of parallel fold in which the limbs are nearly planar and intersect at a sharp angle (Fig. 6-20).

12. *Recrystallization.* Recrystallization of minerals in folds is associated with folds that have formed under high-grade metamorphic conditions. Of course, it should first be determined whether the fold formed before, during, or after the metamorphism. It is often a very difficult problem to distinguish premetamorphic and synmetamorphic structures from one

another because metamorphism is likely to destroy part of the premetamorphic structures through recrystallization. Postmetamorphic structures can be identified if the mechanism of the folding is incompatible with metamorphic conditions. For example, open fractures and other signs of brittle behavior are incompatible with high-grade metamorphic conditions. Fortunately, in this problem guidelines concerning the formation of certain common metamorphic minerals under stress conditions allow us to infer that the presence of particular minerals indicates particular stress conditions. If these minerals are present, it seems logical to assume that the folding took place during the recrystallization which caused the stress mineral to form. Common stress minerals are chloritoid and kyanite. Other minerals such as staurolite, mica, chlorite, talc, epidote, and amphiboles can form under stress but do not necessarily form in stress environments. Leucite, nepheline, sodalite, cancrinite, and scapolite are nonstress minerals and do not form in strong stress fields. Thermodynamic considerations in the reactions necessary to form these minerals have been considered in recent years by Mac-Donald (1957), Verhoogen (1951), and others.

In addition to the crystallization of stress minerals in structures such as folds, actual movement of materials may accompany folding and recrystallization. Fluids present during metamorphism can effect movement of ions from points of great stress to points of less stress. Thus migration of material may be accomplished within units in such a way as to reflect the variations in stress conditions through the units during folding.

13. *Thinning in the hinge.* This is a much rarer condition in folds than is thickening in the hinge. Thickening may result

(a)

(b)

(c)

Fig. 6-21 Folds in metamorphic rocks. (*a*) Note that folding does not involve layers at left. (*b*) Cross folding in gneiss. (*c*) Isoclinal fold with one limb completely thinned out.

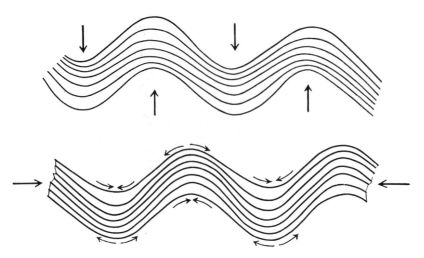

Fig. 6-22 Changes in thickness due to bending and buckling. *(From Ramberg, 1963b.)*

from apparent changes in thickness due to extension of the fold in the axial surface, or from movement of material toward and into the hinge of a fold from the limbs. Thinning may result from extension of material in a bed or from actual movement of material away from the hinge through flowage. Thinning might be expected over a diapiric-type fold. Ramberg (1963b) has depicted thickening and thinning due to buckling of layers that were originally of even thickness (Fig. 6-22).

Conclusions

It remains for us to determine which of the preceding structures occur together most frequently. Most of these various types of structures arise from movement either parallel to or across bedding planes. Structures, notably slip surfaces, tend to form across bedding planes where the bedding has not been active in controlling development of the fold. This condition is frequently found when the rock mass behaved as a relatively isotropic material during folding. Isotropic conditions may be expected in thick masses of salt or clay, in any rock type, and in sections of greatly different lithologies under metamorphic conditions. It should be emphasized here that the condition of isotropy is not fulfilled if there are planes of weakness in the rock mass. Thus a succession of beds of a single rock type will not behave as an isotropic mass if the bedding planes are open or if the strength of the rock across these planes is greatly different from that within the layers.

When the layering controls the fold development, movements parallel to the layering are most prominent. Wedging and drag are likely to occur when the section contains rocks of greatly different physical character. Changes within layers may be from top to bottom of a layer. Particularly within the hinges, fractures are likely in brittle materials over the hinge; thicknesses of more brittle layers are likely to remain nearly constant; thicknesses in ductile layers are likely to vary with migration of material toward fold hinges; saddle reefs may occur; marked changes in shape of the fold with depth are to be expected; and detachment surfaces are likely at depth.

FOLD MECHANISMS

The basic distinction between folds in which slip or shear across bedding dominates and those in which bedding controls deformation and material moves laterally within beds is reflected in the geometrical and genetic classifications. Differences in descriptions of the behavior of rocks in these two general classes of folds tend to reflect individual preferences in terminology more often than a difference of opinion regarding the essential mechanisms involved in the folding process. The problem is to select nomenclature which describes most precisely and accurately what we observe. This is often particularly difficult with folds, because interbedded layers with different physical properties are usually involved and these different layers may respond quite differently to the deformation depending on the conditions under which folding takes place. As a result, one layer in a sequence may yield by flexure accommodated by fracturing and grain rotations, another by slip or breaks that are essentially parallel to bedding, another by lateral movement of material that may be accomplished by complex folding and faulting within that bed, and yet another by development of closely spaced slip surfaces that are essentially parallel to the axial plane of the fold. Whether one of these mechanisms dominates folding or whether each partially influences the deformation is a function of many factors. Donath (1963) groups these factors into two classes:

1. The nature of inherent anisotropy in the rocks
2. The ductilities of the involved rocks

Anisotropies can arise from preexisting structures, bed thicknesses, primary structures of beds, variations laterally and up and down the stratigraphic section in physical properties or primary structure, and variations in thicknesses.

Ductility, by definition, and *competence,* as known by experience, are functions of the physical condition of the rock masses during folding. The physical condition includes the effects of temperature, of confining pressure, of presence or absence of fluids, of the rate of strain, and of the manner of stress application. If the ductility of the rocks in a section being folded is very high throughout, the individual layers should not play a major role in determining the deformation (passive folding), but if the ductility of layers varies greatly, then layers of low ductility may be expected to deform by flexure, whereas those of high ductility accommodate themselves within the space available between the more competent layers. The relation of fields of folding to the mean ductility and the extent of ductility contrast have been discussed by Donath and Parker (1963) (Fig. 6-23). From this plot of ductility contrast against mean ductility we see that:

1. A sequence of low mean ductility deforms through flexural slip.
2. A sequence of high mean ductility deforms by passive folding if the ductility contrast is low, but if the ductility contrast is high, then flexure of the low ductility members may dominate, producing quasi-flexural folds.
3. If there is a low ductility contrast, the fold type depends on the ductility of the sequence (which is a function of the physical conditions of the environment of folding differing with respect to temperature, confining pressure, etc.).

GENETIC FOLD CLASSIFICATION

Various systems of fold classification are in use at the present time, some of which are based solely on the fold shape or geometry. Terms which describe shape should not normally be used to connote the mechanism of folding, but some of them have become so closely as-

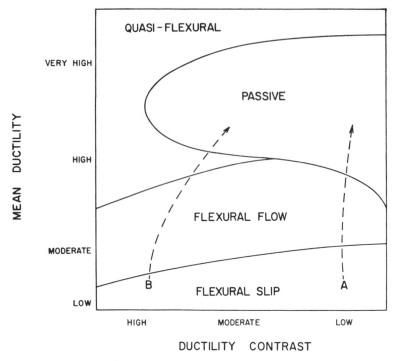

Fig. 6-23 Fields of folding related to mean ductility and ductility contrast. *(From Donath, 1963.)*

sociated with mechanisms of folding that they are used nearly synonymously. For example, the terms *parallel folding* and *concentric folding* connote folding by flexure in which the beds exercise a controlling influence on the development of the folds. *Similar folding,* on the other hand, is often taken to mean folding in which the development of and movement along slip surfaces which cut across the beds are the dominant processes of folding. Such folds are also known as *shear folds* because the mechanism of slippage involves the development of couples which bring about shear or slip along closely spaced cleavages. However, many folds of similar geometry do not show such cleavages or slip surfaces (Fig. 6-24), and even more frequently, slip surfaces are well developed in incompetent layers but the slips do not cross competent layers. A mechanism that seems to apply consists of buckling of the

competent layers with development of slip oriented to bring about thickening in the hinge within incompetent layers (Fig. 6-25).

A third category of folds, also a flow-fold type, is found less frequently. These folds form under conditions which permit flow of the rock, but flowage is not laminar and is not accomplished by movements on closely spaced slip surfaces. Highly irregular forms develop, sometimes called *irregular flow folds.*

To avoid some of the problems involved in the use of such terms as *shear, concentric, flow,* and *ptygmatic,* Donath and Parker (1963) proposed a classification of folds, based on the mechanisms of folding, of three major classes—*flexural, passive,* and *quasi-flexural.* The first two of these classes are subdivided into flexural slip and flow, and passive slip and flow. The basic distinction between flexural and passive folds is whether or not the bedding actively con-

(a)

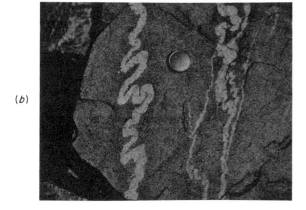

(b)

(c)

Fig. 6-24 (a) Similar-type folds which do not possess slip surfaces parallel to the axial surface; (b) ptygmatic fold; (c) similar-type folds in gneiss.

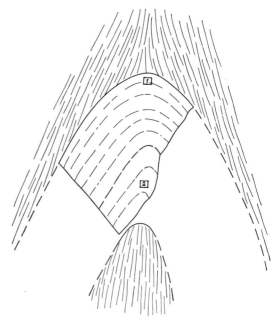

Fig. 6-25 Part of folded quartzite layer sandwiched between mica schist. Schistosity in mica schist indicated by short lines. The short conformable lines in the quartzite represent original layering as indicated by concentrations of mica. (*From Ramberg, 1963b.*)

trols the development of the folds. The types within each of these categories are then distinguished by whether the basic mechanism, within layers for flexural folds or through layers for passive folds, was *slip* along macroscopically discontinuous surfaces, or *flow movements* that do not cause permanent loss of cohesion. The third class, quasi-flexural, is described as follows:*

Under certain conditions individual layers within a folded sequence may be flexed in response to passive behavior in the associated rocks. This relationship represents a gradational class of folding, particularly characteristic in rocks of moderate to high ductility, that is here called quasi-flexural; the geometry and more obvious features of the fold are flexural in general aspect, but the over-all behavior is predominantly passive.

* Donath and Parker (1963).

PTYGMATIC FOLDS

Ptygmatic folds such as those illustrated in Fig. 6-24*b* are among the most curious structures known. Their unusual meandering shape and their changes of thickness, as well as their apparently random orientations relative to other structures, have attracted considerable attention and caused much debate over their origin since Sederholm (1907, 1913) first described them as resulting from movements in rock mobilized by partial melting.

The name *ptygmatic* is applied to a variety of folds which have in common primarily a meandering cross-sectional pattern, but they generally share numerous other features, according to Godfrey (1954). They are found in metamorphic or "granitized" complexes in which at least partial remobilization has occurred. Usually the ptygmatic folds are in veins composed largely of quartz and feldspar which is more coarsely crystalline than the enclosing rocks. A few instances of ptygmatically folded basic veins are known, but these seem to be exceptions. The folded veins do not show internal evidence of brittle fracture or cataclasis, but internal directed structures suggesting internal flow may be found. If there are neighboring veins they usually have harmonious structural relationships with one another, but usually the contact zone of the vein with the country rock shows some deformation.

The question whether all ptygmatic veins originate as a result of the same structural and metamorphic conditions or whether they form through a variety of circumstances is a difficult one to answer. Several convincing arguments have been advanced with corroborating field observations, theory, and experimental results to explain the mode of origin. That these observations and other evidence appear valid strengthens the argument for multiple mechanisms. Two main classes of mechanism have been advanced. The first of these attributes the folds to a passive response of a vein to movements within the country rock at some time after the vein has been emplaced; in this case the folding is secondary. In the second class, folds are attributed to processes acting during emplacement of the vein.

The variety of opinion is clearly shown in the writings of Read, Buddington, Wilson, Kuenen, Ramberg, and Godfrey. Read (1928) states that the "tortuous form results from the resistance to plane fissuring of the country-rock . . . the veins have their original form; they were never plane . . ." and they are "true igneous injections, showing no metamorphic characters." Thus he concludes that the essential physical condition for the formation of ptygmatically folded veins is the "injection into structureless country-rock not readily giving plane fissures."

Buddington (1939) concluded in his study of the Adirondacks that there are two types: one formed similarly to Read's description and the other conformable with plications in the containing schist, for which he concluded that "the injection of the pegmatite occurred in folded rocks during a period of active deformation. Plastic flowage of country-rock and both plastic and magmatic flowage of pegmatite is involved."

Wilson (1952) came to conclusions similar to those of Read: "Those other even more tortuous veins of primary origin, which might be said to be ptygmatic 'in their own right,' and owe their form to their own injection processes." The required physical conditions are that "the country-rock, at the time and place of intrusion, was more mobile than the magmatic material of the veins themselves. The contortions were thus formed by plastic buckling of the vein due to magmatic pressure from behind, with the concomitant displacement of yielding contiguous host-rock."

Kuenen (1938), Ramberg (1959), and others have held the view that ptygmatic folds are secondary and develop under compressive stresses. Ramberg (1959, p. 100) clearly states his reasoning as follows:

. . . He has found no reason to doubt that this striking structure essentially is caused by a component of shortening in host rocks parallel to originally more or less planar veins. Most arguments against this view are probably due to lack of obvious strain features in many ptygmatic veins. This fact, however, only shows that the deformation takes place under somewhat different conditions (greater plasticity or slower strain rate) than those existing under evolution of rocks commonly accepted as tectonites. . . . At the proper difference in competency between vein and host rock—the vein must be somewhat more competent than the host—the vein can only adjust to plastic compressive strain in the host rock by a folding mechanism, provided the vein is properly oriented in relations to the strain geometry of the host rock. . . . Plastic compression along some directions in rock complexes must be associated with simultaneous extensions in directions that make large angles to the compression, provided that volume remains essentially constant during strain. Relatively competent sheets of rocks which make large angles with direction of maximum compression will therefore develop tension fractures or necked-down regions. One should consequently expect boudinage and pinch-and-swell structures to be associated with ptygmatic structures in the field as unseparably as extensive strain is associated with compressive strain in plastic deformation at constant volume. Kuenen 1938, p. 23 notes such field association between stretching and ptygmatic folds. Field experience of the present writer supports this expectation: pinch-and-swell structure of quartz-feldspar veins or boudinage structure of other competent sheet-shaped rocks are generally so intimately associated with ptygmatic structures in the field that a complementary relationship of the kind mentioned above is strongly suggested.

Godfrey (1954) studied ptygmatic structures in an area of the Yukon where coarsely crystalline quartz veins occur in foliated quartzites and schists. Sercite and graphite in the foliation of the country rock were found to continue into and sometimes through the veins. Where the veins were thickened, he found concentrated chlorite and graphite, suggesting growth of the

vein through metamorphism. He concluded that:

> It seems clear that the formation of the ptygmatic folds involved: (1) formation of a coarsely crystalline vein, either cross-cutting or parallel to original bedding or schistosity, by growth in the solid state, involving replacement, recrystallization, and concretionary growth, with development of schistosity in the host rock; and (2) continuous deformation of a plastic, relatively competent "vein" under compressive or shearing forces, while the stress was taken up by viscous flow and shearing in the foliation planes of the host rock.

GEOMETRY OF FOLDS

Fold geometry is described in terms of the changes which are produced in some marker horizon (usually bedding) and our attention is focused on aspects of the process which involve layering. However, as is forcefully brought out by Fig. 6-7, movements parallel to the markers may easily escape our notice. Such movements may be detected through the presence of slip surfaces, slickensides, and changes in thickness within beds, but they may be much more difficult to detect than the same amount of movement transverse to the bedding.

The methods used to study and analyze folds depend to some extent on the size of the folds and the presence or absence of good marker horizons suitable for mapping. Large folds which contain good marker horizons are usually defined by geologic mapping techniques (Fig. 6-5), and their shape is described through use of graphic representations such as structure contour maps (Fig. 6-4), isopach maps, and constructed cross sections. These are described in Appendix A.

During the last two decades, increasing attention has been given to analysis of mesoscopic and microscopic folds in metamorphic terrane and in regions of thick sedimentary sections lacking good mapping horizons. It happens, of course, that such terranes are often either Precambrian or in the younger orogenic belts where deformational history is long, complex, and often involves repeated deformations. Conventional mapping techniques have lacked the resolution needed to define these structural features, and new geometrical techniques have been employed.

Basically, the new methods involve careful collection of large samples of geometrical data on the attitude in space of s surfaces, lineations, and detailed notation of the relations of the various geometrical features to one another in the single outcrop, followed by a comparison from one outcrop to another. The observed data are examined and compared with the statistical distribution of attitudes of points on selected simple hypothetical geometrical models.

Fold Models—Cylindrical and Conical Folds

The form of large portions of many folds can be closely approximated by cylindrical or conic sections. These two shapes can be formed by the rotation of a line. In the case of the cylindrical fold, the line is rotated parallel to itself around a point at a fixed distance from the point. A conical fold is generated by rotating a line, one end of which is fixed. In map view a plunging cylindrical fold and a conical fold are similar, but the two can be distinguished if there is enough geometrical data. The most convenient way to handle these data is to plot them on an equal-area projection as a point diagram. Points representing a large sample of

bedding attitudes taken from all parts of a fold will fall approximately along a great circle in cylindrical folding, and a line can be drawn through the clustering of points to define that great circle. The axis of the fold is the line perpendicular to the great circle, a pie circle; and the attitude, bearing, and plunge of the axis can be directly measured from the equal-area plot (Fig. 6-26) (see Appendix B). The geometry of a conical fold is such that a point diagram of strike and dip measurements on it lie on an arc other than a great circle (Fig. 6-27). The distribution of the sample of data points on the fold is of critical importance in interpretation of point diagrams. It is generally assumed that the sample is evenly distributed across the fold. If this condition is met in the case of a cylindrical fold, the great circles defined by attitude measurements will be uniformly developed, but if a large part of the sample is collected on any one part of the fold the corresponding part of the great circle will appear as a maximum.

From the character of point diagrams constructed from data collected at random over a folded structure, it follows that:

1. Curvilinear folds will tend to be represented by a fairly uniform distribution of points along the great or small circle, and angular folds will be represented by isolated maxima.

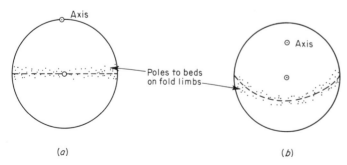

(a)   (b)

Fig. 6-26 Stereographic plots of cylindrical folds (a) with horizontal axis and (b) plunging.

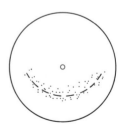

Fig. 6-27 Stereographic projection of a conical fold.

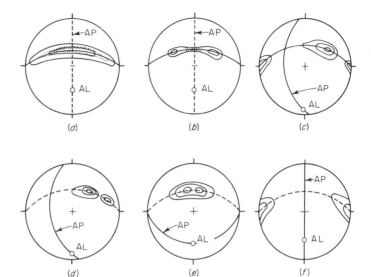

Fig. 6-28 Geometry of some ideal cylindrical folds. AP = axial plane, AL = axial line. Contours (schematic) are of points plotted on lower hemisphere projection. (a) Open fold of uniform curvature; (b) open fold with plane limbs; (c) asymmetrical fold; (d) overturned fold; (e) recumbent fold; (f) isoclinal fold. (*After Dahlstrom, 1954.*)

2. If the radius of hinge curvature is great, there will usually be more points located on the hinge region, and it will be better defined.

3. In the case of an ideal cylindrical fold the axial surface is a great circle which contains the axial line and a point on the pole circle within the crestal scatter pattern and midway between the limb maxima (Dahlstrom, 1954).

4. The position of the axis (using the concept of the axis as a generator line) is defined by the line of intersection, β, of any two planes tangent to a cylinder or cone. The attitude of such a tangent plane is what we measure when the strike and dip of a bed are determined at a point on a fold. Because such measurements are liable to be in error, the line β is most reliable when it is determined by use of data from many points on the fold. If the positions of the successively determined β points (the point of intersection of the line with the hemisphere on the projection is called a β point) are not close, the fold is noncylindrical.

5. The appearances of point diagrams of ideal cylindrical folds are shown in Fig. 6-28 for cases in which the folds are open, isoclinal, asymmetric, overturned, and recumbent.

Similar and Concentric Folds

Charles van Hise (1896) proposed the terms *similar* and *concentric* (also *parallel*) to describe two strongly contrasted fold geometrics, and this usage is still popular. An ideal concentric fold is characterized by the following geometry: (1) The true thickness of the beds, measured perpendicular to bedding, remains constant. (2) The thickness of beds varies considerably with position on the fold when measured parallel to the fold axis. A method for constructing parallel folds is given in Appendix A. One consequence of the uniform-thickness requirement is that the fold shape must change with depth. A cylindrical anticline at one level first is transformed into a cusp and then dies out at depth. Ideal similar folds maintain their shape with depth, but the true thickness of the beds is highly variable from point to point along the fold. Compare the two ideal cases in Fig. 6-29. Most similar folds have strongly developed planar structure oriented

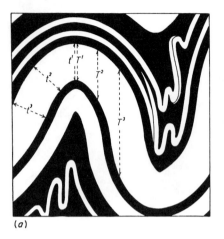 

(a)   (b)

Fig. 6-29 Geometrical features of (a) ideal flexure folds and (b) similar folds. (*From Ramsay, 1962a.*)

approximately parallel to the axial surface. These planes are due to mineral orientation or to fractures and cleavages, and they constitute one of the lines of evidence which point to origin of the folds through a slip-type or laminar-flow-type mechanism. These slip surfaces penetrate through successive layers in the fold, indicating that the individual layers did not exercise much control on the development of the fold form. The layers were passive. Concentric folds, on the other hand, are almost always found in sedimentary piles of varying lithology, and the different types of layers show evidence of quite different mechanisms of yield. Shales, for example, may exhibit a well-developed cleavage (fracture or mineral orientation) more or less parallel to the axial surface in the hinge of the fold, while coarser clastics do not. The individual layers in concentric folding are effective in controlling the deformation.

Although the pattern defined by any layer in a case of ideal similar folding by slip or laminar-flow mechanism may be intricate in cross section, the restoration of the layer is simple. The flow lines are parallel to the axial surface of the fold, and the volume of material of a given layer between any two flow lines is

the same as that in the restored layer between the same two lines.

Concentric folding presents several problems more difficult than those of similar folding. While individual beds may be isotropic, the folded pile usually contains layers of markedly different character, different layers deform by different mechanisms, the folds die out at depth, and movements parallel to bedding are dominant. The more competent (less ductile) beds control the folding, and the less competent layers are sites of accommodating movements. The more ductile layers may have an intricate fold pattern, not reflected above or below, that results from these intralayer movements.

What happens laterally and at depth in concentrically folded sequences can be debated on geometrical grounds. Not only is the thickness of layers constant, but the length of beds in portions of a concentric fold remains constant (Fig. 6-12). Various solutions have been devised to explain this. If the folded layers are envisioned as a compressional feature in which each bed is shortened by the same amount, the bed thicknesses and lengths may be maintained by intricate crumpling and faulting within the cores of the anticlines combined with detachment of the folded beds from the underlying unfolded strata. The volume of the shortened mass is present as an elevated volume over the anticline.

BUCKLING AND BENDING

The terms *buckle fold* and *bending fold* are often used informally in an essentially synonymous sense, but Hills (1953) has distinguished them as two fold types, and Ramberg (1963) pointed out some geometrical and mechanical differences between the two. Buckle folds occur when the layered rock mass is subjected to compression oriented parallel to the layering. Folding occurs if the layers are not physically isotropic and they shear along lines that are more or less parallel to the compression. In the case of bending folds, anisotropy of layers is unimportant and the force causing the bend acts essentially perpendicular to the layers, (Fig. 6-22).

These two types of folds may be distinguished as follows (Ramberg, 1963b):

1. Shortening of a buckled layer tends to form in a direction parallel to the original position of the layer and normal to the fold axis. This shortening may be recognized by such features as strained fossils, boulders, oolites, schistosity, rotated minerals, and *boudins.*

2. Contact strain in a buckle fold tends to die out rapidly up and down. Bending folds do not show a symmetrical distribution of contact strain. If fold amplitude decreases on one side of a sinuously folded layer, it must increase away from the layer in the opposite direction.

3. Before buckling can occur in a single enclosed layer, the competency of that layer must be greater than that of the enclosing layers. Competency contrast is not important in bending.

4. The changes in thickness of originally evenly thick layers is opposite in the cases of bending and buckling (Fig. 6-22).

REAL FOLDS

Concentric and similar folds represent end members in our spectrum of fold types; most real folds lie somewhere between. Shortening of the folded layers is an inherent part of concentric folding. Similar folding can occur without any shortening of layers. Among real folds some intermediate fold types are very common (Figs. 6-30 to 6-32). One of these is the similar-type fold in which the layer thicknesses are not exactly uniform measured parallel to the axial surface, and another is the similar-type fold in which form is not exactly reproduced from layer to layer. When layers of very different ductility are involved, the slip surfaces may be well developed in the shales (phyllites, schists, etc.) but not in interbedded sandstones (quartzites, granitic layers, etc.). These types of intermediate folds have a geometry which is suggestive of concentric folding of the more competent layers accompanied by movement within the less competent layers to produce thickening of hinges, thinning of limbs, and at some stage foliation subparallel to the axial surface.

Classic examples of concentric folds are frequently chosen from the Appalachian Valley and Ridge province, where thick Paleozoic sequences of sandstone and quartzite alternating with shales are thrown into folds tens of miles long and with thousands of feet of wave length and height. These folds have geometrics which closely approximate those of concentric folds, but they are so large that their shape at depth is uncertain.

The best examples of similar folds are found in metamorphic rocks, in salt structures, and in clays. They are most likely to form when the rock is behaving as a relatively isotropic material. This is most likely to occur either when the rock is a uniform mass of low competence or is ductile or when conditions of temperature

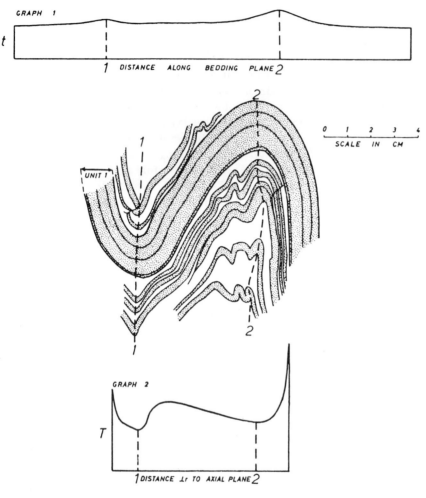

Fig. 6-30 Flexure folds in siltstone with coarse competent bands stippled and fine incompetent bands unornamented. The axial planes of the main folds (1 and 2) are shown as dashed lines. Measurements of the thickness of unit 1, *t*, normal to the bedding planes and its thickness *T* parallel to the axial plane have been graphically recorded. (*From Ramsay, 1962a.*)

and confining pressure reduce the contrast. Even under conditions of high-grade regional metamorphism, different lithologies are apt to retain some differences, which may explain why so many folds that are almost similar are not ideal in their shape. Very rarely can a fold shape be precisely traced downward more than a few feet in folds of similar type.

Flattening of Folds

Ramsay (1962a) concluded that some of the departures from ideal thicknesses could be explained in terms of a flattening of the fold. "Flattening is defined as the process of deformation whereby the original rock shape is plastically changed by compression. This compression results in contraction in a direction

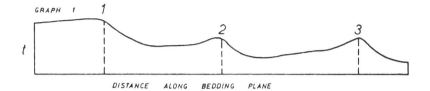

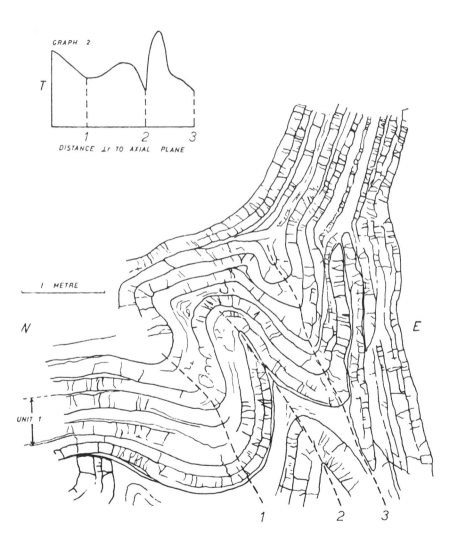

Fig. 6-31 Flexure folds in Cretaceous limestone at Val du Fier, French Jura. The thickness of one limestone bed, unit 1, *t*, measured normal to the bedding planes and its thickness *T* measured in a direction parallel to the axial planes of the folds are recorded in graphs 1 and 2, respectively. (*From Ramsay, 1962a.*)

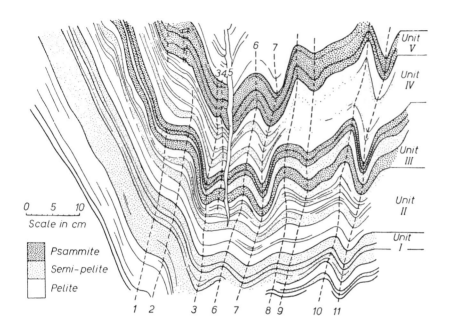

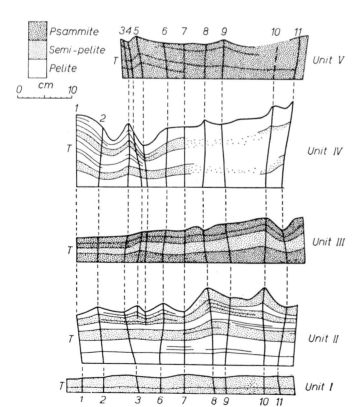

Fig. 6-32 A group of minor folds of similar type in metamorphosed strata from the Moine series of the Scottish Highlands; changes in thickness T in the various folded rock units. (*From Ramsay, 1962a.*)

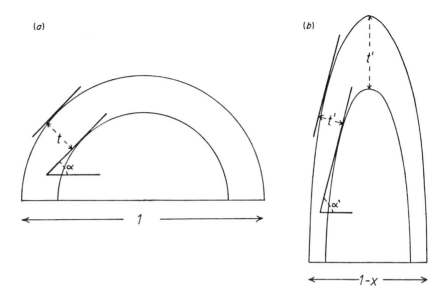

Fig. 6-33 (*a*) A bed of thickness *t* folded by a concentric flexure. (*b*) The geometry of the bed is modified by flattening (*x*): the angle of dip at any point within the flexure is increased (α to α'), and the thickness of the beds is altered (*t* to *t'*). (*From Ramsay, 1962a.*)

parallel to the principal compressive stress and in expansion at right angles to this. . . ." (Ramsay, 1962a.) If a concentric fold is flattened as shown in Fig. 6-33, both the thickness and the dip of the bed at any corresponding points on the fold will change. The amount of change is systematic over the fold and the changes are a measure of the flattening. Flattening curves defined by the relationship between angle of dip and thickness have been calculated (Fig. 6-34) for various percentages of flattening. It is possible by making several measurements of the angle and thickness at different points on a profile of a fold to plot the points on the graph, see which curve they fit, and thereby estimate the percentage of flattening.

Superposed Folds

Recognition of many instances of superposed folds has been one of the results of the application of the new geometrical approaches to

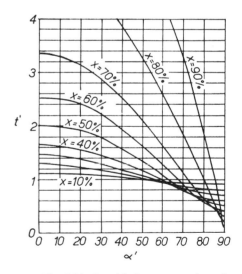

Fig. 6-34 Graphical representation of the change of α' and *t'* with increasing flattening *x*, the original thickness of the beds before flattening, *t*, taken as unity. (*From Ramsay, 1962a.*)

fold analysis, and of increased study of the structure of metamorphic terranes. Two or more superposed folds are perhaps more common than the occurrence of a single fold system in deformed metamorphic rocks. Sometimes these superposed structural features are the result of two distinctly different events as in the case of an early deformation while the rock was semiconsolidated followed by a much later event which took place under conditions of regional metamorphism. Phyllites and schist commonly show an earlier fold system of similar-type folds and a later imposed system of kink folds. Small-scale similar-type folds are also often found in combination with much larger open, cylindrical, or conical folds.

The presence of two fold systems of different character, different geometry, or different trend does not necessarily mean that two separate deformational phases or events took place. Small drag folds are commonly developed during concentric folding on the limbs of larger folds, and small reverse drags are associated with diapiric structures which may have fold form.

Superposed folds may also result from a single deformational event if the deformation is nonaffine. *Affine deformation* is defined as that which proceeds in such a way that lines and planes that existed before deformation are transformed into new lines and planes, but these are not curved in the process. As an example of conditions leading to nonaffine deformation, we might envision a sedimentary basin being deformed in response to a lateral pressure which initially results in formation of a long series of folds. If there is an obstacle in the basin it could have a buttressing effect, causing retardation of the folds along its front and breaking up the orderly fold pattern. We might also envision a region of block faulting in which sedimentary basins are surrounded by basement blocks. If the blocks were moved toward the basin from different directions, an interference fold pattern could easily result.

Within metamorphic piles, cross folding can be introduced as a result of variations in lithologies, as a result of thermal gradients, or as a result of the presence of fluids which cause local variations in the ductility of the rock and its rate of flow. No doubt many superposed folds are a product of changes in the direction of movement in response to changes in the orientation of the stress field, either locally or regionally, during a single period of deformation. If the type of folding and the orientation of directions of movement alone are considered, a large number of possible types of superposition is possible. A partial list will serve to illustrate:

1. Similar-type folds superposed on similar folds with common orientation of slip planes
2. Similar folds superposed on older similar folds with different orientation of slip planes
3. Concentric folds superposed on concentric folds of the same and different orientation of axial surfaces
4. Similar folds superposed on concentric folds with the same and different orientation of axial surfaces
5. Concentric folds superposed on similar folds
6. Kink folds superposed on similar or concentric folds, etc.

It is not difficult to recognize superposed deformation, but it may be impossible to establish the sequence of events or to distinguish two separated phases of deformation from cross folds which are a product of a single event. Culminations and depressions across fold belts constitute a large-scale type of cross folding. On a smaller scale superposed deformations may be recognized where folds of different trends occur in the same area. Not infrequently the crossing of one fold through another is exposed (Fig. 6-21b). Superposed deformation may

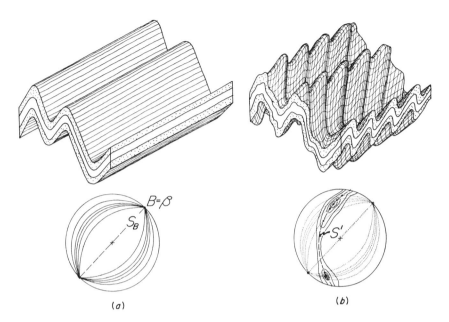

Fig. 6-35 Geometry of superposition of later folds (axes β') on earlier cylindroidal folds (axes β). (*From Weiss, 1959b.*)

sometimes be detected from study of point diagrams of bedding, foliation, lineations, and fold axis data, but it is difficult to generalize the appearance of these point diagrams because there are so many variables. The appearance of the point diagrams obtained by measuring foliations and lineations within a field of superposed folds depends on type of first-generation folds (flexural slip, etc.) and their geometry (cylindrical, etc.; orientation in space; and size); type of second-generation folds and their geometry; relative sizes of the two fold systems; and location of the sample of data.

As an example of superposed fold systems, consider the earlier generation of cylindrical folds with horizontal axes and vertical axial surfaces S_B, which is shown distorted by a second-generation fold system in Fig. 6-35. The original slip surfaces S, the line of their intersection β, and the fold axes of the first-generation folds are shown in a stereographic diagram in Fig. 6-35a. The axial surfaces S' of

the second generation of folds are subparallel, but the resulting axes of the second-generation folds β' do not intersect in a point. They do, however, lie within the axial surfaces S' of the second-generation folds, and they are oriented parallel to the intersection of S and S' in any given part of the field of folding. The axes of the second-generation folds will tend to be concentrated in two clusters as shown in Fig. 6-35b, because the limbs of the first-generation folds do constitute a preferred orientation of S. The concentrations would be even more prominent if the limbs of the first-generation folds had been more planar. The axes of the first-generation folds are dispersed as a result of the rotation which took place during the second folding. When the whole field of folding is considered as in this diagram these first-generation axes are so dispersed that they do not show up at all.

The geometry of superposed fold systems is reviewed in Weiss and McIntyre (1957), Weiss

Fig. 6-36 Unfolding two generations of similar-type folds. (*From Carey, 1962.*)

(1959b), Turner and Weiss (1963), Whitten (1966), and Ramsay (1967).

Determination of Sequence in Superposed Deformations

Evidence of sequence in superposed folds may be found in such key observations as the following:

1. If small-scale folds occurring on larger folds have similar geometrics (axes are parallel, etc.) their development was probably synchronous.
2. If slip surfaces (also foliation in many cases) are folded into angular folds (i.e., kink folds) the angular folds are younger.
3. If similar folds are developed through a

metamorphic rock before a later phase of concentric folding, the direction of asymmetry of the small folds will not change on passing over the hinge of the later folds, but the direction of asymmetry will reverse over hinges of major folds if the minor folds are related to drag movements accompanying formation of the large folds.

4. Slip surfaces are very important indicators. If two generations of similar folds formed by movement on slip surfaces are superposed, the slip surfaces of the older movement will be folded, and the younger slips will be straight. If slip surfaces are parallel to the form of a concentric fold, then either the slips are earlier or they developed as part of the movement ac-

Table 6-1 Classification of Superposed Similar Folds

Strikes	Directrices	Composite symmetry	Pattern
Parallel	Common	Orthorhombic	Overprinting not deducible topologically
Parallel	Oblique	Monoclinic	Hooked patterns, antiformal synclines, and synformal anticlines
Orthogonal	Common	Orthorhombic	Orthogonal domes and basins
Oblique	Common	Monoclinic	Echelon domes and basins, sigmoidal fold axes
Orthogonal	Oblique	Monoclinic	Heart, trident, and anchor patterns
Oblique	Oblique	Triclinic	Skewed heart, trident, and anchor patterns

Source: Carey (1962).

companying development of the concentric fold (see item 3). If similar folds follow concentric folds, the slip surfaces are unfolded.

5. If metamorphism is involved at some stage, the folds may be identified as pre-, syn-, or postmetamorphic, and other conventional means of establishing sequence such as use of intrusions or vein filling may be available.

Carey (1962) has given particular attention to the superposition of one type of similar fold on another. He treats similar folds characterized by slip or laminar-type flow on closely spaced slip surfaces as representing the most common type of fold in metamorphic rocks when they are behaving as nearly isotropic masses. Figure 6-36 shows an example in which a set of similar folds has been modified by later movement

which was also characterized by similar folding. The two sets of similar folds have the same strike, but different attitudes. A cross-sectional sketch is shown at the top. In making restoration the individual layers are identified and traced out, and the axes of symmetry of the most obvious folds are determined. One set of the axes of symmetry is subparallel (about vertical in the drawing), the second set is a sinuous set extending across the diagram. By straightening the axes of symmetry of the folded folds (accomplished by moving points parallel to the axial surfaces of the second set of axes of symmetry), the effects of the second movement are removed; and by doing the same along the now restored first set of axes of symmetry, the bedding is restored to its original form. A classification of superposed similar folds (Table 6-1) and the resulting patterns is made by Carey.

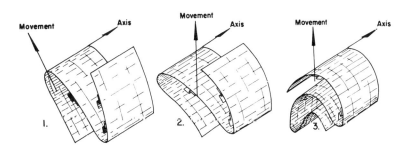

Fig. 6-37 Successive stages of the development of folded folds in unsteady flow by a change in the direction of movement. (*From Wynne-Edwards, 1963.*)

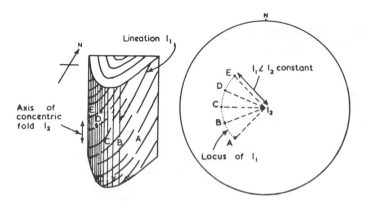

Fig. 6-38 The deformation of an originally rectilinear structure I_1 lying on a surface folded in a concentric manner. In the stereogram, parts of the great circles representing the orientations of the surface at various positions A, B, C, D, and E on the fold have been constructed (dashed lines) together with the location of the I_1 structure at these points. The partial small-circle locus of I_1 is indicated by a dotted line. (*From Ramsay, 1960.*)

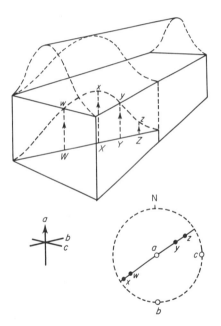

Fig. 6-39 Diagram illustrating the deformation of lineations by similar folding. (*From Ramsay, 1960.*)

Changes in Early Linear Features in Superposed Folds

One fruitful approach to analysis of superposed folds is to consider the way existing linear structural features are modified. Such linear features may be earlier fold axes, mineral lineation, slickensides, etc. Figure 6-38 shows a layered sequence folded by simple concentric folding.

Note that the lineation on the top layer has been deformed, but that the angle between the earlier linear features and the direction of the axis of the fold is constant. Compare this situation with that illustrated in Fig. 6-39, where the lineation is shown deformed by passive slip folding with slip on surfaces parallel to the axial plane. The line defined by W, X, Y, and Z is folded to form the line w, x, y, and z. On the stereographic plot, note that the points all lie in a single plane. The orientation of that plane is governed by the original orientation of the lineation and the direction of tectonic transport during folding. The positions of w, x, y, and z after deformation are shown by points which indicate the plunge of the lineation in the stereogram.

With the preceding background, it should be possible to detect and analyze geometrically superposed folding where lineations are present. Ramsay (1960) has summarized the analysis of different stereogram patterns where an original lineation l_1 has been recognized and a large sample plotted (Table 6-2).

Refolding at Loch Leven, Scotland—An Example

The structural geometry of massive quartzites interbedded with mica schists in a portion of the Scottish Highlands provides a good example of the application of the geometrical techniques in an area of superposed folding (Weiss and McIntyre, 1957). A summary map of the area in Fig. 6-40 shows contoured point diagrams of s surfaces. The regional foliation, termed S, is the most prominent set of structural surfaces in the area, but bedding forms S in the more massive quartzites. S is folded about gently to moderately plunging axes; folds are recumbent. Weiss and McIntyre called these B folds, and they occur on all scales; their limbs are thinned sometimes to zero leaving hinges of quartzite floating in schists; the axial surfaces of many dip gently to the west or northwest; a secondary foliation S_1 is present in some folds and is parallel to the axial plane; the secondary foliation is found in places to become the most prominent and eventually the only foliation. The B folds have a general west-northwest axial trend and are cylindroidal where unaffected by later folding, and many possess a mineral lineation parallel to the axes. Where no B folds are present and S is planar, the lineation persists, and at other places rodlike bodies parallel this direction.

The second generation of structures includes folds with northeast-southwest axial trends which plunge moderately to steeply to the southwest, B^1 folds, and a secondary planar foliation orientated parallel or subparallel to the axial surfaces of the B^1 folds.

Criteria for distinguishing the B and B^1 folds are: (1) Axial surfaces of B^1 folds are vertical irrespective of plunge of the axes. (2) B^1 folds are similar folds with straight limbs. (3) B^1 folds tend to be symmetrical about their axial surfaces and parallel to adjacent folds.

B folds are prominent in subareas 7 to 11, 21, 26, 32, 33, 35, and 37 (Fig. 6-40). They are rare in subareas 20, 25, 28, and 31. S^1 is best developed in subareas 16, 17, 19, 25, 31, and 39. B and B^1 folds are found both together and isolated. The conditions of B fold dominate, B^1 fold dominant, and the two equally developed are figured schematically in Fig. 6-41.

THE OCCURRENCE OF FOLDS

What does the presence of a fold signify? In answering this question we are led to consider the variety of geological circumstances in which folds or fold systems are found. We must be cautious not to assume that the presence of folds means either strong crustal deformation, horizontal crustal shortening, or any other pat interpretation. Fold geometry, rock type, and particularly the relation of the fold to adjacent structural features provide clues to the way folding was generated.

Compression is one of the most obvious po-

Table 6-2   Geometrical Relations of Constantly Oriented Linear Structures l_2 and Variably Oriented Linear Structures l_1 (Stereogram Patterns)

l_1	Angle between l_1 and l_2	Axial planes of l_1 folds	Deduction
Partial small circle on stereogram (partial cone)	Constant	Poles on a small circle	Concentric folding of l_1 by l_2 folds
Arranged on a great circle (plane)	Variable	Poles on a great circle	Similar folding of l_1 by l_2 folds
Arranged on a great circle (plane)	Variable	Poles at a point maximum	Superimposed on initially variable surfaces; l_1 later than l_2
Difficult to place on either great or small circles	Variable	Poles on a great circle with some scatter	Compound folding (similar and concentric) of l_1 by l_2 folds

Source: From Ramsay (1960).

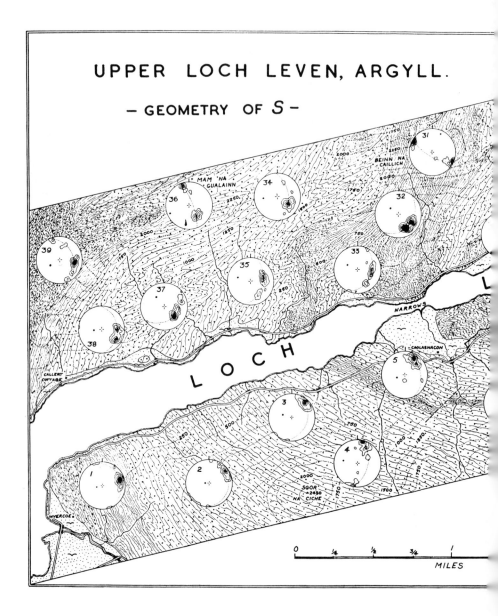

Fig. 6-40 Geometry of S. (*From Weiss and McIntyre, 1957.*)

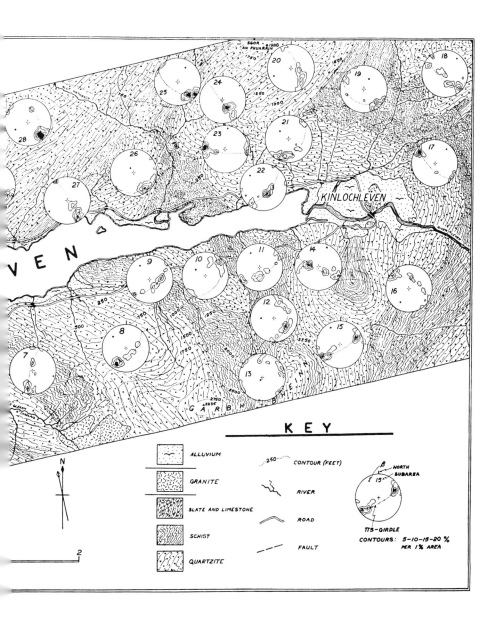

KINLOCHLEVEN

K E Y

ALLUVIUM

GRANITE

SLATE AND LIMESTONE

SCHIST

QUARTZITE

250 ········ CONTOUR (FEET)

RIVER

ROAD

FAULT

CONTOURS: 5-10-15-20 %
           PER 1% AREA

ππS-GIRDLE

NORTH
SUBAREA

N

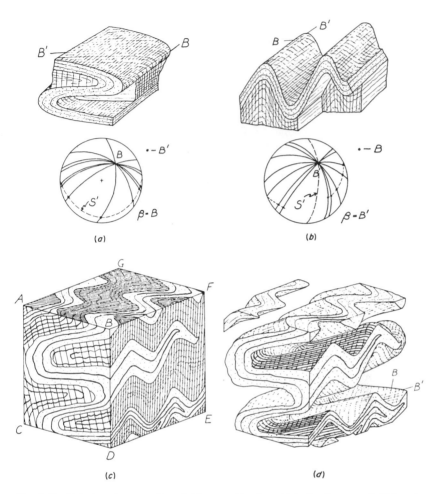

Fig. 6-41 Relations between B and B' axes: (*a*) where B is dominant and B' is subordinate; (*b*) where B' is dominant and B is subordinate. (*From Weiss and McIntyre, 1957.*) (*c*) and (*d*) Relations between equally developed B and B' folds.

tential causes of folding. The compressional origin of folds is one of the oldest interpretations, and it has been examined most thoroughly both experimentally and theoretically. The compressional origin requires careful consideration. Particular care must be used in specifying exactly what is meant by compression. It is easy to think in terms of the experimental models in which layered materials laid in a box with rigid sides and bottom are squeezed between the jaws of a vise. The fixed bottom

and sides and the open top are notable features of this arrangement which ensure the development of a *décollement* at depth. The compressional forces are applied externally in this model. Such a model has been thought to have considerable application in the earth; the continents and oceans basins are considered relatively rigid plates between which geosynclines form and are subsequently compressed in response to crustal shortening resulting from cooling and contraction of the earth. Folded mountain belts have most often been explained in this way. The validity of this idea is being challenged on a number of grounds, and in any case there are no criteria by which any particular fold or fold system can be proven to be a product of crustal shortening. Compression (Fig. 6-42) remains an attractive explanation, but this particular connotation of crustal shortening does not follow. Compression can arise from crowding of sediments within a basin bordered by rigid blocks if the rigid blocks are moved horizontally or vertically relative to one another. This could happen through horizontal compression with pure shortening or by movements of the blocks toward the basin along reverse faults. Another compressional situation can arise through the gravity gliding of material on a slope. Gravity acting as a body force in an inclined layer may induce movements resulting in surficial folding, or folds may be produced ahead of a block that is free in slide.

Folds and faults usually occur together and in many cases the folds are side effects related to the fault. Sedimentary layers are found draped over vertical faults in areas isolated from any other folds or evidences of compression. Where reverse faults or thrusts are associated with folds, it is much more difficult if not impossible to determine whether the folds formed first followed by progressive development of asymmetry and ultimately failure and faulting, or whether the two were more or less synchronous. Folding can occur after thrusting as in the Appalachians where low-angle thrusts are folded.

Nondiastrophic conditions lead to formation of many folds such as the steeply plunging folds found within salt domes (see Chap. 9), folds due to differential compaction of sediment, folds due to gravity sliding within layers of plastic sediment or within layers associated with high pore pressures, folds within and close to plutons, folds due to the flow of glacier ice, and folds due to rock and soil creep or flow.

Drag phenomena induce folding. The most widely recognized types are drags formed in concentric folding in which the drags are asymmetrical toward the fold hinges. However, reverse drags may be formed as in cases of diapiric movements where a very ductile material breaks and is injected through an overlying (or adjacent) more brittle layer. Similar conditions could arise within metamorphic rocks where hotter, less viscous (more ductile) layers at depth start to rise as a dome or fold.

Folds also form in connection with horizontal couples. The folds may occur as a succession of oriented *en échelon* in the sedimentary cover over a more deeply seated strike-slip fault, between such faults, or within zones of lateral displacement where no faults are recognized (Fig. 6-42).

NAPPE STRUCTURE

The term *nappe* is a French word meaning sheet. The original term for a tectonically emplaced sheet was *nappe du charriage*. It has been applied in geology to sheets of rock transported laterally by recumbent folding and thrusting. The term has unfortunately been applied to a variety of features ranging from sheets of conglomerate and basalt deposited and formed in place, to thrust sheets in a variety of degrees of complexity. Some American geologists have confined the use of the term to recumbent folds which have been moved laterally a great distance, usually resulting in shearing out of the lower, overturned limb (Fig. 6-43), but this usage is not accepted by most European geologists. It should be apparent that such a structure may be very similar in field appearance to a thrust sheet showing drag along its front edge. Often the movement has been so great that the nappe has become detached from the beds with which it was originally connected. This source is known as the root of the nappe, and the detached mass of the nappe separated from its roots is a klippe. It is perhaps best, because the name has been applied to such a variety of structures,

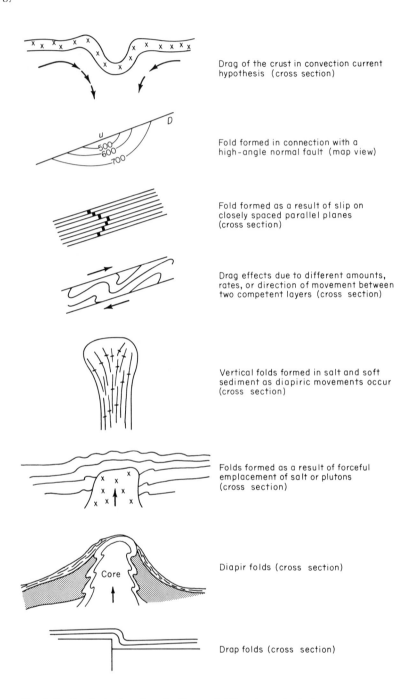

Drag of the crust in convection current hypothesis (cross section)

Fold formed in connection with a high-angle normal fault (map view)

Fold formed as a result of slip on closely spaced parallel planes (cross section)

Drag effects due to different amounts, rates, or direction of movement between two competent layers (cross section)

Vertical folds formed in salt and soft sediment as diapiric movements occur (cross section)

Folds formed as a result of forceful emplacement of salt or plutons (cross section)

Diapir folds (cross section)

Drap folds (cross section)

Fig. 6-42   Geologic situations leading to folding; hypothetical.

Folds formed in sediments deposited contemporaneously with fault movements (cross section)

Folds such as those found in the Malispina glacier where the valley glacier opens out into a plain (map view)

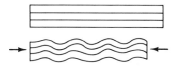

Folds due to local or crustal shortening (cross section)

Folds induced by the down slope movement (cross section)

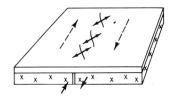

Folds formed in the cover over a deep-seated fault, transcurrent (block diagram)

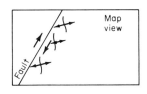

Folds formed near surface as a result of movement along a transcurrent fault (map view)

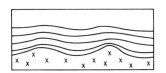

Compaction folds (cross section)

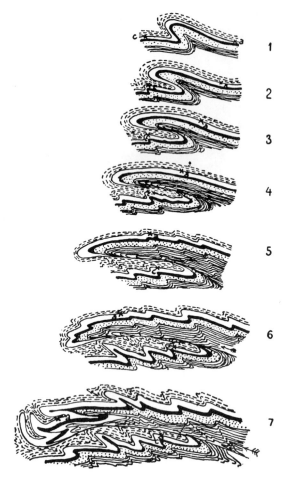

Fig. 6-43 (1) Overfold; (2) to (4), recumbent anticline; (5) to (7), true nappes. [*After Albert Heim (Geologie der Schweiz), from Collet, 1935.*]

argument progressed to how much movement and what direction of movement, and to the location of original source material, the roots, and the important tectonic question of the mechanics of the movement. Many alternatives have been suggested, including low-angle thrusting resulting from horizontal compression, flow of the rock at depth followed by uplift, uplift followed by flow at shallow depths, and vertical uplift followed by gravity sliding.

The theory of nappes has played a major role in the interpretation of the complex tectonic structures of the Alps. The importance of nappes was aptly indicated by Heritsch (1929) when he said: "The fundamental question of Alpine tectonics is the extent to which the Nappe Theory is true."

This statement was made at a time when geologists of Europe were embroiled in a controversy over the extent and manner of application of the theory to Alpine structures. It would be unfair to say that the argument is completely resolved even now, but the view that large-scale complex nappes do exist and that they are one of the most significant features of Alpine geology is universally held. Indeed, nappes have been described in most of the world's orogenic belts and they appear to be one of the characteristic features developed during orogeny. As such they deserve special attention. Such complex structures are not easily identified, as one might guess from the controversy which surrounded them in the Alps, where high relief, excellent exposures, and proximity to many of the great universities of the world allowed exceptional opportunities for their study. We will return later to a regional description of the structure of the Alps.

Arnold Escher van der Linth was the first (1841) to propose large-scale overthrusting to explain Alpine structure. He had studied the geology of the region near Glarus, Switzerland, where he found Permian conglomerates and sandstones overlying Tertiary sediments known as *Flysch,* a marine sequence of interbedded

not to try to define it more specifically than to associate it with the structures of the great thrust masses, thrust sheets, drawn-out recumbent folds, and overturned recumbent folds which are so characteristic of the western Alps. The term was first applied to structures in the Alps which were interpreted as having moved some distance laterally. Much of the early debate about the Alps revolved around the validity of this concept of lateral transport. From the original question of whether or not such movement had taken place, the sands, silts, shales, marls, conglomerates, and breccias, much of which is highly contorted and contains exotic blocks. The Flysch is highly folded and faulted in the Glarus area. It was this Flysch that Escher found in all the valley bottoms for a distance of about 50 km, while the crest and peaks in the same area consisted of horizontal schist and in turn are overlain by limestones containing Liassic fossils.

Apparently Escher was anxious to keep the amount of movement on this nearly horizontal fault at minimum. It must be remembered that this was a new type of structure, and perhaps he was anxious to keep the scale of the overthrust as reasonable as possible. In any case he interpreted the geology of the area as a double fold (Fig. 6-44), two large recumbent folds of opposite orientation. This kept horizontal movement to a minimum. It remained for Marcel Bertrand to replace Escher's double

fold with a single northward-transported structure (Fig. 6-44). In the process, however, it became necessary to interpret the existence of additional overthrust of gigantic size. The origin of the structure of the region was argued, bitterly at times, for a period of 50 years. These arguments centered on questions regarding the concept of the double fold and Bertrand's proposed substitute, the direction of thrusting along each fault, the existence or nonexistence of a recumbent fold with its inverted limb thinned and mylonitized, and the amount of movement. Gradually Bertrand's interpretation of the structure as a great nappe became the accepted view of the Glarus fold.

The appearance of a nappe on a geologic map depends on the relief and topography as well as the complexity of shape of the nappe sheet itself, but an area in the Canadian Rockies of British Columbia (Fig. 6-45), will

Fig. 6-44 Alternative sections across Glarus nappes along a slightly curved north and south line. m = Molasse; f = Flysch; c = Cretaceous; j = Jurassic; t = Trias; p = Permian. (*From Bailey, 1935.*)

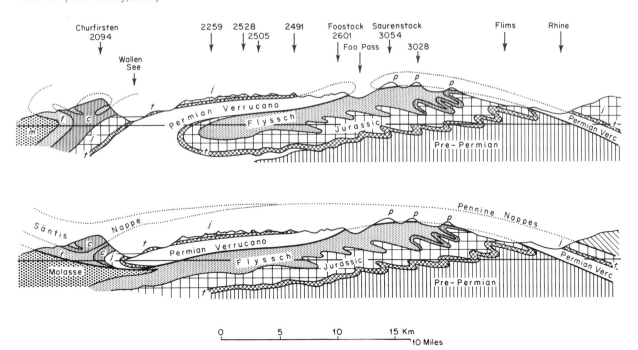

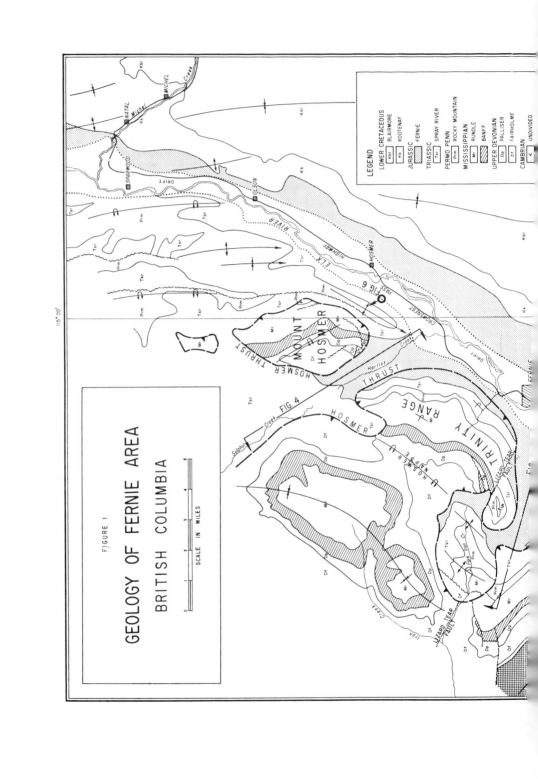

FIGURE 1

GEOLOGY OF FERNIE AREA
BRITISH COLUMBIA

SCALE IN MILES
0 1 2 3 4 5

LEGEND

LOWER CRETACEOUS
Kbl BLAIRMORE
Kk KOOTENAY

JURASSIC
Kf FERNIE

TRIASSIC
Tsr SPRAY RIVER

PERMO PENN
Prm ROCKY MOUNTAIN

MISSISSIPPIAN
Mr RUNDLE
Mb BANFF

UPPER DEVONIAN
Dp PALLISER
Df FAIRHOLME

CAMBRIAN
UNDIVIDED

115° 00'

HOSMER THRUST

MOUNT HOSMER

HOSMER THRUST

Hartley Creek

HOSMER

TRINITY RANGE

U HOSMER TEAR

LIZARD TEAR FAULT

LIZARD TEAR FAULT

Sulphur Creek FIG 4

FIG 6

CRANBROOK

ELK RIVER

HIGHWAY

HOSMER

DRIFT

NATAL
MICHEL
SPARWOOD
MICHEL Creek

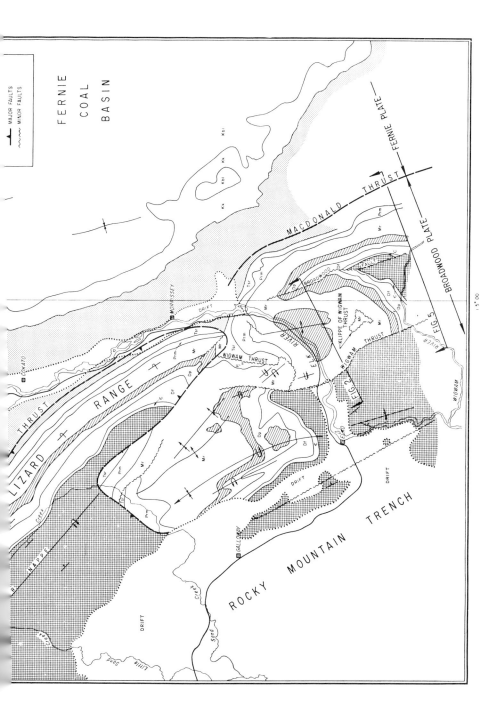

Fig. 6-45 Fernie area, British Columbia. *(From Henderson and Dahlstrom, 1959.)*

serve as an example. Major horizontal transport was involved in this case to bring Precambrian units over Triassic. The sinuous trace of the major fault outcrop is characteristic of low-angle faulting in areas of high relief, as is the klippe at Mount Hosmer. This is combined in this case with larger, overturned fold structures as in the Lizard Range and the Trinity Range.

MODEL EXPERIMENTS IN STRUCTURAL GEOLOGY

A great many geologists have turned to the use of models as a means of trying to understand the formation of natural structures. Though there is much debate about the validity of applying conclusions reached from model studies to interpretation of actual earth structures, it is nevertheless apparent that strikingly similar structures have been produced in models. Moreover, results of model experiments have been influential in the development of structural interpretations. For these reasons some of the most notable experiments deserve our attention. Varying degrees of care have been exercised in the setting up of models. Some have been carefully designed so that the dimensions and physical properties of the materials used are accurately scaled. Many other experiments have been made using materials which approximate only in a general way the rocks they are to represent.

Scale Models

Scale models are designed by selecting appropriate dimensions for the model, choosing a suitable length of time for the experiment to run, and obtaining a material with appropriately scaled density and viscosity. It is convenient to establish model ratios for time, dimensions, and density as follows:

$$\frac{L_1}{L_2} = \lambda \qquad \begin{array}{l} L_1 = \text{length in nature} \\ L_2 = \text{length in model} \end{array}$$

$$\frac{t_1}{t_2} = \tau \qquad \begin{array}{l} t_1 = \text{time in nature} \\ t_2 = \text{time in model} \end{array}$$

$$\frac{\rho_1}{\rho_2} = \delta \qquad \begin{array}{l} \rho_1 = \text{density in nature} \\ \rho_2 = \text{density in model} \end{array}$$

Hubbert (1936) demonstrates that these may be used in turn to establish model ratios for such mechanical quantities as area, volume, frequency, velocity, acceleration, momentum, force, work, power, stress, elastic modulus, and viscosity, which can be expressed in terms of dimension, time, and mass or density. For example, velocity is equal to length per time, acceleration is length squared per time, etc. Since, for the material used in the experiment, such characteristics as viscosity and strength are dependent on the values selected for length and duration of experiment, it is obvious that the selection of materials cannot be random if properly scaled results are to be obtained. The basic criterion used in the scale-model theory is that of dynamic similarity: that all forces of like kinds be proportional. The conditions are approximately satisfied provided inertial forces are negligible, which they are for deformation of plastic or elasticoviscous deformation, and provided the gravitational constant has remained constant. The application of this scale-model theory is found in the experiments of Nettleton (1943) for salt dome formation and Bucher (1956) for formation of fold structures.

THEORY AND EXPERIMENTS IN FOLDING

A variety of factors can be recognized as being important in folding processes. Among these factors are the following:

1. The condition under which folding takes place:
   a. Temperature
   b. Confining pressure
   c. Solutions
2. The character of the folded rocks:
   a. The physical properties of the individual strata at the time of deformation

b. The homogeneity of physical properties within each layer

c. Variations within the stratified section of thickness and rock types

3. The application of the deforming stresses:

    a. The direction of application

    b. The rate at which deformation proceeds

    c. The duration of the applied stress

    d. Uniformity of direction or stress and rate of deformation

Some of the effects of the first of these major categories have already been examined at least insofar as they apply to small samples of rock. Among the most highly significant of the conclusions reached were:

1. Most rocks deform as brittle elastic substances at low temperatures and low confining pressures and high strain rates.

2. At higher temperatures and confining pressures, most rocks tend to exhibit plastic deformation or elasticoviscous flow.

3. Even under relatively low loads, rocks tend to creep when the directed stress is sustained over long periods of time.

These conclusions alone might lead us to expect that several different mechanisms of folding will be found with differences being related to the physical conditions under which deformation occurred. Thus superficial folding of crustal rocks at relatively shallow depth and at low temperatures may best be explained in terms of elastic deformation especially if the folding is of short duration, while folding of rocks at depth, under conditions of metamorphism, or over very long time intervals will likely be accounted for in terms of viscous behavior.

For the purposes of experimental analysis the character of the folded rocks is greatly simplified. Generally the rock units are treated as a stratified sequence in which each layer is considered to be homogeneous, of uniform thick-ness, and of uniform elastic moduli or viscosity. The terms competent and incompetent are also widely used to express marked differences in behavior of different layers. A large number of models of a sequence are obviously possible, including:

1. A single layer unconfined above and below

2. A single layer confined by a fluid below

3. Multiple identical layers confined and unconfined

4. Two competent layers with an incompetent layer between

5. Incompetent layers above and below a competent layer

Several of these models have been analyzed, and we will briefly examine the results.

The third set of factors, application of stresses, is the most difficult to determine in nature and is usually unknown. Very simple and uniform stress fields are applied usually either horizontally or vertically in experimental and theoretical work.

Models of Fold Structures Caused by Gravity

Bucher (1956) used scale models to investigate the role of gravity in the formation of typical structures of orogenic belts. The materials used in these experiments were stitching wax, an elasticoviscous material with a viscosity of 10^6 poises which is very temperature-sensitive, and petrolatum. These materials were selected because the viscosities provide excellent scaled-down equivalents of estimated rock viscosities. There are, of course, many unanswered questions regarding the actual viscosities that rock may have in the earth, particularly during orogeny, but estimates of rock viscosity are assumed to be at least on the right order of magnitude.

The origin of foreland folds such as the folds of the Jura Mountains in the Alps, and the Valley and Ridge folds of the Appalachian Mountains, has been a problem with important implications for the structure of orogenic belts.

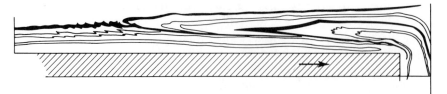

Fig. 6-46 Sketch of wax model in which a nappe formed following uplift caused by compression at depth. (*After Bucher, 1956.*)

There is a considerable amount of evidence to support the view that these foreland folds are shallow folds in a sedimentary veneer that do not extend to great depth (refer to discussion regarding the Appalachian Mountains), and that they formed by gravity deformations in beds that were dipping gently away from the higher central portion of the mountain belt. To simulate this structure, a model consisting of a number of interbedded layers of various colors of stitching wax and grease was constructed so that the top surface at one end was sloping 23°, and a block of wax was placed on top of that end to simulate a thrust block of basement rock. As the wax at the high end of the mass spread under the force of gravity, the layers corresponding to the foreland were thrown into a system of disharmonic folds. The structures in the wax layers are similar to fold and fault patterns in actual mountain belt forelands.

A second set of experiments was designed to simulate the formation of nappelike structures of Alpine type. A bar consisting of several layers of wax of different colors was compressed, by means of a wooden piston driven forward at a slow constant rate, into a thickened wax layer at one end of the bar. Thus wax at the thicker end was forced out and upward. Since the piston moved several times faster than the creep rate of the wax, a pile of wax built up above the general level of the layers in most of the bar. The piston was stopped each night and the wax then gradually spread out, eventually forming a large recumbent fold (Fig. 6-46) with a prominent root at

one end. The forelimb of the anticline is greatly thinned and drawn out; digitations similar to those of Alpine recumbent folds developed in the model, as did surficial folds in front of the nappe. Close to the edge of the nappe the folds are overturned, but farther away from this leading edge the folding dies out. The apparent and actual amount of shortening is another point of interest. The actual shortening which took place was 20 cm, but measurement of the bed's length along the folds, including the nappe, leads to estimates of 80 to 100 cm or nearly five times the actual shortening. Compare the model nappe in Fig. 6-46 with actual cross sections of nappes in Fig. 6-44.

Bailey Willis' Models

One of the first students of models in North America was Bailey Willis, who had produced folds somewhat similar to those of the Appalachian Valley and Ridge as early as 1893, long before the principles of scale-model design were formulated. His models were constructed of layers composed of mixtures of wax, plaster, and turpentine. In the light of scale-model theory it is obvious that some of the layers were much too hard to be suitable for use in scale models, but this was overcome in part by the use of heavy loads of lead shot which built up confining pressure. A number of models were constructed in which the thickness and sequence of hard and soft layers were varied, and variations in initial attitudes of layers were made. In each case the model was compressed by a lateral pressure, and results such as those illustrated in Figs. 6-47 and 6-48 were obtained.

The model illustrated in Fig. 6-47 was constructed so that a thick hard layer overlaid a number of thin hard layers, all of uniform thickness and originally flat-lying. The base material was very soft. The box-shaped folds produced in the experiment are somewhat similar to folds of the Jura Mountains. It is obvious that the folds in the model developed with a rigid basement and by lateral compression accompanied by flow of the soft material into the cores of anticlines and out from under synclines. A similar hypothesis has been advanced to explain the Jura folds.

The development of a thrust fault on the forelimb of an asymmetric anticline was followed in another experiment illustrated in Fig. 6-48. Material of a plastic nature was placed below layers that were firm and flexible at the start of this experiment. As the layers arched upward, faults formed in the less competent layers, and the less competent material moved up into the arch formed by the competent layers along these faults. As shortening continued, the less competent layers were forced to change shape continually. Eventually the steep limb of the fold was pushed under the other limb, and the strata in the inversion were first stretched and then faulted to produce an

overthrust similar to those in the Alps described by Heim.

FOLDING BY ELASTIC BUCKLING

Elastic buckling has been investigated by Currie and others (1962), Biot (1961), Ramberg (1963a), and Price (1967). In the case of folding taking place at shallow depths, the initial deformation is elastic in nature even though the rock behaves as a plasticoviscous material. Such materials exhibit elastic behavior until

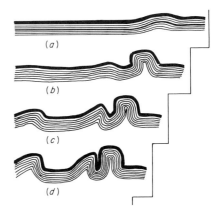

Fig. 6-47 Concentric folds produced in a pressure box. (*Redrawn from Willis, 1934.*)

Fig. 6-48 The rise of the competent anticline continued until it overtopped the piston by which pressure was applied. Then the nearer limb of the fold was pushed under the further limb and the strata in the inversion were stretched, producing an overthrust of the alpine type described by Heim—a stretch thrust. (*Redrawn from Willis, 1934.*)

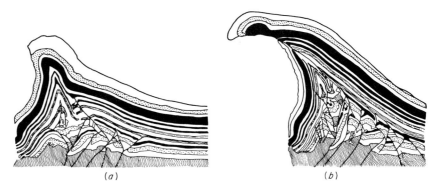

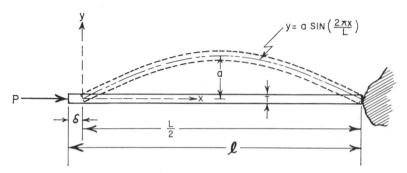

$$y = a \, \text{SIN} \left(\frac{2\pi x}{L} \right)$$

Fig. 6-49 Sketch of the buckling of a weightless beam with hinged ends. (*From Currie, Patnode, and Trump, 1962.*)

the yield strength is reached. The yield strength of a compacted and cemented quartzose rock at temperatures of 200°C and confining pressure of 20,000 psi lies in the range of 50 to 100,000 psi—conditions which might be expected at a depth of 20,000 ft (Price, 1967).

Both field studies and laboratory experiments indicate that stratification, its thickness and arrangement of layers, is significant in determining how a sequence of rocks within a basin will respond to deformation. The competency of members in this analysis is defined by the relative elastic moduli of the interbedded rock types. Both the behavior of these units and the extent to which they can be deformed before they cease to act as continuous members are dependent, to a degree, on the arrangement of units of different competency in the stratigraphic column.

The physical properties and thickness of a dominant member are found to control the fold wavelength that develops in the early stages of deformation in the buckling process. Currie and others (1962) deduce quantitative values to describe the relationships between dominant member thickness and fold wavelength. The following simplifying assumptions are made: that the structures develop in a sequence of strata having essentially infinite areal dimensions, a characteristic Young's modulus E, and that it is subjected to simple shortening.

Case 1. The Euler equation (Price, 1967) allows us to estimate the critical force (P_{crit}) necessary to initiate a sinusoidal buckle under the above conditions if we consider that a single competent layer is buckled in air (Fig. 6-49).

$$P_{\text{crit}} = \frac{\pi^2 \, EI}{L^2} \qquad \text{Euler equation}$$

where E = Young's modulus

I = the moment of inertia of the layer

L = the wavelength of the buckle

Euler's equation was derived from engineering problems carried out under 1 atm of pressure. The critical stress, σ_{crit}, under which buckling is initiated in the earth is equal to the difference between the maximum principal stress and the confining pressure.

The moment of inertia of a buckled layer is a function of the width w and thickness T of the layer:

$$I = \frac{T^3 \, w}{12}$$

If the width of the layer is taken as unity, $I = T^3/12$ and σ_{crit} becomes $\sigma_{\text{crit}} = \pi^2 E T^3/12L^2$. Thus the critical stress is a function of the unit thickness. Price has termed the ratio L/T the *slenderness ratio*.

Biot (1965), Ramberg (1961), and Currie et al. (1962) have shown that when the influence of the medium in which the competent layer is embedded is considered, and assuming that there is no initial change in thickness of the plate, then a sinusoidal wave of wavelength L will be produced as a result of the buckling (Fig. 6-50):

$$L = 2\pi T \sqrt[3]{\frac{E}{6E_0}} \quad \text{or} \quad \frac{L}{T} = 2\pi \sqrt[3]{\frac{E}{6E_0}}$$

where E = Young's modulus of embedded unit
E_0 = Young's modulus of medium in which it is embedded

Here again the slenderness ratio can be found.

The medium in which the competent layer is embedded has to have an elastic modulus less than one-hundredth that of the embedded member to allow elastic instability. Such a marked difference in elastic moduli in nature would exist in the case of a cemented sandstone or quartzite interbedded with thick, very weak materials such as shale, salt, gypsum, clay, and mudstone. Price (1967) cites the ratio of shear moduli for cemented sandstone embedded in mudstone as 1,000:1. Much more common

ratios are in the range of 5:1 to 50:1. The corresponding values for the ratio of L/T of the dominant member are 6:1 to 12:1.

If approximate values for E (10^6 psi) and E_0 are selected, the equation above indicates that the lowest possible wavelength-to-bed thickness ratio for this case is 16:1.

Case 2. In a second example consider a dominant competent layer of thickness, T, located between two layers of thickness, J, which behave elastically and have rigid outer boundaries. The wavelength of the competent layer under these circumstances becomes

$$L = \sqrt[4]{\frac{2\pi^4 E T^3 J}{3E_0}}$$

This equation reduces to a value that is very close to that in the previous example when J is equal to or greater than the wavelength. The equation is useful when the thickness of the medium is less than the predicted fold wavelength.

Fig. 6-50 Sketch of the buckling of a beam in a continuous, infinite medium (left); sketch of the buckling of a beam in a medium made up of vertical columns bounded by rigid members (center); sketch of the buckling of multiple members in an infinite medium (right). (*From Currie, Patnode, and Trump, 1962.*)

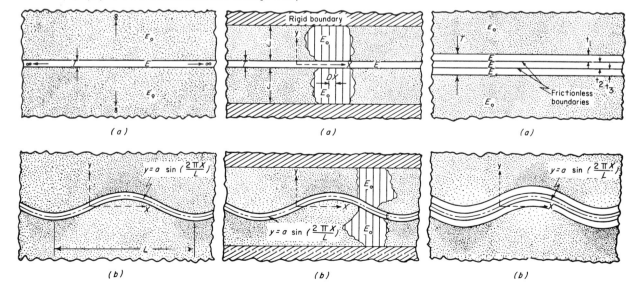

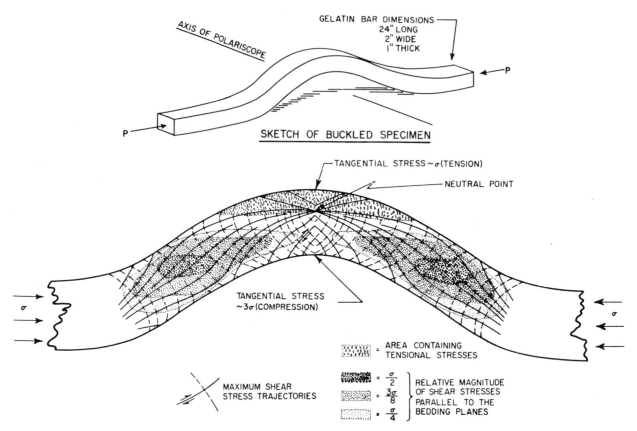

Fig. 6-51   Results of a qualitative photoelastic study of the crest and flanks of a buckled gelatin beam. (*From Currie, Patnode, and Trump, 1962.*)

Case 3.   In a third example of geological importance the single dominant member is replaced by a large number n of thin members having individual thicknesses t and total thickness T. The layers are embedded in an infinite medium with elasticity E_0. The dominant wavelength becomes

$$L = 2\pi T \sqrt[3]{\frac{E}{6n^2 E_0}}$$

This case is the most favorable to elastic instability, but it is dependent on the assumption that the boundaries of individual competent members are frictionless.

To test the above formulas, Currie and others (1962) performed a series of experiments using gelatin layers for incompetent units and gum rubber strips for more competent units. The Young's modulus of the two are 10 and 100 psi, respectively. The use of gelatin has the advantage of making it possible to use photoelastic techniques in which polarized light is transmitted through the gelatin and shows stress patterns such as that depicted in Fig. 6-51. The photoelastic experiments confirm the theoretical predictions of fold development through buckling of a dominant member within a relatively less competent medium.

The theoretical values for wavelengths in sequences that approximate the above conditions were compared with actual field examples of folded sequences by Currie et al. The fold wavelength of a number of folds in sedimentary rocks is plotted against the thickness of the dominant member (Fig. 6-52). The field cases cited give a straight line on a log plot, indicating a linear relationship between fold wavelength and dominant member thickness. Particular care must be exercised in dividing the sedimentary section into competent and incompetent units in this type of field study. Formational boundaries do not always correspond to boundaries separating rock layers of different structural properties. It should also be borne in mind that this analysis applies to initial deformation under conditions favorable to elastic instability. In summary, this study indicates that in cases of buckling the thickness of a dominant member and the relative physical properties of the layers control the wavelength that develops in early stages of deformation.

VISCOELASTIC FOLDING

Biot (1961, 1965) develops a theory of folding of stratified viscoelastic media for the case of folding caused by instability under a compressive load acting in a direction parallel with the layers. The mathematical development of this theory is beyond the scope of this treatment. One of the conditions analyzed is folding of a compressed viscous plate in a viscous medium. This is thought to approximate conditions at depth in the earth during folding which takes place during high-grade metamorphism. The analysis is essentially a study in the growth in amplitude of a sinusoidal wave deflection in a plate through time. Biot found that a dominant wavelength will develop in a restrained bar, in an elastic plate restrained laterally by dashpots, or in a viscous plate in a viscous medium when compressed laterally parallel to the bar or plate.

Fig. 6-52 Log-log plot of the wavelength to dominant member thickness for field examples cited. (*From Currie, Patnode, and Trump, 1962.*)

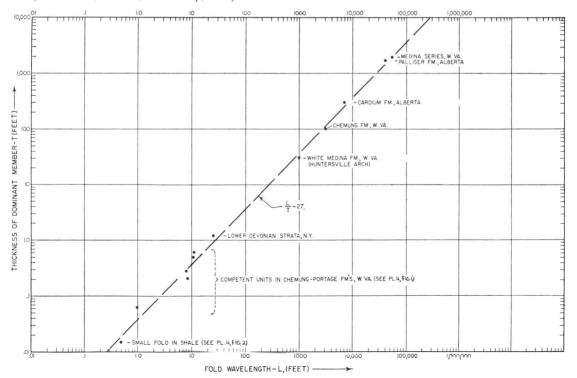

The dominant wavelength is the one for which the rate of increase of the amplitude is maximum. Because the dominant wavelength in these cases has a much larger rate of deformation than others, it is the one which is most likely to form. An equation for the dominant wavelength in the viscous case is

$$\frac{L}{T} = 2\pi \sqrt[3]{\frac{\eta}{6\eta_1}}$$

where η = viscosity of layer
η_1 = viscosity of medium

One interesting conclusion in this case is that the dominant wavelength is not dependent on the compressive stress. The wavelength does depend on the stress for the elastic plate.

Biot extends his theory to define the rate at which an initial wavelength present in the viscoelastic layer is amplified. He finds that the amplification factor for folding of a compressed viscous plate in a viscous medium is a function of the viscosity ratio of the two and time, and that when the amplitude of folding reaches a certain point, the amplitude of folding increases at an explosive rate. The time required for this is a function only of the viscosity ratios.

To illustrate the application of this theory to natural folds, consider this example. If a layer of viscosity $\eta = 10^{21}$ poises is interbedded in other layers of viscosity $\eta = 10^{18}$ poises and is subjected to a compressive load of 10^8 dynes/cm^2 (about 1,450 psi), the time required for the layer to shorten by 25 percent is

$$ti = \frac{\eta}{P} = \frac{10^{21}}{10^8} = 10^{13} \text{ sec} = 317{,}000 \text{ years}$$

and the dominant wavelength is $Ld = 37.5 \times$ layer thickness. These values fall within the range of geologically feasible values.

Biot also analyzed the case of multiple layers N, of identical thickness T and viscosity η (with lubricated boundaries between layers), embedded in a viscous medium η_1, and subjected to a horizontal compression P. The dominant wavelength in this case becomes

$$\frac{L}{T} = 2\pi \sqrt[3]{\frac{N\eta}{6\eta_1}}$$

and all conclusions for the single layers become applicable to the multiple-layer case except that the values are affected by the value of N.

The theory leads to some interesting conclusions which can be applied to field studies of folds and which contributed significantly to our understanding of the folding process. These conclusions are:

1. Within lower stress ranges rocks are elastic for fast deformation. They tend to behave like a viscous medium with viscosities in the range of 10^{17} to 10^{22} poises for slow deformation.
2. Viscous behavior predominates in tectonic folding, and this leads to large deformations without fracture and dependence of fracture on deformation rates.
3. If one assumes that rocks behave as a purely viscous solid, significant folding may appear under relatively low tectonic stresses. In such cases the influence of gravity becomes important near the surface and may be sufficient to prevent folding. Even deep folds may be blocked by the presence of stabilizing density gradients.
4. Incipient folding in a state of initial plastic stress determines a wavelength that is "frozen in." As folding proceeds, high stresses are produced at the fold crests. Cracks or accelerated creep are generated at these points. The bends tend to behave as hinges, and the folding then proceeds by a different mechanism.
5. For purely viscous deformations and when the influence of gravity is not important, the dominant wavelength is independent on the tectonic stress.
6. The dominant wavelength depends on the cubic root of the viscosity ratio, with the consequence that it is not sensitive to large variations in viscosity contrast.

Ramberg (1963a) has investigated models similar to those described above, using the theory of fluid dynamics. He assumed welded layer contacts rather than free-slip models and arrived at a somewhat smaller ratio of wavelength to thickness than did Biot. In a model consisting of multilayers of alternating competence, Ramberg found that many folds will develop if the thickness of the incompetent layer is more than a certain amount, while only one or one-half wave will develop for smaller spacings between incompetent layers.

DEVELOPMENT OF ASYMMETRY IN BUCKLE FOLDS

Price (1967) developed a theory explaining the origin of asymmetrical buckle folds in non-metamorphosed competent sediments. Upright symmetrical folds generally of sinusoidal profile are produced in both the elastic and viscous cases previously considered. Most folds, however, are asymmetrical, and most folds such as those of the unmetamorphosed portions of folded mountain belts probably do not form under conditions in which the rock behaves as either a perfectly plastic or a perfectly viscous material; plasticoviscous behavior is more realistic.

The degree of asymmetry of a fold can be expressed as the ratio of the length of the long limb to the short limb, a ratio that is rarely less than 1.5:1 and sometimes as much as 6:1. Probably the most consistent feature of a system of folds is the attitude of the axial planes which usually are subparallel. Thus the axial planes are perpendicular to the direction of compression or initiating stress in cases of upright symmetrical folds. Price (1967) shows that this is also true of asymmetrical folds which are initiated when the axis of the maximum principal stress is inclined to the unfolded layer (Fig. 6-53). Under this condition a shearing stress is set up which in turn generates a bending moment.

The moment of a force (torque) is the prod-

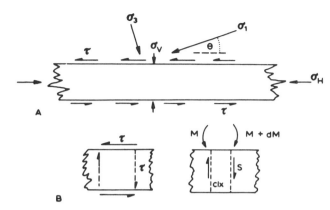

Fig. 6-53 (a) Distribution of stresses normal and parallel to a horizontal competent unit when the axis of greatest principal stress is inclined at an angle θ. (b) Relationship among shear stresses τ, shear force S, and bending moment M. (*From Price, 1967.*)

uct of the force applied normal to an arm or axis and the distance from the point of application of the force to a pivot point. Price (1967) shows that the bending moment, M_{ben}, due to the shearing stress τ varies in a linear manner along the length of a layer from a nodal point and is given by

$$M_{ben} = \tau T L$$

The buckling moment M_{buc} at a point a distance x from a nodal point on the sinusoidal wave train is equal to the product of the critical force needed to initiate buckling and the elastic deflection y at the point.

$$\begin{aligned} M_{\text{buc}} &= P_{\text{crit}} Y \\ &= \sigma_{\text{crit}} T^2 k \end{aligned}$$

where k is dependent on the slenderness ratio L/T. The total moment curve for the layer is then the sum of the bending and buckling moment due to compression along the layer. The total moment curve is asymmetrical in shape (Fig. 6-54), and the resulting fold is asymmetrical. After the fold is initiated and the position of the fold axes determined by elastic failure, the later development of the fold takes place largely by rotation of the limbs.

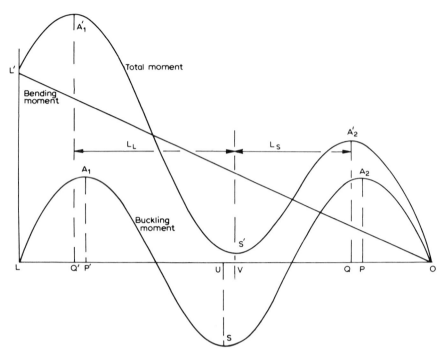

Fig. 6-54 How the bending and buckling moment curves may be combined to give an asymmetrical total moment curve. (*From Price, 1967.*)

Price hypothesizes that the amount of work done in rotating each limb is equal; therefore, the shorter limb rotates through a larger angle.

REFERENCES

Bailey, E. B., 1935, Tectonic essays, mainly Alpine: Oxford, Clarendon Press.

Bailey, E. B., and Mackin, J. H., 1937, Recumbent folding in the Pennsylvania piedmont—preliminary statement: Am. Jour. Sci., s. 5, v. 33, p. 187–190.

Bain, G. W., 1931, Flowage folding: Am. Jour. Sci., v. 22, p. 503–530.

Bain, G. W., and Beebe, J. H., 1954, Scale model reproduction of tension faults: Am. Jour. Sci., v. 252, p. 745–754.

Ball, T. K., 1960, A petrofabric analysis of a fold: Am. Jour. Sci., v. 258, no. 4, p. 274–281.

Bayly, M. B., 1964, A theory of similar folding in viscous materials: Am. Jour. Sci., v. 262, p. 753–766.

Behre, C. H., Jr., 1933, Slate in Pennsylvania: Pennsylvania Geol. Survey Bull. ser. 4, M 16.

Bertrand, M., 1897, Structure des Alpes françaises et recurrence de certain facies sedimentaires: Internat. Geol. Cong., 6th Sess., Comptes rendus, p. 163–177 [1894].

Bhattacharji, Somdev, 1958, Theoretical and experimental investigations of crossfolding: Jour. Geology, v. 66, no. 6.

Billings, M. P., 1954, Structural geology, 2d ed.: Englewood Cliffs, N. J., Prentice-Hall.

Biot, M. A., 1961, Theory of folding of stratified viscoelastic media and its implications in tectonics and orogenesis: Geol. Soc. America Bull., v. 72, p. 1595–1632.

———— 1965, Mechanics of incremental deformation: New York, Wiley, 504 p.

Biot, M. A., and others, 1961, Experimental verification of the theory of folding of stratified viscoelastic media: Geol. Soc. America Bull., v. 72, p. 1621–1632.

Brown, R. W., 1928, Experiments relating to factors

causing localization of folds: Am. Assoc. Petroleum Geologists Bull., v. 12, p. 617–623.

Bucher, W. H., 1933, The deformation of the earth's crust: Princeton, N.J., Princeton Univ.

——— 1953, Fossils in metamorphic rocks: Geol. Soc. America Bull., v. 64, p. 275–300.

——— 1956, Role of gravity in orogenesis: Geol. Soc. America Bull., v. 67, p. 1295–1318.

Buddington, A. F., 1939, Adirondack igneous rocks and their metamorphism: Geol. Soc. America Mem. 7, 354 p.

Bush, J. B., 1957, Introduction to the geology and ore deposits of the East Tintic mining district, in Utah Geol. Soc., Guidebook to the Geology of Utah, p. 97–102.

Busk, H. G., 1929, Earth flexures: London, Cambridge Univ.

Campbell, J. D., 1958, En échelon folding: Econ. Geology, v. 53, p. 448–472.

Campbell, J. W., 1951, Some aspects of rock folding by shear deformation: Am. Jour. Sci., v. 249, p. 625–639.

Carey, S. W., 1954, The rheid concept in geotectonics: Geol. Soc. Australia Jour., v. 1, p. 67–117.

——— 1955, The orocline concept in geotectonics: Royal Soc. Tasmania Proc., v. 89, p. 255–288.

——— 1962, Folding: Alberta Soc. Petroleum Geologists Jour., v. 10.

Cate, A. S., and others, 1961, Subsurface structure of plateau region north-central and western Pennsylvania on top of Oriskany formation: Pennsylvania Geol. Survey, 4th ser., Map.

Chamberlan, T. C., and Salisbury, R. D., 1927, College textbook of geology: New York, Holt.

Chapple, Wm. M., 1968, A mathematical theory of finite-amplitude rock-folding: Geol. Soc. America Bull., v. 79, p. 47–68.

Clark, R. H., and McIntyre, D. B., 1951, The use of the terms pitch and plunge: Am. Jour. Sci., v. 249, p. 591–599.

Clifford, P., and others, 1957, The development of lineation in complex fold systems: Geol. Mag., v. 94, no. 1, p. 1–24.

Cloos, Ernst, 1946, Lineation, a critical review and annotated bibliography: Geol. Soc. America Mem. 18, 122 p., illus.

——— 1947, Oolite deformation in the South Mountain Fold, Maryland: Geol. Soc. America Bull., v. 58, p. 843–918.

——— 1955, Experimental analysis of fracture patterns: Geol. Soc. America Bull., v. 66, p. 241–256.

——— 1964, Wedging, bedding plane slips and gravity tectonics in the Appalachians, in Tectonics of the southern Appalachians: VPI Dept. of Geol. Sci., Roanoke, Va.

Cloos, Hans, 1930, Zur experimentellan tektonik: Die Naturwissenschaften, v. 18.

——— 1936, Einfuhrung in die Geologie: Berlin, Gebruder Borntraeger.

Collet, L. W., 1935, The structure of the Alps, 2d ed.: London, E. Arnold.

Currie, J. B., Patnode, H. W., and Trump, R. P., 1962, Development of folds in sedimentary strata: Geol. Soc. America Bull., v. 73, p. 655–674.

Dahlstrom, C. D. A., 1954, Statistical analysis of cylindrical folds: Canadian Mining Metall. Bull., no. 504, p. 234–239.

Daly, R. A., 1915, Ores, magmatic emanations, and modes of igneous intrusion; discussion of paper by B. S. Butley: Econ. Geology, v. 10, p. 471–472.

Dana, J. D., 1873, On the origin of mountains: Am. Jour. Sci., v. 5, p. 347–350.

De Sitter, L. U., 1939, The principle of concentric folding and the dependence of tectonic structure on original sedimentary structure: Amsterdam, Koninkl. Nederlandse Akad. Wetensch. Proc., v. 42, no. 5, p. 412–430.

——— 1954, Gravitational gliding tectonics—an essay on comparative structural geology: Am. Jour. Sci., v. 252, p. 321–344.

Doll, C. G., and others, 1961, Geologic map of Vermont: Vermont.

Donath, F. A., 1962, Role of layering in geologic deformation: New York Acad. Sci. Trans., v. 24, p. 236–249.

——— 1963, Fundamental problems in dynamic structural geology, in Donnelly, T. W., ed., The earth sciences: Problems and progress in current research: Chicago, Univ. of Chicago, p. 83–103.

Donath, F. A., and Parker, R. B., 1961, Folds and folding [abs.]: Geol. Soc. America Spec. Paper 68, Abstracts for 1961, p. 87–88.

——— 1963, Folds and folding: Geol. Soc. America Spec. Paper 68.

——— 1964, Folds and folding: Geol. Soc. America Bull., v. 75.

Duska, Leslie, 1961, Depth of the basal shearing plane in cases of simple concentric folding: Alberta Soc. Petroleum Geologists Jour., v. 9, no. 1, p. 20–24.

Emmons, Ebenezer, 1863, Manual of geology: New York, 290 p.; Philadelphia, 1860, 2d ed., 297 p.

Escher von der Linth, A., 1841, Verh. Schweizer. Naturf. Gesell. Zurich, p. 54, 58.

Fairbairn, H. W., 1949, Structural petrology of deformed rocks: Reading, Mass., Addison-Wesley.

Fleuty, M. J., 1964, The description of folds: Geol. Assoc. Proc., v. 75, p. 461–492.

Flinn, D., 1962, On folding during three-dimensional progressive deformation: Geol. Soc. London Quart. Jour., v. 118, p. 385.

Ghosh, S. K., and Naha, K., 1962, Recumbent folding in migmatite in the Archean "basement" north of Nathdwana, Rajasthan, India: Am. Jour. Sci., v. 260, no. 4.

Godfrey, J. D., 1954, The origin of the ptygmatic structures: Jour. Geology, v. 62, no. 4, p. 375–387.

Gzovsky, M. V., 1959, The use of scale models in tectonophysics: Internat. Geology Rev., v. 1, no. 4, p. 31–47.

Henderson, G. G. L., and Dahlstrom, C. D. A., 1959, First-order nappe in Canadian Rockies: Am. Assoc. Petroleum Geologists Bull., v. 43, p. 641–653.

Heritsch, F., 1929, The nappe theory in the Alps: London.

Hills, E. S., 1953, Tectonic setting of Australian ore deposits, in Geology of Australian ore deposits: Empire Mining Metall. Cong. (Melbourne), 5th, v. 1, p. 41–61.

Holmes, A., 1920, The nomenclature of petrology with references to selected literature: London, Thos. Murby & Co., 284 p.

Houston, R. S., and Parker, R. B., 1963, Structural analysis of a folded quartzite, Medicine Bow Mountains, Wyoming: Geol. Soc. America Bull., v. 74, p. 197–202.

Hubbert, M. K., 1935, Determination of certain structural features in Illinois, Kentucky, and Alabama by electrical resistance methods: Washington Acad. Sci. Jour., v. 25, p. 506–507.

——— 1937, Scale models and geologic structures: Geol. Soc. America Bull., v. 48, p. 1459.

——— 1951, Mechanical basis for certain familiar geologic structures: Geol. Soc. America Bull., v. 62, p. 255–372.

Jones, K. A., 1959, A petrofabric method of fold analysis: Am. Jour. Sci., v. 257.

Kay, Marshall, 1951, North American geosynclines: Geol. Soc. America Mem. 48.

Kingsley, Louise, 1954, Models for introducing structural geology: Jour. Geol. Education, v. 2, p. 77–79.

Knopf, E. B., and Ingerson, E., 1938, Structural petrology: Geol. Soc. America Mem. 6, 270 p.

Kuenen, P. H., 1938, Observations and experiments in ptygmatic folding: Soc. Geol. Finlande, Comptes Rendus, no. 2, p. 11.

Kuenen, P. H., and De Sitter, L. U., 1938, Experimental investigations into the mechanism of folding: Leidse Geol. Med., v. 10, p. 271–240.

LaForge, Laurence, 1919, The use of the words talus and shingle: Washington Acad. Sci. Jour., v. 9, p. 500–501.

Lahee, F. H., 1952, Field geology, 5th ed.: New York, McGraw-Hill, 883 p.

——— 1961, Field geology, 6th ed.: New York, McGraw-Hill, 926 p.

Leith, C. K., 1913, Structural geology: New York, Holt.

Lewis, W. V., and Maynard, M. M., 1955, Kaokin model glaciers: Jour. Glaciology, v. 2, no. 18.

Link, T. A., 1927, The origin and significance of epi-anticlinal faults as revealed by experiments: Am. Assoc. Petroleum Geologists Bull., v. 11, p. 853.

MacDonald, G. J. F., 1957, Thermodynamics of solids under nonhydrostatic stress with geologic applications: Am. Jour. Sci., v. 255, p. 266–281.

Mathews, W. H., 1958, Geology of the Mount Garibaldi map-area, southwestern British Columbia, Canada: Geol. Soc. America Bull., v. 69, p. 161–198.

McBirney, A. R., 1961, Experimental deformation of viscous layers in oblique stress fields: Geol. Soc. America Bull., v. 72, no. 3, p. 495–498.

McIntyre, D. B., 1950, 1. Note on two lineated tectonites from Strathavon, Banffshire: Geol. Mag., v. 87, no. 5, p. 331–336.

Mead, W. J., 1920, Mechanics of geologic structures: Jour. Geology, v. 28, p. 505–523.

Mertie, J. B., 1959, Classification, delineation and measurement of non-parallel folds: U. S. Geol. Survey Prof. Paper 314-E, p. 91–124.

Nettleton, L. L., 1943, Recent experimental and geophysical evidence of salt dome formation: Am. Assoc. Petroleum Geologists Bull., v. 27, p. 51–63.

Nevin, C. M., 1936, Principles of structural geology, 2d ed.: New York, Wiley, 348 p., [1931, 1st ed., 303 p.].

——— 1949, Principles of structural geology: New York, Wiley.

O'Driscoll, E. S., 1964, Cross fold deformation by simple shear: Econ. Geology, v. 59, p. 1061–1093.

Parker, R. J., and McDowell, A. N., 1955, Model studies of salt dome tectonics: Am. Assoc. Petroleum Geologists Bull., v. 39, no. 12.

Pierce, W. G., and others, 1947, Structure contour map of the Big Horn basin, Wyoming and Montana: U. S. Geol. Survey Oil and Gas Inv. Map 74.

Price, N. J., 1967, The initiation and development of asymmetrical buckle folds in non-metamorphosed competent sediments: Tectonophysics, v. 4, p. 173–201.

Ramberg, Hans, 1959, Evolution of ptygmatic folding: Norsk geol. tidsskr., v. 39, p. 99–131.

—— 1961, Relationship between concentric longitudinal strain and concentric shearing during folding of homogeneous sheets of rocks: Am. Jour. Sci., v. 259, p. 382–390.

—— 1963a, Fluid dynamics of viscous buckling applicable to folding of layered rocks: Am. Assoc. Petroleum Geologists Bull., v. 47.

—— 1963b, Strain distribution and geometry of folds: Geol. Inst. Univ. Uppsala Bull., v. 42, p. 3–20.

Ramsay, J. G., 1960, The deformation of early linear structures in areas of repeated folding: Jour. Geology, v. 68.

—— 1961, The effects of folding upon the orientation of sedimentation structures: Jour. Geology, v. 69, no. 1.

—— 1962a, The geometry and mechanics of formation of similar type folds: Jour. Geology, v. 70, p. 309–327.

—— 1962b, The geometry of conjugate fold systems: Geol. Mag. [Great Britain], v. 99, p. 516–526.

—— 1964, The uses and limitations of beta-diagrams and pi-diagrams in the geometrical analysis of folds: Geol. Soc. London Quart. Jour., v. 120.

—— 1967, Folding and fracturing of rocks: New York, McGraw-Hill, 568 p.

Read, H. H., 1928, A note on ptygmatic folds in the Sutherland granite complex: Summ. Prog. Geol. Survey for 1927, pt. II, p. 72.

Sander, B., 1930, Gefügekunde der Gesteine: Vienna, Springer-Verlag OHG.

—— 1950, Einführung in die Gefügekunde der geologischen Körper: v. I & II, Vienna, Springer-Verlag OHG.

Sanford, A. R., 1959, Analytical and experimental study of simple geologic structures: Geol. Soc. America Bull., v. 70, p. 19–52.

Sederholm, J. J., 1907, Om granit och gneis: Comm. Geol. Finlande Bull., no. 23.

—— 1913, Über ptygmatische faltungen: Neues Jahrbuch Mineralogie, v. 36.

Sougy, J., 1962, West African fold belt: Geol. Soc. America Bull., v. 73.

Spry, Alan, 1964, The origin and significance of snowball structures in garnet: Jour. Petrology, v. 4.

Stillwell, F. L. 1953, Geology of Australian ore deposits: Melbourne, Australian Inst. Mining and Metallurgy.

Stoces, B., and White, C. H., 1935, Structural geology with special reference to economic deposits: Princeton, N.J., Van Nostrand.

Stockwell, C. H., 1950, The use of plunge in the construction of cross-sections of folds: Geol. Assoc. Canada Proc., v. 3, p. 97–121.

Stone, M., and Lambert, J. L. M., 1956, Shear-folding in the Mylor states, near Porthleven, Cornwall: Geol. Mag., v. 93, no. 4, p. 331–335.

Timoshenko, S. P., and Gere, J. M., 1961, Theory of elastic stability, 2d ed.: New York, McGraw-Hill.

Tobisch, Othmar T., 1966, Large-scale basin-and-dome pattern resulting from the interference of major folds: Geol. Soc. America Bull., v. 77, no. 4, p. 393–408, 12 figs., 1 pl.

Turner, F. J., and Weiss, L. E., 1963, Structural analysis of metamorphic tectonites: New York, McGraw-Hill, 560 p.

Van Hise, C. R., 1896, Principles of North American pre-Cambrian geology: U. S. Geol. Survey Ann. Rept. 16, p. 571–843.

Verhoogen, Jean, 1951, The chemical potential of a stressed solid: Am. Geophys. Union Trans., v. 32, p. 41–43.

Weiss, L. E., 1955, Fabric analysis of a triclinic tectonite and its bearing on the geometry of flow in rocks: Am. Jour. Sci., v. 253, p. 225–236.

—— 1959a, Structural analysis of the basement system at Turoka, Kenya: Overseas Geology and Mineral Resources (London), v. 7, p. 3–35, 123–153.

—— 1959b, Geometry of superposed folding: Geol. Soc. America Bull., v. 70, p. 91–106.

Weiss, L. E., and McIntyre, D. B., 1957, Structural geometry of Dalradian rocks at Loch Leven, Scottish Highlands: Jour. Geology, v. 65, p. 575–602.

White, W. S., and Jahns, R. H., 1950, Structure of central and east-central Vermont: Jour. Geology, v. 58, p. 179–220.

Whitten, E. H. T., 1959, A study of two directions of folding: the structural geology of the Monadhliath and Mid-Strathspey: Jour. Geology, v. 67.

Williams, Emyr, 1965, The deformation of competent granular layers in folding: Am. Jour. Sci., v. 263, p. 229–237.

————— 1967, Notes on the determination of shortening by flexure folding modified by flattening: Papers and Proc. Royal Soc. Tasmania, v. 101.

Willis, Bailey, 1893, Mechanics of Appalachian structure: U. S. Geol. Survey Ann. Rept. 13.

————— 1936, Rift-valley types: Pan Am. Geologist, v. 63, p. 304.

Wilson, Gilbert, 1952, Ptygmatic structures and their formation: Geol. Mag. [Great Britain], v. 89, p. 1–52.

————— 1953, Mullion and rodding structures in the Moine series of Scotland: London, Geologists' Assoc. Proc., v. 64, p. 118–151.

Wynne-Edwards, H. R., 1963, Flow folding: Am. Jour. Sci., v. 261, p. 793–814.

7

cleavage, mullion,
rodding, kinks,
and boudinage

ROCK CLEAVAGE

A host of terms (e.g., foliation, flow cleavage, fracture cleavage, schistosity, strain-slip cleavage, slaty cleavage) has been used to designate special types of rock cleavage. All these terms are applied to closely spaced fractures or strongly aligned planar structures of a rock along which the rock tends to break (Fig. 7-1). Some of the terms are genetic and imply mode of origin (e.g., flow cleavage), but unfortunately the mode of origin of cleavage is not clearly understood. Judging from the vast literature on the subject and the strong cases which have been made for first one and then another mode of origin, it seems probable that cleavages can arise under a variety of structural circumstances. Probably it is wise to follow the procedure Sander (1930) applied to metamorphic rocks in designating sets of planes of mechanical inhomogeneity as s surfaces or s planes. Subscripts are used for rocks with more than one plane structure. If bedding can be identified it is one s surface; others are designated S_1, S_2, S_3, etc. and the intersection of S_1 with S forms a lineation, l_1. This procedure at least evades the problem of deciding how each plane formed and the geometrical elements thus defined can be very useful in describing and analyzing the structure. To stop at this point would, however, do a great injustice to the careful studies which have shown so much about the origin of planar features in rock.

Leith (1905) defined two major classes of cleavage, fracture cleavage and flow cleavage, which he differentiated as follows:

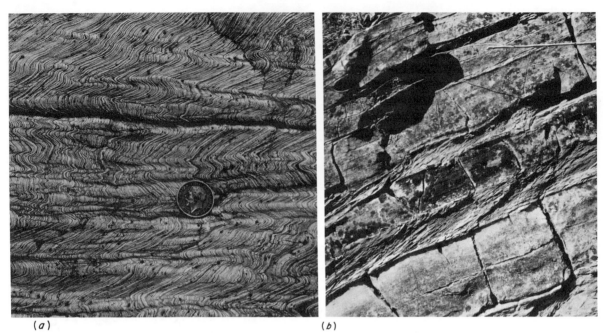

(*a*)   (*b*)

Fig. 7-1   Examples of cleavage. (*a*) Large-scale cleavage (strain slip) in Dartmouth slates, Devon (*Crown copyright*); (*b*) cleavage developed in shale interbedded with uncleaved limestone of the Edinburg formation, Virginia; (*c*) cleavage in argillaceous limestone of Edinburg formation, Virginia; (*d*) strain-slip cleavage in schistose grits (*Crown copyright*).

Fig. 7-2   Microfold in Martinsburg slate showing transport parallel to slaty cleavage. (*From Maxwell, 1962.*)

Fracture cleavage (also called false cleavage, strain-slip cleavage) is conditioned by the existence of incipient, cemented, or welded parallel fractures and is independent of a parallel arrangement of the mineral constituents.

Flow cleavage (also called slaty cleavage, schistosity) is dependent on the parallel arrangement of the mineral constituents of the rock.

If the argument of mode of origin is left out, these definitions allow a reasonably clear way to differentiate cleavages into at least two categories. That the "mode of origin" argument can be elaborate is shown in the following brief outline of ideas on the formation of schistosity (these apply to flow cleavage in general) discussed by Turner (1942) in a review article on the origin of schistosity. Arguments have been made for the origin of schistosity by one or a combination of the following:

(c)

(d)

1. Development of slip surfaces in rocks during plastic deformation
2. Ruptural deformation of the whole rock
3. Rotation of rigid grains in a plastically flowing matrix
4. Plastic deformation of individual grains
5. Rupture of grains
6. Syntectonic crystallization
7. Posttectonic crystallization

Modern experimental results concerning the effects of many of the above are discussed in the section on theory and experiment in rock deformation (see Chap. 5). Briefly, processes of cataclastic and plastic deformation and re-crystallization have been called on to explain the origin of flow cleavage. We will return later to some of these arguments, but it is important first to examine some of the charac-teristic features of cleavage from a purely descriptive point of view.

Slaty Cleavage

Slaty cleavage is simply flow cleavage as it occurs in slate. The slates of Pennsylvania studied by Behre (1933) and Maxwell (1962) are selected for description here. The slates are found in the strongly deformed Appalachian fold belt, and occur in the Upper Ordovician Martinsburg formation, which is composed of shale, sandy shale, and some arkosic sand-stones in a section estimated to be 11,000 ft thick. Slaty cleavage is found in the fine-grained portions of the formation. The most abundant minerals in slate are fine micaceous minerals identified usually as muscovite or sericite, quartz fragments, and commonly some carbonate, pyrite, graphite, and rutile needles.

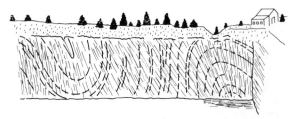

Fig. 7-3 Typical folding of the slate beds; cleavage shows as oblique lines from upper left to lower right. (*From Behre, 1933.*)

The micaceous minerals particularly have a very high degree of parallel orientation in the Pennsylvania slates, and this results in such prominent cleavage that bedding is often obscured. When bedding is traced, however, it is found to be folded, and the folds appear to have been formed as a result of minute movements parallel to the slaty cleavage (Fig. 7-2). The folding is similar in type, and folds show marked crestal thickening.

The cleavages lie approximately parallel to the axial planes of the folds. In regions where

Fig. 7-4 Tectonic history of the Delaware water gap area. (*From Maxwell, 1962.*)

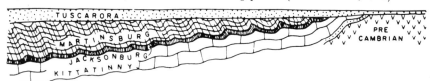

I. END OF TUSCARORA DEPOSITION

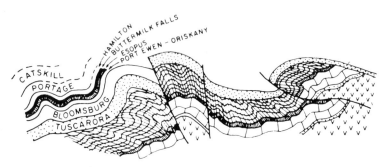

II. END OF APPALACHIAN DEFORMATION

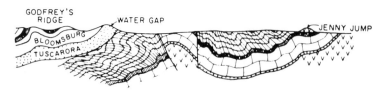

III. CROSS-SECTION, DELAWARE WATER GAP AREA
NEW JERSEY - PENNSYLVANIA

this condition is found, it becomes possible to determine the approximate attitude of the axial plane of the fold and the position of the fold axes relative to any given outcrop on the fold limbs. This is possible because the cleavage intersects the top of a bed in such a way that the acute angle of intersection opens toward the anticlinal axis while the obtuse angle opens toward the adjacent syncline (Fig. 7-3). Care must be exercised in the use of this method because cleavage is not always parallel to the axial plane, and the method can fail if the beds are upside down, if there has been deformation after formation of cleavage, or if there is more than one cleavage direction. In Pennsylvania there has been post-slaty cleavage deformation which has caused structures ranging from gentle flexures to strong folding, and in some places a fracture cleavage is imposed on the slaty cleavage (Fig. 7-4). Despite these later deformations, the slaty cleavage in the Martinsburg formation is of regional scope and is roughly parallel over the region.

Although the cleavage does not usually show in interbedded sandstones, the contacts of sandstone with the slate are tightly welded and show no shearing parallel to the contact. A slate-sandstone contact is shown in Fig. 7-5 in which the sand appears injected into the slate as dikes. Partially as a result of this type of relationship, Maxwell concludes that the cleavage and folding formed while the sediment was still unconsolidated.

Fracture Cleavage

Two generations of cleavage, one with the characteristics of flow cleavage and a later one involving rupture of the earlier cleavage, are encountered. Sometimes the two may be clearly differentiated but at other places one appears to grade into the other as in the metasedimentary rocks of east-central Vermont (White, 1949). White found two cleavages, one the schistosity of the rock and the second a fracture cleavage, in the eastern part of the area he studied. The fracture cleavage (White prefers

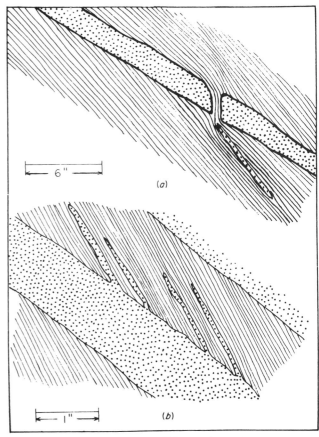

Fig. 7-5 Sandstone dikes parallel to slaty cleavage. (*From Maxwell, 1962.*)

the term *slip cleavage*) cuts the earlier schistosity and appears as parallel fractures, cutting the limbs and axial planes of small scale crinkles in the schistosity. The fracture cleavage is parallel to the axial planes of the small crinkles. The fracture cleavage becomes increasingly developed toward the west until (in a distance of 4 miles) it grades into true schistosity without deflection. Thus there is a progressive rotation of the earlier schistosity by movements along the fracture cleavages until the old schistosity disappeared into the plane of the new schistosity. This was accompanied by growth of new micas parallel to the new schistosity. In another example described by

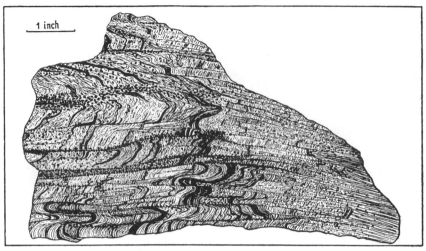

Fig. 7-6 Polished specimen of phyllite showing limbs of folds, displaced by shear zones and subsequently recrystallized. Biotite crystalloblasts along the shear zones are coarser than those elsewhere in the phyllite. At lower right, the zones are so closely spaced as to obliterate the original beds. Siliceous layers shown in solid black. (*From Balk, 1936.*)

Balk (1936), shown in Fig. 7-6, foliation of a phyllite is shown displaced along closely spaced shear zones. The displacements are clear at the left, but biotite crystalloblasts are coarser along the shear zones than elsewhere in the rock and the foliation is obliterated completely to the right.

The fracture cleavage mentioned earlier in the Pennsylvania slate belt is found in silty and calcareous beds as well as in some of the slates. The cleavage surfaces are often distinct cracks separated from one another by thin plates of rock showing little or no parallel alignment of minerals. The fracture cleavages are often only subparallel, and their surfaces may be rough, irregular, and discontinuous. The cleavages tend to be parallel to axial planes of associated folds only in the fold hinge, and they maintain an obtuse relationship with the bedding. The cleavage fans out across the fold and dips toward the axial planes of anticlines. That some slip occurred parallel to beds is shown by bending of the cleavages along bedding surfaces.

Observations on the Occurrence of Cleavage
It will prove useful to summarize some of the characteristics of cleavages and to make some additional observations before turning to the question of the origin of cleavages.

1. *Spacing.* Flow cleavage tends to pervade the rock in slates but in schists, spacing of the planes of schistosity may vary from a few millimeters to fractions of an inch apart. Fracture cleavages vary in spacing from millimeters to inches.
2. *Rock type.* Cleavages are most common in fine-grained rocks and tend to be less developed in sandstones than in silts, shales, or limestones.
3. *Relation of cleavage to folds.* Folds in slate appear to have formed by movements along parallel cleavages. In Pennsylvania these are parallel to the axial plane. Another common pattern in flow cleavage is that of fanning cleavages (see E. Cloos' work, described in Chap. 13). The cleav-

ages dip slightly toward the axial planes of the anticlines. Fracture cleavages tend to strike in the same direction as the strike of the axial planes on which they occur, but their dips show greater divergence from the axial plane as they fan across fold axes.

4. *Variations in degree of development, in spacing, and in attitude where rocks of different lithologies occur.* The cleavages often appear to be "refracted" on passing from one layer to another of different character. Often this is due to having flow cleavage developed in one lithology and fracture cleavage in another.

5. *Movement along and between cleavages.* It appears that the folding in the Pennsylvania slate is due to movements parallel to flow cleavage. Movements can also occur parallel to fracture cleavage, giving rise to chevron-shaped folds or a variety of other structures, i.e., small folds, kinking, or shear offsets. De Sitter (1964) calls the thin slivers of rock between cleavages *microlithons*. When folding or kinking occurs between cleavages, a shortening normal to the cleavages is indicated.

6. *Fracture and flow cleavage occurring together in a rock mass.* It is likely that progressive movements along fracture cleavage can lead to the formation of a new cleavage with the characteristics of flow cleavage.

7. *Recrystallization—probably prominent in the development of flow cleavage, particularly in schists.* The mineral constituents owe their large size to processes of recrystallization. In some schists and phyllites it is clear that recrystallization was contemporaneous with movements parallel to the flow cleavage. This is shown by the presence of "rolled or snowball" garnets which show rotation during growth.

8. *Shortening normal to cleavages.* Deformed oolites, fossils, pebbles, and other primary

geological objects in rocks with flow cleavage show clearly that shortening normal to the principal cleavage plane often accompanies the development of cleavage, and that elongation is parallel to the cleavage.

Hypotheses of the Formation of Flow Cleavage

A basic question in considering the origin of cleavage is whether all types of flow cleavage originate in the same way. Should we expect to define a single process by which cleavage forms in slate, phyllite, and schist? Do the processes differ for each? Or is it possible that any one type may originate by several different processes under different conditions

Much attention has been given to the idea that slate, phyllite, and schist represent three progressive stages in the metamorphism of shale, with the main difference lying in the prominence of shearing movements in the development of slate. The orientation of minerals in these three metamorphic rocks is generally ascribed to:

1. Mechanical rotation of existing minerals
2. Mechanical flattening of existing minerals
3. Recrystallization and growth of new minerals
4. Combinations of the above

The first of these ideas was suggested by Sorby (1853) on the basis of petrographic studies of slate and artificially compressed clay. He concluded that the mica flakes and other planar minerals were rotated into parallel positions normal to the compression. The rotations were envisioned as being those of rigid grains in a plastically flowing matrix. This idea, especially in combination with rupturing and extension of grains and recrystallization, has been popular. Recent experimental work has shown more clearly the process by which plastic deformation in rocks occurs. Mechanical flattening of grains occurs through a process of brittle fracture, by granulation, by gliding within mineral grains, by slip between layers of atoms, by twinning, and by recrystallization. The rolled garnets found in some phyllites show clearly that recrystallization was contemporaneous with movements parallel to cleavage.

Crystallization contemporaneous with deformation has long been recognized as an important process in the development of schistosity; and the few instances of little deformed fossils preserved in schistose rocks are sufficient evidence to show that recrystallization without strong distortion of the rock does sometimes take place. The mechanisms which have been suggested for syntectonic recrystallization include solution and redeposition according to Riecke's principle, which holds that the solubility of a strained face of a crystal is increased. Thus material tends to dissolve most rapidly from points of strain, to be transported by solution, and to be redeposited elsewhere in the fabric where strain is less. The rock fabric tends toward the development of a foliated structure with the foliation normal to the principal stress direction, both by a process of flattening and by deposition of dissolved material in unstressed positions.

Experimental work with calcite and marble has produced some interesting results which bear on recrystallization. Marbles strained slowly at temperatures from 400 to 800°C undergo some recrystallization. New crystals have a strongly developed preferred orientation of the c crystallographic axis in a position normal to the maximum stress direction. Turner and Weiss (1963) conclude that "the driving force of syntectonic recrystallization is the augmented free energy due to strain in the lattice; and diffusion, moreover, seems to be facilitated by accumulated lattice defects."

So far our attention has been directed to flow cleavage as a product of metamorphism. Maxwell (1962) has proposed a strikingly different alternative for the development of slaty cleavage. His theory is derived from the evidence which points to development of cleavage

in the Pennsylvania slates before the rock was consolidated. Evidence of the unconsolidated nature of the sediment at the time of cleavage formation includes:

1. Sandstones interbedded with the slate were injected along cleavage directions as dikes, a process associated with unconsolidated sand.
2. The sands and slates are folded into similar-type patterns. Apparently the bedding exercised little control in folding; the folds are passive, indicating that the sands were incompetent materials.
3. The cleavage formed in Late Ordovician time; cleavage of the same orientation and character does not occur in younger units. It is unlikely that the sediment was deeply buried.
4. The main micaceous mineral in the slate is illite, and recent studies indicate that illite and even chlorite can be generated in marine environments at low temperatures and low pressures. Thus the usual metamorphic conditions of high temperature and pressure are unnecessary to account for micaceous minerals of slate.

Maxwell (1962, p. 300) summarizes his hypothesis as follows:

In the early stages of compaction a clay may be visualized as an open network of clay plates and fibers with water-filled interstices. As compaction proceeds, water is expelled, and the clay particles rotate, approaching parallelism as more and more water is expelled (Buessem and Nagy, 1954). If the process proceeds slowly and water pressure remains essentially hydrostatic, the load is carried by the clay particles, friction and bearing strength increase, and in later stages compaction occurs only at the expense of considerable deformation of the clay particles. In the process proposed in this paper, it is assumed that a thick sequence of impermeable shaly sediments accumulated just prior to deformation and that escape of pore water was so slow that abnormally high pore pressures characterized the sequence when deformation began. The resulting compression tended to increase the pore-water pressure which may very well have approximated the lithostatic pressure through much of the formation; perhaps even locally lithostatic pressure was exceeded, with resulting instabilities giving rise to fluid flow perpendicular to the maximum pressure. Flowage parallel to cleavage . . . may well be of this origin, as may be the peculiar downward-injected sandstone dike of [Fig. 7-5].

During deformation, flattening, rotation, and extensive flowage parallel to cleavage resulted in a near-parallel orientation of clay particles. This in turn destroyed the original network of clay particles which held the water so tenaciously; permeability increased in the plane of the cleavage and in the direction of the grain, facilitating the rapid dewatering of the slaty rocks as the last stages of the slaty cleavage episode. Thereafter the rocks were relatively brittle, as indicated by the post-slaty cleavage deformation.

Hypotheses on the Origin of Fracture Cleavage

As in the case of flow cleavage, it seems probable that a number of different structural conditions give rise to fracture cleavage. No really satisfactory distinction can be drawn among joints, fractures, and fracture cleavage except one based on spacing, and even it is not always satisfactory. Fracture cleavages may be spaced on the order of a few millimeters apart. The fractures illustrated in Fig. 7-6, for example, were referred to as shears by Balk, and it is evident that shearing movements have taken place along them. At the same time, though, these appear to be excellent examples of the fractures called fracture cleavage by others. The term *fracture cleavage* has been applied to closely spaced fractures located in a variety of structural positions, and their origin has been attributed to a number of mechanisms. For example:

1. Fractures parallel to a fault and attributed to shear.
2. Fractures along which movements have

occurred, giving rise to shear or similar-type folds.
3. Fractures parallel to axial planes of chevron- or accordion-type folds.
4. Fractures parallel to axial planes of kinks in foliation of schistose rocks; also in slate.
5. Fractures in the hinge zones of competent layers in concentric folds and attributed to extension fracturing. Fractures much farther down on the limbs and approximately normal to bedding have similarly been attributed to extension as the fold amplitude has increased.
6. Fractures originating from interbed shearing during folding as a result of couples generated by movements along bedding surfaces in concentric-type folding.

If all these fractures are to be considered fracture cleavages, several mechanisms are needed to generate them. The three most commonly employed are shearing, extension, and flattening. The first two of these have been discussed previously in the chapter on fractures. De Sitter (1964) emphasizes the role of flattening in development of cleavages of both types. He calls the rock slivers between two cleavages microlithons and points convincingly to the folding and kinking within the microlithons as evidence of the shortening of the rock normal to the cleavages. Thus these cleavages arise as a result of flattening accompanied by movements in planes normal to the maximum stress direction.

MULLION AND RODDING

The terms *mullion* and *rodding* have been applied to columnlike structures found in folded sedimentary and metamorphic rocks. Mullion structure has the external appearance of intersecting columns; internally the columns are composed of whatever type of country rock they bound. Rods have a more distinct cylindrical form and usually are composed of quartz. G. Wilson (1953) uses this difference in com-

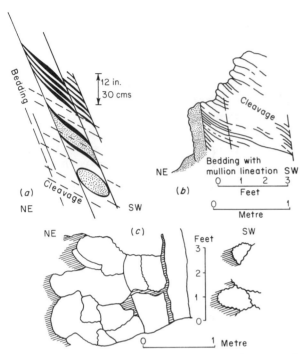

Fig. 7-7 (a) and (b) The development of cleavage mullions, with examples; (c) profiles of irregular mullions. (*From Gilbert Wilson, 1953.*)

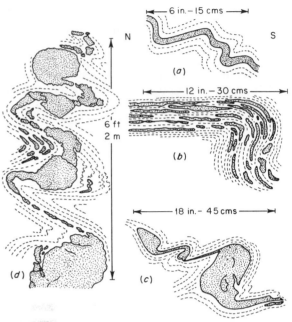

Fig. 7-8 (a) Slightly folded quartz vein parallel to the bedding; (b) stretched and folded quartz lenses parallel to the bedding; (c) and (d) profiles of quartz rods developed in the apices of small-scale folds. (*From Gilbert Wilson, 1953.*)

position as a means of distinguishing the two types of features. The origin of mullions and rods has been interpreted in quite different ways by various geologists, and it is probable that similar types of structures can originate by different means. Essentially the difference in interpretation revolves around the question of whether the rods and modified columnar forms are developed parallel or perpendicular to the direction of movement. Terms such as *slickensides grooving* have been applied to "parallel striated and grooved prisms suggesting logs of wood" (Fermor, 1909, in Wilson 1953), and the rod and mullion forms often seen on fault planes are well known. Such structures have almost certainly formed by movements parallel to the grooves or rods.

A very different mode of origin is proposed

for the mullion and rods described by G. Wilson (1953) in the Scottish Highlands. Wilson recognized three types of mullions: bedding or fold mullions, cleavage mullions, and irregular mullions. Fold mullions are cylindrical undulations of bedding, as shown by the conformable laminations of bedding within the mullions. Cleavage mullions are formed by the intersection of cleavage with bedding; they are often quite angular prisms for this reason (Fig. 7-7). The contacts between thin and massive beds are corrugated by asymmetrical rolls. A third variety of mullion characterized by highly irregular outline in cross section is described but not explained by Wilson. The mullions are remarkably constant along their lengths and are parallel to the fold axes of the larger folds on which they are located.

G. Wilson (1953) described quartz rods at Ben Hutig in Scotland as follows:

There is every gradation between plane or flatly lenticular quartz-veinlets on the one hand, and cylindrical quartz-rods on the other. Both are the products of quartz-segregations which were formed during the folding, shearing and metamorphism of the country-rocks. Some veins are undistorted and clean-cut, these must have been formed at the end of the period of movement. Others that formed during the movements were distorted, folded, or even rolled to varying degrees, and are now seen as rods. The original quartz-segregations developed along three main planes of weakness in the rocks, and can be locally subdivided into (i) those which lie along planes of secondary cleavage or foliation; (ii) those whose formation was controlled by original bedding; (iii) those which filled fissures oblique to those two important structural surfaces.

KINKS—KINK BANDING

The term *kink* is used to describe the abrupt bending or rotation of cleavage, foliation, or bedding planes. It was first recognized by Clough (1897), who called the bands produced by kinks *strain bands*. Kinks are common features of thinly foliated, fine-grained rocks such as phyllites. The foliation between kinks is usually planar, and the kink itself may be a very abrupt flexure of the foliation or a fracture (which accounts for the name *joint drag*, sometimes applied). Terminology applied to kinks is illustrated in Fig. 7-9. The zone of rotation may be sharp, producing chevron or angular folds, or it may be curved as shown. Another common characteristic of kink bands is that two sets of zones, inclined to one another and showing opposite senses of rotation, occur to-

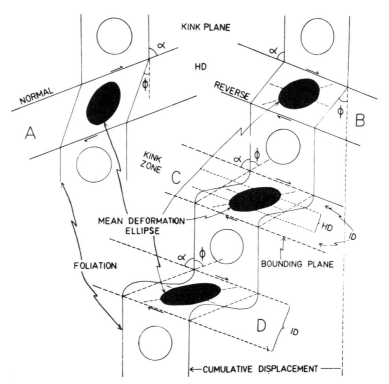

Fig. 7-9 Geometry and terminology of kink bands. (*From Dewey, 1965.*)

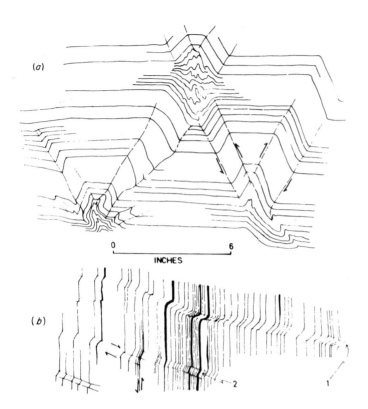

(a)

0 ‖————————————————‖ 6
INCHES

(b)

Fig. 7-10 Late folds in black Carboniferous slates on the southern side of the Beara Peninsula, County Cork, Ireland. (a) Conjugate folds at the Slath; (b) kink bands at Black Ball head. (*From Dewey, 1965.*)

gether; these are called *conjugate sets* (Fig. 7-10).

Dewey (1965) has proposed recognition of four different types of kink bands: joint-drag kink bands, segregation kink bands, pelitic strain bands, and shear kink bands (Fig. 7-11).

1. Joint-drag kink bands. A kink band is a joint drag when the kink plane is a fracture or a fault along which the foliation is externally rotated. Within the foliation, internal rotation occurs by slip or gliding along foliation planes. This type of deformation is thought to occur in brittle materials and at a rapid rate.
2. Segregation kink bands. These have weakly developed kink planes. The foliation is pulled apart and the voids are often filled with quartz or calcite. The development of voids indicates shallow deformation.

3. Pelitic strain bands. This type of kink is defined on the basis of the changes which have taken place within the foliation during the development of the bands. The long limbs are semipelitic, the kink band is pelitic. A margin of sericite and muscovite occurs on the kink band from which quartz has migrated (Fig. 7-12).
4. Shear kink bands occur as similar-type folds developed by continuous shear. Note the absence of kink planes.

The first two of these categories are generally recognized as kinks. Some geologists may prefer to consider the third and fourth examples of shear folding.

The differences in nature of the above four types of structures tend to dissuade one from looking for a single mechanism to explain the mechanics of the origin or the implications of kinks. Kinks are commonly attributed to late-stage deformation, and particularly the joint drags and segregation kink bands seem to fall into this category. In these two cases the mechanism of formation involves primarily slip between foliation layers. Pelitic strain bands and shear kink bands would appear to form under conditions of higher confining pressure and by shearing.

Paterson and Weiss (1966) formed kink bands in phyllite experimentally using very high confining pressure (5 kbars) and room temperature. Specimens were deformed in compression with various orientations of foliation, and gliding along foliation occurred readily when foliation was favorably oriented (up to about 45°) with development of kinks, conjugate folds, and tightly oppressed similar folds. Surprisingly, deformation was found to proceed by growth of the kinked region (Fig. 7-13) up to as much as 50 percent shortening, and parts of some of these specimens retained an undeformed appearance after 50 percent shortening. Boundaries of deformed domains are kink surfaces across which the foliation is sharply bent.

BOUDINAGE

Lohest (1909) applied the term *boudinage structure* to sausage-shaped bodies of one rock layer sandwiched between layers of different rock

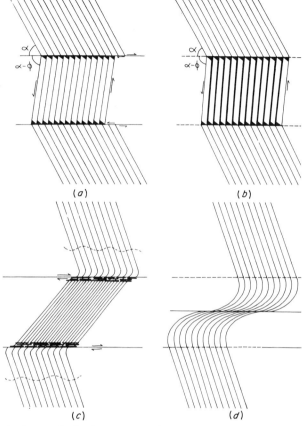

Fig. 7-11 Idealized geometry of four types of kink band. (*a*) Joint drag; (*b*) segregation kink band; (*c*) pelitic strain band; (*d*) shear kink band. (*From Dewey, 1965.*)

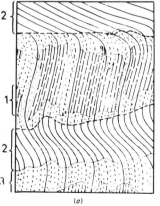

Fig. 7-12 Camera lucida drawings of a thin section of a semipelite showing kink bands, Glenummera, Central Murrisk, County Mayo, Ireland. (*a*) × 15; (*b*) × 60. 1 = semipelitic normal long limb; 2 = pelitic rotated short limb; 3 = long limb with large magnetite and strainfree quartz porphyroblasts. (*From Dewey, 1965.*)

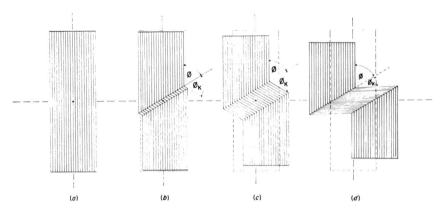

Fig. 7-13 Progressive deformation by kinking. (*a*) Undeformed; (*b*) and (*c*) increased shortening by lateral migration of kink boundaries with $\phi = \phi_k$ unchanged; (*b*) and (*d*) increased shortening by further deformation within kink band, ϕ_k becoming smaller than ϕ and foliation laminae becoming thinner and longer. (*From Paterson and Weiss, 1966.*)

type. He distinguished the layers as fractured (making the *boudins*) and unfractured. The rock types were schists and gneisses in this case, but very similar structures have been widely described in layered sequences ranging from semiconsolidated sediments to low- and high-grade metamorphic rocks. Significant differences in competency (ductility) between the rock in the *boudins* and the enclosing rock are generally found, and this is usually taken as the reason for the development of the structure.

Excellent detailed descriptions of boudinage are given by Wegmann (1932), Ernst Cloos (1947), and Ramberg (1955). *Boudins* may be separated from one another, but often they occur as a linked chain, and the individual bodies are usually elongate in the plane of the layering. The three-dimensional shape of *boudins* is poorly documented, but in cross section they are usually symmetrical about a plane parallel with the layering. Many *boudins* are more or less equidimensional in the plane parallel to layering, and they are commonly shaped like rhombs or parallelograms (Ramberg, 1955). Rod-shaped bodies oriented perpendicular to the mineral elongation in adjacent schists are also known. The edges of *boudins*

may be sharply defining rectangular blocks which have simply separated. The material composing the *boudins* must have been both brittle and strong relative to the enclosing materials in such cases. *Boudins* with a barrel-shaped cross section are far more common. This shape arises from plastic flowage and lateral elongation of the body. Lens-shaped bodies may be produced in extreme cases of plastic flowage. Ramberg distinguishes lens-shaped *boudins* produced by plastic flowage behind a tensional rupture from *boudins* produced by complete necking-down during plastic stretching by the structure at the tapered ends. Where the plastic flowage took place after rupture, the upper and lower edges of the *boudin* are drawn out farther than the central portion of the *boudin*.

Boudins are sometimes rotated or deformed by shearing, but such cases appear to be due to superposition of deformations and are not an integral part of the process by which most *boudins* originate.

Structures within incompetent layers support the idea that there has been plastic flowage within the material parallel to the layering and directed toward the places where the *boudins* separated. Sometimes the layering is curled around the edge of the *boudin*. A drag fold may be formed in the zone of separation if flowage continues. Such zones of separation are sites of secondary mineral growth in metamorphic rocks, and in cases of extreme replacement the structure within the zone is totally obscured.

Most students of boudinage agree that it results from elongation parallel to the layering in a sequence of materials of varied competence in which the more brittle material is broken while the more ductile rock flows. We might expect the nature of the structure to depend on the ductility contrast; hence we would consider structures ranging from simple pinch

and swell features to rectangular *boudins* as products of similar processes in cases of varying ductility contrast.

Elongation in a rock sequence may result from a variety of conditions—stretching as a result of tensile stress, compression perpendicular to the direction of elongation, or a stress couple. Ramberg favors the second of these alternatives as the most general condition. The evolution of the structure may be viewed in terms of a model consisting of a competent layer sandwiched between two incompetent layers. As the sequence is compressed between two rigid plates, plastic flowage occurs within the incompetent layers from the center toward

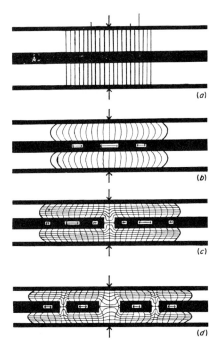

Fig. 7-14 Successive steps during formation of boudinage structures. (*a*) State prior to compression. The black layer in the middle is the competent body on either side of which incompetent bodies exist (vertically lined regions). Compressive stress is transmitted by means of two stiff sheets (black). (*b*) Compression has started; the plastic flowage in the incompetent layers is indicated by the distortion of the originally vertical lines. Arrows in the competent black layer indicate tensile stress. (*c*) A more advanced step than (*b*). Competent layer is now ruptured in the middle where tension was greatest. The network in the incompetent layer indicates pattern of flowage. This network is not a further evolution of the deformed network in (*b*), but rather the evolution of an

imaginary rectangular network not shown in (*b*). Horizontal arrows show tensile stresses in the competent layer. (*d*) A stage more advanced than (*c*). Competent layer has ruptured at two new places. The pattern of the network indicates plastic flowage in the incompetent layers during evolution from (*c*) to (*d*). Again, the deformed network in (*d*) is supposed to have developed from a rectangular imaginary network not shown in (*c*). (*From Ramberg, 1955.*)

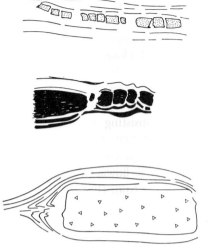

Fig. 7-15 Sketches showing natural boudinage. (*Drawn from photographs in Ramberg, 1955.*)

the margins. Depending on the boundary conditions, flowage would be possible in a single direction (giving rise to rod-shaped *boudins*) or in multiple directions. The flowage exerts drag on the competent layer, fracturing it or at least separating older fractured blocks (Fig. 7-14). The magnitude of the tensile stress built up in the competent layer depends on such factors as the magnitude of the compressive stress, the rate of flow, viscosity coefficients, boundary conditions between the competent and incompetent layers, area of contact, and thickness.

If it is assumed that deformation can be treated as a case of viscous flow for the incompetent layer and elastic deformation in the competent layer before failure, then mathematical relationships among compressive stress, rate of flow, magnitude of tensile stress in the *boudin* layer, and size of *boudins* can be formulated (see Ramberg, 1955, for derivation and all formulas). The stress at the center of the competent layer S_0 is found to be given by:

$$S_0 = -\frac{Zi}{Zc}(P_0 - P_L)$$

where Zi and Zc are thicknesses of the compe-

tent and incompetent layers and $(P_0 - P_L)$ is the pressure gradient in the incompetent layer. Surprisingly, the viscosity coefficients of the layers do not determine this value. It is concluded that the viscosities control only the rate at which the *boudins* form.

REFERENCES

Anderson, E. M., 1948, On lineation and petrofabric structure: Geol. Soc. London Quart. Jour., v. 104, p. 99–132.

Bader, H., 1951, Introduction to ice petrofabrics: Jour. Geology, v. 59, no. 6.

Balk, Robert, 1936, Structural and petrologic studies in Dutchess County, New York: Geol. Soc. America Bull., v. 47, pt. 1.

Behre, C. H., Jr., 1933, Slate in Pennsylvania: Pennsylvania Geol. Survey Bull., no. 16.

Bless, F. D., 1955, Further study of cleavage tendencies in quartz [abs.]: Geol. Soc. America Bull., v. 66 (12), pt. 2, p. 1531–1532.

Buessem, W. R., and Nagy, B., 1954, The mechanism of the deformation of clay: Clay and minerals: Natl. Acad. Sci., Natl. Research Council, pub. 327, p. 480–491.

Cloos, Ernst, 1946, Lineation: Geol. Soc. America Mem. 18.

——— 1947, Boudinage: Am. Geophys. Union Trans., v. 28, p. 626–632.

Crook, K. A. W., 1964, Cleavage in weakly deformed mudstones: Am. Jour. Sci., v. 262, p. 523–531.

Dale, T. N., 1892, On plicated cleavage-foliation: Am. Jour. Sci., 3d. ser., v. 43, p. 317–319.

De Sitter, L. U., 1964, Structural geology, 2d ed.: New York, McGraw-Hill, 587 p.

Dewey, J. F., 1965, Nature and origin of kinkbands: Tectonophysics, v. 1, p. 459–494.

Fairbairn, H. W., 1935, Notes on the mechanics of rock foliation: Jour. Geology, v. 43, p. 591–608.

Gonzaley-Bonorino, F., 1960, The mechanical factor in the formation of schistosity: Internat. Geol. Congr., 21st, v. 18, p. 303–316.

Hancock, P. L., 1965, Axial-trace-fractures and deformed concretionary rods in South Pembrokeshire: Geol. Mag. [Great Britain], v. 102, p. 143–163.

Haughton, S., 1856, On slaty cleavage and distortion of fossils: Philos. Mag., v. 12, p. 409–421.

Holinquist, P. J., 1931, On the relations of the boudinage structure: Geol. Fören. Stockholm, v. 53, p. 193–208.

Leith, C. K., 1905, Rock cleavage: U. S. Geol. Survey Bull., v. 239.

Lohest, M., 1909, De L'origine des veines et des geodes des terrains primares de Belgique: Soc. Géol. Belgique Annales, v. 36B, p. 275–282.

Maxwell, J. C., 1962, Origin of slaty and fracture cleavage in the Delaware water gap area, New Jersey and Pennsylvania, *in* Petrologic studies— a volume to honor A. F. Buddington: Geol. Soc. America.

Mead, W. J., 1940, Folding rock flowage and foliate structures: Jour. Geology, v. 48, p. 1007–1021.

Oertel, Gerhard, 1962, Extrapolation in geologic fabrics: Geol. Soc. America Bull., v. 73, p. 325–342.

Paterson, M. S., and Weiss, L. E., 1961, Symmetry concepts in the structural analysis of deformed rocks: Geol. Soc. America Bull., v. 72, p. 841–882.

—— 1966, Experimental deformation and folding in phyllite: Geol. Soc. America Bull., v. 77, no. 4, p. 343–374, 20 figs., 9 pls.

Ramberg, Hans, 1955, Natural and experimental boudinage and pinch and swell structures: Jour. Geology, v. 63, no. 6.

—— 1960, Relationships between length of arch and thickness of ptygmatically folded veins: Am. Jour. Sci., v. 258, no. 1, p. 36–46.

Sander, B., 1930, Gefügekunde der Gesteine: Vienna, Springer.

Sharpe, D., 1849, On slaty cleavage: Geol. Soc. London Quart. Jour., v. 5, p. 111–129.

Sorby, H. C., 1853, On the origin of slaty cleavage: Edinburgh New Phil. Jour., v. 10, p. 137–147.

—— 1856, On the theory of slaty cleavage: Philos. Mag., v. 12, p. 127–129.

Turner, F. J., 1942, Current views on the origin and tectonic significance of schistosity: Royal Soc. New Zealand Trans., v. 72, pt. 20.

—— 1948, Mineralogical and structural evolution of metamorphic rocks: Geol. Soc. America Mem. 30.

Turner, F. J., and Weiss, L. E., 1963, Structural analysis of metamorphic tectonites: New York, McGraw-Hill, 560 p.

Walls, R., 1937, A new record of boudinage structure from Scotland: Geol. Mag. [Great Britain], v. 74, p. 325–332.

Wegmann, C. E. 1932, Note sur le boudinage: Soc. geol. France Compte Rendu, v. 5, pt. 2, p. 477–489.

Weiss, L. E., and McIntyre, D. B., 1957, Structural geometry of Dolradian Rocks at Loch Leven, Scottish Highlands: Jour. Geology, v. 65, no. 6.

White, W. S., 1949, Cleavage in east-central Vermont: Am. Geophys. Union Trans., v. 30, p. 587–594.

Wilson, Gilbert, 1946, The relationship of slaty cleavage and kindred structures to tectonics: Geol. Assoc. London Proc., v. 57, p. 263–302.

—— 1953, Mullion and rodding structures in the Moine series of Scotland: Geol. Assoc. Proc., v. 64, p. 118–151.

—— 1961, The tectonic significance of small scale structures, and their importance to the geologist in the field: Ann. Soc. Geol. Belgium, v. 84, p. 423–548.

Wilson, M. E., 1953, Early Precambrian rocks of western Quebec: Geol. Soc. America Bull., v. 64, p. 1492.

8
primary
sedimentary structures

Study of primary sedimentary structural features is important to the structural geologist because he must often rely on primary features in order to determine which side of a sedimentary layer was originally the top. Stratification is also significant because it is through our understanding of the primary shape and attitude of strata that we are able to perceive that they are deformed and measure the amount of that deformation.

STRATIFICATION

No feature of sedimentary rocks is more universal than stratification. This feature arises through slight variations in any of the physical or chemical characteristics of sediment that occur essentially vertical to the bedding. Among the factors that cause stratification are differences between layers in: (1) chemical composition, (2) grain size, (3) degree of sorting, (4) degree and type of packing, (5) cohesion, (6) cementation, (7) permeability or porosity.

The conditions under which sediment is deposited impart distinctive characteristics to the layering. This is reflected in the nature of the layers, in the arrangement of the material within the strata, in features on the bedding planes, and sometimes in the layer shape of the sedimentary unit. Some stratification arises directly from sedimentation as in the cases of varves, layering in deep sea carbonate and siliceous oozes, evaporites in playa lakes and behind fringing reefs, and chemical precipitates in general. The layering is formed indirectly when the water is agitated so that sediment is reworked, and previously deposited sediment is broken up and redeposited. This is most likely to occur in shallow water. Still other layers form under combined conditions of direct and indirect stratification. A few examples will illustrate the range of types of stratification. The term *varve* is applied to regular layering or lamination due to annual changes in sedimentation. Glacial varved clay and silt is an excellent example. This sediment is found to form under conditions such as those in glacial lakes in which a fine dark layer is deposited during the winter when the surface of the lake is frozen and the source of sediment cut off by ice and snow. A thick, coarser, and lighter-colored layer is deposited in spring and summer when the sediment size in the water is increased. Varves can also be formed in lakes in temperate regions where remains of plankton form a large part of the sediment. The amount of plankton reaches a peak of abundance in late spring, while evaporation with increased calcium carbonate deposition reaches a peak in late summer. For more detail the student is referred to the work of Bradley (1929) on the Green River shales.

One of the classic examples of still-water deposition is the Jurassic Sea of Bavaria in which the Solenhofen limestone was deposited. This limestone is so fine-grained and uniform that it has been widely used as a lithographic stone. The limestone is thought to have formed in a lagoon between reefs which acted as sediment traps to cut out coarser sediment. The water must have been unagitated because the layering is very regular and fossils of such delicate features as feathers are preserved in the sediment.

The deep ocean basins are largely covered by finely stratified sediment, most of which has slowly settled through thousands of feet of water. Skeletal remains of diatoms, foraminifera, and other plankton provide one of the main sources. Red clays presumably derived from meteoritic dust accumulated over vast periods of time also constitute widespread deposits in the deep seas. Volcanic ash is locally important, and closer to continents, the finer clays transported far out from streams and glaciers are important. All these deposits assume blanketlike form as the particles of sediment settle on the existing submarine topography.

The other primary source of deep sea sediment is the turbidity current. These deposits differ from other types of deep sea sedimentary deposits both in the form of the deposit, which is lobate in plan, and in composition and internal structure. Turbidity current deposits are commonly associated with submarine slumps at river deltas or continental shelves, especially where streams carrying heavy loads of sediment have built up deposits on steep slopes. The material in the turbidity current deposits is usually sand, silt, or other normally shallow-water deposits, and may contain invertebrate shells and even grass. These are found deposited on typical deep sea sediments as off the Grand Banks (Heezen, Ericson, and Ewing, 1952) in bathyl and abyssal depths. Typically these deposits contain graded bedding, and the clastic sands sometimes show current ripple marks. In a number of instances large blocks of material have been transported.

Graded Bedding

Sediments or sedimentary rocks are said to be graded when there has been a sorting of sizes and separation of these vertically to some extent within the sequence. A simple experiment approximates the physical conditions. Place a poorly sorted sediment into a long cylinder and shake until all the sediment is in suspension, then set the cylinder down. At this point all sizes are distributed at random through the cylinder and the only force acting on the mixture aside from the momentum of the agitated water is gravity. Physical formulas (Stokes' law) have been devised for the purpose of analyzing settling velocities, and these formulas show that the velocity with which particles settle is a function of the viscosity of the liquid and the diameter and density of the particles. The symbols are

$$V = \frac{2}{9} \frac{ga^2(d_1 - d_2)}{\eta}$$

where V = settling velocity
   a = radius of sphere
d_1 and d_2 = densities of sphere and medium
   g = gravitational force
   η = coefficient of viscosity

In general terms the largest and most dense fraction settles fastest, and thus the lowest layer is composed mainly of the larger and more dense fragments mixed with a small percentage of finer materials that were close to the bottom when settling started. At a later time all but the smallest fraction will have settled out and the bedding will have a distinct graded character. Kuenen (1952), Kuenen and Migliorini (1952), and others have demonstrated the formation of graded bedding in clastic sediment that has slumped, formed a turbidity current, and settled out in a sedimentation tank. Among the notable instances of graded bedding in modern sediments are the turbidity current deposits that have been described in the North Atlantic Ocean basin. Since they were first recognized many cores containing coarse clastic sediments have been taken in the deep sea, and many of these exhibit graded bedding. It seems very probable that deposition from density currents may be one of the most important processes of sedimentation on the continental rises and in the deep ocean basins, and particularly within basins surrounded by over-steepened submarine slopes.

Ideally graded deposits show a gradual decrease in grain size from bottom to top of a layer, but unfortunately for those wishing to use graded bedding to distinguish the top of beds, conditions sometimes exist during sedimentation which give rise to abnormal grading. For example, a reversal in grain size may be present. This would not occur if conditions were just like those described in our experiment. One main difference lies in the fact that the water is often in motion in nature. Eddies may be effective in keeping smaller fractions in suspension. Also in the case of turbidity currents the flow may be laminated with a turbulent zone near the top and increasing velocity in depth. Sediment is concentrated toward the bottom of density currents. Some of the abnormalities may be related to the rate and character of sediment supplied to the turbidity current and the tendency for lighter particles to be removed.

Exotic blocks

The term *exotic blocks* is applied to large fragments or blocks of rock which occur within sedimentary deposits that were laid down under conditions which would seem to be incongruous with the deposition of the blocks. Large blocks of reef material are found in deposits of the Delaware basin, west Texas, but it seems clear that these are masses from the reef which encircle the basin and that they were moved by sliding or slumping from the reefs into the

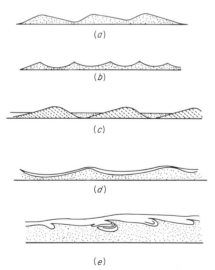

Fig. 8-1 Ripple marks. (*a*) Current ripples; (*b*) oscillation ripples; (*c*) current ripples showing internal cross lamination and coarse particles collected in troughs; (*d*) current ripples showing a thin shale layer deposited with greatest thickness in troughs of ripples; (*e*) antidune ripple. (*From Shrock, 1948.*)

basin where shales were being deposited. At the present time, large blocks are sometimes transported by streams from the mountains along the California coast into the sea where they are slid or are transported in turbidity currents into much deeper water than that in which they might normally be expected to be found.

Of less certain origin are boulders such as those found in the Johns' Valley shale of Pennsylvanian age in the western Ouachita Mountains. Here exotic blocks ranging in age from Cambrian to Mississippian are found in a normally marine shale. Some of the blocks are from 10 to 100 ft in diameter. They were apparently derived from the Arbuckle Mountains, but how they were transported so far from their source is a problem. Ice rafting has been suggested, but there is no clear evidence that glaciers were present at that time, the blocks are not striated, and there are no tillites. An alternate interpretation is that the blocks were emplaced by means of submarine slump and gravity sliding. In this case the blocks broke loose and moved down initial dips on the sea floor, sliding on a mud base or within a mud flow.

The bedded character in the case of indirect stratification is due to agitation, typical of shallow water. Agitation is the movement of water largely as a result of wave action and long shore currents. There is vigorous agitation near shore where energy is still available when oscillating water affects the sea bottom. This agitation is capable of moving sand- and mud-sized particles with ease but probably not gravel. The energy needed to break up sediments and move gravel and larger sizes is produced by the action of breaking waves, particularly storm waves.

Where indirect stratification has been important, bedding is likely to show such evidence of the agitation as reworked deposits, the presence of broken shell fragment beds, coquina, edgewise conglomerates, or flat pebble conglomerates. Edgewise and flat pebble conglomerates are formed when thin bedded sediments are broken up in agitated waters. The conglomerate is likely to be edgewise if settling is rapid and there is much loose sediment in which platy fragments can become embedded. The fragments of flat pebble conglomerates settle approximately in the original plane of bedding.

Examples of the products of combined direct and indirect stratification are found where there is a fluctuation of sea level due to glaciation or any other cause. The immediate result is a mixing of deposits of shallow and deeper water environments. For example, a succession of layers might be found to contain layers of mud interbedded with broken fragments of shells, then mud and silt indicating a deepening of water, and finally mud with few shells which are whole and must have settled in deep, quiet water where they were undisturbed.

SIGNIFICANT MARKINGS ON BEDDING PLANES*

The main purpose of this treatment is to outline some of the most common types of primary structures and point out their use in determining the top of beds. Markings on bedding are of both organic and inorganic origin. These may be briefly outlined as follows:

Inorganic Marks

Ripple marks

Asymmetrical (current) ripples: The top and bottom are usually indeterminant unless the internal structure of the ripple shows cross lamination (Fig. 8-1). In the case illustrated, the laminae are parallel to the steep slope and the ripple has been buried by fine sediment laid in horizontal beds. Note also that the coarser grains are accumulated in the trough.

Symmetrical ripples: Good for top determina-

---

* Students should refer to Shrock (1948) and Middleton (1965) for more complete details and to Pettijohn and Potter (1964) for some of the best photographs of primary sedimentary features available.

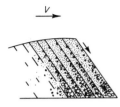

Fig. 8-2 Sorting at the lee face of a dune due to sliding. (*From Brush, 1965.*)

tion. These ripples have pointed crest and rounded troughs resulting from oscillatory water motion.

Interference ripples: Usually the top is indeterminant. These are complex ripples formed by interference wave motion resulting from combined oscillation and current action. Many complex forms result, some of which have sharp crests that may be used for top determination.

Antidune ripples: Good for top determination. These ripples form when the water velocity becomes so great that the sediment below the surface moves. These ripples move upstream by a process of erosion on the downstream face and deposition on the upstream face. At some stages in the movement, sharp crests are formed (Fig. 8-1).

Linguoid ripples: The top is indeterminant. These are modified ripples which have a tongue-shaped form. They resemble mud flows.

Metaripples: Good for top determination. These are large ripples formed on a coarse base material showing long wavelengths. Fine sediment is deposited to give the large ripples their asymmetry.

Channels (Fig. 8-3)

Tidal channels: Good for top determination. These are drainage channels developed on tidal flats as the tide goes out. They are usually dendritic in plan and of U-shaped cross section.

Rill marks: Good for top determination. These are very small dendrite-shaped channel systems formed along beaches as the water flows seaward. They are modified where the flow is intercepted by rocks or shells. Some rill

systems join seaward, and others split, forming distributaries seaward.

Lobate rill marks: Good for top determination. These are lobate-shaped, strongly asymmetric depressions aligned in the direction of flow of strong currents.

Grooves: Good for top determination. Under this heading we may include such features as grooves formed by floating or suspended objects which have projections that are dragged across a soft sediment base leaving a groove.

Cut and fill structures: Good for top determination. These are usually short channels with lens-shaped cross section which are later filled. The manner of filling varies, but commonly the fill is essentially the same as the material into which the channel was cut. The fill tends to possess structures somewhat similar to deltaic deposits. The layering is inclined into the cut channel, and generally these inclined beds have a slightly curved form, concave upward. Often there are numerous cuts, so that previously filled channels are recut and one cut and fill feature is imposed on earlier ones. The truncated surfaces, as they are always on top, provide a good key to which way is up. The conditions of formation are similar to those under which braided streams form.

Mud cracks: These familiar features develop most readily in fine sediment subjected to alternate drying and wetting. The thin layers of mud tend to be broken into a complex system of polygonal shaped pieces. As drying takes place the pieces tend to curl upward. Usually the cracks are filled and the top is easily recognized by the convex surfaces of the cracked layers. If the layer of cracked mud has been subjected to agitation sufficient to turn the plates over, great care should be taken in judging the top.

Objects dropped into sediment

Raindrop impressions: Raindrops leave imprints in soft sediment in the form of small craters with rimmed edges. Depending on the consistency of the mud, it may rise slightly in the center of the crater.

Rocks falling into sediment: If the sediment is soft, the layers are likely to be strongly bent immediately under a falling rock to conform to its shape. In some instances the uppermost layers may even be penetrated. Essentially flat layers may form around the top part as filling goes on around the rock, but if soft sediment is deposited over the rock, compaction will eventually cause the overlying layers to be gently arched.

Fulgurites: When lightning strikes sediment, the quartz present is usually fused to form a glass. The form of such features is tubelike with bifurcations pointed downward.

In addition to the features described above, it is sometimes possible to identify the top of a bed by finding collapsed caves, cave deposits, buried soil profiles, erosional features on unconformities, pot holes, etc.

Organic Markings

Among the multitude of animals which live in shallow water there are a number which leave tracks or trails or which bore into the sediment, leaving marks which are useful for the purpose of determining tops of beds. Usually the tracks and trails consist of furrows and ridges left in a pattern which is typical of the type of animal. In such cases it is necessary to know the pattern left by the particular animal. The top can then be determined from the relative distribution of ridges and furrows in the pattern. In simple cases the trail is a single, rather straight groove, but more complicated patterns are more typical. Footprints in soft sediment are more readily identified.

Many invertebrates burrow in sediment. One worm tube (*Scolithus*) is nearly always found perpendicular to bedding in sandstone or quartzite. It is a useful guide when the bedding is not apparent. Most borings are useful to determine the top of beds only if the starting point of the boring can be seen, but many worm borings are so complicated they are of little use. The burrows may have a small ridge left around the entrance to the hole where material removed from the hole has been built up.

DIVERGENT STRUCTURES BETWEEN BEDDING PLANES

Of the various sedimentary structures found between bedding planes, two stand out as particularly significant. These are (1) cross laminations such as those arising on deltas, dune deposits, and scour and fill structures and (2) divergent structures due to movement of materials within beds after initial deposition and before or during the processes of consolidation, compaction, and cementation (see Chap. 9). The first of these two categories is sometimes important as a means of identifying tops of beds and the second because these structures can be

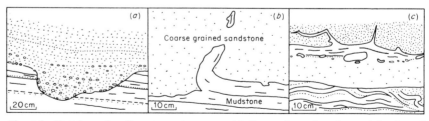

Fig. 8-3 Sketches of sedimentary structures. (*a*) Scour channel at base of laminated pebbly sandstone; (*b*) overfold of mudstone at base of massive coarse-grained sandstone; (*c*) layer of pebbles along bedding plane. (*From Crowell and others, 1966.*)

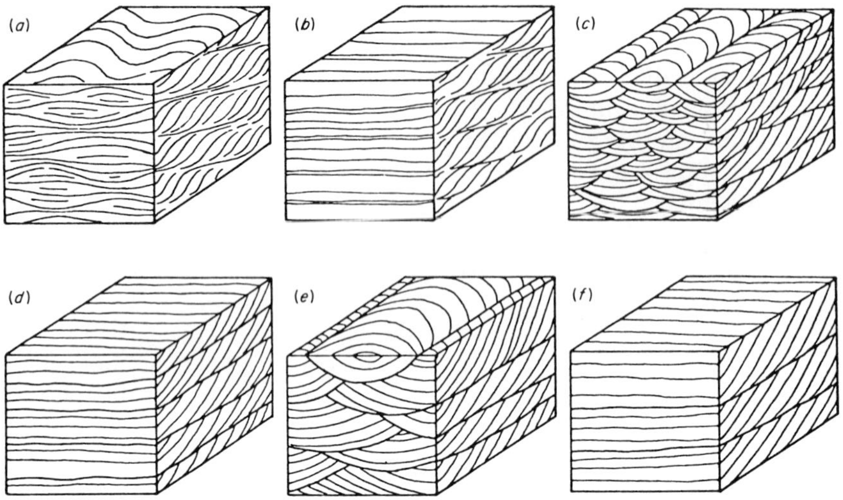

Fig. 8-4 Common types of cross stratification considered to be generated by migration of asymmetrical ripple marks. (*a*) Small-scale cross-stratified sets showing pinch and swell structure and gradational contacts resulting from small-scale linguoid ripples; (*b*) cross-strata in small-scale planar sets with gradational contacts resulting from small-scale straight ripples; (*c*) small-scale trough cross-stratified sets resulting from small-scale linguoid ripples; (*d*) small-scale planar cross-stratified sets resulting from migration of small-scale straight ripples; (*e*) large-scale trough cross-stratified sets resulting from large-scale lunate and possibly linguoid ripples: (*f*) large-scale planar cross-stratified sets resulting from straight large-scale ripples. (*From Allen, 1963.*)

easily confused with secondary deformation—particularly when they occur on a large scale.

Cross Laminations

Cross laminations of different origins have distinctive geometries which usually makes differentiation possible. Deltaic cross bedding is composed of three sets of bedding. The more thickly inclined beds, foreset beds, thin out in the direction of current movement and become tangential to the underlying bedding plane as bottomset beds. The topset beds are usually composed of sediment in the process of being moved toward the delta front, and consequently the topset beds are often eroded away, leaving truncated foreset beds. The truncated surface is the top. Such deltaic bedding is common in lakes, streams, and on coasts and occurs on all scales.

While it is true that the truncated edge is the top edge in cross-bedded strata, it is important to know that the intersection to the foreset beds with the lower beds can be quite abrupt in some cases. This may lead to formation of cross bedding which is apparently truncated at both top and bottom. Such cross bedding is commonly thought to form under conditions of rapid sedimentation and is called *torrential cross bedding*.

Cut and fill structures with cross-laminated beds were referred to earlier. A great range of geometric shapes is possible in exposures of cross-laminated beds. This range arises both from the original form of the deposit and from the angle of the exposed section through it. Complication in form is also caused by changes in the direction of the currents. This is easy to visualize in the case of a braided stream in

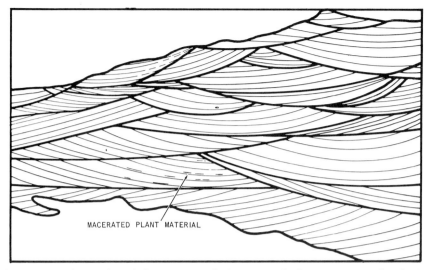

MACERATED PLANT MATERIAL

Fig. 8-5 Complex series of festoon cross beds (perpendicular to current direction). Maximum thickness of pictured section 7 ft. (*From Frazier and Osanik, 1961.*)

which the path of water is constantly changing in such a way that old deposits are being cut and removed as new ones are deposited. Allen (1965) believes that many common types of cross stratification (Fig. 8-4) are generated by migration of asymmetrical ripple marks.

It is not always easy to distinguish cross-bedded dune deposits from water-laid deposits, but some criteria for their recognition have been established. Very large cross-bedded deposits, several hundred feet high, are probably sand dunes, which occur rather commonly on that scale. Festoon-type cross bedding (Fig. 8-5) is much more likely to develop in water, and it is often possible to make the distinction by noting the relation of the deposit to adjacent sedimentary rock units. The character of the sand grains is also important. Frosted grains and very well-sorted grains are more typical of sand dunes. Further evidence can sometimes be found in studies of ripple marks which may appear on the surfaces of the laminations. The ratio of the wavelength to the amplitude of the

ripple is likely to be 14:1 or higher for wind ripples but lower for water current ripples.

REFERENCES

Allen, J. R. L., 1963a, Asymmetrical ripple marks and the origin of water laid cosets of cross strata: Liverpool Manchester Geol. Jour., v. 3, p. 187–236.

―――― 1963b, The classification of cross-stratified units, with notes on their origin: Sedimentology, v. 2, no. 2, p. 93–114.

Bradley, W. H., 1929, The varves and climate of the Green River formation: U. S. Geol. Survey Prof. Paper 158, p. 87–110.

Brush, L. M., Jr., 1965, Sediment sorting in alluvial channels: Soc. Econ. Paleontologists and Mineralogists Spec. Pub. no. 12, p. 25–34.

Crowell, J. C., and others, 1966, Deep-water sedimentary structures Pliocene Pico formation Santa Paula Creek, Ventura basin, California: California Div. Mines and Geol. Spec. Rept. 89.

Frazier, D. E., and Osanik, A., 1961, Point-bar deposits, Old River locksite, Louisiana: Gulf Coast Assoc. Geol. Soc. Trans., v. 11, p. 121–138.

Heezen, B. C., Ericson, D. B., and Ewing, Maurice, 1952, Turbidity currents and sediments in North America: Am. Assoc. Petroleum Geologists Bull., v. 36, p. 489.

Kuenen, P. H., 1952, Classification and origin of submarine canyons: K. Nederlandse Akad. Wetersch. Proc., ser. B, v. 55, p. 464–473.

Kuenen, P. II., and Migliorini, C. I., 1950, Turbidity currents as a cause of graded bedding: Jour. Geology, v. 58, p. 91–127.

Middleton, G. V., ed., 1965, Primary sedimentary structures and their hydrodynamic interpretation: Soc. Econ. Paleontologists and Mineralogists Spec. Pub. no. 12.

Pettijohn, F. J., and Potter, P. E., 1964, Atlas and glossary of primary sedimentary structures: New York, Springer-Verlag.

Shrock, R. R., 1948, Sequence in layered rocks: New York, McGraw-Hill, 507 p.

structures in unconsolidated sediment and salt

COMPACTION

The process of compaction sets in almost as soon as a sediment is deposited and it continues as the deposit is buried under progressively greater thicknesses of overburden. Differential compaction is responsible for much of the thickening and thinning that is seen in sedimentary units composed of lenses of sandstone in shale, responsible for warping of layers of sediment over enclosed consolidated rocks, and responsible for the splitting of coal seams; on a larger scale it may play a decisive role in the development of domes over buried topographic features. Even many of the structural features now found in hard, consolidated rocks exposed in folded mountain belts are thought to have formed when the sediment was unconsolidated or semi-consolidated. Major thrust faults, fold systems, and even slaty cleavages have been attributed to conditions arising in unconsolidated rock. Thus it is important that we examine some of the characteristics of such rocks and the environments in which they occur.

The range of sediment sizes is vast and a wide range of sizes and degrees of sorting is encountered in nature; however, the most marked differences in behavior are found among those particles which are of colloidal size, clays, and the larger fragmental materials such as sand or silt. Since most of the sediments with which we are concerned were deposited in water, the process of compaction takes place in a two-phase system consisting of water and solid fragments. It is in the nature of the way water is held in the sediment that sand and clay differ so greatly.

Water in a sediment consisting of large fragments is held in pore spaces between the solid fragments. Porosity is a measure of the volume of the pore space, and is expressed as a percentage of the the total volume of the rock. If the sediment is composed of perfectly spherical particles and is perfectly sorted so that all particles are the same size, the porosity is a maximum if the spheres are packed so that each sphere is centered over the sphere below. Porosity is a minimum if the spheres of one layer are centered over the spaces between spheres of the next lower layer. Of course, most sediments do not consist of either perfect spheres or perfectly sorted sizes. When sedimentation takes place slowly and sediment consists of various sizes, the smaller sizes tend to fill pore spaces between larger fragments, resulting in a closely packed sediment with relatively little pore space. If sedimentation is fast or if the sediment consists of irregularly shaped particles, a loosely packed sediment may result with a high porosity. The platy fragments may form a boxwork fabric, or small cavities may be formed in loosely packed sediment, yielding very high porosities. Open cavities do not last long as compaction begins. As weight builds up, the loose cavities collapse and grains tend to shift in such a way as to reduce porosity. This process takes place provided it is possible for the water to be expelled. Unless the water can move out of the sediment, little compaction can occur since water is not highly compressible. Most fragmental rocks are permeable, and the water can therefore be forced upward as compaction occurs. The porosity of a sand might well be in the range of 30 to 40 percent when loosely packed and reduce to 20 to 30 percent in tight packing under compaction. Although the range of values may vary considerably from rock to rock,

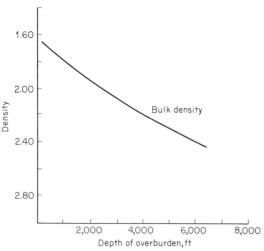

Fig. 9-1 Relation of shale density to depth of overburden in Venezuelan wells. (*From Hedberg, 1936.*)

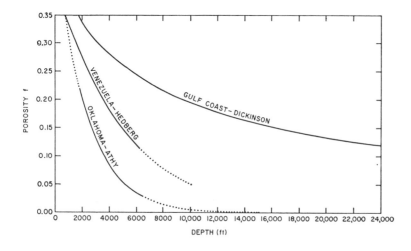

Fig. 9-2 Comparison of depth-porosity relationship in wells of Oklahoma, Venezuela, and Gulf Coast. (*From Rubey and Hubbert, 1959.*)

the difference in the pore space due to compaction will not vary greatly from 10 to 20 percent (Fig. 9-1), and this is in marked contrast with clays.

Water is held in clays both between the individual particles or aggregates of particles and within the crystal lattice as absorbed water. Porosity varies depending on the type of clay mineral involved, the degree of dispersion of the clay particles, and the degree and arrangement of aggregates of particles. As compaction of clay takes place, water is first forced out of the spaces between aggregates, but as water is lost, the rate of decrease of porosity is lowered. A film of water surrounds each clay colloid, and as the thickness of this film is reduced, the rate of water loss is retarded. Figure 9-2 shows the observed changes of porosity of clay-rich sediments from the Gulf Coast, Venezuela, and Oklahoma with depth in drill holes. Some clays have a porosity on the order of 60 to 80 percent at the surface. Compare the change in porosity of clay, shown in Fig. 9-2 with that of sand, shown in Fig. 9-3, for any given depth. The great difference in the behavior of the two is strikingly apparent.

These differences in behavior account for many of the structures resulting from differential compaction. Sandstone lenses, concretions, or blocks of consolidated rocks found enclosed within clay will compact less than the clay. Thus, as compaction occurs, the bedding developed within the clay will be deflected over the sand or rock, producing a small domical structure. Similar features are formed in tuffaceous deposits which compact more than do buried objects such as lava flows or trees.

Many structures in coal are formed as a result of shrinkage and compaction which accompanies the alteration of peat to coal. Between 10 to 30 ft of peat is estimated to produce a 1-ft coal seam. Since peat forms in swamps, coal deposits often contain sandy stream channel deposits or deposits laid around the margin of the swamp, and most coal seems to have been deposited under conditions of long-term slow

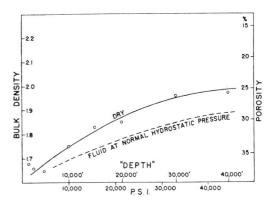

Fig. 9-3 Compaction of sand at room temperature and 1 atm fluid pressure. Upper curve—observed results. Lower curve—estimated values if normal hydrostatic pressure for each depth were present during experiment. (*From Maxwell, 1960.*)

subsidence, often marked by slight interruptions. This condition has given rise to the splitting of coal seams (Fig. 9-4), and in combination with transformation of peat to coal and differential compaction has created *fish tailing,* or splitting of a single thick coal seam into a large number of thinner seams laterally interbedded with other sediment. For example, the famous Ten Yard coal seam of England is found to change from a single seam 30 ft thick into a system of 12 thinner seams interbedded with sandstone and shale, making a section 500 ft thick in a distance of 5 miles. Presumably the thickness of peat required to make the 30-ft seam was nearly equal to the thickness of the peat, sand, and clay at the edge of the swamp when the peat was being deposited.

Clastic dikes are another interesting feature of coal seams that are related to shrinkage and compaction. When peat begins to shrink, some lateral as well as vertical changes in dimensions occur. The peat cracks, and if water-filled sand is below the peat, it may be forced into the crack, producing a clastic dike. As compaction of the coal continues, the clastic dike becomes folded (Fig. 9-5).

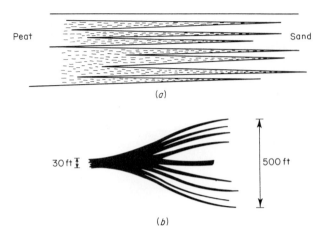

Peat   Sand

(a)

30 ft   500 ft

(b)

Fig. 9-4 Cross sections of splitting of coal seams. (a) Interfingering of sand and peat as initially deposited near swamp margin; (b) fishtail resulting from differential compaction.

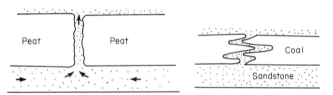

Peat   Peat   Coal

                                     Sandstone

Fig. 9-5 Formation of folded sandstone dike in coal seams.

PLAINS-TYPE FOLDING

Folds, particularly broad open domes and nose-shaped structures, are found in regions that are far removed from orogenic belts. The midcontinent of North America is notable for examples of such structures. Over large portions of this region, near-surface exposures indicate nearly flat-lying beds, but subsurface drilling demonstrates that the lower beds are tilted, or broadly folded over buried topographic features that existed on old erosion surfaces. One of the largest of these buried features is the Nemaha

Mountain Range which extends over 200 miles north-south from eastern Nebraska to Oklahoma. The ridge is composed of granite with maximum relief of nearly 2,000 ft yet anyone familiar with the region knows there is no mountain range on the ground surface. The ridge is completely buried under Pennsylvanian sedimentary rocks. It is several miles wide at the top and is slightly asymmetric, having a steep eastern flank (see the United States Tectonic Map, 1961). The gentle homoclinal dips of Pennsylvanian rocks are interrupted over the ridge to form long, broad, open anticlinal ridges.

Powers (1922, 1931) described folds which he called *plains-type folds,* characterized by their association with buried hills. They are in effect the reflection of the buried topography into the overlying sedimentary veneer. Several mechanisms have been offered to account for this reflection, including renewal of movements within the rocks making up the buried hills and compaction. Both processes undoubtedly can be shown to be operative in different cases. The Augusta oil field of Kansas is an example of one of the structures formed over the Nemaha ridge. Structure contour maps drawn on the Permian and Ordovician oil producing horizons are illustrated in Fig. 9-6. The domes overlie buried hills, but the structure has been modified by uplift and faulting along the granite ridge.

SUPRATENUOUS FOLDS

The name *supratenuous fold* is applied to folds arising as a result of compaction. In the case of a buried topography it is most likely that sedimentation was already occurring on the flanks of the hills before the hills were submerged. There would be a tendency for the irregularities in the topography to hold less sediment than the valleys between, until the relief disappeared and a thinning of beds was produced toward high topographic features. If compaction goes on at a rate comparable to the rate of deposition, the beds in the valleys show a tilt away from the hills by virtue of the variations in thickness even before the hills are buried.

Assume for simplicity that the hills become buried until the surface of sediment is nearly level above them. The amount of compaction is then a function of the type of sediment and the thickness of the section being compacted. Because this thickness is greater over low areas in the old topography, more compaction occurs there than over hills producing a fold in the units over the buried hill.

Nevin and Sherrill (1929) have shown some of the effects that the original shape of the hill may have on the compaction or supratenuous folds formed over it. If the hill is symmetrical,

the compaction folds over it are also symmetrical and the line that bisects the hill also extends through the crest of the overlying folds. If the hill is asymmetrical, the compaction folds are also asymmetrical but the line connecting the crest of the compaction folds does not coincide with the line that bisects the angle between the two sides of the hill. Instead, the crest line of the compaction folds is nearer the vertical. The top of each succeeding bed is moved in the direction of the lower slope of the buried topography as the series rises.

PORE PRESSURE

It has been more or less implied through the preceding discussion that water is readily re-

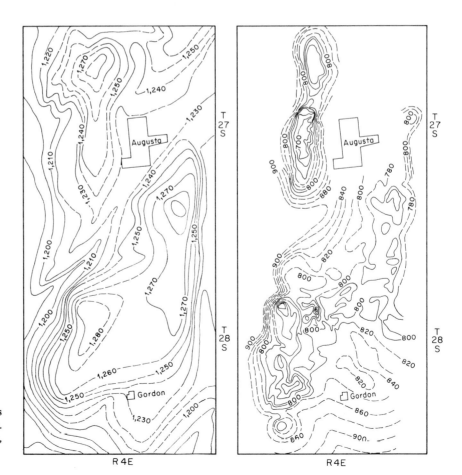

Fig. 9-6 Structure contours in the Augusta field, Kans. (*After Berry and Harper, 1948.*)

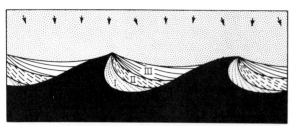

Fig. 9-7 Pointed mud wisps and lee-side cross laminae differentially deformed during deposition. The deformation is an effect of current drag that occurs during sediment fallout from overlying turbulent suspension. (*From Sanders, 1965.*)

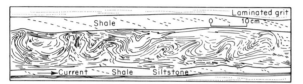

Fig. 9-8 Convolute bedding in fine grit with undisturbed, current-bedded base lying between shales with cleavage. (*From Kuenen, 1953.*)

moved from sediments undergoing compaction. This is not always true. Shales and clay are not generally very permeable, and thus it is difficult to remove water from a thick deposit of clay. Water tends to be forced into sands and out along the water sediment contact. Water can become confined either within the clay sediment or in pore spaces of sands from which the water is prevented from escaping by overlying impermeable layers. When this happens, pressures are exerted on the water by the weight of the overlying sediment-water mixture, and very high pressures can be built up in the water. This water pressure, called *pore pressure,* can essentially "float" the sand. Such high pressures are encountered in oil fields, sometimes with disastrous results. Pore pressure can reduce the internal friction of sand and thus induce landslides, and as we have seen, it may be significant in large-scale thrust faulting. High pore

pressure is of critical importance in the formation of many soft-sediment structural features. The sandstone dikes found in coal and other sediments result from the upward injection of saturated sand under pressure into fractures. The presence of layers of high pore pressure would doubtless contribute to basin-directed slump and sliding of stratified sequences.

POSTDEPOSITIONAL DEFORMATION

A great many structures in sedimentary rocks are recognized as having formed in the interval between initial deposition and final consolidation. In many cases, as with turbidity currents, it is very difficult to distinguish syndepositional deformation from that which follows shortly thereafter. Structures known as *convolute bedding, slump structure,* and *flow casts* are of this type.

Sanders (1965) describes an interesting example of a syndepositional deformation in which the passage of a turbulent suspension causes deformation of the sediment that makes up the bed over which the current passes. Evidence of the interaction of the suspension and the bottom sediment is shown when upward-growing projections from the bottom are found. Such structures may consist of mud wisp with adjacent, deformed cross laminae (Fig. 9-7). The cross laminae were deposited to the lee of the rising mud, but were subsequently overturned by further upward movement of the mud and deformed by effects of current drag during sediment fallout from the overlying suspension.

Important factors in the development of postdepositional deformation are the hydroplastic nature of clay and mud deposits, the saturation of clastic sediments with water which when trapped in an accumulating pile of sediment can attain a quicksand characteristic due to pore pressure in the water, the pressure of overlying deposits, the initial dip of the stratification, and the effects of current action as in the case described above.

Convolute bedding (Fig. 9-8) is a name coined by Kuenen (1953) to apply to peculiarly deformed laminations which have the following characteristics:

1. Crumpling of the laminations increases in intensity upward in a bed and then gradually dies out again, so that the upper laminae of the same bed are again flat.
2. No rupture of laminae has occurred. The lamination planes can be traced across several undulations showing rounded distortions.
3. Only one bed is affected at a time, and there is only one system of distortions in a single bed, but this disturbance can be traced laterally for great distances in all directions within that bed.
4. The affected bed shows no external irregularities in thickness.
5. The degree of distortion is of almost equal intensity in two planes, one parallel, the other at right angles to the original slope.

Undisturbed current bedding or lamination may occur below in the same bed and the undulations may be smoothed off in the same manner before the deposition of the bed came to an end. Hence the deformation took place during sedimentation by the turbidity current and this process cannot have occupied more than a few hours, probably much less.*

Not all students of convolute bedding agree entirely with this conclusion. Davies (1966) has reviewed the literature dealing with the origin of convolute lamination. Among the ideas offered to explain its origin are (1) gravity-induced plastic flow, (2) injection of sediment from below, (3) plastic deformation of ripple marks coupled with loading pressure, (4) sliding of overlying sediment deforming a bed by shear, (5) quicksand movement, (6) deformation of cohesive sediment in response to shearing effects set up by high-velocity currents, (7) intrastratal laminar flow, and (8) localized thixo-

* Kuenen (1953).

tropic flow coupled with loading. It seems probable that not all convolute bedding originates in the same way.

Flow casts and slump structures may resemble convolute bedding, and we may certainly expect transitional forms. Flow casts or load casts are features which arise from the filling of negative features in a bedding surface produced by the flowage of the soft underlying sediment. Frequently the condition is one in which sand fills pockets produced in a hydroplastic deposit such as clay. Rounded bag-shaped surfaces are produced between the two layers, and the plastic sediment wedges in between. A distinction between load casts and convolute bedding is found in that convolute bedding occurs within the plastic layer itself, while load casts develop between two beds of different mechanical properties.

Kuenen (1953) distinguishes the characteristics of slump structures as follows:

. . . Occurrence between undisturbed beds, rupture of the beds at the higher end (pull-apart structures, generally not exposed or not obvious), piling up or thickening of beds at the lower end, beheading of anticlines, the dying out downward of the deformation, less seldom also upwards, balled up structures of sandy or calcareous beds surrounded by more plastic material (clay or lime mud), sliding planes, faults, general irregularity of structures often showing similar intensity in sections parallel and at right angles to the slope, internal rupture of bedding planes, brecciated masses, abrupt changes in thickness of beds, the partaking of more than one bed in the movements, irregular surface sometimes smoothed off by a graded bed or by infilling with laminated deposits, the duplication of beds on top of each other.

Convolute bedding, load casts, and slump structures are schematically illustrated in Fig. 9-9.

DIAPIRS

Diapirs are structural features in which a mobile core material is injected through overlying, less mobile layers. Formation of diapirs

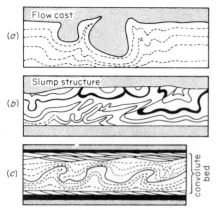

Fig. 9-9 Diagram showing some soft-rock deformation types. (*a*) Load cast, developed by plastic deformation of a bed under a later load; (*b*) slump structures due to horizontal movement of beds after deposition; (*c*) convolute bedding developed during deposition of the bed without horizontal movement. (*From Kuenen, 1953*.)

is favored by any natural condition of instability in a sedimentary pile. The two most common conditions are for materials of low density or high ductility to be overlain by higher-density, less ductile layers. Most diapirs in sediments are associated with salt, gypsum, anhydrite, and clay. Salt, gypsum, and anhydrite are of low density and high ductility. When such beds are buried under sediments of normal density, an unstable condition is created, and diapiric structures can form even in the absence of strong externally applied stresses. This is the case in the Gulf Coast salt domes, which will be considered in detail.

Many diapirs are associated with anticlines and develop during the process of folding, when the response of interbedded materials of highly different competence or ductility to the compressive stresses results in arching or folding of the less ductile layers and flowage of the more ductile beds. This may occur when weak clays are interbedded with clastic beds; when salt, gypsum, or other ductile layers are present, or in metamorphic terranes when differences in ductility arise from differences in the response of rocks to the metamorphic conditions.

The Blinman dome, a feature in the Flinders Range of Australia, is a good example of one type of diapir. A large mass of breccia forms the core of a domal feature in this case. There is only minor peripheral faulting although other similar breccias do occur along faults in the Flinders Range. The regional structure of the rim rock is domal with dips on the order of 35°, but the rim turns up and is nearly vertical where the core material comes in contact with the rim. There are tear faults in this upturned rim rock. The core material consists of breccia of dismembered fragments of a great many rock types which are known to occur in stratigraphic succession below the rim rock of the dome. Some of the pieces are quite large (the largest block within the breccia is 1 by 2 miles), but most of the breccia fragments are much smaller, ranging in size down to fragments of microscopic size. The fragments near the contact are oriented crudely parallel to the contact. Ring and radial structures are seen within the breccia on aerial photographs, and these are thought to be breccia pipes. A gravity low situated over the dome suggests a density contrast between the breccia material and the surrounding material. The domes seem to be localized in a region where the Willouran series is very thick (12,000 ft). These sediments, which occur commonly in the breccia core, are composed primarily of micaceous siltstone and laminated shales. Thus thickness of the unit as well as diastrophism may contribute to the movements which lead to the formation of the diapiric domes (Coats, 1964).

SALT STRUCTURES

Structures related to salt in the United States Gulf Coastal Plain have been responsible for entrapment of much of the oil and gas of that region. Exploration in the region and interest in the formation of these salt bodies have been intense since the discovery of Spindletop, the first salt dome oil field in the United States, which came in as a gusher in 1901. The presence of salt springs in the region had been known near Natchitoches, La., since the early 1700s, and salt was mined during the Civil War. A salt quarry that was opened in the Avery Island dome in 1862 is still an important source

of salt today. Many ideas concerning the origin and emplacement of the salt have been advanced (see DeGolyer, 1926).

The present conception, based on thousands of wells around salt structures and a vast

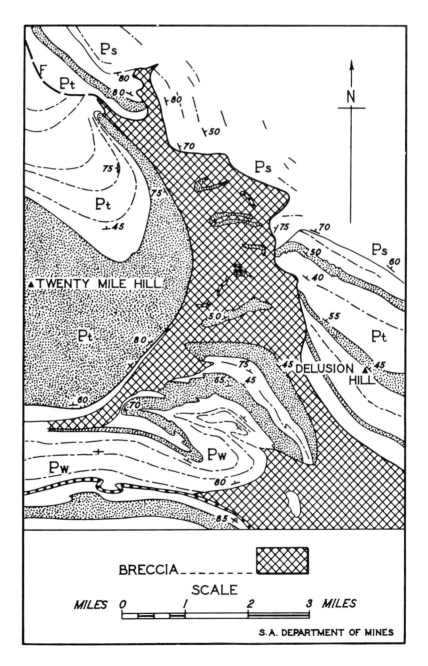

Fig. 9-10 Witchelina diapir; a near-vertical cross section of the diapiric structure. (*From Coats, 1964.*)

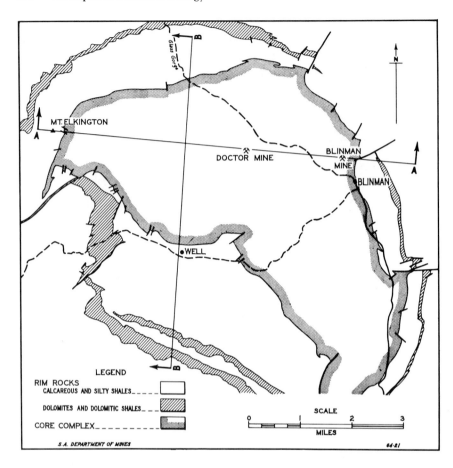

Fig. 9-11 Plan of the Blinman dome. (*From Coats, 1964.*)

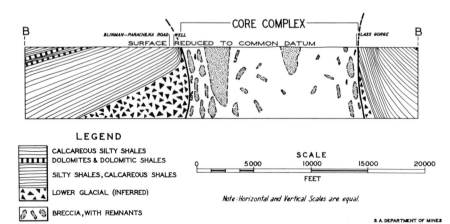

Fig. 9-12 Geological cross section of the Blinman dome diapir. (*From Coats, 1964.*)

amount of geophysical data, is that the salt was originally deposited as an extensive sedimentary unit in a large basin. It was later buried under increasingly greater loads of unconsolidated Cenozoic sediment which caused the salt to flow and locally to force its way up through the overlying sediments which have a higher density than the salt. Some of the salt intrusions have elliptical or circular shapes and taper at depth. Tops of salt bodies are buried at a great variety of depths, ranging from the surface to many thousands of feet, and some are rising today. As the salt is intruded the overlying sediments are domed, faulted, and forced apart to allow the salt to move upward. The salt movements and structures related to it are thought to have formed independently of tectonic activity.

THE GULF COAST SALT BASIN

Despite the great accumulation of knowledge about the Gulf Coast and salt domes, there are still many unanswered questions regarding the formation of the salt. A thick layer of bedded salt overlying anhydrite and associated with red beds and other evaporites has been penetrated by wells in Arkansas, northern Louisiana, and east Texas. These beds, known as the Louann salt, are thought by most geologists to be the source of the salt found in domes throughout the region. The Louann salt is gray, nearly clear, coarsely crystalline, and contains streaks of anhydrite. It is underlain by the Werner formation, which consists mainly of anhydrite, with minor red beds and gravel, and it is overlain by the Norphlet formation, a sequence of red beds. In the region of good subsurface control, these units lie between the unconformity separating late Paleozoic units, rarely penetrated in wells in the coastal plain, and the Upper Jurassic Smackover formation. This places the date of the salt formation somewhere between Permian and Late Jurassic. Palynological evidence indicates an age of Late Triassic to Early Jurassic.

The shape and extent of the basin containing Louann salt and the source of the salt are both unsolved problems. There is reasonable control on that portion of it which is found in the Coastal Plain (Fig. 9-13) but the southern edge of the basin is presently indeterminant. The salt extends at least as far as the edge of the present continental shelf, and many workers in the region believe that the salt may have been laid in a basin that covered all the Gulf region and that it is the same salt deposit penetrated in Cuba and from which the salt domes in the Tehuantepec region of Mexico originate. There are several closed depressions in the central part of the Gulf where it may be that salt has risen to the surface, broken into the water, and been dissolved.

Certainly the salt deposit would not be expected to be of uniform thickness. The thinned edge of the salt is known in southern Arkansas where the salt disappears northward. Wells into the salt show its thickness to be more than 1,300 ft in south Arkansas, 1,200 ft in northwest Louisiana, and 800 ft in east Texas; and all of these are thicknesses penetrated near the edge of the salt basin. The salt is covered by such great thicknesses of sediments farther south that no wells have reached it. Various estimates have been made of the thickness toward the south. These range from 4,000 to over 17,000 ft; a widely accepted figure is 5,000 ft average thickness with probable large ranges of variation depending on the original depositional topography and, of course, on subsequent movement of the salt both laterally and vertically. Because the salt has moved so extensively, it is difficult to estimate its original thicknesses.

One of the problems encountered in trying to define the mode of origin of the salt is the excessive thickness of salt present relative to the amount of underlying anhydrite. The proportion of the two does not correspond to the relative amounts of these two that can be precipitated from sea water today. Because the anhydrite would be precipitated first it has been

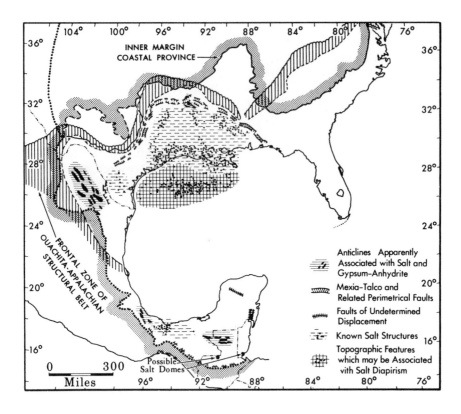

Legend:
Anticlines Apparently Associated with Salt and Gypsum-Anhydrite

Mexia-Talco and Related Perimetrical Faults

Faults of Undetermined Displacement

Known Salt Structures

Topographic Features which may be Associated vith Salt Diapirism

Fig. 9-13 Probable salt structures, Gulf of Mexico basin. *(From Murray, 1966.)*

suggested that highly concentrated brines were introduced into the Louann salt basin during deposition. These could possibly have come from the Permian basins of western Texas or from the Sabinas basin of Mexico. Another widely accepted idea is that concentration took place in an environment where bars or barriers of some type allowed water into the basin or parts of it only after the water was partially evaporated and part of the calcium sulphate precipitated. The shape of this basin is much disputed. Some propose a lagoonal environment, others suggest local basins, and still others consider that the Gulf may have been a vast closed sea at the time.

A schematic illustration of one of the postulated development histories of the basins is found in Fig. 9-14. The initial stage represents deposition of the salt over an extensive area with some possible highs over which deposition was thin. The second stage, close to the end

of the Cretaceous, depicts subsidence of the basin and accumulation of Jurassic and Cretaceous sediments with the consequent formation of some salt domes. The last two stages depict the gradual extension of the areas of subsidence toward the coast with consequent accumulation of sediments and activation of salt intrusion.

Salt-related Structures in the Gulf Coast

Much more detailed information is available about salt structures toward the margins of the salt basins, where wells have been drilled through the salt, than in the deeper parts of the basin, where only those structures over and around the salt are well defined and we are forced to rely much more on seismic data. We will turn presently to the fault and domal structures over the salt and to the flowage structures within the salt after considering the general shapes of the salt bodies. Several salt bodies of distinctly different shapes are known. These include:

1. *Salt swells along faults at the edge of the basin.* These are best seen in the zone of normal faults (e.g., Mexia-Talco zone). The salt wells up along the upthrown sides of the faults, forming domes or folds with 500 to 600 ft of closure at the depth of the salt. These occur in the area where the salt is thinning.
2. *Salt pillows.* These resemble the first category but are not associated with faults. They are doubly plunging swells which appear often to be aligned.

3. *Deep-seated salt domes, buried at depths of 1 to 2 miles.* Sediments are domed and faulted over these bodies, but piercement of the sediments by the salt is minor. The shallower these domes are, the more faulting tends to be associated with them. Those below 12,000 ft have little associated faulting.
4. *Piercement domes.* The salt has forcefully intruded the overlying sediment by moving up along complex faults in some instances and by displacement of the unconsolidated sediments.
5. *Residual salt features called turtle structures in northern Germany.* These are

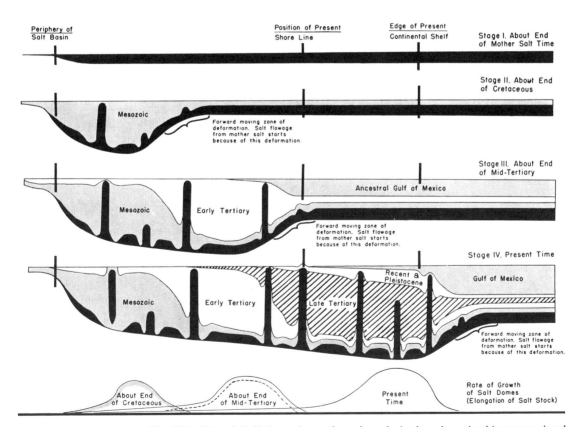

Fig. 9-14 Rise of Gulf Coast domes through geologic time shows in this cross-sectional account (top to bottom) of four stages in deposition of sediments atop mother salt bed by rivers, streams, and prehistoric seas. Domes were supposedly triggered by difference in static load of sediments at, and ahead of, area of deposition. (*From Hanna, 1959.*)

structures which result from the with-
drawal of salt from around the edges into
piercement domes, leaving a body with
thinned edges.

One of the important unsolved problems
concerning these salt structures is the role of
the "basement" underlying the salt. Much of
it is too deep to have been penetrated. Where

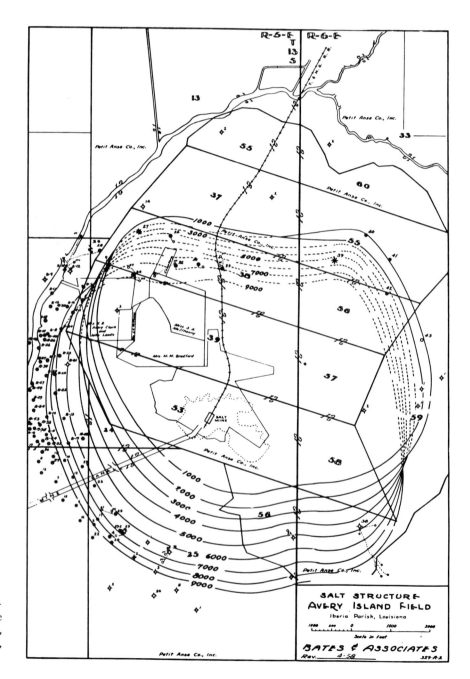

Fig. 9-15 Structure contours of Avery Island dome on top salt. (*From Bates, Copeland, and Dixon, 1959.*)

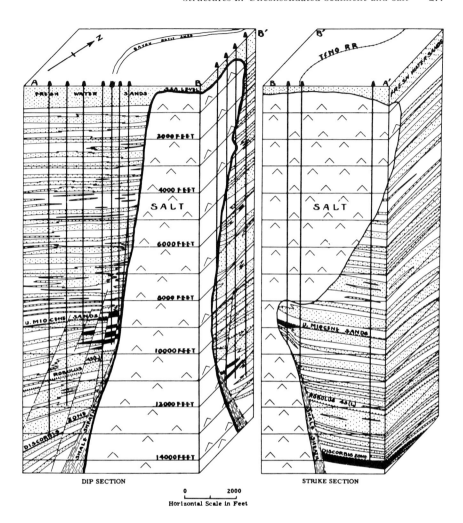

Fig. 9-16 Generalized block diagram of Avery Island dome. (*From Bates, Copeland, and Dixon, 1959.*)

data are available, they suggest that the surface on which the salt was deposited is relatively undeformed, but faults have been interpreted in this basement. Some students of the region think movements on these faults have initiated the development of salt ridges from which the domes and swells have originated. Support for this argument is found in the apparent alignment of many domes, and in the salt swells located along faults at the edges of the salt basin. In any case the dominant process in the development of structures appears to be directly related to the mobility of the salt.

Avery Island Dome

Salt has been mined at Avery Island since the Civil War. The salt dome has intruded to the surface, and its shape is reflected in the topography of the island. Because the dome is so close to the surface, its shape has been carefully studied. It is a warped ellipse in map view, and on the north side there is an overhanging lip (Fig. 9-15). The shape of the dome is also depicted in block diagrams (Fig. 9-16) which show the way in which salt has flowed laterally near the surface overhanging part of the sedi-

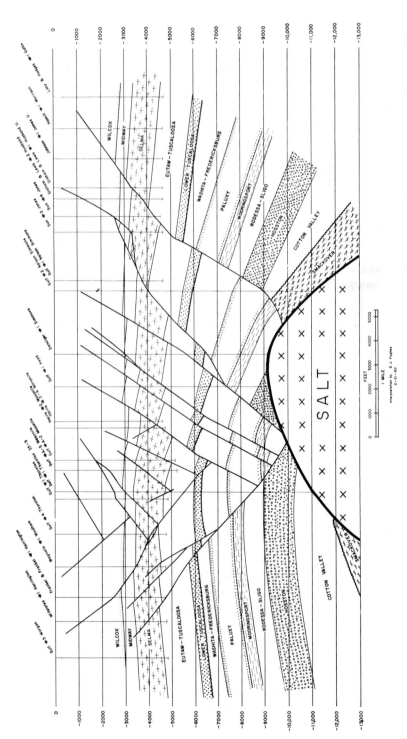

Fig. 9-17 East-west cross section of the Heidelberg structure, Jasper County, Miss., illustrating actual fault pattern over deep-seated salt dome. (*From Hughes, 1960.*)

ments. A sheath of shale and a postulated system of faults at depth are also shown.

Fault Patterns Associated with Salt Structures

A characteristic pattern of normal faulting is found over salt domes. The pattern may be complex in detail, but in general there are two or more major faults forming a graben over the dome. The strike of these major faults parallels the long axis of the dome when the dome is elongate. Frequently the major fault bifurcates, splitting into two or more normal faults which form a step-fault pattern with the downthrown side of the fault toward the center of the dome. Cross sections across domes where there is good subsurface control (Fig. 9-17) usually show an intersecting network of normal faults with dips ranging from 70° to a low of 30°. In surface expression these faults have characteristics of grabens and radial fault patterns (Fig. 9-18).

Changes of dip and changes in the amount of throw with depth are especially interesting aspects of these faults. These changes are reflected in the cross section (Fig. 9-19): however, it will also be apparent that not all faults show the same type of change in dip. In general, faults tend to increase in throw and decrease in dip with depth. An exception to this appears in Fig. 9-19, in which the faults become steeper, from dips of 45° to nearly 60°, where they pass from the Upper Cretaceous to the Lower Cretaceous formations. Hughes (1960) points out that this is common where control is good, and that it is probable that these same faults flatten in dip at greater depths.

The fault patterns have been closely dupli-

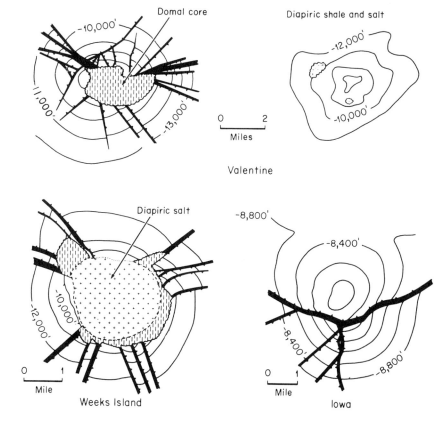

Fig. 9-18 Structure of upper surface of *Cibicides hazzardi* zone (Chickasawhayan), Iowa dome, Calcasieu and Jefferson Davis Parishes, La., showing major, simple-offset fault with subsidiary radial faulting. Sediments enclosing Weeks Island dome, Iberia and St. Mary Parishes, La., are deformed by radial fault pattern at top of S sand (Upper Miocene) where it is in contact with diapiric salt (crosses) and diapiric shale (vertical dashed lines). Maps of Valentine dome, Lafourche Parish, La., disclose configuration of (1) upper surface of diapiric salt and shale (right) and (2) upper surface of *Bigenerina humblei* zone (Miocene) where it is in contact with domal core of salt and shale. (*All figures after Atwater and Forman, 1959; From Murray, 1966.*)

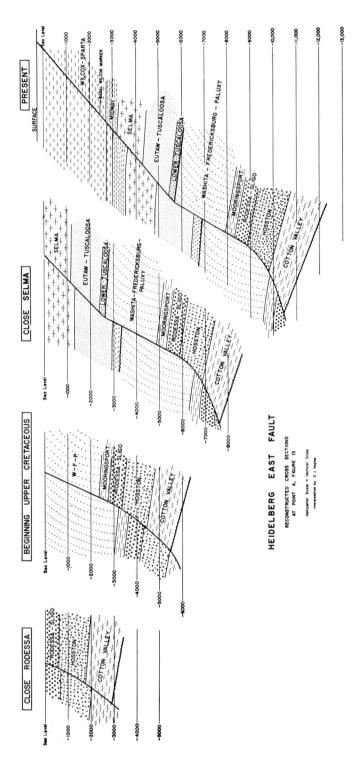

Fig. 9-19 Stages in growth of the East Heidelberg fault, Jasper County, Miss. Fault is reconstructed at various times, assuming zero throw on each horizon at time of deposition of that horizon.

cated through model experiments such as those performed by Currie (1958) and shown in Fig. 9-20. In addition to the principal fault or faults, there are usually a number of smaller subsidiary faults that develop as *antithetic faults*. The major faults at least have grown through a long period of time, as sediments have been deposited over domes that had already begun to rise. Hughes' interpretation of the stages in the growth of the fault through the overlying sediments as they were deposited is shown in Fig. 9-19. Notice that the stratigraphic throw has increased on the fault from top to bottom. This is thought to be due to lengthening of the section in the downthrown beds, and to the presence of wedges below unconformities that are preserved in the downthrown side but not on the upthrown block.

Deformational Pattern within Salt Domes

Mines located in the top of near-surface salt domes have afforded an unusual opportunity to study the structure of the salt body and to determine directly the character of the processes by which the salt has been intruded. Detailed maps have been made of portions of salt mines at Grand Saline salt dome, Van Zandt County, Tex.; Winnfield dome, Winn Parish, La. (Fig. 9-21); and Weeks Island salt dome, La. All reveal a structural pattern showing in the salt darker layers, usually anhydrite, that can only be interpreted as flowage.

Grand Saline Salt Dome

One of the classic studies of salt domes is that of Balk (1949) in which he analyzes the structure of the interior of the Grand Saline salt

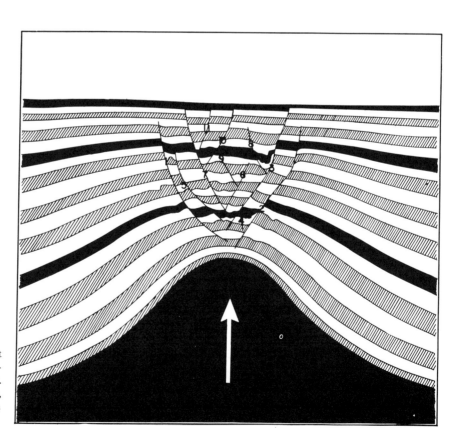

Fig. 9-20 Graben fault pattern formed in sectional model experiment. (*Modified after Currie, 1956; redrawn from Hughes, 1960.*)

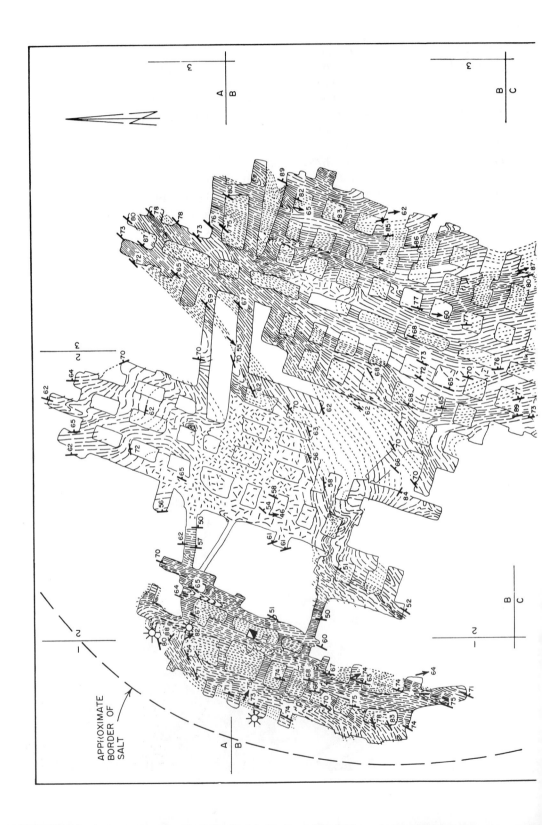

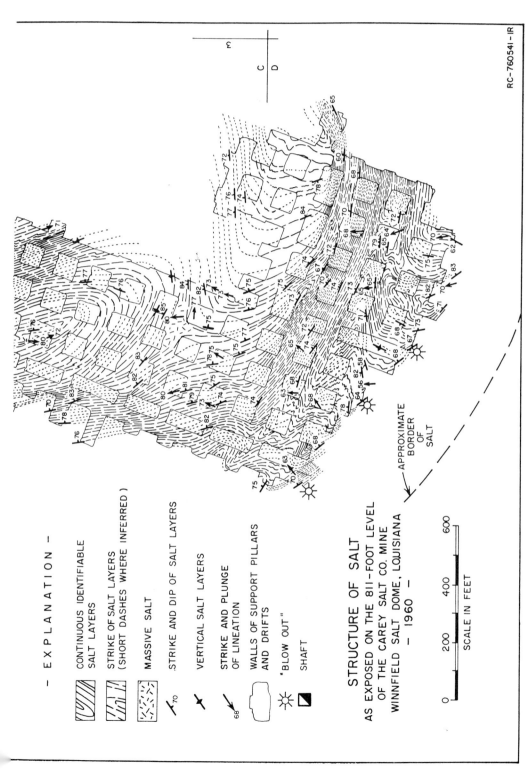

Fig. 9-21 Structure of salt as exposed on 811-ft level of Carey Salt Company mine, Winnfield salt dome, La. (*From Hoy, Foose, and O'Neill, 1962.*)

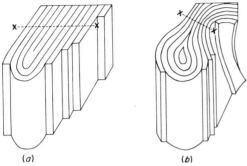

Fig. 9-22 Block diagram of fold in salt. (*a*) Typical iso-clinal fold with vertical axes. (*b*) Closed fold resulting from constriction during vertical movements. Note thinning of beds along *XX*, complete attenuation of some beds, and lessened dip in outer parts of constricted area. (*From Kupfer, 1962.*)

dome through study of megascopic features. He found that layers of salt and anhydrite are visible throughout the mined parts of the dome, and that these layers dip very steeply, presumably parallel to the edge of the dome. These layers were found to be intricately folded elsewhere in the dome, and the axes of nearly all the folds plunge nearly vertically. Many of these are isoclinal folds in which the beds show slip planes parallel to the axial planes; however, none of the slippages causes a complete break in the bedding (Fig. 9-22). Balk (1949, p. 1803) describes the folds as follows:

> In contrast to the monotonous sequence of parallel layers of salt on vertical walls, the ceilings of rooms and tunnels exhibit an impressive array of folds. Few structural features express the remarkable evolution of a salt dome through deformation as tellingly as the wonderful sweep and beauty of single beds, or swarms of salt layers, trending in broad, smooth curves across the spacious ceilings of large, electrically lighted rooms, forming here a large isoclinal fold, there grouped in numerous smaller flexures that reconcile diverging trends of larger folds.
>
> . . . It is probably significant that only in this section (one to two hundred feet from the border of the dome) are folds almost lacking. The salt here displays straight layers, striking east and west and dipping about 65° southward. . . .

Salt folds vary greatly in size. Some are small, insignificant features, involving only a few, or one single layer. Wave lengths of small contortions are a few inches at most, but where larger groups of layers are involved, wave lengths may increase to more than 100 feet. There are gently curved, open folds as well as tightly compressed, isoclinal folds. The innumerable folds which vary the orientation of their limbs in a bewildering manner, have one element in common; all their axes are parallel, in nearly vertical attitudes. . . .

There are literally thousands of smaller folds, superposed on the limbs of the larger folds. In a series of straight beds, shear folds may appear on a single layer only, either along its entire course, as far as it can be examined, or over a short distance only. . . . The limbs of the shear folds may be isoclinal, or may diverge in directions, causing rows of zigzags, or chevrons. . . . Salt layers whose cross sections approach the axial plane zone as smooth curves are abruptly thrown into scores of isoclinal contortions.

The axial planes of these small shear folds are without exception parallel with the axial planes of the folds on which they are found. Followed through the mine, their directions vary over short distances, and nowhere have shearing movements cut through the limbs of folds. . . .

It seems, therefore, that the shear folds developed in response to the same stresses that governed the direction of compression of the larger folds.

Lineations formed through the alignment of minerals are found throughout the mine. Those formed of anhydrite are pencil-shaped aggregates. There is a similar alignment of anhydrite crystals none of which deviates more than 20° from the vertical. Balk found that the pencils are composed of rows of relatively small crystals. The *b* crystallographic axes of the crystals were not found to be perfectly aligned, but would instead be concentrated in a cone-shaped area. Halite crystals tended to show an elongation oriented vertically.

In addition to the fold patterns and crystal elongations, a number of other observations bear on the formation of the dome. These negative features were noted by Balk (1949, p. 1811):

1. Not a single fracture is exposed in the mine.

2. Nowhere is salt displaced by a fault.

3. Salt layers are nowhere crossed by others, and there are no unconformable contacts between layers. Where groups of salt layers approach each other with contrasting strikes, a zone of compact salt intervenes.

4. No brine or gas is encountered, except as microscopic interpositions in halite crystals.

5. No inclusions of foreign rocks have been found in this mine.

A theory regarding the movement of salt toward the salt dome and into it has been proposed by Escher and Kuenen (1929).

While the direction of principal propagation of the whole material is centripetally inward and upward, the converging motion of all particles generates peripheral, tangential stresses. Their varying directions would be represented by horizontal lines, drawn on the surface of the cone. As these stresses act parallel with the layers, they constitute shearing stresses. If the material chosen is homogeneous, there is a continuous gradation of the rate of yielding from one small area to another, but if the mobility of adjacent layers varies abruptly, the rates of yielding will also vary abruptly so that one layer, or one group of layers, must slip over or under adjacent layers.... Thus there originates around the periphery, at the base of the dome, numerous folds whose axes trend radially, and plunge outward from the dome in all directions.

A simple and familiar way of reproducing this fold pattern is to raise several horizontal sheets through a horizontal ring. . . . As each mass of salt approaches the axis of the dome, the direction of principal propagation becomes steeper. Therefore, the axes of the folds turn also into progressively steeper directions until, at high levels in the dome, there should remain only a multitude of folds with nearly vertical axes.

Subsequently Muehlberger (1959) mapped details of the band patterns in the ceiling of the Grand Saline salt dome.

In the Winnfield dome (Hoy, Foose, and O'Neill, 1962), bedding in the layered anhydrite and halite as well as the fold axes dips and plunges steeply toward the center of the dome. Pencil-shaped aggregates of anhydrite were found parallel to the fold axes with plunges of 70° and more. These are interpreted as evidence for upward and outward movement of the salt during its diapiric emplacement. Toward the outer edge of the salt, the spacing of layers is closer and the pattern of folding is more complex. The folds, which range in size from inches to 200 ft, are isoclinal with steeply plunging axes. Many lineations formed by anhydrite pencils several inches in diameter and over a foot long were found to plunge toward the center of the dome and vary steeply, over 70°, again suggesting the nearly vertical direction of movement.

At Weeks Island dome, Kupfer (1962) has described folding of bedding which has resulted in the formation of long, vertical pipelike bodies which are isoclinally refolded (Fig. 9-23).

Formation of Salt Domes

The most widely held concept regarding the mechanics of the formation of salt domes is that described by Nettleton (1934) in which the salt rises from the original bedded deposit of salt as a result of the instability which exists when salt is overlain by a thick sequence of higher-density sediments. This theory has gained acceptance because it accounts for the formation of the observed features by a process which does not require lateral deformation folding, and because it can be used to explain the origin and behavior of salt and the structural features associated with salt bodies. Nettleton concluded that salt domes formed as a result of fluid movement under gravitational forces because salt is lighter than the surrounding sediments, and because the domes all have a nearly circular form, suggesting that their shape is controlled by yielding and flow and not as a result of fracturing or faulting.

The contrast between the density of salt and the surrounding sediments provides a gravitational motive force which is, as will be shown,

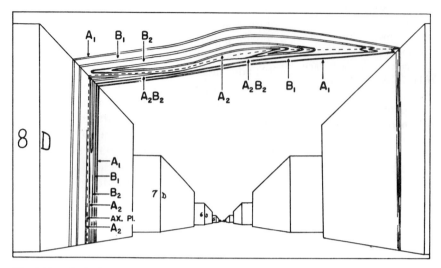

Fig. 9-23 Block diagram of refolded fold; corridor D-8 to D-7. If salt structure is unfolded along dashed line representing trace of axial plane, a second axial plane is revealed between B_1 and B_2. Thus $A_1 = A_2$ and $B_1 = B_2$. Character of beds as seen in walls and ceilings—sharp here and vague there, wide here and narrow there, and similar details not shown in sketch—strongly suggests this refolding. (*From Kupfer, 1962.*)

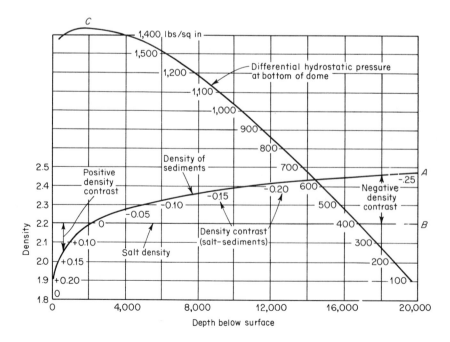

Fig. 9-24 Density contrast and differential pressure at bottom of salt column, Texas Gulf Coast. (*Redrawn from Nettleton, 1934.*)

sufficient to cause the salt flow. The density of the salt (2.2) does not vary with depth, but the density of the surrounding sediments increases with depth as a result of increasing overburden. A plot showing the predicted change in density of sediments with depth (Fig. 9-24) also has a curve showing the differential hydrostatic pressure to be expected at the bottom of the salt column. Below a depth of 2,000 ft the density of the sediment exceeds that of the salt. The differential hydrostatic pressure ranges from a few hundred pounds per square inch to nearly 1,400 lb/in.², certainly enough to cause solid flowage of the salt. Experiments have shown that salt will flow at differential pressures of this order of magnitude. It should be pointed out that some salt domes have apparently formed under overburdens of as little as 1,000 m.

Nettleton (1943) and others, notably Parker and McDowell (1955) and Dobrin (1941) have conducted scale-model experiments to simulate the formation of salt domes; however, salt was not used. Stages in the development of three of these experiments by Nettleton are shown in Fig. 9-25.

SALT STRUCTURES OF NORTHERN GERMANY

More than 200 salt stocks and similar features are now known in the oil- and gas-producing

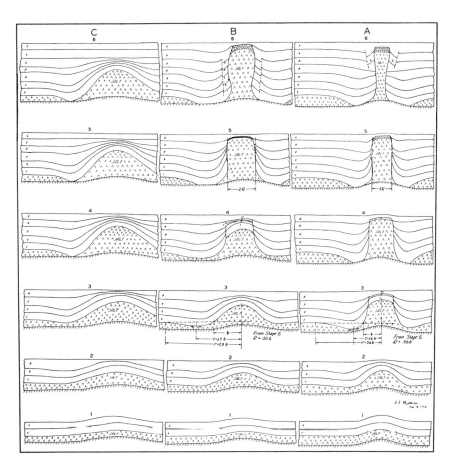

Fig. 9-25 Formation of salt dome structural form in scale-model experiments. (*From Nettleton, 1934.*)

Fig. 9-26 Salt structures in north-west Germany. *(From Trusheim, 1960.)*

region of northern Germany (Fig. 9-26). Here the mechanics of formation of the bodies is thought to be very similar to that in the United States Coastal Plain (Trusheim, 1960) although the general geologic setting and the shapes of many of the salt structures differ from those normally associated with American Gulf Coast domes. Since the salt in the German basin is shallower than the salt of the United States Coastal Plain, the structure of the German basin is better known. In addition to stocks which resemble Gulf Coast domes, there are salt pillows and salt-walls (Fig. 9-27), most of which are oriented roughly parallel to one another with a few notable exceptions which have almost meandering courses. Some of these walls are nearly 60 miles long.

The mother salt was deposited in northern Germany in the Permian on a basement surface of very low relief. The salt was deposited in the lower and middle Permian in the deepest parts of the basin, but later in the period it was laid down throughout the basin so that the thickness of the salt now varies from a few feet at the edges to more than 1,000 m in the deepest portions of the basin. The sedimentary cover overlying the salt consists of Mesozoic and Cenozoic sediments which attain a maximum thickness of between 3,000 and 4,000 m. The salt stocks and walls have risen from the deepest portions of the basin, and the salt pillows are concentrated in the shallower portions, suggesting that the salt thickness and the weight of overlying strata determine the form of the salt structures.

The pre-Permian salt basement is little deformed with the exception of a few known fault and fracture systems, but the overlying section is often strongly deformed with features such as folds, normal and thrust faults, and flowage features, all of which have formed independently of the underlying basement (Trusheim, 1960). A thickness of about 1,000 m of sediment is required to start salt flowage and migration. Various ideas have been put forth in Germany to explain the initial movements. These range from attributing the initial movements to faulting, to fracture zones in the basement, and to initial difference in thickness of the salt due to tectonic activity.

Trusheim suggests "that the development of a salt structure normally began with the salt pillow stage. The salt pillow consists of a salt accumulation, which is plani-convex, at first hourglass-shape, later dome-shape, and usually almost symmetrical. . . ." These features as well as the salt stocks have peripheral sinks. If the supply of salt is maintained, the pillow structure swells, its flanks become steeper and eventually form shearing cracks in the overlying sediment, and the diapir stage begins in which vertical salt movement dominates the development of the structure.

Some of the American domes come close to the surface, and apparently some of these domes in Germany broke through the surface and flowed out as salt extrusions (possibly under unconsolidated sediment) or "salt glaciers" flowing over and around brecciated rock and sediment.

Some typical structures associated with these salt intrusions are illustrated in Fig. 9-28. Trusheim (1960, p. 1527) described their formation as follows:

Many salt structures in Northern Germany are asymmetric especially in the deeper levels. . . . The salt has been forced obliquely upward, through a half-open "trapdoor" so that in cross section the salt body has assumed the appearance of a duck's head. The salt paste, during the upward thrust, probably intruded along the inclined shearing planes, and consequently initiated the asymmetric development of the diapir. [Fig. 9-28.] In this way one of the German salt plugs ever becomes detached from its source of supply, and rises into higher levels as a rootless, drop-shape salt body. [Fig. 9-29.] In general, it may be stated that even neighboring salt stocks can be of very different construction. No two salt stocks are alike.

. . . Almost all the larger structures [in northern Germany] are limited to the postsaline strata. In general, the intensity of folds and faults decreases with depth. As a rule, they do not continue into the presaline basement. . . . The transformation of structural relief is a typical consequence of the salt migration. Old swells are buried under younger troughs, and, conversely, older trough-fills may be converted into younger anticlines. These phenomena occurred because the salt that had accumulated in the core of the existing swells broke through upward, and as a result, the roof of the swell collapsed. The depressions arising over the existing swells were continuously filled with basin sediments, whose volume more or less

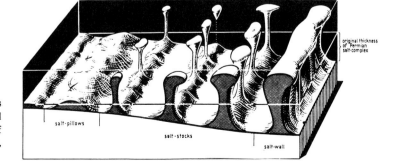

Fig. 9-27 Diagram of different types of salt structures in relation to original thickness of Permian salt complex of northwest Germany. (*From Trusheim, 1960.*)

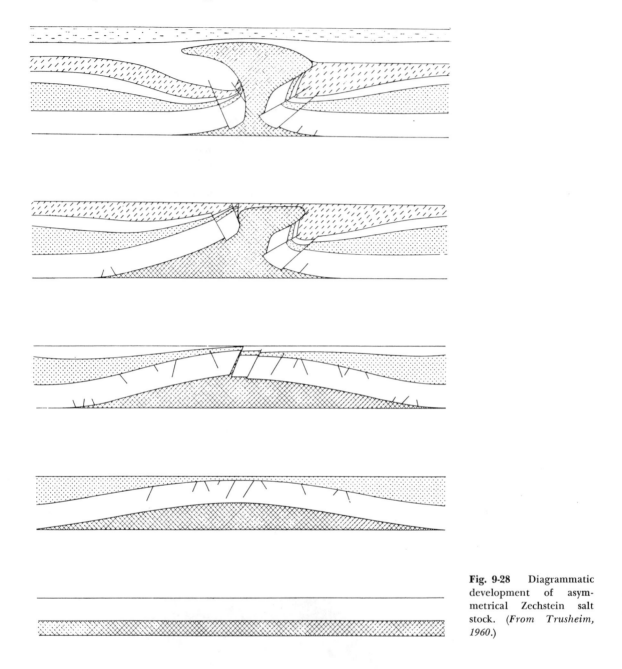

Fig. 9-28 Diagrammatic development of asymmetrical Zechstein salt stock. (*From Trusheim, 1960.*)

equals that of the salt which has moved away. Simultaneously, the trough-fill already in existence was transformed into a pseudo-anticline, because the flanks of the existing trough flattened out more and more. Accordingly, such turtle-shaped structures owe their faulting not to a later, "updoming" of the trough-fill, but exclusively to the collapse of the swell regions.

TECTONIC SALT STRUCTURES

Sedimentary basins in which salt has accumulated are found in Holland, Germany, Denmark, Rumania, Russia, Siberia, Iran, Saudi Arabia, Palestine, Algeria, Morocco, Spain, Portugal, Egypt, France, and the Western Hemisphere from Alberta to Argentina. Where the thickness of the salt and overlying sediments is great, and where there has been tectonic activity following the deposition of the salt, the salt has exhibited a high degree of mobility and has consequently been an important factor in the determination of the structures formed. In the United States Gulf Coast and in northern Germany the salt features appear to have formed almost completely independently of external stresses other than the force of gravity. The behavior of the underlying rocks in these areas does not appear to have played an important part in the movements

which caused the salt to penetrate overlying rock layers and to form domes and other structures, although it has been suggested that movements in the rocks beneath the salt may have been important in initiating the salt movement.

In other areas salt, gypsum, and anhydrite have played an important role in the development of large-scale structural features when external stresses have apparently been applied. Massive gypsum beds are involved in the folds and faults of the Jura Mountains of France and in the Alps. It has been suggested that the salt beds in the Jura Mountains have functioned as a gliding surface over which the sedimentary veneer is folded and faulted and below which the basement is undeformed relatively. Salt and shale beds are said by some to function in a similar manner in the fold and fault belt of the Appalachian geosyncline.

In the region of southern France a salt basin formed during the Triassic over the area immediately north of the modern Pyrenees Moun-

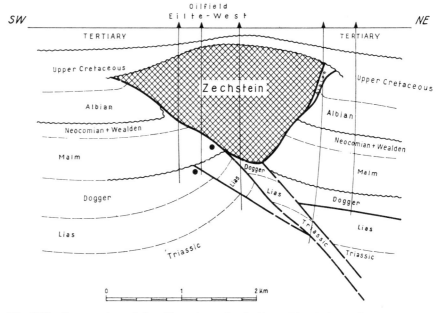

Fig. 9-29 Cross section of droplike salt stock of Eilte (with oil field Eilte-West below salt body). Ascent of salt might be associated with fault zone below salt body. This interpretation is that suggested by E. Plein. (*From Trusheim, 1960.*)

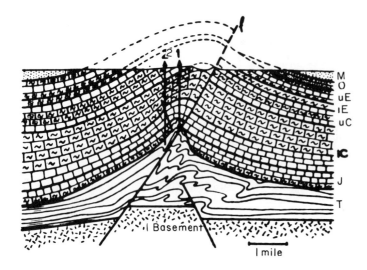

Fig. 9-30 Interpretative cross section of Audignon anticline. *(After Bonnard and Maugis redrawn from Dupouy-Camet, 1953.)*

tains. Approximately 7,000 ft of Triassic sediment accumulated and was followed by additional sediment between 8,000 and 23,000 ft thick. This sequence was deformed at several times corresponding to various phases of the tectonic activity in the Pyrenees. Structures involving the salt include isolated salt domes, piercement folds with salt plug cores, anticlines over deep diapiric plugs, salt dikes along faults, and erratic salt outcrops probably connected with unexposed faults. These structures are related to deep fractures and faults in the underlying basement rocks (Dupouy-Camet, 1953), as shown in Fig. 9-30, but both tectonic forces and density differences have been important in their formation. Notice how the fault which originated as a normal fault in the basement rock has evolved to become a thrust fault in the overlying sedimentary sequences as a result of the movement of the salt layer.

The salt structures of Rumania are famous. In the region southeast of the Transylvanian Alps, salt deposited in the Mesozoic was covered by great thicknesses of unconsolidated sediment before the main orogenic phases of deformation occurred in the Pliocene. Walt Small (1959, p. 455) describes the conditions of deformation as follows: "With 10,000-15,000 feet of sediments, most of which were unconsolidated, ly-

ing on a sloping foundation of the Carpathian foreland, it is easy to visualize the long strike folds pressing forward and down the slope as the uplift of the Carpathians reached its climax. Salt and salt breccia, along with fluids and gases entrained along lines of movement, served as lubricants."

Carter and Elston (1963) review the role of salt in the development of anticlines in Colorado and Utah.

COLLAPSE STRUCTURES IN SALT BASINS

A very different type of structure from the salt domes and piercements of the Gulf Coast and the high mobility of salt in tectonically deformed areas is found in the great Silurian salt basin of central North America, where removal of salt has promoted subsidence and collapse of overlying rock units. A large area of probable collapse of units above the Salina salt formation is mapped by Landes (1945) under Lake Michigan and Lake Huron. Surface evidence is seen in the vicinity of the Straits of MacKinac where great masses of brecciated rocks, some up to 1,500 ft in vertical dimension, are found in the otherwise slightly deformed Silurian and Devonian section. Some of the blocks have moved down hundreds of feet in the collapse features, but others are only slightly tilted.

The idea of salt solution in this region is not new. As early as 1933 Newcombe suggested that Lake Huron and Lake Michigan originated in depressions caused by solution and removal of salt. The outcrop belt of the salt is under water, in part, making leeching a probable cause. The thickness of salt in the salt basin is not at all uniform. Variations in thickness are due to thinning toward basin margins, non-deposition over reefs, and solution. Some parts of the basin have no salt, others are greatly thinned. The breccias of MacKinac Straits represent one type of structure related to the solution and removal of the salt. Other subsidence structures are known in Ontario and at the Kimball pool, where structures in units over the salt can be directly related to salt thickness.

REFERENCES

Andrews, Donald I., 1960, The Louann salt and its relationship to Gulf Coast salt domes: Gulf Coast Assoc. Geol. Soc. Trans., v. 10, p. 215–240.

Atwater, G. I., and Forman, M. J., 1959, Nature of growth of southern Louisiana salt domes and its effect on petroleum acc.: Am. Assoc. Petroleum Geologists Bull., v. 43, p. 2592–2623.

Balk, Robert, 1949, Structure of Grand Saline salt dome, Van Zandt County, Texas: Am. Assoc. Petroleum Geologists Bull., v. 33, p. 1791–1829.

Barton, D. C., 1933, Mechanics of formation of salt domes, with special reference to Gulf Coast salt domes of Texas and Louisiana: Am. Assoc. Petroleum Geologists Bull., v. 17, p. 1025–1083.

Bates, F. W., Copeland, R. R., Jr., and Dixon, K. P., 1959, Geology of Avery Island salt dome, Iberia Parish, La.: Am. Assoc. Petroleum Geologists Bull., v. 43, p. 944–958.

Berry, G. F., Jr., and Harper, P. A., 1948, Augusta field, Butler County, Kansas, in Structure of typical American oil fields: Am. Assoc. Petroleum Geologists, v. 3.

Borg, Iris, and others, 1960, Experimental deforma-

tion of St. Peter sand—a study of cataclastic flow: Geol. Soc. America Mem. 79, p. 133–191.

Bornhauser, Max, 1958, Gulf Coast tectonics: Am. Assoc. Petroleum Geologists Bull., v. 42, p. 339–370.

Carter, F. W., and Elston, D. P., 1963, Structural development of salt anticlines of Colorado and Utah, in Backbone of the Americas: Am. Assoc. Petroleum Geologists Mem. 2.

Coats, R. P., 1964, The geology and mineralization of the Blinman dome diapir: South Australia Geol. Survey, Rept. Inv. no. 26.

Currie, J. B., 1955, Role of concurrent deposition and deformation of sediments in development of salt-dome graben structures: Am. Assoc. Petroleum Geologists Bull., v. 39, no. 12.

———— 1956, Role of concurrent deposition and deformation of sediments in development of salt-dome graben structures [Mississippi]: Am. Assoc. Petroleum Geologists Bull., v. 40, p. 1–16.

Davies, R., 1966, Concentration of mica by water flotation: Geol. Soc. America Bull., v. 77, p 661–662.

DeGolyer, E., 1926, Origin of North American salt domes, in Geology of salt-dome oil fields: Am. Assoc. Petroleum Geologists, Tulsa, p. 1–44.

———— 1934, Origin of North American salt domes, problems of petroleum geology: Am. Assoc. Petroleum Geologists Bull., v. 38, p. 629–678.

Dobrin, M. B., 1941, Some quantitative experiments on a fluid salt dome model and their geologic implications: Am. Geophys. Union Trans., Ann. Mtg., 22d, p. 528–542.

Dupouy-Camet, J., 1953, Triassic diapiric salt structures, southwestern Aquitaine basin, France: Am. Assoc. Petroleum Geologists Bull., v. 37, p. 2348.

Escher, B. G., and Kuenen, P. H., 1929, Experiments in connection with salt domes: Leidsche Geologische Mededeelingen, v. III, pt. 3, p. 151–182.

Hanna, M. A., 1934, Geology of the Gulf Coast salt domes, problems of petroleum geology: Am. Assoc. Petroleum Geologists, Tulsa, p. 629–678.

———— 1959, Salt domes: Favorite home for oil: Oil and Gas Jour., v. 57, p. 138–142.

Heard, H. C., and Rubey, W. W., 1966, Tectonic implications of gypsum dehydration: Geol. Soc. America Bull., v. 77, p. 741–760.

Hedberg, H. D., 1936, Gravitational compaction of clays and shales: Am. Jour. Sci., v. 31, p. 241–287.

Hoy, R. B., Foose, R. M., and O'Neill, B. J., Jr., 1962, Structure of Winnfield salt dome, Winn Parish, La.: Am. Assoc. Petroleum Geologists Bull., v. 46, p. 1444–1460.

Hughes, Dudley J., 1960, Faulting associated with deepseated salt domes in the northeast portion of the Mississippi salt basin: Gulf Coast Assoc. of Geol. Soc. Trans., v. 10, p. 155–173.

Kuenen, P. H., 1953, Significant features of graded bedding: Am. Assoc. Petroleum Geologists Bull., v. 37, p. 1044–1066.

Kupfer, Donald H., 1962, Structure of Morton Salt Company mine, Weeks Island salt dome, Louisiana: Am. Assoc. Petroleum Geologists Bull., v. 46, no. 8, p. 1460–1467.

Landes, K. K., 1945, Mackinac breccia, subsurface stratigraphy and regional structure, *in* Geology of the Mackinac Straits region: Michigan Geol. Survey Div. Pub. 44, Geol. Ser. 37.

Mattox, R. B., ed., Holser, W. T., Ode, H., McIntire, W. L., Short, N. M., Taylor, R. E., and van Siclen, D. C., assoc. eds., 1968, Saline deposits: Geol. Soc. America Spec. Paper 88.

Maxwell, J. C., 1960, Experiments on compaction and cementation of sand: Geol. Soc. America Mem. 79, p. 105–132.

Moore, D. G., and Scruton, P. C., 1957, Minor internal structures of some recent unconsolidated sediments [Gulf of Mexico]: Am. Assoc. Petroleum Geologists Bull., v. 41, p. 2723–2751.

Muehlberger, W. R., 1959, Internal structure of the Grand Saline salt dome, Van Zandt County, Texas: Texas Univ. Bur. Econ. Geology, Rept. Inv., no. 38, 24 p.

Murray, G. E., 1966, Salt structures of Gulf of Mexico basin: Am. Assoc. Petroleum Geologists Bull., v. 50, p. 439–478.

Nettleton, L. L., 1934, Fluid mechanics of salt domes: Am. Assoc. Petroleum Geologists Bull., v. 18, p. 1175–1204.

——— 1943, Recent experimental and geophysical evidence of mechanics of salt-dome formation: Am. Assoc. Petroleum Geologists Bull., v. 27, p. 51–63.

——— 1955, History of concepts of Gulf Coast salt dome formation: Am. Assoc. Petroleum Geologists Bull., v. 39, p. 2373–2383.

Nevin, C. M., and Sherrill, R. E., 1929, Studies in differential compacting: Am. Assoc. Petroleum Geologists Bull., v. 13, p. 1–22.

Ocamb, Rayburn, 1961, Growth faults of south Louisiana: Gulf Coast Assoc. Geol. Soc. Trans., v. 11, p. 139–175.

Omara, S., 1964, Diapiric structures in Egypt and Syria: Am. Assoc. Petroleum Geologists Bull., v. 48, p. 1116.

Parker, Travis J., 1951, Scale models as guide to interpretation of salt-dome faulting: Am. Assoc. Petroleum Geologists Bull., v. 35, no. 9, p. 2076–2086.

Parker, Travis J., and MacDowell, A. N., 1955, Model studies of salt-dome tectonics: Am. Assoc. Petroleum Geologists Bull., v. 39, p. 2384–2470.

Powers, Sidney, 1922, Reflected buried hills and their importance in petroleum geology: Econ. Geology, v. 17, p. 233–259.

——— 1931, Structural geology of northeastern Oklahoma: Jour. Geology, v. 39, p. 117–132.

Raistrick, Arthur, and Marshall, C. E., 1939, The nature and origin of coal and coal seams: London, English Universities Press.

Read, John L., 1959, Geologic case history of Slocum dome, Anderson County, Texas: Am. Assoc. Petroleum Geologists Bull., v. 43, p. 958–973.

Richter-Bernberg, G., and Schott, Wolfgang, 1959, The structural development of Northwest German salt domes and their importance for oil accumulation: World Petroleum Cong., 5th, sec. I, Paper 4.

Rubey, W. W., and Hubbert, M. K., 1959, Role of fluid pressure in mechanics of overthrust faulting: Geol. Soc. America Bull., v. 70, p. 167–206.

Sanders, J. E., 1965, Primary sedimentary structures formed by turbidity currents and related resedimentation mechanisms, *in* Primary sedimentary structures and their hydrodynamic interpretation: Soc. of Econ. Paleontologists and Mineralogists Spec. Pub. no. 12, p. 192–219.

Small, W. M., 1959, Thrust faults and ruptured folds in Rumanian oil fields: Am. Assoc. Petroleum Geologists Bull., v. 43, p. 455.

Smith, Derrell A., 1961, Geology of South Pass Block 27 oil field, offshore, Plaquemines Parish, Louisiana: Am. Assoc. Petroleum Geologists Bull., v. 45.

Trusheim, F., 1960, Mechanism of salt migration in northern Germany: Am. Assoc. Petroleum Geologists Bull., v. 44, p. 1519–1541.

Woods, R. D., 1956, The northern structural rim of the Gulf basin: Gulf Coast Assoc. of Geol. Soc. Trans., v. 6, p. 3–9.

part two
tectonics

10
the earth's interior and major crustal elements

The development of the major structural features of the crust is intimately related to the earth's interior. While there are a number of strongly contrasting theories about such fundamental geological questions as the origin of continents and ocean basins, the causes of mountain building, and the permanence of continents, the nature of the earth's interior has an important bearing on such theory. If we knew the nature of the interior more precisely, many of the problems listed below involving the crust would be much easier to solve:

1. Did the continents originate by differentiation from ultrabasic rocks of the mantle, the sialic differentiates rising to the surface, being pushed into a single large plate by convection currents, and later being broken up and drifting apart to their present position?
2. Or have continents formed by gradual acretion, growth around sialic nuclei by incorporation of marginal geosynclines?
3. Have continents drifted apart in the geologic past, like rafts of granitic material floating on a sea of basalt, or are the continents deeply rooted in the mantle?
4. Do large convection cells in the mantle exert drag on the crust and cause the development of folded mountain belts?
5. Is the earth cooling and contracting, or is it actually expanding?
6. Are there processes of large-scale melting or phase changes going on in the interior which cause uplift and subsidence in the crust?

In order to evaluate the arguments made for these various theories and to establish a background for understanding the setting of the crust, we will review some of the evidence concerning the earth's interior.

Direct observations of the interior are very limited. The deepest wells are just over 25,000 ft deep and these are drilled on continents with crustal thicknesses on the order of 125,000 ft. Preliminary holes drilled in the ocean in preparation for attempts to drill into the mantle also fall far short of the top of the mantle. Other direct observations on deep rock are obtained through study of rocks (all ultra-basic—dunite, peridotite, or eclogite) erupted from volcanoes believed to be deep-seated because they are associated with deep earthquakes. Peridotite intrusions such as the diamond pipes

of South Africa also appear to be derived from very great depths. Similar ultrabasic intrusions occur commonly in orogenic belts.

Finally we can examine folded mountain belts in which rocks have been uplifted from depths of perhaps 50,000 ft and exposed for our inspection by erosion. These rocks occur in the regions of greatest crustal thickness and so do not expose subcrustal materials. Thus it is impossible to examine the earth's interior directly. For this reason the conventional methods of geologic field study can not be used to study the interior. The principal tools by which we know the nature of the deeper crust and interior are geophysical—seismic, gravitational, and magnetic. The data obtained by these methods are interpreted in terms of surface geology and laboratory investigations, particularly those dealing with the behavior of rocks and minerals under high temperatures and confining pressures.

DEFINING THE CRUST

The crust of the earth is now defined in terms of seismic discontinuity discovered by Mohorovicic and named Moho or M discontinuity in his honor. The M discontinuity is recognized throughout most of the earth by a sharp increase in the velocity of compressional waves from about 6.0 to 8.0 km/sec. The methods used by Mohorovicic involved seismic refraction techniques. The method has been followed using earthquakes, small TNT blasts produced in water in the oceans, quarry blasts, and more recently, underground nuclear explosions. The crust so defined has several marked characteristics:

1. The continents and ocean basins have different thicknesses of crust. The average continental thickness is 35 km. The oceanic crust thickness ranges between 5 and 10 km. Typical sections are illustrated in Fig. 10-1.

2. The main areas of departure from the average continental and oceanic thickness

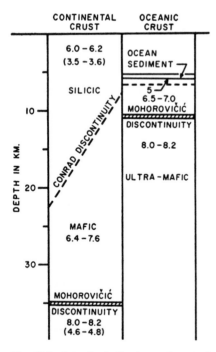

Fig. 10-1 Seismic indications of crustal layering in continental shields and ocean basins. Compressional and shear velocities (in kilometers per second) are shown. Shear velocities are in parentheses. (*From Press, 1961.*)

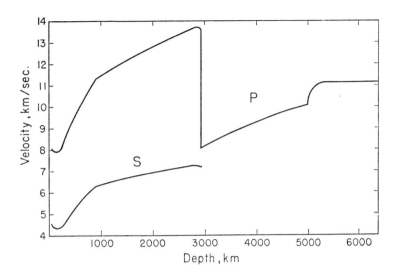

Fig. 10-2 Gutenberg's latest velocities. *(From Bullard, 1957.)*

lie in long narrow belts in the regions of island arcs, folded mountain belts where crustal thicknesses of 50 km have been observed, and midoceanic ridges where no sharp M discontinuity is observed.

The composition of crustal materials is a sedimentary veneer with a bulk chemical composition similar to granite. Shield areas and other exposures of deep continental rocks are predominantly granites and granitic gneisses. Basic materials, primarily andesite and basalt, make up a small fraction of the exposed continental rocks. Basalt and other basic rocks are exposed as dikes and sills, and in a few places, notably the Columbia River Plateau and in the Deccan Plateau of India, large volumes of basalt occur on continents. Thus the continents are primarily granitic, but a source of basalt must be present at depth under continents. The oceans, on the other hand, are underlain by extensive basaltic materials, judging from the predominance of basaltic volcanic products on the mid-Atlantic ridge, the basalt dredged from sea mounts, and lava coming from active volcanoes both in the Atlantic and in the Pacific.

Seismic velocities of the subcrustal materials ($P = 8.1$ km/sec) are similar to those indicated by experimental work for ultramafic rocks such as dunite and peridotite at the temperatures and pressures which prevail at the level of subcrustal rocks. Thus the composition of the mantle is interpreted to be one of the ultrabasic rock types. Velocities in the higher portions of the continental crust ($P = 6.0$ to 6.2 km/sec) are velocities found also experimentally to be characteristic of granite, while the lower parts of the continental crust and most of the standard oceanic crust have velocities ($P = 6.5$ to 7.6 km/sec) of basalt. This twofold division of the continental crust is not confirmed everywhere.

DEEPER SEISMIC DISCONTINUITIES

Seismologists have long recognized a three-part division of the earth's interior: the crust, the mantle, and the core. These were all discovered through study of travel times of earthquake shock waves. The crust-mantle discontinuity is marked by the sudden velocity increase of P waves. The mantle-core break is marked by the disappearance of shear waves, suggesting a liquid core. Subsequently the core was divided into an inner and outer core, the inner core being characterized by somewhat higher P-wave velocities (Lehmann, 1936). Velocities of compressional, P, and shear, S, waves at various depths in the interior are illustrated in Fig. 10-2. It is immediately apparent from this that there are at least two additional breaks within the mantle. The first is a zone between 50 and 200 km in which velocities decrease, called the *Gutenberg low-velocity zone,* and the second is a break at about 900 km in which the rate of increase of velocities of both *P* and *S* with depth decreases.

DENSITY VARIATION

The variation of density with depth in the earth's interior is calculated by use of seismic velocities which are known to depend on the elastic constants of the materials through which the seismic wave travels. Density distribution is limited by estimating the probable density of the top of the mantle from the composition of ultrabasic rocks thought to be derived from the mantle, or alternatively, by using estimates based on stony meteorites which are interpreted as the mantle rock of disintegrated or unformed planets. Additional limiting factors include the estimated mass and moment of inertia of the earth now derived from satellite data. The der-

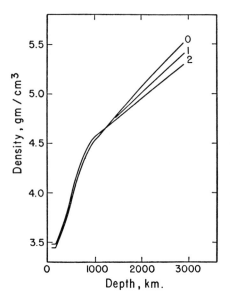

Fig. 10-3 The density variation in the mantle. (*From Clark, 1963.*)

ivation of density values from these data and discussion of the elaborate limitations of the various assumptions made in the calculations cannot be cited here (see Clark, 1963, for a review), but curves showing a range of values obtained according to three slightly different assumptions are illustrated in Fig. 10-3.

HETEROGENEITY OF THE MANTLE

Certainly the outer part of the mantle is the most important part of the subcrustal portion of the earth insofar as the structure of the crust is concerned. Processes acting in this portion of the mantle have direct effects on the crust; materials are believed to enter the crust from this zone; movements here are called on to exert drag on the crust; the crust may have been derived from these rocks. Because so many critical geological questions focus on the character of the mantle, much attention is being given to study of the outer mantle.

Composition of Mantle Rocks

Rocks which have apparently come from the outer mantle are all ultrabasic, but the most direct evidence of heterogeneity of mantle rock is found by comparing these rocks. They occur as inclusions in basalts, as kimberlites, and as associated ultrabasic xenoliths. The main minerals which occur in the ultrabasic inclusions in basalts are olivines, enstatite, and augite. They occur in a rock with density in the range of 3.30 to 3.33 g/cm^3. The proportions of these minerals are highly variable, ranging from dunite, 100 percent olivine, to rock without olivine. The major xenoliths from kimberlite (a peridotite) are eclogites which contain garnet and mica as well as olivine. Thus subcrustal rocks show mineralogical variation. Unfortunately the occurrence of such rocks is so limited that it is impossible to obtain an accurate idea of the distribution of such variations as may exist. Heat-flow measurements also indicate possible variation in the composition of the mantle. The average rate of heat flow is about

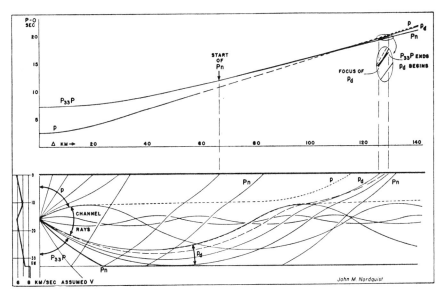

Fig. 10-4 Wave paths of longitudinal waves in the lithosphere channel and corresponding travel times. (*From Gutenberg, 1954.*)

the same through continental and oceanic crusts, 1.2 μ cal/cm² sec. The heat from continents is thought to come from the decay of radioactive minerals which are abundant in granitic rocks, but the source of heat flow through the oceanic basaltic crust must have some other explanation. Possibly the explanation lies in the composition or differences in character of the mantle under oceans and continents, or it may be that the oceanic crust is younger and still cooling.

LOW-VELOCITY ZONE IN THE MANTLE

The discovery of a low-velocity zone near the top of the mantle must be ranked as one of the most important recent discoveries in earth science. Gutenberg (1948) and Gutenberg and Richter (1954) postulated the existence of such a low-velocity zone at a depth of 60 to 150 km for P waves when he observed a shadow-zone effect for earthquake shock waves (Fig. 10-4). If velocity increases steadily with depth, then a shock wave should travel out from the focus

as a continuous wavefront, but if a low-velocity zone occurs at depth, the waves become channeled into it and create a shadow effect. Effects are different depending on the depth of the focus relative to the low-velocity zone. If the focus is in the zone then a larger part of the energy remains in the channel formed by the low-velocity zone. For waves that pass downward into the zone to move back up into higher-velocity materials over the zone, they must first be refracted through the zone into lower high-velocity materials. In the time taken for these movements the waves are traveling laterally as well, and a shadow zone is therefore created. The existence of the low-velocity layer has been confirmed by studies of amplitudes of P waves produced by nuclear explosions (Romney, 1959). Geophysicists are currently seeking data which will explain the cause of this low-velocity zone.

The significance of the low-velocity layer depends on the physical conditions responsible for it. One suggestion is that it occurs where the effect of increasing temperature with depth

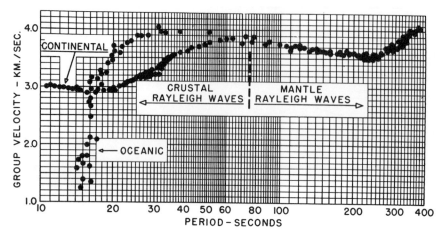

Fig. 10-5 Observed dispersion of Rayleigh waves in the period range 10 to 400 sec. *(After Ewing and Press, 1956)*

of burial exceeds the effect of the weight of overburden, hence a zone of increased plasticity. The depth of the zone is about that predicted for the generation of primary basaltic magma. It is in this depth range that temperatures come close to those required for partial melting of basalt. The majority of earthquakes associated with volcanic activity in the circumpacific belt occur in this depth interval. If the zone is one of high temperature and increased plasticity or low shear strength, then this zone may be of critical importance in regard to continental drift, polar wandering, and crustal deformation.

STUDY OF CRUST AND MANTLE BY SURFACE WAVES

In addition to the seismic reflection and refraction techniques, other ways of using shock waves are being employed to study the crust and mantle. These involve analysis of the dispersion of surface waves, Love and Rayleigh waves. Love waves are a type of shear wave that involves lateral movement in a horizontal plane. They come into existence as a result of horizontal layering and they are dispersive, that is, waves with different periods travel with different phase and group velocities. Rayleigh

waves move by retrograde elliptical motion, and can exist on the free surface of a solid as non-dispersive waves, but in practice they too are dispersive in the layered earth. The shorter Rayleigh waves travel in upper layers, but those of longer wavelength penetrate to greater depth and are thus affected by the elastic properties of materials at depth.

To measure and plot dispersion, each peak on a wave train of surface waves is plotted against the arrival time of that peak. The slope of the curve thus obtained is a measure of the frequency at the time represented by that point. A group velocity can then be calculated and plotted against the period (Fig. 10-5).

The interpretation of surface wave dispersion is accomplished by computing theoretical curves for various models and comparing the observed dispersion curves with the models. Observed dispersion data for long-period Rayleigh waves fit theoretical curves based on models with the Gutenberg low-velocity zone better than do those based on models with a steady increase in velocity with depth (Dorman, Ewing, and Oliver, 1960). Studies of surface-wave dispersion have led in recent years to the following conclusions that are pertinent to the structure of the crust and mantle.

1. Velocity increases with depth in the continental crust as predicted by Conrad.
2. The low-velocity zone in the mantle appears to occur throughout the earth under continents and ocean basins with the minimum velocity at a depth of approximately 140 km.
3. The upper mantle under continents and various ocean basins is different. Several suggestions have been made to explain this difference. One is that the level of the low-velocity zone is shallower under the Pacific than under continents (Dorman, Ewing, and Oliver, 1960). A second is that the level is the same but the velocity is lower in the zone under the ocean (Aki and Press, 1962).

The phase velocity obtained from surface-wave data show an excellent correlation with Bouguer gravity anomalies. Figure 10-6 is a profile across the United States showing this correlation and topography.

DEFINING THE CRUST BY GRAVITY ANOMALIES

Because the rock materials of the continental crust have lower densities than those of the mantle, we might expect Bouguer gravity anomalies to show some relation to the thickness of the crust. Woollard (1959) has compiled records which illustrate the relations between gravity anomalies and topography and crustal thicknesses. Figure 10-7 shows a plot of crustal thicknesses measured by means of seismic refraction data, data on thickness derived from phase velocities of surface waves, and Bouguer anomalies. Notice that the Bouguer anomalies define a curve—not a straight line. The anomalies over deeper parts of the continental crust are greater than they would be if a straight-line fit were made. It appears that the density of the crustal rocks increases in deeper parts of the continental crust. This is thought to be due to thickening of an intermediate, basaltic layer rather than to change in the upper sialic layer. This is confirmed by seismic studies. Figure 10-8 shows

Fig. 10-6 Profile across the United States, showing the relation of Rayleigh-wave phase velocity to topography and Bouguer anomaly. Depths to the discontinuity are inferred from the phase velocity. *(After Ewing and Press, 1960)*

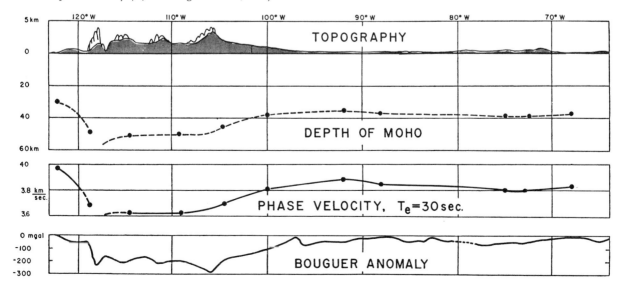

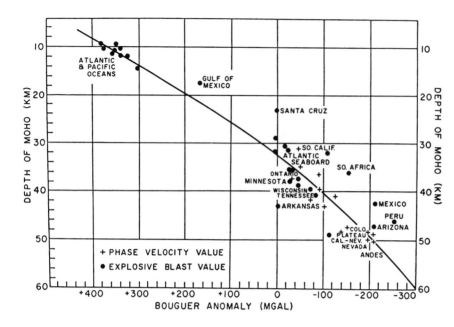

Fig. 10-7 Relation between the Bouguer gravity anomaly and the thickness of the crust. Circles = points plotted from seismic refraction data; crosses = points plotted from data on phase velocity of surface waves. *(After Woollard, 1959.)*

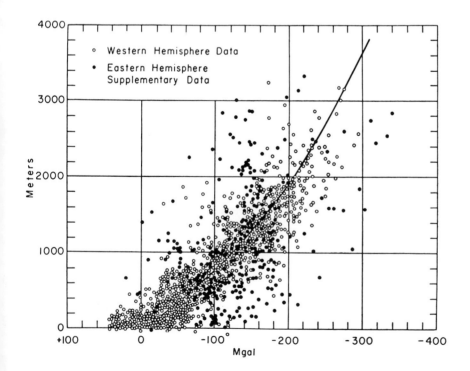

Fig. 10-8 Relation between the Bouguer gravity anomaly and topographic elevation. *(After Woollard, 1959.)*

the relation between topography and Bouguer anomalies. In both cases a positive correlation is seen.

Using the relation between gravity anomalies and crustal thickness, maps have been made of the crust-mantle contact. One such map for the United States is illustrated in Fig. 10-9. These are based on Bouguer anomalies and Bouguer isostatic anomalies corrected for surficial geology.

STRUCTURAL DIVISIONS OF THE CRUST

Because it is not practical to cover the details of the structure of every feature on earth and,

indeed, because many are not yet known in detail, it is useful to establish criteria by which major sections of the crust can be classified. By doing this we hope to recognize a major framework of the crust and find a basis for comparing, contrasting, and relating different crustal elements. We must at the same time try to avoid the pitfalls of thinking in terms of oversimplified stereotyped models, for detailed comparisons of structural elements of the same type often reveal striking differences.

It is not easy to find criteria for defining structural divisions which can be applied uniformly to all parts of the earth. We know the topography of parts of the continents with precision, but our knowledge of submarine topog-

Fig. 10-9 Crustal thickness; crustal and mantle velocities. *(After Pakiser and Zietz, 1965.)*

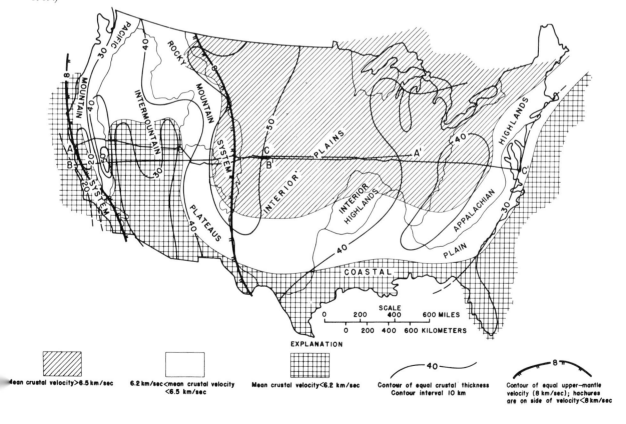

EXPLANATION

Mean crustal velocity>6.5 km/sec

6.2 km/sec<mean crustal velocity <6.5 km/sec

Mean crustal velocity<6.2 km/sec

Contour of equal crustal thickness
Contour interval 10 km

Contour of equal upper-mantle velocity (8 km/sec); hachures are on side of velocity<8 km/sec

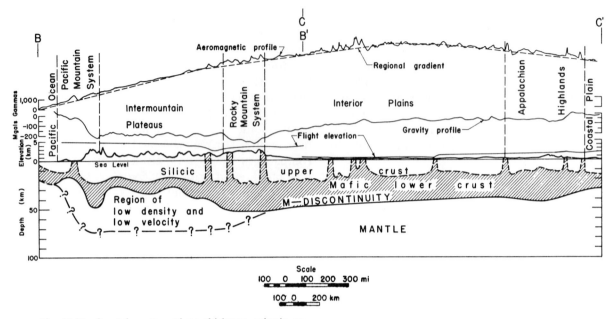

Fig. 10-10 Crustal cross section: thickness, seismic velocities, gravity, and magnetic fields. *(After Pakiser and Zietz, 1965.)*

Fig. 10-11 Hypsographic curve of the earth's surface (mean elevations given by dashed lines). *(Redrawn from Bucher, 1933.)*

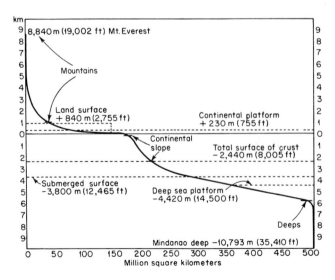

Fig. 10-12 Graph showing the two frequency maxima of elevation on the earth's surface. Solid line = actual frequency of elevations based on a contour interval of 100 m; dotted line = hypothetical frequency of elevations representing the result of disturbances of a single equilibrium level, with deformation accomplished as easily downward as upward. *(From Wegener, 1922.)*

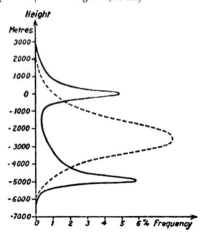

raphy is still in an early stage of development. Since methods of surface geological study used on continental areas can not be applied in ocean basins, we are forced to rely even more heavily on topography in the oceans. The criteria most readily applied are geophysical observations of seismic discontinuities, gravity anomalies, heat-flow measurements, magnetic anomalies, and the geography of earthquake epicenters. Thus the criteria available are essentially topographic, geologic, and geophysical.

The best-defined division of the crust is between continents and ocean basins, with a third, highly varied division where the transition from continents to ocean basins occurs. The following points summarize differences between continents and ocean basins:

1. Topographically the surfaces of the continents stand high. The level of the top of the oceanic crust is low. This is clearly pointed out in the hypsographic curve of the earth's surface (Fig. 10-11). Two distinct levels nearly 5 km apart on the average can be recognized on earth (Fig. 10-12).

2. Petrographically the rocks which occur on continents are rich in quartz and aluminum; granites and gneisses are common on continents, and the bulk chemical composition of the continental crust is granitic. Lavas on continents are generally rhyolites, andesites, and some basalt. Rocks found under the ocean basins are, with the exception of the thin sedimentary veneer, basaltic or ultrabasic. Poldervaart (1955) summarized the bulk compositions of rock from four divisions of the crust (Table 10-1).

3. Structural differences are not easily documented, but some structural inferences about the ocean basins can be made from geophysical and petrological evidence. A most significant difference is that young folded mountain belts of the types found in the Alpine-Himalayan, Appalachian, Caledonian, and Cordilleran belts have not been recognized and are thus presumed to be absent from the oceanic crust. Thus the processes and conditions which give rise to folded belts appear not to exist in the oceans. On the other hand the mid-oceanic ridges have no counterparts of comparable dimensions on the continents.

4. Seismic discontinuities indicate prominent differences between continents and ocean basins. Typical sections of continental and oceanic crust defined on seismic data are illustrated in Fig. 10-1. The differences in level of the M discontinuity is the most striking difference. Figure 10-13 shows a generalized seismic section from the Pacific based on seismic and surface-wave data. The section shows water, sediment, a crust with velocity and density comparable to basalt, and the low-velocity channel in the mantle. The twofold division of the continental crust, indicated by the Conrad discontinuity which shows up prominently in

Table 10-1   Percentage Composition of the Lithosphere

	SiO_2	TiO_2	Al_2O_3	Fe_2O_3	FeO	MnO	MgO	CaO	Na_2O	K_2O	P_2O_5
Oceanic region	46.6	2.9	15.0	3.8	8.0	0.2	7.8	11.9	2.5	1.0	0.3
Suboceanic region	49.5	1.9	15.1	3.4	6.4	0.2	6.2	13.2	2.5	1.3	0.3
Young folded belts region	58.4	1.1	15.6	2.8	4.8	0.2	4.3	7.2	3.1	2.2	0.3
Continental shield region	59.8	1.2	15.5	2.1	5.1	0.1	4.1	6.4	3.1	2.4	0.2
Lithosphere	55.2	1.6	15.3	2.8	5.8	0.2	5.2	8.8	2.9	1.9	0.3

Source: Poldervaart (1955).

the section from Ludlow, Calif., to Boise, Ida. (Fig. 10-14), is not found in the oceanic crust. The only common discontinuity in the oceanic crust occurs between the semiconsolidated sedimentary veneer and the basaltic layer.

A less well-defined difference between continents and oceans is found in the character of the low-velocity layer of the upper mantle discussed earlier. Either the layer is at a different level or the velocity reduction is different under continents and oceans.

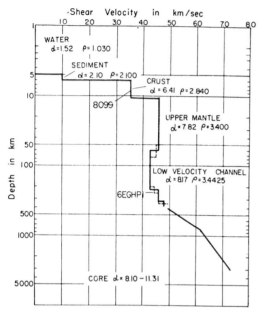

Fig. 10-13 Generalized structure for the Pacific basin. *(From Ewing and others, 1962.)*

Fig. 10-14 Variations in crustal thickness and an intermediate crustal layer from Ludlow, Calif., *B*, to Boise, Ida., *B'*. *(From Pakiser, 1963.)*

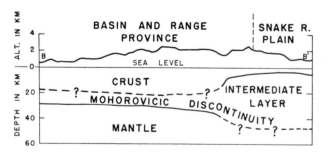

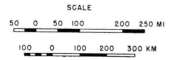

5. Heat-flow observations have now been made over large areas of the crust. Figure 10-15 shows a contoured orthogonal function representation of 757 heat-flow values. Contours are in ergs per centimeter squared second; 92 were made on continents, 665 in oceanic regions. The heat flow shows no positive correlation with type of crust but appears to be related instead to the height of the geoid (MacDonald, 1964).

The differences in heat production of different rocks are striking (e.g., granite 285 ergs/g year, basalt 58 ergs/g year, dunite 0.08 ergs/g year). Despite this difference the granitic continental crust fails to be clearly differentiated from the basaltic oceanic crust on the basis of heat-flow measurements. This is interpreted by MacDonald as indicating that the differences in the continents and ocean basins extend deep into the mantle.

6. Gravity data also tend to support the idea that differences between oceans and continents extend into the mantle. The gravity field of the earth shows that average values are the same over continents and oceans. This means that the mass per unit area is the same beneath oceans and continents despite the prominent differences in the density of the rocks in the two. This indicates that differences in the density of deeply buried material must compensate for surface inequalities in density (MacDonald, 1964) not compensated for by differences in elevation.

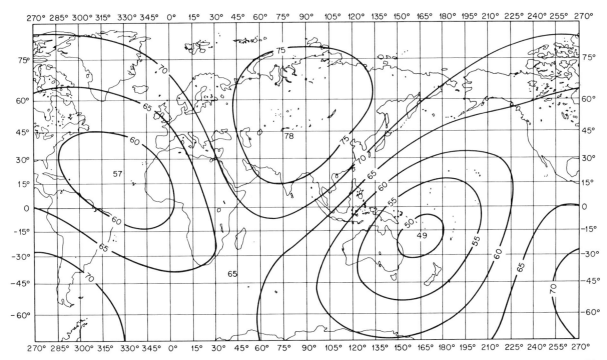

Fig. 10-15 Orthogonal function representation of weighted averages for the $5 \times 5°$ grid. *(From Lee and MacDonald, 1963.)*

Subdivisions of Continental and Oceanic Crust
Each continent can be subdivided into many parts on the basis of surface geology, but two principal types of structural provinces are found on every continent. These are the shield areas in which Precambrian igneous and meta-morphic rocks are most prominent in outcrop over vast areas, and the younger orogenic belts in which Paleozoic or younger sedimentary sequences accumulated, often in great (30,000 to 50,000 ft) thicknesses, and are folded, faulted, intruded by large batholiths, and often partially metamorphosed. The shield areas may be drawn to include stable platformlike areas surrounding the Precambrian outcrop area which are covered by relatively thin undeformed sedimentary veneers. The central United States east

of the Rocky Mountain front, north of the deformed belt in Oklahoma and Arkansas, and east of the Appalachian basin is essentially of this character, and may be conveniently thought of as an extension of the Canadian shield. There are local departures from the characteristics associated with the idealized crustal element. Shields are generally seismically stable, yet there are numerous earthquakes in southern Ontario. The idea of thin sedimentary veneer over the central platform of North America breaks down where great basins such as the Michigan basin with many thousands of feet of Paleozoic sediment have accumulated (but not been deformed as in orogenic belts). There are also numerous areas of block faulting within shields and stable platform areas.

Ocean basins constitute a second major division of the crust, but as research has proceeded the number of areas of anomalous crust within the oceans has increased. The midocean ridges and oceanic rises are the most prominent of these. We are also confronted with a major problem in recognizing crustal divisions within the large and highly significant zones which lie between the ocean basin proper and the continents. Around the margins of the Pacific Ocean this zone is one of Cenozoic orogeny. Young folded mountain belts lie along the western margin of North and South America; well-defined arcuate island belts occur in the northern and western Pacific; and a highly complicated pattern of arcs and strewn islands characterizes the southwest Pacific. The Atlantic margins stand in marked contrast. Young orogenic belts touch the Atlantic only in the Caribbean region; the margins are often broad coastal plains and shelf areas such as those found in eastern North America, and at several places old orogenic belts run out into and are lost within the Atlantic. This happens in the Atlas Mountains of North Africa, the Pyrenees in Spain and France, the Caledonides in England, and the Appalachians in Newfoundland.

Great care must be exercised in classifying crustal elements because the pitfalls of stereotyped thinking may follow any faulty classification. Both the continental shields and the abyssal plains of the oceans have been called *cratons*. They do have some things in common: few earthquakes occur in either, both are relatively flat, and neither is the site of a young folded mountain belt or of a midocean ridge (by definition). But our knowledge of the two is hardly comparable. We can examine the shields in detail, and the history of stability of shields is well established on the basis of geologic facts, but this is not true of abyssal plains. There we can only be puzzled by the thin sedimentary veneer if, like a shield, it has a history of stability since Precambrian times. A number of geologists now question this proposition and are investigating the possibility that

the ocean floors are much younger features, perhaps even as young as Mesozoic.

It is certainly misleading to group all features between ocean basins and continental areas into a single category of "continental margins," and we do not yet know enough about the structure of this zone to know how many different classes of structures are actually involved. The margin of the eastern (a coastal plain and shelf) and western (a modern orogenic belt) United States, the margin off northeast Asia (an island arc), the margin off northwest Africa (an orogenic belt ends at the coast), and the margin off Chile (a trench) are all sufficiently different to justify different classes. Some of these may represent different stages in the development of a single general class of structural element. Even with the category of island arcs we may question the validity of grouping the near-perfect arc of the Aleutians with the poorly defined island grouping extending from New Guinea to the New Hebrides.

In conclusion, it is valuable to classify crustal elements in order to simplify thinking in terms of global structural patterns, but the models accepted must be flexible until our knowledge justifies more concrete conclusions. Examples of some of the major types of crustal elements are discussed in the following chapters.

REFERENCES

Aki, K., and Press, F., 1961, Upper mantle structure under oceans and continents from Rayleigh waves: Geophys. Jour. Royal Astron. Soc., v. 5.

Anderson, D. L., 1962, The plastic layer of the earth's mantle: Sci. Am., July.

Benioff, Hugo, 1954, Orogenesis and deep crustal structure—additional evidence from seismology: Geol. Soc. America Bull., v. 65, no. 4.

Berry, M. J., and Knopoff, L., 1967, Structure of the upper mantle under the western Mediterranean basin: Jour. Geophys. Research, v. 72, no. 14, p. 3613–3626.

Birch, A. F., 1952, Elasticity and constitution of the earth's interior: Jour. Geophys. Research, v. 57, p. 227–286.

———— 1953, Elasticity and constitution of the earth's mantle: Geol. Soc. America Bull., v. 64, no. 5, p. 601–602.

———— 1954, The earth's mantle—elasticity and constitution, *in* Bucher, W. H., ed., Symposium on the interior of the earth: Am. Geophys. Union Trans., v. 35, p. 79–85.

———— 1958, Differentiation of the mantle: Geol. Soc. America Bull., v. 69, p. 483–486.

Bucher, W. H., 1933, The deformation of the earth's crust: Princeton, N.J., Princeton Univ., 518 p.

———— ed., 1954, Symposium on the interior of the earth: Am. Geophys. Union Trans., v. 35, no. 1, p. 48–49.

Bullard, E. C., 1957, The density within the earth: Kon. Nederland. Geol. Minjb. Genoot. Verh. Geol. Ser., pt. 18, p. 23–41.

Clark, S. P., Jr., 1963, Variation of density in the earth and the melting curve in the mantle, *in* Donnelly, T. W., ed., The earth sciences: Rice University (Chicago, Univ. of Chicago, *Publisher*).

Cook, K. L., 1962, The problem of the mantle-crust mix: lateral inhomogeneity in the uppermost part of the earth's mantle, *in* Advances in geophysics, no. 9: New York, Academic.

Dorman, James, Ewing, Maurice, and Oliver, Jack, 1960, Study of shear-velocity distribution in the upper mantle Rayleigh waves: Seismol. Soc. America Bull., v. 50, p. 87.

Ewing, Maurice, and Press, Frank, 1956, The long-period nature of S waves [abs.]: Am. Geophys. Union Trans., v. 37, no. 3, p. 343.

———— 1960, Determination of crustal structure from phase velocity of Rayleigh waves, Part III: The United States: Geol. Soc. America Bull., v. 70, p. 229–244.

Ewing, Maurice, and others, 1962, Surface wave studies of the Pacific crust and mantle, *in* Crust of the Pacific basin: Am. Geophys. Union Mon. 6.

Gilluly, James, and others, 1968, Principles of geology, 3rd ed.: San Francisco, Freeman.

Gutenberg, Beno, 1948, On the layer of relatively low wave velocity at a depth of about 80 kilometers: Seismol. Soc. America Bull., v. 38, p. 121–148.

———— 1951, Internal constitution of the earth: Princeton, N.J., Princeton Univ.

———— 1954, Low-velocity layers in the earth's mantle: Geol. Soc. America Bull., v. 65.

Gutenberg, Beno, and Richter, C. F., 1949, Seismicity of the earth and associated phenomena: Princeton, N.J., Princeton Univ.

———— 1954, Seismicity of the earth, 2d ed.: Princeton, N.J., Princeton Univ., 201 p.

Hodgson, J. H., and Skoens, A. E., 1964, Seismicity and earthquake mechanism, *in* Odishaw, Hugh, ed., Research in geophysics, no. 2, Solid earth and interface phenomena: Cambridge, M. I. T.

Holmes, Arthur, 1965, Principles of physical geology: New York, Ronald.

Holsen, W. T., and Schneen, C. J., 1957, Polymorphism in the earth's mantle: Am. Geophys. Union Trans., v. 38.

Lee, W. H. K., ed., 1965, Terrestrial heat flow: Baltimore, Am. Geophys. Union Pub. 1288, 276 p.

Lee, W. H. K., and MacDonald, G. J. F., 1963, The global variation of terrestrial heat flow: Jour. Geophys. Research, v. 68, p. 6481–6492.

Leet, D. L., and Judson, Sheldon, 1965, Physical geology, 3rd ed.: Englewood Cliffs, N.J., Prentice-Hall.

Lehmann, I., 1936, P': Pubs. Bur. Central Seismol. Intern. Trav. Sci., v. 14, p. 87–115.

Lovering, J. F., 1958, The nature of the Mohorovicic discontinuity: Am. Geophys. Union Trans., v. 39, p. 947–955.

MacDonald, G. J. F., 1964, The deep structure of continents: Science, v. 143, p. 921–930.

Oliver, J., and Isacks, B., 1967, Deep earthquake zones, anomalous structures in the upper mantle, and the lithosphere: Jour. Geophys. Research, v. 72, no. 16, p. 4259–4275.

Pakiser, L. C., 1963, Structure of the crust and upper mantle in the western United States: Jour. Geophys. Research, v. 68, no. 20, p. 5747–5756.

Pakiser, L. C., and Zietz, Isidore, 1965, Transcontinental crustal and upper mantle structure, *in* U.S. Program for the Internat. Upper Mantle Project, Prog. Rept. 1965: Natl. Acad. Sci., Natl. Research Council, Washington.

Poldervaart, Arie, 1955, Chemistry of the earth's crust, *in* Crust of the earth: Geol. Soc. America Spec. Paper 62.

Press, Frank, 1959, Some implications on mantle and crustal structure from G. waves and Love waves: Jour. Geophys. Research, v. 64.

———— 1961, The earth's crust and upper mantle: Science, v. 133, p. 1455–1463.

Press, Frank, and Ewing, Maurice, 1955, Earthquake surface waves and crustal structure, *in* Geol. Soc. America Spec. Paper 62, p. 51–60.

Ringwood, A .E., 1962a, A model for the upper mantle: Jour. Geophys. Research, v. 67.

———— 1962b, Mineralogical composition of the deep mantle: Jour. Geophys. Research, v. 67.

Romney, Carl, 1959, Amplitude of seismic body waves from underground nuclear explosions: Jour. Geophys. Research, v. 64, p. 1489–1498.

Spencer, E. W., 1962, Basic concepts of physical geology: New York, Crowell.

Tatel, H. E., and Tuve, A., 1955, Seismic exploration of a continental crust: Geol. Soc. America Spec. Paper 62, p. 35–50.

Thompson, G. A., and Talwani, Manik, 1964, Geology of the crust and mantle, western United States: Science, v. 146, p. 1539–1549.

Verhoogen, J., 1954, Petrological evidence on temperature distribution in the mantle of the earth: Am. Geophys. Union Trans., v. 35, p. 85–92.

Wegener, Alfred, 1922, The origin of continents and oceans: London, Methuen.

Woollard, G. P., 1959, Crustal structure from gravity and seismic measurements: Jour. Geophys. Research, v. 64.

11

the north american continental craton and its stable margin

THE NORTH AMERICAN CRATON

The North American continent may be divided into several large structural units: a centrally located craton, the Canadian shield and its southern extension, bordered by the Appalachian Mountain system on the east, the Mesozoic and Cenozoic orogenic systems on the west, the exposed remnants of Paleozoic orogenic belts along the south. The Arctic Ocean obscures the character of the northern side of the shield. The Gulf of Mexico geosyncline and the complex zone between North and South America form the remaining element. The term *craton* is applied to those regions of the earth which have exhibited long-term stability. In the case of North America this includes central Canada over which Precambrian rocks are exposed and the extension of this shield south into the United States and west toward the Canadian Rockies. The approximate borders of the craton may be taken as the Rocky Mountain frontal structures, the Quachita-Wichita belts in the south, and the Appalachian basin on the east. Such boundaries include a large area covered by a relatively thin sedimentary veneer (compared with a geosyncline) and a number of basins in which significant subsidence and sediment accumulation has taken place, but in which the sedimentary units have not been strongly folded, intruded, or metamorphosed. The outlines of some of these major basins, the Illinois, Michigan, and Appalachian, and their associated arches are illustrated in Fig. 11-1.

Compared with the regions surrounding it, the craton has exhibited

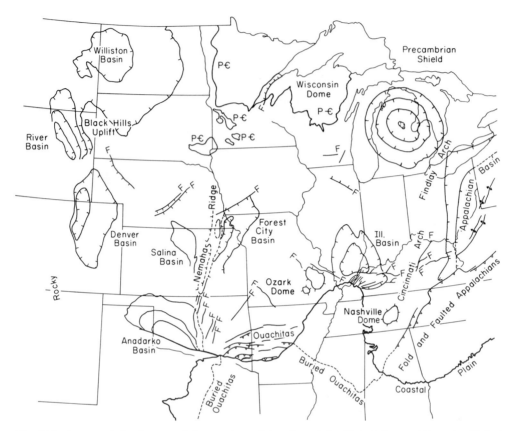

Fig. 11-1 Structural sketch map of the continental interior of the United States. (*After the United States Tectonic Map, 1961.*)

marked stability since the start of the Paleozoic. There is evidence of the existence of large faults in the basement of the craton, which may have undergone considerable displacement since the Paleozoic. A mountain range trending north-south, the Nemaha Range, which is bounded on its eastern side by a fault, lies buried along the eastern border of Oklahoma. Studies of subsurface geology of the midcontinent have revealed a long history of movements which caused unconformities, the development of large open folds, broad flexures, and faults in the sedimentary veneer. Many of these structures are attributed to movements in the Precambrian basement rocks, or to compaction over basement topography or structures. The

basement rock of the craton has also subsided and been covered by thick accumulations of sediment along its margins, particularly as shown by the great pile of sediment in the Appalachian basin of Tennessee, West Virginia, and Pennsylvania.

In contrast with the craton, the geosynclinal belts have exhibited long-term instability. The Appalachian geosyncline has been the site of accumulations of 30,000 to 50,000 ft of Paleozoic sedimentary rock in a long, relatively narrow trough. These sedimentary accumulations were repeatedly deformed with major pulses of deformation occurring in the late Precambrian, Late Ordovician, Middle Devonian, and late Paleozoic. Instability during this time was characterized by uplift, folding and thrusting of the sediments, intrusion of huge batholiths, and metamorphism of large volumes of rock. The structural pattern and history of instability is even more complex along the western edge of the craton, where deformation of the Paleozoic geosyncline has been complicated by the superposition of later geosynclines and major Jurassic and Late Cretaceous orogenies, Tertiary block faulting, and late Tertiary and Pleistocene deformation. The character of these bordering belts will be treated later in some detail, as will the character of the continental margins.

Crustal thickness maps (Fig. 10-9) have now been prepared as part of the International Geophysical Year Upper Mantle Project. The distribution of thicknesses is only roughly correlated with the structural divisions evident from surface geology. The crust is slightly thicker under the Appalachians, it is reasonably uniform under the craton, and the most notable variations occur in the western states where Mesozoic

and Cenozoic orogeny have taken place.

The Precambrian rocks of the Canadian shield consist largely of granites, granitic gneisses, and schists although a great variety of other rocks is represented as well. The scarcity of well-preserved fossils and the lack of sedimentary marker horizons of regional extent have made synthesis of the structure a difficult task, as have the vast size of the area, the extensive cover of glacial lakes and swamps, and the cold climate. That the shield consists of a number of Precambrian orogenic belts superimposed and welded together has long been recognized, but the precise correlation of events within the belts and the delineation of boundaries of the belts has varied with time and author. The key to recognition of these belts has been the use of radiometric dating techniques. Gastil (1960) compiled dates from Precambrian rocks throughout North America and has delineated the date provinces illustrated in Fig. 11-2. Other important tools have included regional aeromagnetic

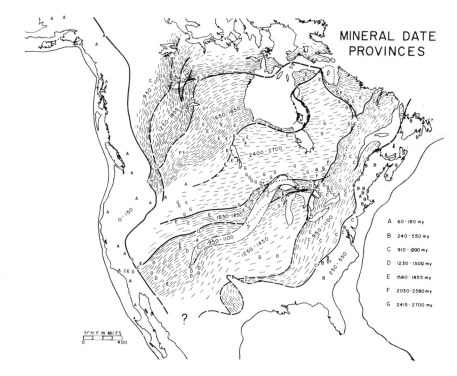

Fig. 11-2 Precambrian orogenic belts of North America. Age ranges for each belt, obtained by radioactive dating methods, are indicated in millions of years. *(Courtesy of Dr. Gordon Gastil.)*

Fig. 11-3 Structural trends in Canadian shield. *(From Stockwell, 1965.)*

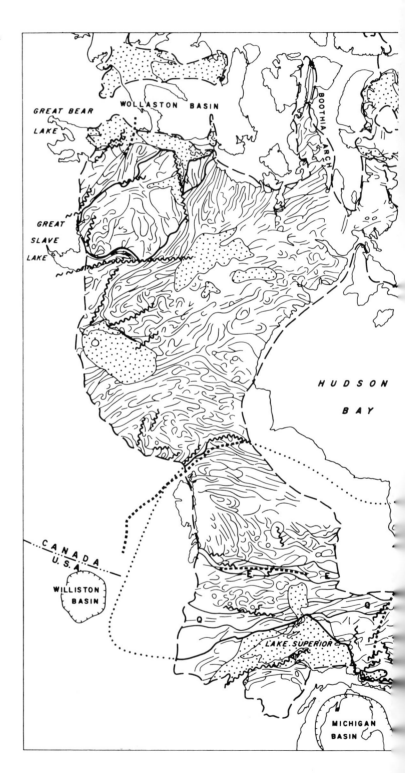

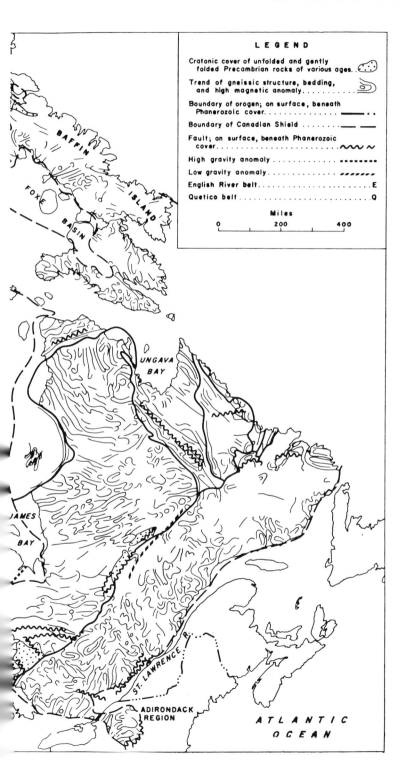

LEGEND

Cratonic cover of unfolded and gently
folded Precambrian rocks of various ages.

Trend of gneissic structure, bedding,
and high magnetic anomaly...........

Boundary of orogen; on surface, beneath
Phanerozoic cover................

Boundary of Canadian Shield ....

Fault; on surface, beneath Phanerozoic
cover.......................

High gravity anomaly ....

Low gravity anomaly..............

English River belt......................E

Quetico belt............................Q

Miles

0   200   400

Fig. 11-4 Tectonic map of the Canadian shield. *(From Stockwell, 1962.)*

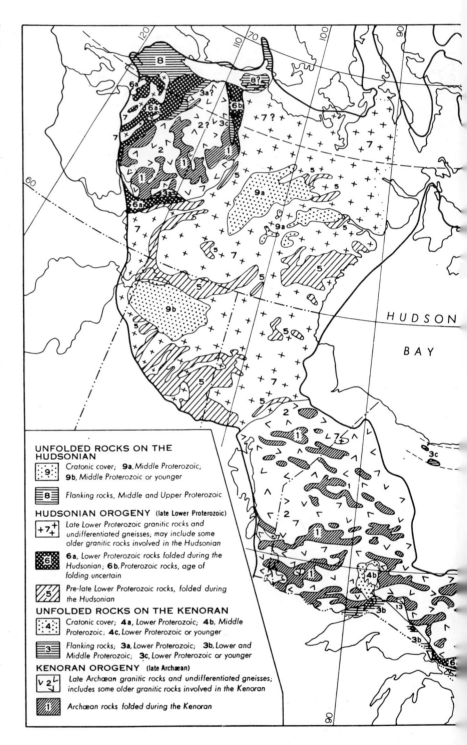

UNFOLDED ROCKS ON THE HUDSONIAN

9 Cratonic cover; **9a**, Middle Proterozoic; **9b**, Middle Proterozoic or younger

8 Flanking rocks, Middle and Upper Proterozoic

HUDSONIAN OROGENY (late Lower Proterozoic)

+7+ Late Lower Proterozoic granitic rocks and undifferentiated gneisses; may include some older granitic rocks involved in the Hudsonian

6 **6a**, Lower Proterozoic rocks folded during the Hudsonian; **6b**, Proterozoic rocks, age of folding uncertain

5 Pre-late Lower Proterozoic rocks, folded during the Hudsonian

UNFOLDED ROCKS ON THE KENORAN

4 Cratonic cover; **4a**, Lower Proterozoic; **4b**, Middle Proterozoic; **4c**, Lower Proterozoic or younger

3 Flanking rocks; **3a**, Lower Proterozoic; **3b**, Lower and Middle Proterozoic; **3c**, Lower Proterozoic or younger

KENORAN OROGENY (late Archæan)

V2V Late Archæan granitic rocks and undifferentiated gneisses; includes some older granitic rocks involved in the Kenoran

1 Archæan rocks folded during the Kenoran

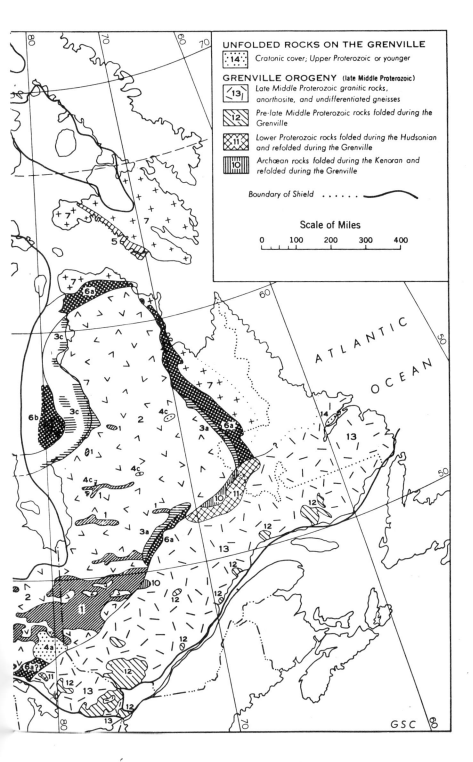

UNFOLDED ROCKS ON THE GRENVILLE

`:14:` Cratonic cover; Upper Proterozoic or younger

GRENVILLE OROGENY (late Middle Proterozoic)

`13` Late Middle Proterozoic granitic rocks, anorthosite, and undifferentiated gneisses

`12` Pre-late Middle Proterozoic rocks folded during the Grenville

`11` Lower Proterozoic rocks folded during the Hudsonian and refolded during the Grenville

`10` Archæan rocks folded during the Kenoran and refolded during the Grenville

Boundary of Shield . . . . . .

Scale of Miles

0   100   200   300   400

ATLANTIC

OCEAN

GSC

maps, now available for large parts of Canada, and reconnaissance geologic mapping from aerial photographs. These have been used in connection with detailed studies of smaller areas by more conventional field mapping methods to locate major structures, identify structural trends, and outline large intrusions. The results of these efforts will shortly appear on the new Tectonic Map of Canada.

Four major periods of orogeny have been identified: Kenoran (2,390 million years), Hudsonian (1,640 million years), Elsonian (1,280 million years), and Grenville (880 million years) (Stockwell, 1965). The absolute ages are only approximations. Each of these orogenies was followed by deep erosion and later deposition

of new sedimentary material. The rate at which new radiometric dates, results from photo interpretation, and aeromagnetic data are being accumulated is noteworthy in the Canadian shield. An unfortunate consequence of this is that boundaries of structural provinces, the number of orogenies, and regional interpretation are subject to change. The establishment of such boundaries is complicated because some of the orogenies affected older orogenic belts and consequently reset the radiometric "clocks" in the older belts.

Two types of tectonic maps representing advance information from the new Canadian Tectonic Map of the Canadian shield will serve to outline more recent interpretations of the

Fig. 11-5 Precambrian geology in the western Great Lakes region. (*From Goldich and others, 1961.*)

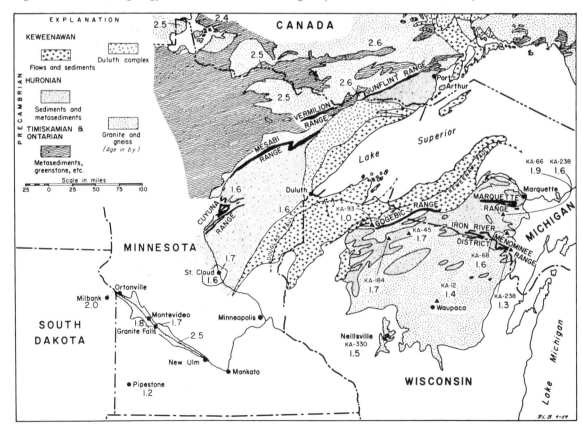

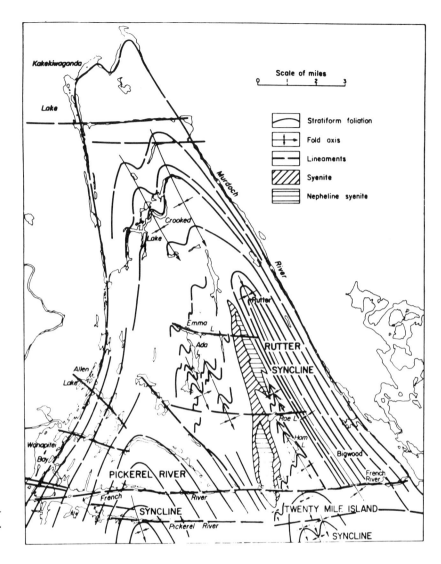

Fig. 11-6 Structural features, French River area. *(From Hewitt, 1956.)*

tectonics of the shield. Figure 11-3 shows structural trends in the shield. The trend lines, which are long and straight, generally represent surface traces of long tight folds; the curvilinear features are more open folds or tight folds bent by batholithic intrusions or around mantled gneiss domes. The second map (Fig. 11-4) outlines areas affected by three of the Precambrian orogenies. The Elsonian orogeny affected the small area shown blank along the Atlantic Coast between the latitudes 54 and 60° N.

Two provinces of the Precambrian shield, the Grenville and the Superior, are known in much greater detail than the others. The Grenville province extends northeast parallel with the St. Lawrence. This province also includes the Adirondacks and is the same age as the Precambrian exposed throughout the Appalachian region. The Superior province includes the region around Lake Superior (Fig. 11-5) and north to Hudson Bay.

CHARACTER OF STRUCTURES IN THE BASEMENT

The full range of metamorphic and igneous structures is found in North American Precambrian rocks, as well as large, slightly deformed sedimentary deposits and vast lava flows. The origin of much of the granitic gneiss remains to be determined. Both mantled gneiss domes and discordant plutons are abundant, and map patterns frequently suggest refolding of earlier structures. Some idea of the types of structures may be obtained by examining the structure of the French River area, the Harvey-Cardiff area, and the western Adirondacks, all of which are within the Grenville province.

The French River area (Fig. 11-6) is located in Ontario, and the major structure is a system of plunging folds formed in granitized metasedimentary rocks. The large areas of unlabeled material in the figure are granitic gneisses (Hewitt, 1956). Mapping in the terrane was aided by the presence of a prominent quartzite horizon. The Rutler syncline is isoclinal and plunges southward. The intensity of folding appears to increase toward the west. Evidence that the gneisses here are products of granitization is found in the partial conversion of the quartzite to granite, the well-developed fold structure in the foliated and layered gneisses, and the abundance of replacement of other minerals by microcline in thin section.

The geology of the Harvey-Cardiff arch reveals a very different type of structure. Here a line of granite gneiss domes of northwest trend forms an arch over 40 miles long (Fig. 11-7). Granite and gneiss are exposed in the domes. Anticlines and synclines in the well-foliated gneisses of the Burleigh dome indicate its metasedimentary origin. The Anstruther dome has a migmatite border and resembles the mantled gneiss domes such as the Baltimore gneiss dome described in Chap. 13. The structure of the mantled domes is interpreted as having formed under conditions which promoted mobility of the domes and their mantles in both cases. Hewitt (1956) thinks it probable that the Cheddar dome differs from the Anstruther dome in that a magma formed in the former and migrated farther upward, while in the latter the rock reached only a stage of incipient mobility

with some plastic flowage. The Centre Lake (Cardiff) pluton represents still a higher level of intrusion. It possesses both a center of upward intrusion and flank structures where magma has broken through as granite and syenite sheets to invade the country rock. Thus the plutons in this region seem to form a progressive sequence from granitic gneisses formed in place and showing structures associated with metasedimentary rocks in the south to intrusive plutons in which magma formed and intruded the country rock in the north.

Our third example from the Adirondacks is from an area in which the map pattern (Fig. 11-8) showing bodies of granite, gneisses, marbles, and quartzites is quite complicated (Buddington, 1956). The mixed gneisses are a combination of altered metasedimentary rocks and thin intrusive sheets. The heavy line separates an area of predominantly metasedimentary rocks from one of mainly igneous and meta-igneous origin, and there has been considerable movement along this boundary as is shown by intense deformation of the mylonite and by the slickensides developed along it. The Stark complex is a tight anticline formed in a thick sheet of hornblende gneiss; the western limb of the structure was later cut out by intrusion of younger granite. The rocks west of the Stark complex are involved in a large isoclinal syncline overturned toward the southeast and dipping 25 to 50° N.

Many structural features in Precambrian rocks are difficult to decipher because they have had a complex history; often first generation of sedimentary structures has later been deformed. Sometimes the last structures imparted to the mass formed during a time when the rock was partially mobilized, with the result that we now encounter structures ranging from those characteristic of brittle behavior through the range of ductile behavior to that of viscous magma.

Complex fault patterns and regional fracture patterns are characteristic of Precambrian rocks in the shield. These zones show up on aerial photographs as multidirectional patterns. Fre-

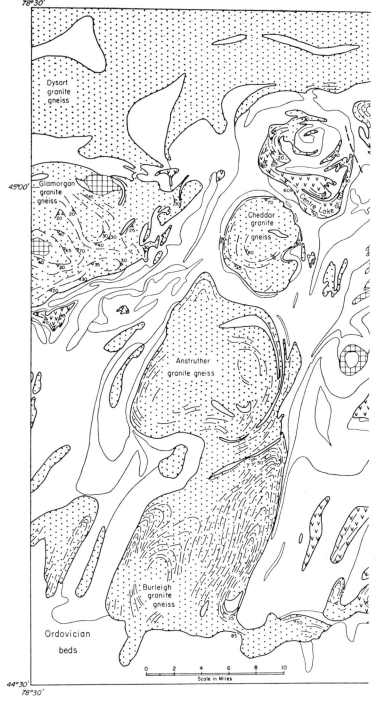

Fig. 11-7 Harvey-Cardiff arch, Canadian shield. *(From Buddington, 1959.)*

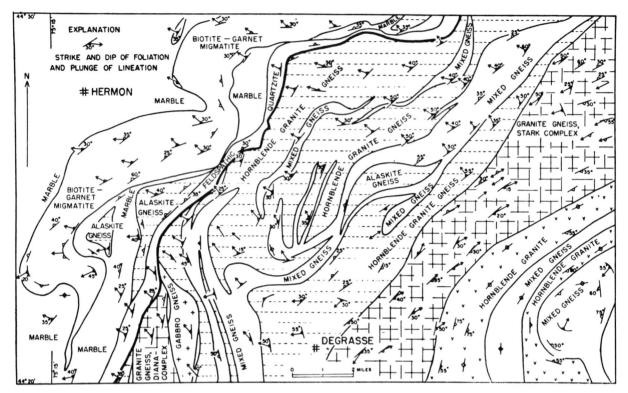

Fig. 11-8 Details of overturned isoclinal syncline on northwest flank of relatively rigid unit of Stark complex. The lineation is subperpendicular to the trend of the major fold axes, northwest Adirondacks. The heavy line marks the boundary between the belt on the northwest in which rocks of the Grenville series predominate and the belt on the southeast in which igneous rocks and orthogneisses are predominant. (*From Buddington, 1956.*)

quently these lineaments are shatter zones many feet wide; some are occupied by dikes, and many are known as faults of considerable displacement. They are not related to the fold structures of the metamorphic rocks in which they occur, or if they are the relationship is obscured by the multiplicity of directions. Displacements along such zones are now known to be a key factor in the determination of many structures in the American midcontinent and in the Middle Rocky Mountains.

Midcontinent Gravity High

The Bouguer anomaly gravity map of the United States shows a very pronounced positive anomaly with marginal negative anomalies situ-

ated over the Duluth lopolith along the western edge of Lake Superior. It is offset to the east at the south end of Lake Superior but continues as a broad flat high to Minneapolis where a second eastward offset occurs. The high continues southwest across Iowa and terminates in the southeastern corner of Nebraska. Negative anomalies of similar trend can be followed well into Kansas. The anomaly has been described by Craddock and others (1963) in Minnesota where the anomaly has highs of +53 mgals flanked by subparallel lows of −75 and −89 mgals which have been traced from Lake Superior southward (Fig. 11-9). The maximum coincides with a belt of Keweenawan basic igneous rocks estimated to be 29,000 ft thick where the basement is exposed near Minneapolis. Craddock interprets the high as being due to a southward continuation of these thick igneous rocks, and the lows as being due to adjacent Keweenawan sedimentary sequences estimated to be 11,000 ft thick.

The positive anomaly also parallels the St. Croix horst and is characterized in this region by a broad flat over the crest of the horst and by bands of steep gravity gradient over the basement faults which bound the horst. This horst was elevated in late Precambrian time.

Southwest of Minneapolis the gravity anomaly bends sharply to the southeast before resuming a southwesterly trend. This could be due to the primary shape of a volcanic fissure along

which basic rocks are localized, or it could reflect an offset in the basement along a transcurrent fault. A northwest-trending dip-slip fault has been described in the Paleozoic rocks along this trend (Sloan and Danes, 1962) as is shown on the United States Tectonic Map (Fig. 11-10).

The continuation of the midcontinent gravity high across Iowa is also postulated as representing a continuation of the Precambrian Keweenawan basalt flows. This high has been tentatively connected with another high which extends across the Michigan basin (see B in Fig. 11-9) (Rudman, Summerson, and Hinze, 1965). Magnetic data show highs coincident with this anomaly. Still another high may be traced

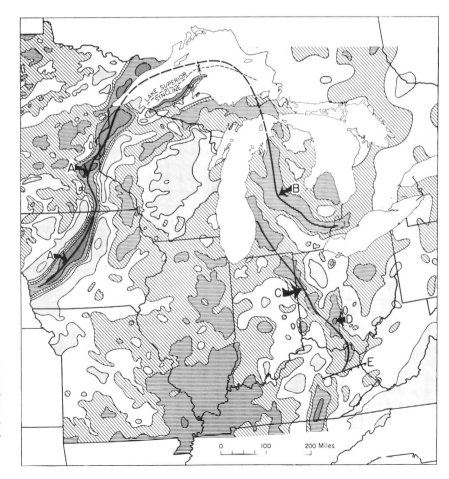

Fig. 11-9 Bouguer gravity anomaly map of the midwestern United States. (Lettered features identified in text.) *(Modified from Woollard and Rose, 1963, and Thompson and Miller, 1958; from Rudman, Summerson, and Hinze, 1965.)*

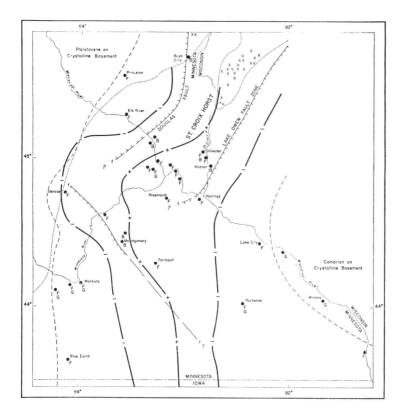

Fig. 11-10 Regional geologic-tectonic map of Precambrian rocks. *(From Craddock, Thiel, and Gross, 1963.)*

across Michigan and Iowa and into Kentucky, and it too has been interpreted as resulting from basement basalts or ultramafics. Wells which have penetrated to the Precambrian have revealed basic rocks in central Iowa and in Ohio, adding strength to the argument that extensive volcanic flows occur in the midwestern continental interior.

CONTINENTAL MARGINS

A great diversity of structural situations is found on continents near their margins. Along some, as in the eastern United States, gently tilted strata of a coastal plain lie on the eroded surface of a long-stabilized, folded mountain system basement. These strata extend out under the continental shelf. Modern geosynclinal accumulations are buried in an elongate trough parallel to the Gulf Coast of the United States;

recently active mountain belts are arranged parallel to the western coast of North and South America; young folded mountain belts intersect the coast at high angles as in England, northern Spain, and northwest Africa; Precambrian shield rocks lie along the eastern coast of South America and Africa; and modern island arc systems lie along the continental margins of much of the Pacific. Even these island arcs are varied in their structure and relationship to continental margins. Thus we must be careful about generalizing the nature of continental margins or interpreting the geophysical data in the marginal zones in terms of preconceived notions of marginal structure. We do not now possess detailed knowledge of the subsurface in marginal zones in many parts of the world.

Guilcher (1958, 1963) concludes that continental margins may be classified in a twofold system, as constructional or diastrophic. Some of the main divisions within this classification, illustrated in Fig. 11-11, include:

1. *Constructional:* A subsiding type with a wide shelf and a thick sedimentary basin (e.g., eastern North America, northwestern Europe). (Fig. 11-11*a.*)
2. *Diastrophic:* A flexural type in which there is no significant sedimentation (e.g., Provence, France). (Fig. 11-11*b* 1.)
3. *Diastrophic and constructional combined:* (e.g., West and South Africa). (Fig. 11-11*b* 2.)
4. *Diastrophic:* A faulted type with the irregularities in the basement filled up by sedimentation (e.g., Queensland, Australia). (Fig. 11-11*c* 1.)
5. *Diastrophic:* A block-faulted type with erosion on ranges and sedimentation in the basins (e.g., southern California). (Fig. 11-11*c* 2.)

6. *Diastrophic:* A fissured type with glacial overdeepening in transverse valleys (e.g., Norway, Labrador, east Antarctica). (Fig. 11-11*d.*)

Continental Margin of Eastern North America

South of Florida the structure of the continental margin of North America is complicated by the Antilles Island arc. North of Florida the continental margin is characterized by a broad coastal plain which is emergent from New York south and submerged from New York north. Undeformed or slightly deformed Cretaceous to Recent sedimentary units underlie this Coastal Plain. They lie unconformably on the Paleozoic and Precambrian structures of the Appalachians (Fig. 11-12). Seismic profiles and wells drilled in the emerged Coastal Plain allow relatively accurate determination of the slope of the crystalline basement under the Coastal Plain (Fig. 11-12). This unconformity slopes

Fig. 11-11 Types of continental margins. (*a*) Constructional, subsiding type; wide shelf, wide and thick sedimentary basin; e.g., eastern North America, northwestern Europe. (*b*1) Flexured type; no significant sedimentation; e.g., Provence (at Nice, no shelf at all). (*b*2) Flexured type with narrow shelf and sedimentary wedge; intermediate between (*a*) and (*b*1); probable examples, West and South Africa. (*c*1) Faulted type; irregularities in basement filled up by sedimentation; probable example, Queensland. (*c*2) Block-faulted type; sedimentation in downfaulted basins, erosion on ranges; e.g., continental borderland of southern California. (*d*) Fissured type; glacial overdeepening in transverse valleys; e.g., Norway, Labrador, east Antarctica. (*Redrawn from Guilcher, 1963.*)

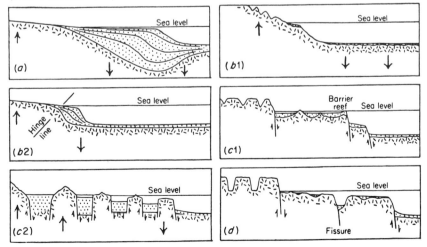

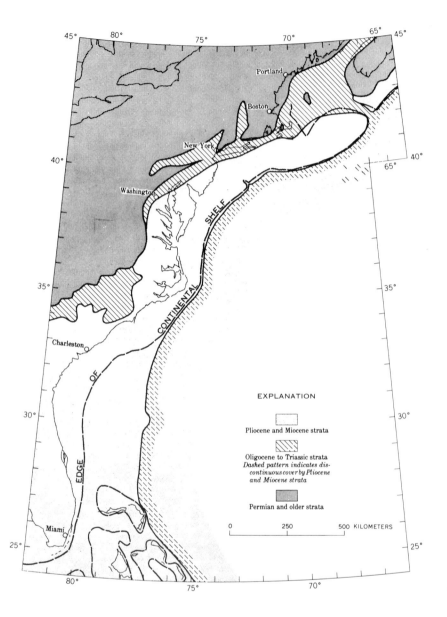

EXPLANATION

□ Pliocene and Miocene strata

▨ Oligocene to Triassic strata
*Dashed pattern indicates dis-
continuous cover by Pliocene
and Miocene strata*

■ Permian and older strata

0   250   500 KILOMETERS

Fig. 11-12 Map of continental shelf and slope showing distribution of pre-Pleistocene strata. *(From Emery, 1966.)*

gently seaward and follows the shape of the coast from Cape Cod to Cape Fear, N.C. South of the Cape Fear arch the trend of the basement swings southwestward across Florida into the Gulf region.

The technique of continuous seismic reflection profiling using sparker discharge of suffi- cient energy to penetrate at least the upper sedimentary layers has made it possible to determine the shape of these layers very rapidly. Analysis of profiler records (Uchupi and Emery, 1967) indicates that the continental margin between Nova Scotia and the Florida Keys has been formed by building up of the continental shelf and building out of the continental slope, at least during the Cenozoic. The shelf has been built up by deposition of between 200 and 1,000 m of Cenozoic sediment. The slope has been extended seaward by 5 to 35 km during the same interval, with the most rapid construction taking place where the slope is flanked by the Blake Plateau. The Cenozoic sedimentary beds can be traced continuously from the continental slope to the rise off Nova Scotia, but from New England southward the beds of the slope appear to cover those of the rise and the Blake Plateau.

Some profiler records show beds which appear to have become detached and to have slid downslope, and records obtained off the Florida Keys (Fig. 11-13) appear faulted by high-angle faults.

Deep structural cross sections obtained by seismic profiles across the East Coast margin from Cape Hatteras north (Fig. 11-14) reveal great thicknesses of low-velocity sedimentary rock, buried beneath the continental slope and the continental rise. Note that the M discontinuity appears in only two of these sections and that it is steeply inclined as it drops from oceanic to continental levels. This drop is even more pronounced in the section based on gravity anomalies (Fig. 11-15). The belt of great sediment thickness along the eastern United States is subparallel to the coast (Fig. 11-16) and represents an accumulation that is comparable in size and thickness to that of the Paleozoic Appalachian geosyncline (Fig. 11-17). The age of the sediment is uncertain. It may be equivalent in age to the present Coastal Plain sedi-

Fig. 11-13 Profiles between Cape Kennedy and Key West. Miocene (M) rock was dredged by Gorsline and Milligan (1963) in vicinity of profile 67. (*From Uchupi and Emery, 1967.*)

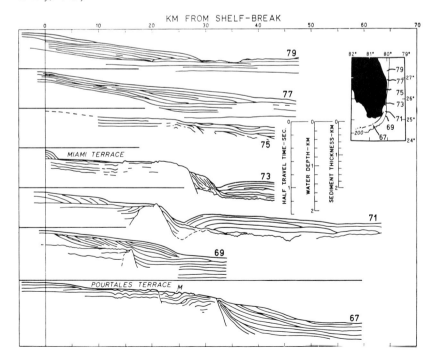

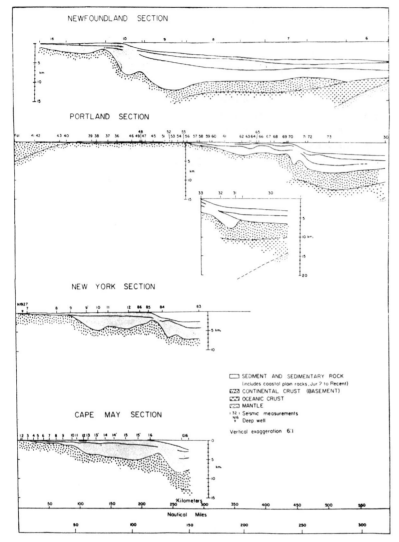

Fig. 11-14 Structure sections from seismic refraction measurements. East coast of North America. *(From Drake, Ewing, and Sutton, 1959.)*

ment; it is Cenozoic where penetrated in wells on the continental shelf, but it could be much older, even Paleozoic. This sedimentary accumulation lies in two deep troughs separated by a basement ridge. The two have been likened to the Paleozoic Appalachian miogeosyncline and eugeosyncline (Drake, Ewing, and

Sutton, 1958). Although there is no active volcanism in the outer trough, partially buried seamounts and associated high magnetic anomalies indicative of past volcanic activity are found.

The shape of the trough appears anomalous at about 40° N latitude. The trend of the accumulations swings into an east-west line along which the Kelvin seamount group is situated to the east and one of the faulted Triassic basins to the west. The great bend of the Appalachian fold system in Pennsylvania occurs along this same line, and it has been suggested that this line is a major fault or fracture zone at depth (Woodward and Drake) running transverse to the structural trends of the older mountain system and the modern continental margin structure.

This great trough does not appear to continue to the south. The structure changes as the rise of the northeastern margin passes into the Blake Plateau. Since a basement high lies under the Florida peninsula, the geosyncline-like accumulation does not cross northern Florida into the Gulf of Mexico.

Seismic and magnetic studies east of Florida in the region of the Blake Plateau and the Bahama basin have demonstrated that this is an area of complex structure unlike that depicted in cross sections across continental margins farther north (Hersey and others, 1959). Several major faults have been postulated, and the basement may be complexly block-faulted (Fig. 11-18). Block faulting developed on a regional scale in the Appalachians during the

Fig. 11-15 Gravity and structure sections, Portland, Me., line. (*From Drake, Ewing, and Sutton, 1959.*)

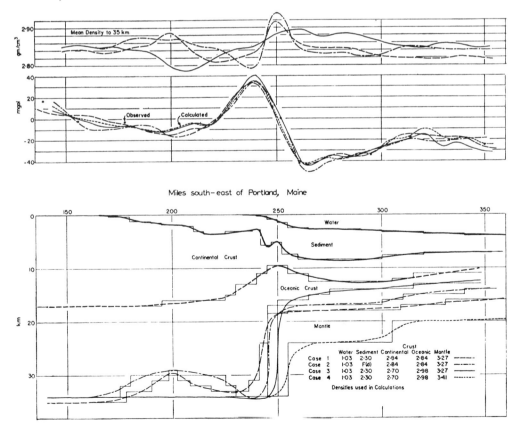

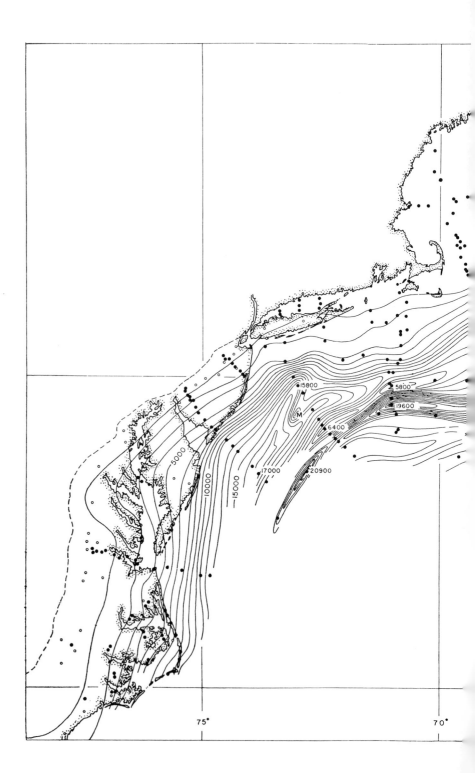

Fig. 11-16 Isopach map of total sediment thickness. *(From Drake, Ewing, and Sutton, 1958.)*

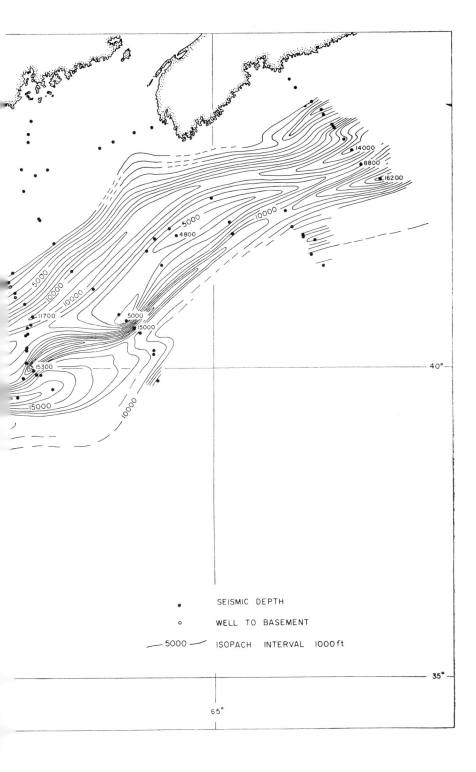

SEISMIC DEPTH

WELL TO BASEMENT

————— 5000 —————   ISOPACH INTERVAL 1000 ft

35°

65°

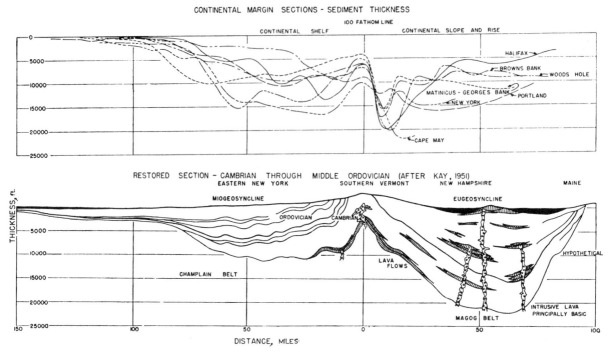

CONTINENTAL MARGIN SECTIONS - SEDIMENT THICKNESS

Fig. 11-17 Comparison between restored geosynclinal section (after Kay, 1951) and isopachous sections off the east coast of North America. (*From Drake, Ewing, and Sutton, 1959.*)

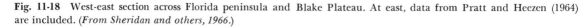

Fig. 11-18 West-east section across Florida peninsula and Blake Plateau. At east, data from Pratt and Heezen (1964) are included. (*From Sheridan and others, 1966.*)

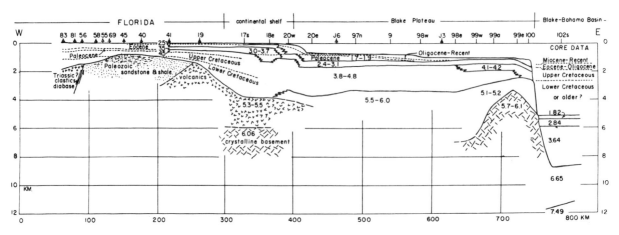

Triassic. Grabenlike structural features containing Triassic terrigenous sediment are located on the eastern side of the Piedmont in North Carolina, and Triassic basins buried beneath Coastal Plain sediments have been found in North and South Carolina and Georgia. Proponents of continental drift have indicated a post-Carboniferous age for the initiation of drift around the Atlantic. Thus this block faulting could be an expression of the initial extension as the Atlantic began to open. If this interpretation is correct, block faulting should be widely developed in basement rocks along the continental margins. One fault of northerly trend is mapped along the steep slope from the Blake Plateau to the Blake Bahama basin. Other faults of eastern trend cross the Blake Plateau and strike more nearly parallel with the northern coast of the Gulf of Mexico. This block faulting marks the southern end of the deep trough off the northeastern coast.

The basement structure in southern Florida is known in part from deep wells (Fig. 11-19). Rocks of Precambrian to Silurian age have been found in wells deep enough to penetrate the unconformity between Paleozoic and Jurassic

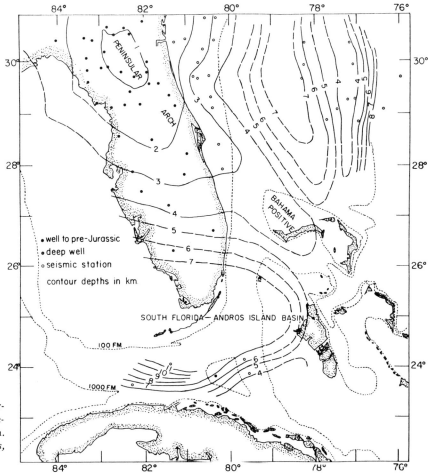

Fig. 11-19 Generalized subsurface structure map; top of pre-Jurassic basement is datum. (*From Sheridan and others, 1966.*)

and Cretaceous Coastal Plain sediments (Applin, 1951). Magnetic anomalies in this region and on the Blake Plateau trend toward the west, across the Appalachian structural trend and toward the Ouachitas (King, 1959). It has been suggested that the Ouachita structures may continue east toward the Bahamas (Drake, Heirtzler, and Hirshman, 1963).

GULF OF MEXICO

The Gulf of Mexico and the surrounding Coastal Plain are of great interest economically because of the widespread occurrence of oil and gas in the region. Exploration has led to extensive deep drilling and geophysical work which reveal a structural province quite different from those previously described. Mesozoic and Cenozoic sediment accumulation in the United States Coastal Plain and under the continental shelf and slope is of geosynclinal proportions and has come to be known as the Gulf of Mexico geosyncline. We are prompted to wonder what relation this geosyncline bears to those geosynclines now deformed as orogenic belts, and what connection there may be between this accumulation and the thick sediment accumulation under the continental slope of eastern North America. The Gulf also lies in close proximity to the island arc system of the Caribbean, just north of the equatorial orogenic belt so often pointed out by students of global tectonics; finally we must question the origin of the Gulf—is it a small ocean basin, a floundered continent, or of some intermediate character?

Pre-Mesozoic rocks form the basement of the Gulf and Coastal Plain region. The late Paleozoic orogenic belts are unconformably overlain by Cretaceous and younger strata at the southern end of the Appalachians, in the Ouachita, and in the Marathon Mountain region. This Paleozoic basement was composed of highly consolidated sedimentary, metamorphic, and igneous rocks long before any of the structure now

found in the Coastal and Gulf region formed. Control that may have been exerted by older structures on the present structure is still obscure; however, faults arising in the basement have been suggested as a contributing factor in the initiation of salt dome formation.

Marine Triassic deposits are not found in the Gulf region either in exposure or subsurface. The sedimentary sequence from Upper Jurassic to Recent is well developed—a thickness of 45,000 ft is cited at the Texas coast (Colle and others, 1952). This raises the interesting question of whether the Gulf region was emergent during the Triassic and Early Jurassic, and subsequently sank, or whether the Gulf formed as a result of movement of continents in the Jurassic so that the continental crust was separated and subcrusted material was exposed, as suggested by continental drift hypotheses. A third possibility is that the margins of the Gulf were emergent and the Triassic deposits are yet to be found offshore. Starting in the Jurassic, however, and continuing to the present, a vast sheet of sediment has been deposited. The structures in this sheet have been controlled and influenced by:

1. The original shape of the depositional surface
2. Significant lateral changes in facies which have created effects of differential compaction
3. Broad regional warping and movement of the basement as in the Mississippi embayment, and as shown by widespread unconformities
4. The presence of a thick layer of salt

In addition we may surmise that there has been a tendency for the unconsolidated sediments to move toward local depressions in their vicinity, that the steep sediment faces at the edge of the continental shelf have been subject to slump as is suggested by the highly irregular topography found on parts of the shelf, and

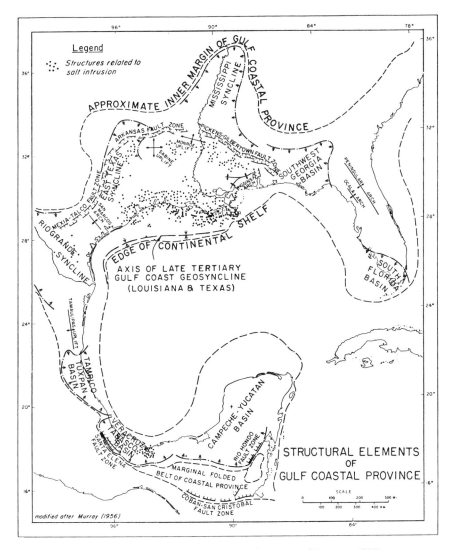

Fig. 11-20 Sketch map of the Gulf region. *(From Atwater and Forman, 1959.)*

that possibly some older basement structures have been rejuvenated during the more recent movements.

The zone of high-angle normal fault, the Mexia-Balcones zone and others, in the American Coastal Plain is one of the most prominent regional structures (Fig. 11-20). These faults occur in a belt of Cretaceous-Eocene outcrop; they are locally arranged *en échelon* and consist of step faults and graben and horst structures. The south side of the zone is down when viewed on a regional scale. This zone is usually interpreted in terms of regional movement toward the Gulf either as a result of a gentle flexure in the basement rock or as a distributed mass movement which has pulled away from

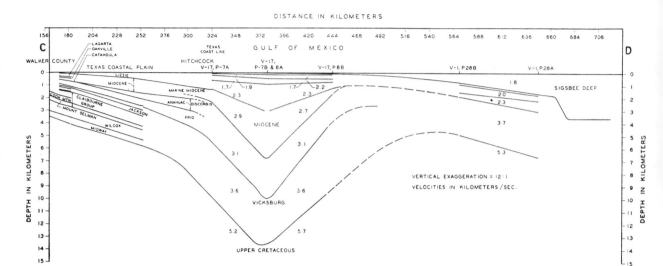

Fig. 11-21 Structure section *C–D* from Walker County, Tex., *C,* to Sigsbee escarpment *D.* (*From Antoine and Ewing, 1963.*)

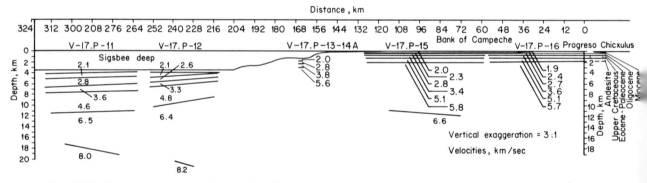

Fig. 11-22 Structure section *E–F* from Sigsbee Deep *E* to Progreso, Mexico *F.* (*From Antoine and Ewing, 1963.*)

the thin margins of the wedge of sediment as thickening has taken place in the geosyncline. Other zones (Wilcox, Vicksburg, and Frie) of flexure and normal faulting, also down a few hundred to over 1,000 ft to the south, have been found in the subsurface, but these either die out upward in the Miocene sediment or are not recognized at the surface.

Geophysical Studies

Seismic refraction profiles have been made across the Gulf region (Ewing and others, 1955, 1962;

Antoine and Ewing, 1963) (Figs. 11-21 and 11-22). These profiles were drawn along a line from east Texas to the Yucatan Peninsula. The striking result of these profiles is that the M discontinuity lies at a depth of about 17 km under the Sigsbee Deep and is thus much more shallow than under the continents to either side. The possibility of a floundered continent in the Gulf seems eliminated. A great thickness of sediment, velocity 2.15 to 3.2 km/sec, presumably the Tertiary and Recent deposits typical of the Gulf Coast geosyncline, were found.

These were about 9 km thick at the northern edge of the Sigsbee Deep and thinned to 5 km in the center of the deep. The layer 6.2 to 7 km/sec, possibly the Paleozoic basement, could be crystalline rock, limestone, dolerite, or perhaps even gabbro.

Recent work (Figs. 11-21 and 11-22), allows a more precise correlation of refraction results with stratigraphy both in Yucatan and in Texas. A southern edge of the Gulf Coast geosyncline appears probable north of the Sigsbee Deep (Antoine and Ewing, 1963). This is marked by a broad ridge. A number of circular rises were found in the Sigsbee Deep, called Sigsbee knolls. These rise several hundred meters above the abyssal floor of the deep and are the tops of nearly vertical columns apparently intruded into the sediment. They are interpreted as salt domes (Ewing and others, 1962). Sediment appears to reach the Sigsbee Deep which contains a 5-km thickness, probably Tertiary and Recent.

Seismic profiles off the Florida shelf show that it is similar to the Campeche bank. Cretaceous units lie at depths of less than 4 km. The top of the basement, 5.6 to 6.0 km/sec, is thus very near the surface compared with that in the Gulf Coast geosyncline. The pre-Mesozoic basement in Florida (Fig. 11-18) has the shape of a broad nose rising to the north. This, in combination with the seismic section across the shelf, delimits the eastern boundary of the Gulf Coast geosyncline, which does not connect with the thick deposits under the Atlantic slope.

REFERENCES

Antoine, J., and Ewing, J., 1963, Seismic refraction measurements on the margins of the Gulf of Mexico: Jour. Geophys. Research, v. 68, p. 1975–1996.

Applin, P. L., 1951, Preliminary report on buried pre-Mesozoic rocks in Florida and adjacent states: U.S. Geol. Survey Circ. 91, p. 1–27.

Atwater, G. I., and Forman, M. J., 1959, Nature of growth of southern Louisiana salt domes and its effect on petroleum accumulation: Am. Assoc. Petroleum Geologists Bull., v. 43, p. 2592–2622.

Buddington, A. F., 1956, Correlation of rigid units, types of folds, and lineation in a Grenville belt [New York and New Jersey], in Thompson, J. E., ed., The Grenville problem: Royal Soc. Canada Spec. Pub. no. 1, p. 99–118.

―――― 1959, Granite emplacement with special reference to North America: Geol. Soc. America Bull., v. 70, p. 671–747.

Colle, Jack, and others, 1952, Sedimentary volumes in Gulf Coastal Plain of United States: Geol. Soc. America Bull., v. 63, p. 1193–1200.

Cooke, H. C., 1947, The Canadian shield: Canada Geol. Survey Econ. Geol. Ser. no. 1, p. 11–97.

Coons, R. L., Woollard, G. P., and Hershey, Garland, 1967, Structural significance and analysis of mid-continent gravity high: Amer. Assoc. Petroleum Geologists Bull., v. 51, no. 12, p. 2381–2399.

Craddock, Campbell, Thiel, E. C., and Gross, Barton, 1963, A gravity investigation of the Precambrian of southeastern Minnesota and western Wisconsin: Jour. Geophys. Research, v. 68, p. 6015–6032.

David, T. W. E., 1950, The geology of the commonwealth of Australia: London, Arnold.

Drake, C. L., Ewing, M., and Sutton, G. H., 1959, Continental margins and geosynclines: the east coast of North America, north of Cape Hatteras: Phys. Chem. Earth, v. 3.

Drake, C. L., Heirtzler, J., and Hirshman, J., 1963, Magnetic anomalies off eastern North America: Jour. Geophys. Research, v. 68, no. 18.

Drake, C. L., and Woodward, H. P., 1963, Appalachian curvature, wrench faulting, and off shore structures: N.Y. Acad. Sci. Trans., ser. II, v. 26.

Emery, K. O., 1966, Atlantic continental shelf and slope of the U.S.: U. S. Geol. Survey Prof. Paper 529-A.

Emery, K. O., and Zarudski, E. F. K., 1967, Seismic reflection profiles along the drill holes on the continental margin off Florida: Geol. Soc. America Prof. Paper 581-A.

Ewing, J., Worzel, J. L., and Ewing, M., 1962, Sediments and oceanic structural history of the Gulf of Mexico: Jour. Geophys. Research, v. 67.

Ewing, M., and Antoine, J., 1966, New seismic data concerning sediments and diapiric structures in Sigsbee deep and upper continental slope, Gulf of Mexico: Am. Assoc. Petroleum Geologists Bull., v. 50, no. 3, p. 479–504.

Ewing, M., Ludwig, W. J., and Ewing, J., 1965, Oceanic structural history of the Bering Sea: Jour. Geophys. Research, v. 70, no. 18, p. 4593–4600.

Ewing, M., Worzel, J. L., Ericson, D. B., and Heezen, B. C., 1955, Geophysical and geological investigations in the Gulf of Mexico: Geophysics, v. 20.

Gastil, G., 1960, Continents and mobile belts in the light of mineral dating: Internat. Geol. Cong., 21st, Norden, p. 162–169.

Gill, J. E., 1948, The Canadian Pre-Cambrian shield: Structural geology of Canadian ore deposits: Canadian Inst. Mining Metallurgy Trans.

——— 1949, Natural divisions of the Canadian shield: Royal Soc. Canada Trans., s. 3, sec. 4, v. 43, p. 61–69.

——— 1952, Mountain-building in the Pre-Cambrian shield: Internat. Geol. Cong., 18th, London, v. 13, p. 97–104.

Goldich, S. S., and others, 1961, The Precambrian geology and geochronology of Minnesota: Univ. Minnesota and Minnesota Geol. Survey Bull., v. 41, 193 p.

Gough, D. I., 1967, Magnetic anomalies and crustal structure in eastern Gulf of Mexico: Am. Assoc. Petroleum Geologists Bull., v. 50, no. 2, p. 200–211.

Guilcher, A., 1958, Coastal and submarine morphology: London, Methuen; New York, Wiley.

——— 1963, Continental shelf and slope, in Hill, M. N., ed., The sea: New York, Wiley, v. 3.

Hales, A. L., 1960, Seismic and gravity research on crustal structure in South Africa: Jour. Geophys. Research, v. 65, no. 7.

Heitanen, A., 1938, On the petrology of the Finnish quartzites: Comm. Geol. Finlande Bull., no. 122.

Hersey, J. B., Bunce, E. T., Wyrick, R. F., and Dietz, F. T., 1959, Geophysical investigation of the continental margin between Cape Henry, Virginia and Jacksonville, Florida: Geol. Soc. Am. Bull., v. 70.

Hewitt, D. F., 1956, The Grenville region of Ontario, in The Grenville problem: The Royal Soc. Canada Spec. Pub. 1, p. 23–41.

Holmes, A., 1949, The sequence of the Pre-Cambrian orogenic belts in south and central Africa: Internat. Geol. Cong., 18th, London, 1948.

Kay, G. M., 1951, North American geosynclines: Geol. Soc. Am. Mem. 48.

King, P. B., 1959, The evolution of North America: Princeton, N.J., Princeton Univ.

Krause, D. C., 1966, Seismic profile showing Cenozoic development of the New England continental margin: Jour. Geophys. Research, v. 71, no. 18, p. 4327–4332.

Lowdon, J. A., and others, 1963, Age determinations and geological studies, including isotopic ages: Geol. Survey Canada, Rept. 3, Paper 62–17, p. 5–120.

MacGregor, A. M., 1951, Some milestones in the Pre-Cambrian of southern Rhodesia: Geol. Soc. South Africa Trans. and Proc., v. 54, p. xxvii.

Magnusson, N. H., 1965, The Pre-Cambrian history of Sweden: Geol. Soc. London Quart. Jour., v. 121, p. 1–30.

Muehlberger, and others, 1967, Basement of the continental interior of the United States: Am. Assoc. Petroleum Geologists Bull., v. 51.

Pakiser, L. C., and Zietz, Isidore, Transcontinental crustal and upper mantle structure (in press—1965), in U.S. Program for the Internat. Upper Mantle Project: Prog. Rept. 1965: Natl. Acad. Sci., Natl. Research Council, Washington.

Rudman, A. J., Summerson, C. H., and Hinze, W. J., 1965, Geology of basement in midwestern United States: Am. Assoc. Petroleum Geologists Bull., v. 49, p. 894–905.

Sheridan, R. E., and others, 1966, Seismic-refraction study of continental margin east of Florida: Am. Assoc. Petroleum Geologists Bull., v. 50, no. 9, p. 1972–1991, 13 figs., 1 table.

Sloan, R. E., and Danes, Z. F., 1962, A geologic and gravity survey of the Belle Plaine area, Minnesota [Ms. submitted to Minnesota Acad. Sci., 9 p.].

Stevenson, J. S., ed., 1962, The tectonics of the Canadian Shield: Royal Soc. Canada Spec. Pub. 4, 180 p.

Stockwell, C. H., 1962, Structural trends in the Canadian shield, in The tectonics of the Canadian shield: Royal Soc. Canada Spec. Pub. 4, 180 p.

——— 1965, Structural trends in the Canadian shield: Am. Assoc. Petroleum Geologists Bull., v. 49, p. 887–894.

Thompson, J. E., ed., 1956, The Grenville problem: Royal Soc. Canada Spec. Pub. 1.

Uchupi, Elazar, and Emery, K. O., 1967, Structure of continental margin off Atlantic Coast of U.S.:

Am. Assoc. Petroleum Geologists Bull., v. 51, no. 2, p. 223–234.

Wegmann, C. E., 1929, Biespiele tektonischer analysen des grundgebirges in Finland: Comm. Geol. Finlande Bull., v. 87, no. 8, p. 98–127.

Wilson, M. E., 1939, The Canadian shield, Geologie der Eerde, *in* Ruedeman, R., and Balk, R., eds., Geology of North America: Berlin, Borntraeger.

—— 1948, An approach to the structure of the Canadian shield: Am. Geophys. Union Trans., v. 29, p. 691–726.

—— 1949, Some major structures of the Canadian shield: Canadian Inst. Mining Metallurgy Trans., v. 52, p. 231–242.

Zietz, I., and others, 1966, Crustal study of a continental strip from the Atlantic Ocean to the Rocky Mountains: Geol. Soc. America Bull., v. 77, p. 1427–1448.

12
a case study of an orogenic belt— the alps

STRUCTURE OF THE ALPS

The Alps of France, Switzerland, and Austria form one of the most intensively studied structural units of the earth's crust; but the complexity of the structural and stratigraphic problems there are such that much still remains to be done before a complete understanding of the evolution of this belt is obtained. We are fortunate, however, in having such a beautifully exposed and well-known section of one of the world's great orogenic belts. Were it not for the highly dissected, glaciated mountains of the Alps with their deeply exposed valley walls and cirques, it is hard to estimate how long it would have taken for us to realize that structures of the type exposed there could exist.

The Alps are part of the Tethys orogenic belt which extends from southern Spain and North Africa in a meandering pattern across southern Europe, through Turkey into the Himalayas, and finally merges with the island arc systems of southeast Asia. Attention here will be focused on one small part of that mighty belt—the western portion of the Alps.

The western Alps have been subdivided into a number of structural units by Collet (1935), as follows:

1. The Jura Mountains
2. The Swiss Plateau

3. The Prealps
4. The High Calcareous Alps
5. The crystalline Hercynian Massifs
6. The Pennine nappes
7. The zone of roots
8. The Calcareous Alps of the south, or Dinarides

THE JURA MOUNTAINS

The Jura Mountains are situated in the foreland of the Alps but separated from the highly deformed Alps by the Swiss Plateau which is underlain by unfolded Tertiary deposits. Because the deposits of the plateau are little deformed, it is difficult to understand what connection, if any, exists between the deformation in the Alps and the fold and fault belt of the Juras.

The region of the Jura Mountains is crescent-shaped, following the broad curve of the Alps and being wider (44 miles) in its central part than at either end. The Juras are readily divided into two parts: (1) the outer (northwestern) zone, a plateau reflecting the underlying flatness of the strata, which are little deformed but which have been tilted and broken by high-angle faults which break through them and cause displacements in the Hercynian basement; and (2) an inner zone of folds broken in places by thrusting and offset by transverse faults. Folds in this belt are numerous, and the folding is reflected in the topography in that the anticlines form ridges and the synclines form valleys. While the folds die out toward either end of the belt, approximately 160 anticlines have been counted.

The basement rock in this region is composed of deformed Paleozoic (Hercynian) rocks. This basement is exposed north and west of the Jura in the Black Forest, Vosges, and Central Plateau massifs, but these large areas are disconnected and separated by basins and major fault valleys such as the Rhine graben. Thus the basement is broken by faults along

which there has been considerable displacement. The covering sedimentary rocks on this basement are Mesozoic and Tertiary rocks which show a general thickening from north to south and from east to west. The aggregate thickness of the sediments, all of which represent shelf deposits in the northwest, is approximately 3,000 m compared with 4,600 m in the southeast. Most of the Triassic sediment in these sequences is conglomerates, sands, shales, and marls, a large part of which was deposited in shallow water or in continental environments: the Jurassic and Cretaceous beds are predominantly limestones, but also of shallow-water origin; and the overlying Tertiary is Molasse, partly continental and partly marine in origin. The sedimentary pile thus consists of rocks of varying competencies interstratified in a sequence of variable but great thickness. One part of the Triassic, the Muschelkalk, deserves special mention because it is composed in part of thick beds of anhydrite and gypsum which are the oldest units identified along the axes of the anticlines and along thrust faults. This has been widely interpreted to mean that older rocks are not involved in the faulting and folding. Buxtorf has interpreted this zone of gypsum as a probable plane of *décollement* (literally, ungluing) over which the sedimentary veneer has folded and faulted in response to a lateral shove (from the Alps), and beneath which the basement was unaffected by the deformation (Fig. 12-1). It should be pointed out that the level of the salt is well below the ground surface over most of the region so that the basement-veneer relationship cannot be directly observed. One problem in this interpretation is how a lateral push could be transmitted across the Swiss Plateau without deforming the rocks there at the same time.

Numerous alternatives have been offered to explain the mechanism of deformation in the Jura fold belt, but as in the case of Appalachian foreland folds, the basic argument centers around the role of the basement as opposed to

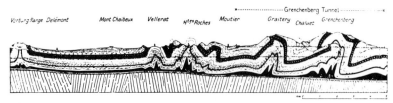

Fig. 12-1 Section showing *décollement* of the folded Jura. (*After Buxtorf, 1916; from Bailey, 1935.*)

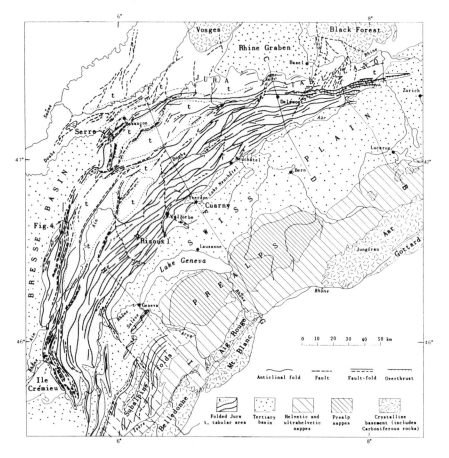

Fig. 12.2 Tectonic map of the Jura Mountains and adjacent area. (*From Pierce. 1966: compiled from Bersier, 1934; Christ, 1934; and Lugeon, 1941; tabular areas from Dreyfuss, 1960.*)

lateral movement over a plane of *décollement*. The large-scale plan of the deformed belt is illustrated by a tectonic map in Fig. 12-2, on which the following characteristics of the tectonic plan are shown:

1. Anticlines are far more numerous in the central part than at the ends of the belt.
2. Many of the anticlines split, forming two or more anticlinal ridges which follow sub-parallel trends.

3. The longer folds have arcuate axial traces.

4. Many of the folds have strong changes in trend where they meet transverse faults.

5. Transverse faults cut across the fold belt, usually intersecting the folds at angles of about 45°. The most prominent of these have left-lateral displacement.

6. A second system of high-angle faults and fractures trending north-northeast occurs in the western portion of the Jura and is subparallel to the fault system of the Rhine graben. Many of the faults and fractures underwent movements contemporaneous with those in the Rhine graben.

7. A thrust fault emerges at the northeast end of the fold belt. Movement has been from south to north along all of these.

Apart from the origin of the fold system, the geometry of the Jura folds is of great interest. Box- and fan-shaped folds as well as the more common symmetrical and asymmetrical shapes are beautifully exposed in the Jura Mountains. Many of the folds are demonstrably disharmonic, and in extreme cases synclines are situated above anticlines. Often the folds are broken on one limb by faults, and movements on some faults have brought older units up along bedding thrust.

At the southern end of the Juras, the Swiss Plateau division dies out, the narrow southern end of the Juras converges on the southern Alps (Fig. 12-3), and the Jura can be divided into three longitudinal divisions. The easternmost of these consists of long subparallel synclinal valleys and anticlinal ridges; in the central zone the anticlines are separated by fault zones; and in the westernmost zone the strata are gently tilted on a series of fault blocks.

Several areas within the central portion of the folded Juras show no signs of the folding and faulting which surrounds them, according to Wegmann. Valleys cut deeply into these areas and drill holes appear to confirm that no *décollement* has occurred over these apparently stable zones. If this is true it is difficult to en-

vision that folds and faults beyond the stable areas formed by means other than basement deformation.

A number of students of the Juras have proposed hypotheses to explain the origin of the folds in terms of offsets in the basement, notably Aubert, Wegmann, and Pavoni. Different types of movement plans have been suggested, one of which proposes lateral movements in the basement along transverse fault zones (Fig. 12-4), resulting in drag and faulting in the overlying sedimentary veneer. Certainly the basement is faulted where it is exposed, and movements in the basement have occurred within the right time interval to be the cause of the Jura folding. Even if the main movements responsible for the folding did originate by basement faulting, the salt beds still must have played an important role in the deformation through development of local *décollement* and disharmonic folding.

THE SWISS PLATEAU

The high plain which lies between the Jura Mountains and the Alps is called the Swiss Plateau. It has the form of a very large open syncline and contains a thick section (4,500 m in eastern Switzerland) of undeformed sediments, deposits of Tertiary sediment known as Molasse. The Molasse contains both fresh-water and marine deposits of a variety of rock types, primarily sandstone, conglomerate, coals, and limestone derived largely from the high Alps. Molasse deposits are found on both sides of the Alps, and the deposit at the edge of the Swiss Plateau is itself folded and overridden by the front of some of the nappes.

When the base of the Molasse is exposed, it rests on Flysch deposits. These two terms were originally used in the Alps and they are now widely applied to sediments in orogenic belts. It is therefore useful to contrast them as they occur in the Alps (after Trumpy, 1960):

1. Flysch sediments formed within the Alpine

geosyncline; Molasse formed within basins outside the geosyncline or in basins on the Alps.

2. Flysch sediments are entirely marine; Molasse was laid down in shallow, brackish seas.

3. Flysch was deposited starting with the first folding movements but ended before the main deformations; Molasse was deposited during and after major deformation.

4. Some of the sediments of the two are very similar, especially the sandstones, but the

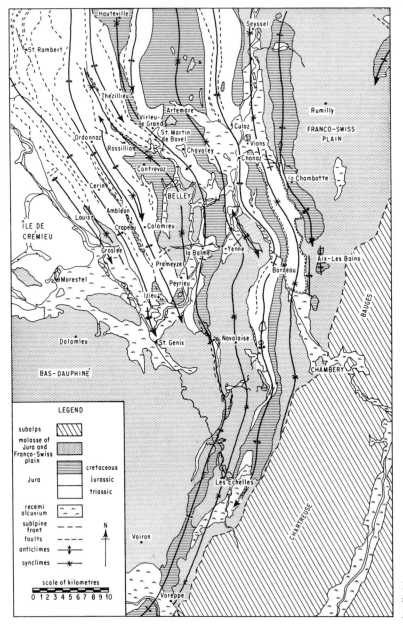

Fig. 12-3 Structural map of the southern French Juras. (*Redrawn from Ager and Evamy, 1963.*)

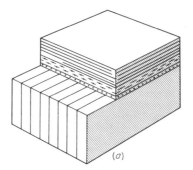 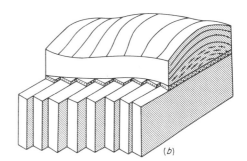

Fig. 12-4 Schematic representation of a way folds may be formed in the cover by fault movements in the basement. (*According to Wegmann, 1961.*)

(*a*)   (*b*)

Molasse contains significant quantities of coal, argillaceous material, and small quantities of shelly limestone.

5. Molasse contains deltaic deposits of coarse conglomerate and marine shoreline conglomerates that are absent from the typical Flysch.

6. Flysch deposits show graded bedding, cyclothems, coarse cross bedding, and ripple marks.

7. Beds in the Molasse are much thicker than those in the Flysch and the Molasse conglomerates contain boulders up to 50 m in diameter.

THE PREALPS

The Prealps stand out as a sort of frontal projection of the high Alps into the Swiss Plateau (Fig. 12-5). The intensely folded and faulted rocks which compose these mountains are Mesozoic and early Tertiary, thus they predate most of the Tertiary Molasse deposits of the Swiss Plateau. Furthermore, these Mesozoic units are not continuous structurally or stratigraphically with Triassic and Jurassic rocks of the High Calcareous Alps which are immediately adjacent to the southeast. Outcrops of Tertiary and Cretaceous strata form an intervening belt. More detailed comparison shows that the Triassic and Jurassic units of the Prealps are of different facies and thickness from those of the same age in the nearby High Calcareous Alps.

Hans Schardt (1898) was the first to conceive that this mountain mass, 120 km long and 40 km wide, the Prealps, is a great klippe (Fig. 12-6) of rocks derived from some place far to the south and now resting on a base of younger Tertiary deposits. He had worked in the region for many years and recognized the importance of this view in explaining the structural details of the superimposed nappes known in the exposed peaks of the Prealps. Five main nappes are known, the Simme, Breccia, Klippe, Niesen, and Col nappes in descending order, and these bear the relations to one another that are shown in map and sectional view in Figs. 12-6 and 12-7.

The highest nappe, the Breccia nappe, outcrops mainly at the southwest end of the Prealps, where it lies with fault contact partially on the High Calcareous Alps and partially on the Prealps Klippe nappe. Other scattered erosion remnants of the Breccia nappe are found farther north on the Klippe nappe. The position of the Breccia nappe on the High Calcareous Alps, which are also nappes, is important because it demonstrates clearly that the Breccia nappe was emplaced after the formation of the High Calcareous Alps nappes and must therefore have come from a great distance south. This interpretation is supported by the significant differences between facies of the rocks in the Breccia nappe and those of comparable ages nearby.

A number of other characteristic structural relations of the Prealps can be seen illustrated

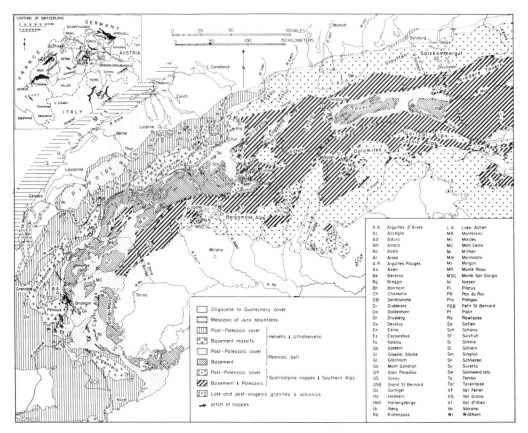

Fig. 12-5   Tectonics sketch map of the Alps. (*From Trümpy, 1960.*)

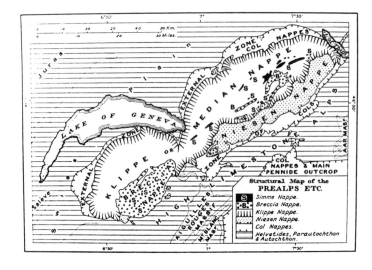

Fig. 12-6 Structural map of the Prealps. (*From Bailey, 1935.*)

in cross section in Fig. 12-7. Note that, along the northwestern edge of the Col nappes, Flysch is faulted onto the younger Molasse and that Flysch is in turn overridden by Jurassic strata of the Klippe nappe.

Such questions as the direction of movement of the nappes, how far they have moved, and what mechanism accomplished this movement have been long debated, but it is interesting that modern interpretations resemble those originally set forth by Schardt, who interpreted the nappes as having come from the south, traveling great distances by gravity sliding. In particular, he envisioned the Klippe nappe as having originated either as a fold which became faulted as movement proceeded, or as a clean-cut thrust which was elevated, broke away from its root and began gliding downhill, down the northwestern slope of the Pennine Alps which were moving northward at the same time. Support for the concept of gravity sliding is found in the character of the Flysch deposits associated with the nappes of the Prealps. The Niesen Flysch, for example, contains fragments of pre-Triassic schist of a type found in the Pennine Alps far to the south. The Flysch in the Prealps contains conglomerates which develop into breccias containing huge angular blocks of granite and into gneiss interbedded with fossiliferous shale. Schardt came to interpret these as having developed as landslides and screes along the advancing edge of the Klippe nappe. As the mass moved, it presumably sheared off the crystalline schist from the tops of exposed ridges in the Pennines.

THE HIGH CALCAREOUS ALPS AND THE HERCYNIAN MASSIFS

The High Calcareous Alps, Hercynian basement massifs, and Pennine Alps form a pattern of concentric zones which swing in a great arc through nearly 90° from the Mediterranean Coast at Nice to the Austrian Alps. The basement, the Hercynian Massifs, outcrops as the Argentera, Pelvoux, Belledonne, Aiquilles Rouges, Mont Blanc, Aar, and Gotthard Massifs (Fig. 12-5). These massive blocks are composed of pre-Carboniferous metamorphic and igneous rocks containing small areas of infolded late Paleozoic sedimentary rocks. These massifs are surrounded and separated from one another by a highly deformed cover of post-Paleozoic sediments which form a much wider outcrop belt on the north and west sides of the zone of massifs. Within the belt of massifs the larger blocks are separated from one another by depressions, as indicated by arrows in Fig. 12-5, showing the plunge of the basement, as between the Aar-Gotthard and Aiquilles Rouge–Mont Blanc Massifs. The plunge of these massifs and the overlying cover are most important because they provide the exposures which allow inferences about the structure at depth within the deformed pile. The down-structure method of viewing maps and cross sections is most reward-

Fig. 12-7 Section across Prealps. m = Molasse; f = Flysch; n = Nummulitic; c = Cretaceous; j = Jurassic (with breccias separately ornamented); C.N. = Col Nappes; K.N. = Klippe Nappe; B.N. = Breccia Nappe. (*From Bailey, 1935.*)

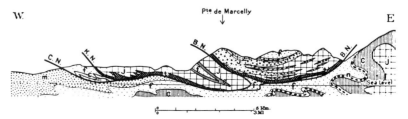

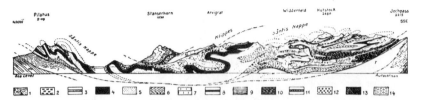

Fig. 12-8 Section across the High Calcareous Alps of central Switzerland. [*Based on Arbenz, Tobler, and Buxtorf's work; after Albert Heim (Ceologie der Schweiz) (with simplifications).*] 1 = Molasse Mo, Flysch, and Nummulitic limestones; 2 = Upper Cretaceous; 3 = Gault; 4 = Barremian; 5 = Hauterivian; 6 = Valanginian; 7 = Upper Jurassic; 8 = Argovian-Oxfordian; 9 = Dogger; 10 = Lias; 11 = Trias (Autochthon); 12 = Trias (Prealps); 13 = Crystalline schists; 14 = Cretaceous; T = Tertiary. (*From Collet, 1935.*)

ingly used in the Alps, allowing construction of the cross sections which graphically depict the complexity of the nappes.

It is also important to notice that some of the massifs are divided longitudinally by narrow zones of post-Paleozoic sediment, also highly deformed, as between the Aar and Gotthard Massifs.

It was a portion of the High Calcareous Alps at Glarus that the nappe theory was first established as the significant tool for interpretation of Alpine structure. The High Calcareous Alps, like the Prealps, are now viewed as a massive pile of thrust sheets and recumbent folds. As in the Prealps, some of the nappes are apparently far removed from their point of origin or roots, and others can be traced back to their original position.

Characteristic features of the structure of the High Calcareous Alps are brought out in a generalized cross section in Fig. 12-8. The superposition of one nappe on another is clear, but the complexity of the relationships is not immediately apparent. At the Jungfrau, Paleozoic crystalline rocks are brought on top of Jurassic sediments which can be followed upside down under the crystalline complex. Toward the northwest, the Jurassic sequence which mantles the crystalline rocks is thrust onto a complex recumbent fold of Jurassic, and down the mountainside, the Jurassic sequence is repeated beneath this recumbent syncline four times.

The repetitions show through the preservation of thin, drawn-out remnants of Cretaceous and lower Tertiary units on the upper layers of the Jurassic. These lower faults are subparallel to bedding, but some of them can be traced back into zones of shearing that involve the basement complex. This shearing out of the basement and the development of inverted recumbent folds is even better shown in the section from the Morgenhorn to the Breithorn.

The sections discussed above illustrate only details of a portion of a region in which many nappes are piled one on the other. Problems in interpretation arise in trying to decide where each nappe originated and in integrating the individual nappes into a general movement picture. It seems that some of the nappes have developed from shearing of the sedimentary veneer off the basement blocks along faults in the basement (Fig. 12-9). Other of the nappes must have come from the zone between the basement blocks. One such zone is the Chamonix zone, a narrow belt of steeply dipping Triassic and Jurassic strata located between the Mont Blanc and Aiquilles Rouges Massifs. The sedimentary veneer here has been sheared out as though crushed between the jaws of a giant vise (Fig. 12-10). These zones of shearing provide the most logical source areas for the nappes of the High Calcareous Alps, and indeed some of the nappes can be traced back into these root zones.

THE PENNINE ALPS

The Pennine Alps are often referred to as the internal zone of the Alps, the High Calcareous Alps and Hercynian massifs being an external zone. Complex nappe structures and shearing along zones originating in the crystalline basement characterize both zones. Here also thrust sheets are piled one on another. Basement rocks make up a large portion of the Pennine zone southeast of the Gotthard Massif, but farther to the west the Mesozoic cover is more widely exposed. The Pennine zone is distinguished by high-grade regional metamorphism which affected the zone during the Tertiary, and by the widespread occurrence here of basement rocks. This zone represents the deeper portion of the orogenic belt. It plunges eastward beneath the thrust sheets of the Austroalpine zone, but reappears through a window of the Hohe Tauern in Austria. The nappes of the Pennine Alps are composed of crystalline cores mantled in schists or sedimentary rocks, and they are developed on a grand scale.

The *Schistés lustrés* (also called the *Bündner Schiefer*) make up a significant part of the metamorphics, and because they contain fossils it can be shown that they include metasediments ranging in age from Triassic to Eocene.

The major structural elements of the Pennine Alps are illustrated in Fig. 12-5. Large masses of granite and gneiss appear, surrounded by covers of *Schistés lustrés* or Mesozoic sedimentary rocks. The relationships of the basement rocks and this cover can be seen at many places in the highly dissected ranges as at the Matterhorn where *Schistés lustrés* underlie highly deformed, recumbently folded older basement gneisses. Here in the Pennines the basement floor of the geosyncline was actively deformed; it was folded and sheared out along faults with movements amounting to at least several miles. This much can be clearly demonstrated. Arguments concerning the Pennines center largely on the degree and amount of basement mobilization and movement. Argand

(1916) conceived of a structure of the Pennines in the early 1900s which stood for many years as the masterpiece of Alpine synthesis. He envisioned each of the major pre-Triassic basement elements in the Pennines, the Dent Blanche, Monte Rosa, Saint Bernard, Monte Leone, Lebedun, and Antiogio as large-scale nappes in which the basement gneisses had be-

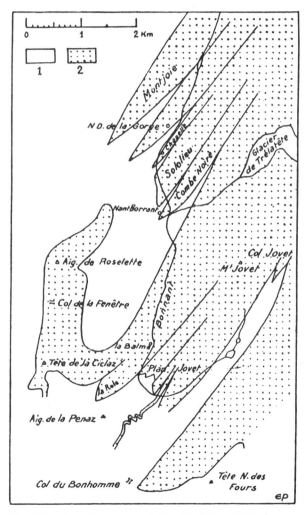

Fig. 12-9 Geological map of the southwest extremity of Mont-Blanc, showing the crystalline wedges. (*After E. Paréjus.*) 1 = Trias and Lias; 2 = crystalline schists. (*From Collet, 1935.*)

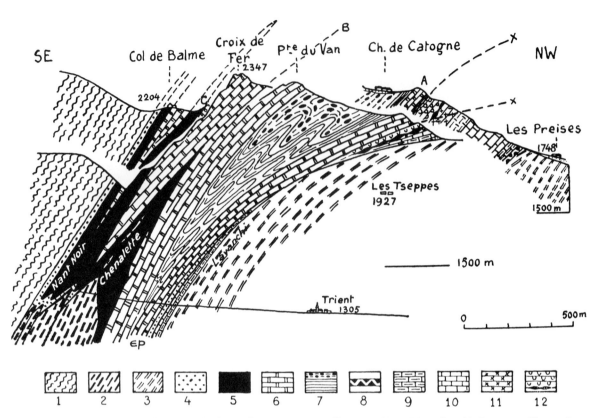

Fig. 12-10 Section across the Zone of Chamonix. *(After E. Paréjas.)* 1 = Mont Blanc Massif; 2 = crystalline wedges; 3 = Aiguilles Rouges Massif; 4 = Trias; 5 = lower Lias; 6 = middle Lias; 7 = upper Lias; 8 = Dogger (Bajocian-Bathonian); 9 = Argovian; 10 = upper Jurassic; 11 = Lower Cretaceous; 12 = Tertiary. *(From Collet, 1935.)*

come mobilized, moved into the overlying cover of Mesozoic or Tertiary rocks, and were transported many miles northwest (Fig. 12-11). He reconstructed the sequence of events as the pile of nappes developed, explaining in a most ingenious manner the great variety of structural detail. Modern students of the Pennines are not so enthusiastic for the grand synthesis, and are less inclined to accept the section of Argand's work which is based on the down-structure method of viewing the geologic maps. They tend to think instead that movements have been over smaller distances, that many of the movements have been gravity sliding, that basement movements have been more commonly by

shearing than by actual folding, and that the nappes are not of such a grand regional scale.

It was the driving of the Simplon tunnel (1895 to 1905) that set the stage for the view of large-scale basement folding such as that proposed by Argand. The tunnel was driven through a nappe involving basement gneisses; it demonstrated that the basement rocks were actually involved in large-scale recumbent folding as shown in Fig. 12-12. This is highly significant and in strong contrast with nappe structures of the outer zone and the Prealps where the sedimentary veneer alone is highly folded, although the Hercynian Massifs are sheared, broken, and displaced by faults.

Metamorphism is most marked in the Pennine zone, although metamorphism has affected the Mesozoic cover outside the Pennines slightly. Even within the Pennines, metamorphism is highly variable. Mesozoic rocks in France are very slightly altered but to the northwest the *Schistés lustrés* are more affected. In Switzerland the metamorphic grade is higher, and abundant biotite, staurolite, kyanite, and garnet are present in the Jurassic rocks of the Pennine nappes. It has been suggested (Bearth, 1962) that there were two main phases of metamorphism—an earlier one which produced lawsonite and pumpellyte in the outer Pennine zones and galuco-phane and choloritoid in the inner zone, and a later one which produced kyanite and sillimanite in the inner zone. The isograds cut across the nappe structure and thus appear to be later.

Salt and gypsum deposits of the Triassic have played an important role as lubricants in the movement of nappes in the outer part of the Pennines. As the folding and faulting of the basement occurred, the salt beds were rolled up and lubricated the movement of the basement masses as they pushed northwards. Masses of other rock became caught up in the salt which now completely encases them. Some of the salt outcrops can be traced for distances of tens of kilometers along the strike.

THE ROOT ZONE—THE INSUBRIC LINE—THE DINARIDES

The roots of the basement nappes of the Pennines were interpreted by Argand (1916) to lie in a zone at the southeastern edge of the Pennines where large masses of basement gneisses separated by *Schistés lustrés* or dolomitic marbles are found standing nearly vertical. This is a zone of intense deformation and high-grade regional metamorphism. Some of the sedimentary units are crushed and drawn out into lenticular masses. The large area of basement exposure, the Sesia-Lanzo zone, is still interpreted as the root zone of the Dent Blanche nappe located far north in the Pennines. Along

Fig. 12-11 Cross section through the Alps. *(After Argand, 1916; from Collet, 1935.)*

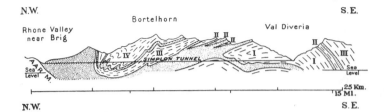

N.W.   S.E.

Bortelhorn   Val Diveria

Rhone Valley
near Brig

N.W.   S.E.

Fig. 12-12 Section across the Pennide core: I = Antigorio; II = Lebendun; III = Monte Leone; IV = Saint Bernard; V = Monte Rosa; VI = Dent Blanche. The section follows the Simplon tunnel. (*After Schardt, 1898; from Bailey, 1935.*)

the southeastern edge of the Sesia-Lanzo zone there is a line of major faulting, called the *Insubric line,* which separates the complex basement structures of the Pennines from the little-deformed region to the south, the Dinarides.

Structural units of this southern part of the Pennines, as represented by the Sesia-Lanzo, become much more widely distributed toward the east and make up the largest part of the eastern Alps. They have been viewed as great nappes which have moved out over the Pennine elements, as is suggested by the large window in which Pennine elements are exposed at Tauern, south of Innsbruck, Austria. As in the Pennines, however, there is currently much debate about the amount of movement and the continuity of individual nappe features in these elements, known as the *Austroalpine nappes.*

ALPINE GEOSYNCLINE SYNTHESIS*

The significance of the Alpine Flysch and Molasse has already been pointed out. Some additional aspects of the stratigraphy of the geosyncline are highly significant in any structural interpretation of the Alps. The basement of the Alpine geosyncline was composed of deformed and metamorphosed Paleozoic and possibly Precambrian rocks. This basement was beveled by an erosion surface before Triassic time, when deposits of dune sand, lagoonal deposits, and salt beds were deposited. This salt has figured prominently in the structural de-

* Refer to Trümpy (1960) and Ramsey (1963).

velopment of the Juras and some of the Pennine nappes. The areas of Triassic salt deposition were in a basin on the north side of the present Alps and were separated by land from the main area of the Tethyian geosyncline to the south.

Deeper water transgressed the region in the Jurassic, and thick deposits of shale and marl were deposited in elongate basins. It appears probable that the margins of some of these basins were active high-angle faults from which large breccia slides developed. Similar breccia slides occur in the Cretaceous deposits, and some of these breccias contain large quantities of basement rocks. Toward the southeast, Cretaceous submarine volcanoes extruded and intruded basic magma—presumably as pillow lavas, spilitic rocks with serpentine—into the sediments. In the Late Cretaceous, conditions across the geosyncline were very uniform and marly sediments were deposited. One of the most striking features of this geosynclinal accumulation is that it is nowhere more than about 3,000 m thick. It was during the Late Cretaceous that the first compressional deformation took place in the geosyncline. As folds began to rise, their erosion products were deposited on the flanks of the uplifts in what were to become the internal Flysch basins. As the folding continued, the Flysch deposits themselves were caught up in the folding and faulting, and the Flysch spread, first filling adjacent troughs in the geosyncline and finally pouring out into the areas beyond the geosyncline. The location of the uplifts in the geosyncline appears to bear no consistent relationship to the form of the

Mesozoic sedimentary basins. The first nappes of the eastern Alps are dated as Late Cretaceous, the earliest in the western Alps are late Eocene, and the youngest Flysch is Oligocene; therefore, by the time the last Flysch was deposited, large parts of the Alpine nappes had already formed.

As the main thrusting accompanied by metamorphism and granitization took place, erosion was attacking the uplifted mountain mass, and the erosion product, the Molasse, was deposited on the flanks. By Miocene time the Alps were eroded to a broad and low but hilly surface. Then uplift was renewed in the Pliocene and Pleistocene, accompanied by volcanic activity and some slight faulting.

REFERENCES

Ager, D. V., and Evamy, B. D., 1963, Geology of the southern French Jura: Proc. Geol. Assoc., v. 74.

Arbentz, P., 1912, Der Gebirgsbau der Zentralschweiz. Verh. der Schweizer: Naturforsch. Ges. 95 Jahresvers., Altdorf, Teil 2.

Argand, Emile, 1912. Les nappes de recouvrement des Alps occidentales Carte structurale. 1/500,000. Matériaux Carte géol. Suisse, N. S. Livraison 31, planche 1 (carte spéciale No. 64), Berne.

——— 1916. Sur láre des Alpes occidentales: Eclogae geol. Helv., v. 14, p. 145–191.

Bailey, E. B., 1935, Tectonic essays: Oxford, Clarendon.

Bearth, P., 1962, Versuch eines Gliederung alpin metamorpher Serien der Westalpen: Min. pertegr. Mitt., Schweiz, v. 42, p. 127–137.

Bersier, Arnold, 1934, Carte tectonique du Jura, Fasc. I, pl. 3, *in* Guide géologique de la Suisse: Soc. Géol. Suisse.

Bertrand, M., 1897, Structure des alpes françaises et récurrence de certain faciès sédimentaires: Internat. Geol. Cong., 6th Sess., 1894, Comptes rendus, p. 163–177.

Bucher, W. H., 1952, Geologic structures and orogenic history of Venezuela: Geol. Soc. America Mem. 49.

Buxtorf. A., 1908, Geologische Beschreibung, des Weissensteintunnels und seiner Umgebung Beitr. z. geol. Karte de. Schweiz N. F. XXI, Bern.

——— 1916, Prognosen und Befunde beim Hausenstein-basis und Grenchenberg tunnel, und die Bedeutung der letzteren für die Geologie des Juragebirges: Basel, Naturf. Gesell. Verh., v. 27.

Collet, L. W., 1927, The structure of the Alps: London, E. Arnold, 289 p.

——— 1935, The structure of the Alps, 2d ed.: London, Arnold.

Collet, L. W., and Paréjas, ed., 1920, Le chapeau de sédimentaire des Aiguilles Rouges de Chamonix et le Trias du Massif Aiguilles Rouges-Gastern: C. R. Soc. Phys. Hist. Nat., v. 37, no. 2, Genève, 1920.

De Sitter, L. U., 1953, Essai de géologie structurale comparative de trois chaînes tertiaires, Alpes Pyrénées, et Hout-Atlas: Soc. belge. geologie, 13.t., 62, f. 1, p. 38–58.

Evison, F. F., 1960, On the growth of continents by plastic flow under gravity: Geophys. Jour. Royal Astron. Soc., v. 3, p. 155–190.

——— 1961, Rock magnetism in western Europe as an indication of continental growth: Geophys. Jour. Royal Astron. Soc., v. 4, p. 320–335.

Heim, Albert, 1878, Untersuchungen uber den Mechanismus der Gerirgbildung: Basel.

Heim, Albert, and Schmidt, C., 1911, Geologische Karte der Schweiz 1/500,000, 2e Auflage, Neudruck.

Kay, G. M., 1947, Geosynclinal nomenclature and the craton geological note: Am. Assoc. Petroleum Geologists Bull., v. 31, p. 1289–1293.

Krasser, L. M., 1939, Der bau der Alpen, ein Hilfsbuch zur einfuhrung, viii: Berlin, Gebruder Bertraeger.

Liniger, Hans, 1958, Vem bau der Alpen: Munchen, Ott Verlag Thun., p. 236.

Lombard, A. E., 1948, Appalachian and Alpine structures—a comparative study: Am. Assoc. Petroleum Geologists Bull., v. 32, p. 709–744.

Lugeon, M., and Gagnebin, E., 1941, Observations et vues nouvelles sur la géologie des Prealpes romades: Univ. Lausanne Lab. Géol. Bull. 72.

Oberholtzer, J., 1933, Geologie der Glarneralpen: Bern, Switzerland (privately published).

Pierce, W. G., 1966, Jura tectonics as a décollement: Geol. Soc. America Bull., v. 77, p. 1265–1276.

Ramsey, J. G., 1963, Stratigraphy structure and metamorphism in the Western Alps: Geol. Assoc. Proc., v. 74.

Schardt, Hans, 1898, Les régions exotiques du ver-
sant Nord des Alpes Suisses: Soc. vaudoise Sci.
Natl. Bull., v. 34, p. 113–219.

Strand, Trygve, 1961, The Scandinavian caledonides—a review: Am. Jour. Sci., v. 259, p. 161–172.

Trümpy, Rudolph, 1960, Paleotectonic evolution of
the central and western Alps: Geol. Soc. America
Bull., 71, p. 843–908.

Weber, F., 1904, Über den Kali-Syenit des Piz Giuf
und Umgebung (Östl. Aarmassiv): Beitr. z. geol.
Karte de. Schweiz. N. F. 14 e Lief 44, Bern.

Wegmann, Eugene, 1961, Anatomie comparée des
hypothèses sur les plissements de couverture (le
Jura plissé): Uppsala Univ. Geol. Inst. Bull., v.
40, p. 169–182.

Wyllie, P. J., 1965, A modification of the geosyncline
and tectogene hypothesis: Geol. Mag. [Great
Britain], v. 102, no. 3, p. 231–245.

13
anatomy of a folded mountain belt— the appalachians

STRUCTURAL FRAMEWORK OF THE APPALACHIAN MOUNTAINS

It was on the basis of studies in the region of the northern and central Appalachians that James Hall proposed his concept of the geosyncline. In an address before the American Association for the Advancement of Science, he outlined his view of the development of the folded mountain belt. He recognized that the rocks exposed in the folded belt had originally been deposited as shallow marine sediment in seas that occupied the eastern margin of North America in the Paleozoic. These sediments—composed largely of sand, mud, and limy deposits—accumulated slowly in a long, relatively narrow belt that gradually subsided until a great thickness of sediment, estimated to be between 30,000 and 40,000 ft, had accumulated. That this sediment accumulated in shallow water is shown by the ripple marks, mud cracks, and shallow-water fossils found throughout the stratigraphic section. The thickness of units within the belt of subsidence was recognized as being far greater than that of units of comparable age in the Midwest on the craton, the stable continental interior. Hall concluded that the sedimentary rocks of the geosyncline became folded during the subsidence of the geosyncline and that they were uplifted later by a regional upwarping.

Hall's concept of the geosyncline as a long, relatively narrow belt of mobility in the earth's crust, characterized by thick sediment accumulations and strong deformation, has survived to the present, but the folds and faults are no longer generally interpreted as having formed during subsidence. The systematic and persistent asymmetry of the folds toward the northwest and the

movement of overthrust blocks to the northwest argue against their formation during subsidence. The movement is consistently toward the craton—toward the margin of the geosyncline, not the center.

The Coastal Plain and the ocean form the eastern boundary of the Appalachian Mountains at present. Along most of this eastern and southern margin, Cretaceous or Tertiary sediments lie unconformably on the old sedimentary, igneous, and metasedimentary rocks of the Appalachian Piedmont. In New England the ocean forms the eastern edge. The character of this margin is important; because of it we are unable to obtain a very precise understanding of the eastern part of the Appalachians, or what the geosyncline was like during the millions of years while the sediments were accumulating, nor is it possible to tell how far to the east the mountains may have extended 200 million years ago after the last important phase of orogenic deformation was over. Coastal Plain sediments also obscure the southern end of the Appalachians covering probable connections between the southern Appalachians and the Ouachita Mountains and its probable continuation to the Marathon Mountains of western Texas.

South of Maine the Appalachians can be divided longitudinally into two major provinces, a western province of deformed sedimentary rocks and an eastern province of igneous and metamorphic rocks (Fig. 13-1). Two areas, one in New England and a second in southeastern Pennsylvania and Maryland, provide the best opportunities to correlate the sedimentary units of the west with the metamorphic rocks to the east. To the east lie the Precambrian sedimentary, metasedimentary, and igneous rocks along with extensive areas of strongly deformed and metamorphosed Paleozoic sediments and intrusives. Basins of Triassic sediments bounded by high-angle faults lie mainly in this eastern zone. The Precambrian exposures are located primarily in a central

Fig. 13-1 Appalachian physiographic provinces. (*From Spencer, 1965.*)

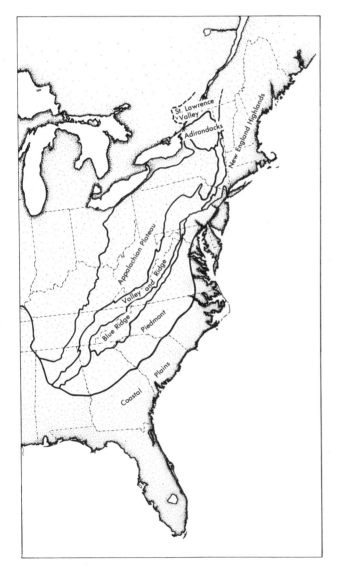

position and stand out prominently today as the Smoky Mountains, Blue Ridge, Reading uplift, Green Mountains, and other western New England domes. The folded and faulted belt of Paleozoic sedimentary rocks lies immediately west of these Precambrian exposures. This belt is narrowest in the north along the Hudson and Champlain valley, where it is confined between the extensive exposures of Precambrian igneous and metamorphic rocks of the Adirondack dome and the New England metamorphic rocks. Strongly folded and thrust-faulted Cambrian and Ordovician sedimentary rocks lie in these valleys. These can be traced south through the valleys of Pennsylvania and Virginia to Alabama, but toward the south the folded belt increases in width and from Pennsylvania southward the folding and faulting involves all Paleozoic sedimentary units.

As expressed in present surface exposures, the character of deformation in the western or sedimentary provinces of the southern and central Appalachians varies both from east to west and from south to north. In general the intensity of folding as expressed by the degree of asymmetry and the tightness of the folded structures tends to decrease from southeast to northwest across the folded belt. From south to north, closely spaced low-angle thrust faults pass into folds, and eventually in northern Pennsylvania and New York the middle and upper Paleozoic sedimentary units are only broadly warped. The Appalachians are divided into a number of physiographic and structural divisions. Divisions frequently referred to here are:

Appalachian Plateau: A large elongate structural basin in the western part of the southern and central Appalachians. Flat-lying or gently warped middle to upper Paleozoic sequences are maturely dissected.

Valley and Ridge: The folded and thrust-faulted belt of lower and middle Paleozoic sedimentary sequences exposed in an almost continuous belt from Canada to Alabama. This province is a southern Appalachian province represented in the north by the Hudson and Champlain valleys.

Blue Ridge: The prominent ridge of Precambrian igneous and metamorphic rocks best developed in Virginia. The Smoky Mountains are a southern continuation of it. The ridge dies out in Maryland, but the Reading Mountains and New Jersey highlands are composed of similar rock types and lie along trend with the Blue Ridge.

Piedmont: The metamorphic and igneous province in the southern Appalachians east of the Blue Ridge.

New England highlands: The igneous and metamorphic provinces of the New England Appalachians.

Adirondack Mountains: A structural dome composed of Precambrian igneous and metamorphic rocks located west of the folded belt in New York.

Triassic lowlands: Basins containing Triassic continental sedimentary rocks deposited in block-faulted basins. These lowlands include the Connecticut Valley, New Jersey lowlands, Gettysburg basin, Culpepper basin, Richmond basin, Danville basin, and Deep River basin.

As the Appalachians are traced northward into New Brunswick, Nova Scotia, and Newfoundland, the character of the belt changes. The well-defined narrow fold and fault belt of the south passes into a more open fold system. The edge of the fault belt seems to pass into the St. Lawrence River; the metamorphic and igneous province of New England is lost under late Paleozoic sedimentary sequences; and the clear, longitudinal twofold division is lost. Attention is here focused on that portion of the Appalachian system which lies within the United States.

Division of the Geosyncline

The term *miogeosyncline* is applied to the region of Paleozoic sedimentary rocks west of the belt defined by the Blue Ridge and New England Precambrian domes. Most of these units are compact and tightly cemented and some of the shales are locally altered to slate, but otherwise the rocks are unmetamorphosed; there are almost no intrusions in them, and they are largely sandstones, shales, limestones, dolostones, and mixtures of these. The individual units often have great lateral extent, many being traced for hundreds of miles along the geosyncline, but quite commonly the units change character and thickness rapidly when traced across the geosyncline. It is difficult to trace units across the geosyncline because successively younger rocks are exposed toward the west into the Appalachian Plateau. Precambrian sedimentary units are exposed at the Blue Ridge, but northwest of the Valley and Ridge, Carboniferous rocks cover the older sequences. It has been largely from the study of miogeosynclinal sequences that the history of Appalachian tectonics has been interpreted.

Several major angular unconformities help to delineate diastrophic episodes in the geosyncline, but the changing character of the sediments supplied to the geosyncline has proved to be the most important key. The source of most of these sediments appears to have been outside the area where the miogeosynclinal rocks are now exposed. Much of the great volume of clastic sediment has the general shape of huge clastic wedges which thicken to the east, suggesting source areas in the region now occupied by the Blue Ridge, Piedmont, and New England highlands. Some sediment was undoubtedly derived locally from folds which rose in the miogeosyncline, but this is of minor importance compared with the external sources.

Many geologists have recognized a cyclic pattern in geosynclinal sedimentation. Pettijohn (1957) describes two cycles in the Paleozoic of the middle Appalachians—one from Early Cambrian to Middle Silurian, and a second from Late Silurian through the Carboniferous. These are characterized by a preorogenic facies, chiefly orthoquartzite and carbonates; a euxinic facies, characterized by black shales, and commonly chert; a Flysch facies in which the sandstones become coarser and cleaner, and in which they show cross bedding and other current structures. These various facies are thought to be tectonically controlled, reflecting initially slow, shallow marine sedimentation on a flooded craton or its margin; a rapid basining and starved sedimentation; then basin filling by turbidity flows and other gravity processes taking place in deep water; and later basin filling by paralic sedimentation.

A Precambrian igneous and metamorphic complex is exposed in the Blue Ridge Mountains, in the Adirondacks, in the Reading Prong of the New England highlands, and in a number of large domes and anticlines in the northern Piedmont and New England. These rocks have radiometric ages of 1 billion years or more. They are clearly Precambrian, but considerable doubt exists concerning the age of some of the metasedimentary sequences which rest nonconformably on these Precambrian complexes in the Piedmont and in New England. These are intruded by plutonic series which are Paleozoic, and a few fossils have been found in the metasedimentary units, but others (including most of the Piedmont metamorphic rocks) are not fossiliferous, and their age has been variously interpreted as Precambrian or lower Paleozoic.

The oldest of the unmetamorphosed clastic sequences is found in the Smoky Mountains where the Ocoee series is composed largely of clastic materials with minor amounts of interbedded limestone. This sequence is estimated to be as much as 30,000 ft thick, and it is probably of late Precambrian age. Thus a major source area, one of considerable height or size, is necessary to explain the origin of this sedimentary pile very early in the geosyncline's history.

A clastic sequence known as the Chilhowee is found along the northwestern flanks of the

Blue Ridge throughout most of its length. This sequence is composed of quartzite, sandstone, graywacke, shale, and minor amounts of volcanic ash. It is several thousand feet thick and reaches a maximum of nearly 6,000 ft. Its source is still debated. Cross-bedding studies have indicated western sources at some localities. Unlike many of the other major clastic sequences, the Chilhowee does not have a wedge-shaped distribution.

Carbonates were deposited in the miogeosyncline during most of the Cambrian and Lower Ordovician. These sections of limestone and dolomite contain some shales and minor amounts of sandstone, but the carbonate character is typical from the southern to the northern end of the Appalachians in the United States, and the section reaches thicknesses in excess of a mile in places.

A second major clastic wedge was flooding into the geosyncline in the Smoky Mountain region by the Middle Ordovician; the sands and shales of this deposit spread north and west, reaching a maximum thickness of nearly 8,000 ft, but it thinned out rapidly.

Uplift and strong deformation were affecting the northern Appalachians in Vermont, New York, and Pennsylvania by the end of the Ordovician. A clastic wedge, the Queenstown delta, spread westward and is preserved in Pennsylvania and New York. One of the major unconformities is found in this region, and the orogeny is called the Taconic orogeny. Silurian conglomerates lie on Precambrian gneisses at Green Pond, N.J.; much of the folding and thrusting of the northern Appalachian region in New York and Vermont is thought to be of this age. Silurian sands and conglomerates spread widely down the geosyncline.

A second major uplift took place in the New England area about the middle of the Devonian. The famous Catskill delta formed from the erosion products of this uplift. These clastic sequences measure over 7,000 ft thick in New York, and sands and shales are prominent in

Devonian sequences far to the south. Unlike so many other clastic wedges, the Catskill beds have not been folded or thrust-faulted by later movements in the region where they are thickest, nor has it been possible to distinguish the structures associated with this deformation, the Acadian orogeny, from those of earlier age in large parts of the New York–New England region. There are, however, a number of large plutons of this age in New England and in the Piedmont.

Carboniferous sedimentary sequences are thick over much of the Appalachian geosyncline; however, they are not present east of the Valley and Ridge, presumably because they have been eroded away. Great thicknesses of Mississippian clastic sediments are found in eastern Tennessee (about 6,000 ft thick) and in Pennsylvania and West Virginia (where sandstones and conglomerates are several thousand feet thick). These sections thicken toward the east also. Pennsylvanian sequences are predominantly clastic and they are very thick (over 10,000 ft) in Alabama. They thin gradually into Pennsylvania, but sections are still several thousand feet thick.

All Paleozoic units through the Pennsylvanian are folded and faulted in the southern Appalachians. This condition plus the absence of major angular unconformities in the Paleozoic section of the central and southern Appalachians has given rise to the importance assigned to the late Paleozoic orogeny, the Appalachian orogeny. It is clear from the consideration of the sedimentary record that the designation of only three orogenies in the Paleozoic (Taconian, Acadian, and Appalachian) is misleading. Major uplifts over large regions are necessary to provide the clastic sediments which spread into the miogeosyncline in one area or another in every period of the Paleozoic.

Orogenic deformation ceased at the end of the Paleozoic and was followed by block faulting which gave rise to the Triassic basins, fault troughs filled with continental sediment which

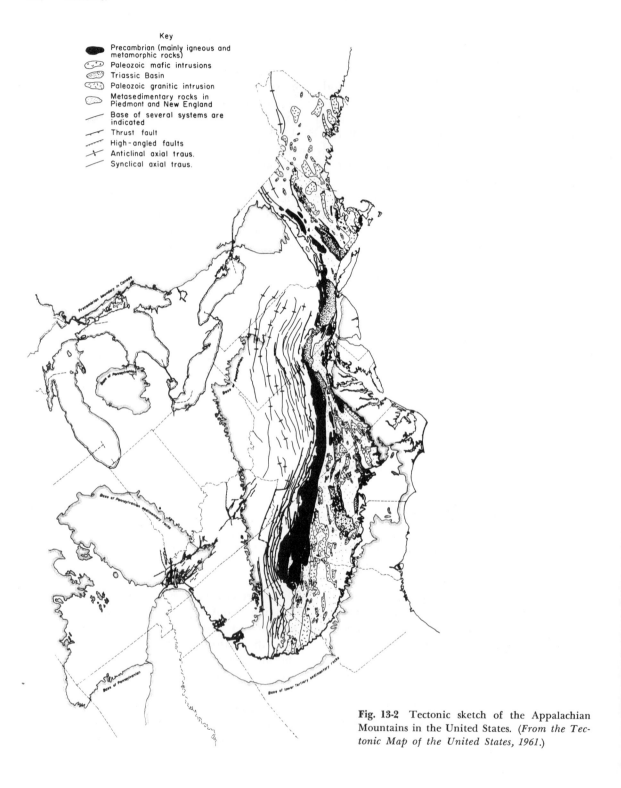

Key

Precambrian (mainly igneous and metamorphic rocks)
Paleozoic mafic intrusions
Triassic Basin
Paleozoic granitic intrusion
Metasedimentary rocks in Piedmont and New England
Base of several systems are indicated
Thrust fault
High-angled faults
Anticlinal axial traus.
Synclical axial traus.

Fig. 13-2 Tectonic sketch of the Appalachian Mountains in the United States. (*From the Tectonic Map of the United States, 1961.*)

has been tilted (but not folded) by postdepositional movements on the faults. Basaltic sills and dikes were emplaced during deformation.

The question of the relationship between the miogeosynclinal units and the more complex metamorphic rocks and intrusions in the Piedmont and in New England has long been debated. Kay (1951) cites evidence which indicates that this eastern zone is what he has termed an *eugeosyncline*. Thus the Appalachian geosyncline had two parts, eastern and western. The eugeosyncline was the site of accumulation of great thicknesses of sediment during the Paleozoic, which included volcanics and graywacke as well as the rock types found in the miogeosyncline. It was into these sequences that great intrusions were emplaced during the orogenies that affected the geosyncline, and it was here that rocks were metamorphosed and highly deformed. This eugeosyncline was the core of the orogenic belt in every sense.

The view that a continental borderland was located east of the miogeosyncline during the Paleozoic stands in strong contrast to the concept of the eugeosyncline. That the source of sediment for the miogeosyncline was to the east during much of the Paleozoic is indicated by variations in sediment thickness and coarseness across the geosyncline and current directions interpreted from cross bedding. The eastern source was persistent over long periods of time and throughout much of the geosyncline, although western sources are also indicated from time to time, and during long intervals of the Upper Cambrian and Ordovician no land source is needed for the carbonate sequences. The exact location of the eastern borderland has not been exactly determined. For a long time most of the Piedmont metamorphic rocks were thought to be Precambrian, and the Blue Ridge, Piedmont, and New England regions were therefore selected. Over the years more and more of these rocks have been shown to be Ordovician, Devonian, and Carboniferous in-

trusions and Paleozoic metasedimentary materials. Thus the borderland of the East has become less distinct. The Blue Ridge remains a possibility, the region covered by the Coastal Plain sediments is a possible location, and the age of some of the metasedimentary rocks in the Piedmont is still questioned, particularly a sequence known as the Glenarm series and its equivalents which now appear to be of a Precambrian age and thus a possible source area. These occur in the unlabeled parts of the Piedmont (Fig. 13-2).

Structures of the miogeosyncline

In the southern portion of the miogeosyncline, sedimentary units ranging in age from Cambrian through Pennsylvanian are folded and faulted. The strongest deformation lies in a belt about 75 miles wide that is covered at the southern end by Cretaceous units. In the southern portion of this belt most of the folds are asymmetrical toward the northwest and are cut by thrust faults. Thrust faults are prominent in surface exposure from Alabama to central Virginia.

The character of this southern faulted zone is much better known in surface plan than it is at depth. Many parts of the folded and faulted belt have now been mapped as quadrangle reports at the scale of 1 in. to 1 mile. Since relief in the region amounts to as much as several thousand feet, some ideas regarding changes at depth can be formulated, but there are very few deep wells in the belt. Thus the true nature of the structure at depth is largely hypothetical, and there is much debate over the question of how deep the deformation extends. Do the thrust faults become bedding faults at some depth below which unfolded and unfaulted strata prevail, or do the folding and faulting continue into the Precambrian crystalline complex below the miogeosyncline? Other closely related questions concern the structure in the Appalachian basin. Few faults outcrop in the Appalachian basin, but because oil and gas occur widely through this belt many wells have been drilled and faults are frequently encountered in these wells.

Thrust faults of the southern Appalachians Smoky Mountain region*

The structure of the southern end of the miogeosyncline is dominated by thrust faults. These faults are shown on the geologic map of eastern Tennessee and the maps of the Great Smoky Mountain area in Fig. 13-3. Fourteen or more faults may be crossed in a traverse across the mountain system from the western edge of the Great Smokies, where Precambrian sedimentary sequences are thrust onto Cambrian units, to the Cumberland escarpment of the Appalachian Plateau. These faults occur in lower Paleozoic units. They are usually parallel to the strike of the beds. The beds are folded into northeast-trending folds, and the faults occur on one or both limbs. Many of the faults dip steeply at the ground surface, but they can be shown to be folded in other localities.

Most of the major faults have outcrops of the Cambrian Rome or Elbrook formations on the overthrust side, indicating that the faults moved along or within the units. Both of these formations are composed in large part of shale, and it is apparent from the mode of deformation within them that they have behaved as incompetent materials during the deformations. It is interesting to note that at no place west of the fault of the Great Smoky–Blue Ridge front have units older than the Rome been brought to the ground surface. It has been argued that this is no coincidence, and that the reason is that the faults originate in the Rome formation.

Certain types of fault patterns recur in the fault belt. Major faults split into two or more faults of parallel trend, one or more of which may die out or pass into a fold. Some rejoin the major fault, others appear to be lost in one of

the thick shale sequences, and *en échelon* patterns are sometimes encountered.

A more complex pattern is found at the margin of and within the Great Smoky Mountains (Fig. 13-3). Here the great piles of clastic sediment which comprise the Ocoee and the Chilhowee are thrust onto Paleozoic rocks which range in age from Ordovician to Mississippian. Klippes and windows are found in this region. Paleozoic rocks are exposed in windows where the overthrust Ocoee series has been cut by erosion. Note also that the frontal thrust is offset along transverse "tear" faults in places.

A striking feature of the Great Smoky Mountain is the window on the east side of Grandfather Mountain, where Paleozoic rocks are exposed in a window through old Precambrian metamorphic and plutonic rocks. This is interpreted to mean that most of the Ocoee has been thrust over the eastern edge of the miogeosyncline. The minimum distance from Grandfather Mountain to the western edge of the mountains is 6 miles, and much greater transport is possible. The sequential development of the Great Smoky fault is shown in Fig. 4-21, as inferred by King (1964).

Relation of gravity anomalies to structure*

The following observations can be made if a map of Bouguer anomalies* is compared with the Tectonic Map of the United States (1962):

1. A strong trend parallel to surface structures shows in the gravity anomalies.
2. The strongest positive anomalies generally lie over the Blue Ridge–Piedmont region, while negative anomalies characterize the Valley and Plateau regions. However, the negative anomalies lie over the Smoky Mountain region and extend into the Piedmont farther south.

* A Bouguer gravity map of the United States was published in 1965 by the U. S. Geol. Survey. The student should refer to it for comparison of anomalies with structure in other parts of the country.

* Refer to King (1964), Rodgers (1953), Hadley and Goldsmith (1963 a and b).

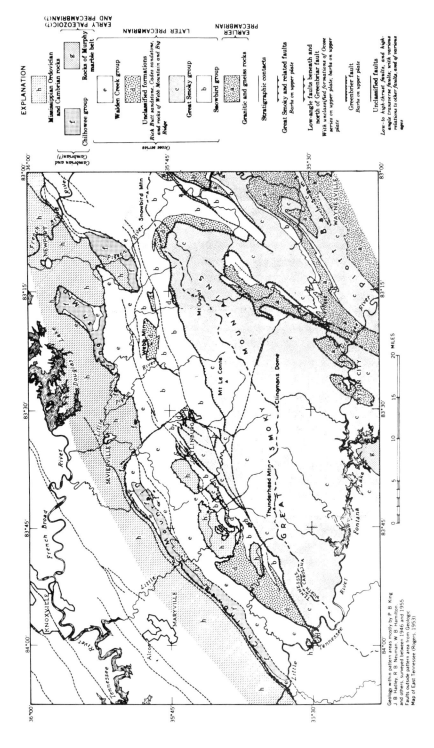

Fig. 13-3 Geologic map of the Great Smoky Mountains and vicinity showing Ocoee series and adjacent formations and the groups into which the Ocoee is divided. (*From King, 1964.*)

EXPLANATION

h — Mississippian Ordovician and Cambrian rocks

g — Rocks of Murphy marble belt

f — Chilhowee group

Cambrian and Cambrian(?)

e — Walden Creek group

d — Unclassified formations
Rich Butt sandstone, Cades sandstone, and rocks of Webb Mountain and Big Ridge

LATER PRECAMBRIAN (Ocoee series)

c — Great Smoky group

b — Snowbird group

EARLIER PRECAMBRIAN

a — Granitic and gneiss rocks

Stratigraphic contacts

Great Smoky and related faults
Barbs on upper plate

Low-angle faults beneath and north of Greenbrier fault
With unclassified formations of Ocoee series on upper plate; barbs on upper plate

Greenbrier fault
Barbs on upper plate

Unclassified faults
Low- to high-thrust faults, and high-angle transverse faults, with various relations to other faults, and of various ages

EARLY PALEOZOIC(?) AND PRECAMBRIAN(?)

Geology within pattern areas mostly by P B King
J B Hadley, R B Neuman W B Hamilton
and others, surveyed between 1946 and 1955
Faults outside pattern area from Geologic
Map of East Tennessee (Rogers, 1953)

3. The gradient between the positive and negative anomalies forms a narrow belt which runs the length of the Appalachians. The base of this belt follows the western edge of the Precambrian uplifts from central Virginia northward, but to the southwest the base crosses the Blue Ridge and extends to the Brevard zone (King, 1959).

The divergence of the base of this gradient across the Blue Ridge coincides approximately with the development of low-angle thrust faults along the northwestern edge of the Blue Ridge, and as shown on Fig. 13-2, the number of thrusts increases markedly to the south. Thus the gravity data lend support to the idea that the Precambrian basement exposed in the southern Appalachians is underlain by lower-density (probably Paleozoic) sedimentary rocks (Watkins, 1964).

Structure of the Appalachian Plateau

Northwest of the exposed belt of steeply asymmetrical folds and thrust faults lies the Appalachian Plateau, located mainly in western Pennsylvania and West Virginia. Upper Paleozoic rocks outcrop over most of this area, and their regional structure, as evidenced by surface mapping, is that of a broad asymmetrical synclinorium. The southeast limb is steepest and the axis appears to plunge southwestward as a long sweeping arc. The western edge of this structure is defined by the Cincinnati arch (Fig. 13-2), and its northern continuation, the Findlay arch. The synclinorium passes into the nearly flat-lying units of the Catskill Mountains to the north, and these are truncated by the Mohawk and Hudson River valleys. There is no structure equivalent to the plateau north of New York.

The southeast side of this region, sometimes referred to as the Appalachian Structural Front, is defined by the steep west limbs of anticlines along the Nittany anticlinorium, by the Hyndman and Wills Mountain anticlines in Penn-

sylvania, by the Wills Mountain anticline in Virginia, and then by the outcrop of the St. Clair thrust southward to the Pine Mountain thrust (Gwinn, 1964) (Fig. 13-4).

Until recent years most of our knowledge of this portion of the central Appalachians was based on surface mapping. These maps reveal a system of doubly plunging folds with trends which parallel the folds and faults of the Valley and Ridge, sweeping in a broad arc through Pennsylvania and then again in the opposite direction at the southern end of the synclinorium. The folds appear to die out toward the northwest. No prominent thrust faults are exposed in this region, and the strata are essentially horizontal, particularly in the western portion.

One of the striking peculiarities of the structural pattern is that while the relief of the anticlines decreases to the northwest, some of the anticlines are asymmetrical toward the southeast and the southeastern limbs are steeper. This appears inconsistent with the idea of northwestward tectonic transport in the Appalachians. Another unusual feature evident at the surface is the general fold pattern. Many of these major folds are 50 miles long and some are as much as 100 miles long. In some instances, they form an *en échelon* pattern, but in numerous other places the folds plunge, sometimes abruptly. Lines drawn through the points at which these plunges occur (Fig. 13-4) define northwest-trending lines which suggest transverse faults. Most of these are not faults at the surface, but small transverse faults do occur at the surface in Pennsylvania near one of the lines defined by plunge of folds and abrupt changes of structural trend.

New and unsuspected structures have been uncovered through drilling for oil and gas in the plateau region. Wells drilled through units which are only broadly arched at the surface encounter fault breccias, repeated sections, and other complications at depth, particularly at the base of the Devonian section. The few wells drilled into Ordovician units reveal that below

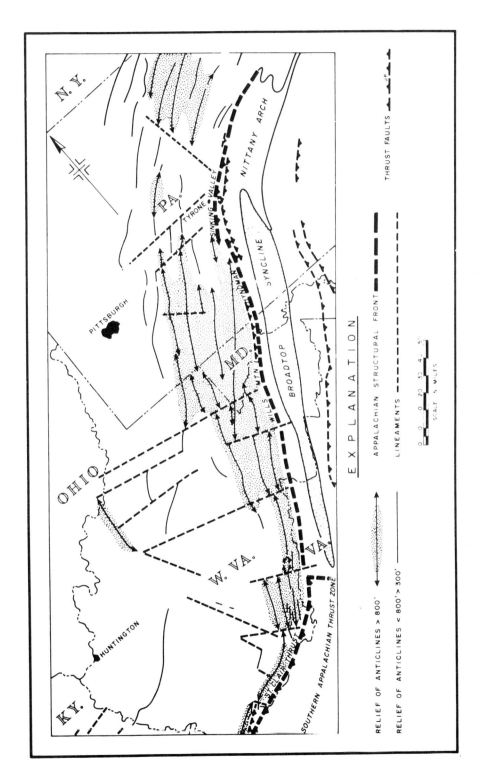

Fig. 13-4 Map of surface anticlinal axes and structural relief, lineaments, and important faults of the central Appalachian Plateau and the northwestern Valley and Ridge provinces. (*From Gwinn, 1967.*)

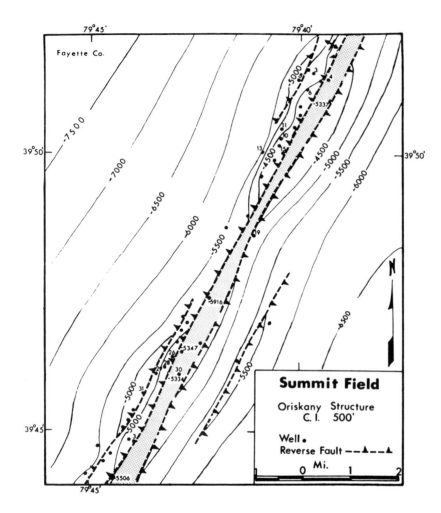

Fig. 13-5 Depressed axial zone, Oriskany sandstone level, Summit field, Chestnut ridge anticline, Fayette County, Pa. The South Summit pool is on the northwest flank of the anticline near the lower left corner, and the North Summit pool is on the upper right. (*From Gwinn, 1964.*)

the Lower Devonian limestones, structures again become simple. Dipmeter surveys indicate flat-lying units (Gwinn, 1964). From the generalized stratigraphic section of this region, it is clear that rock units with very different physical properties occur repeatedly in the sections. The complicated structures occur mainly in that part of the section which contains several thousand feet of shale. The character of the structural complication is seen in the structure contour map of the Summit field in Fig. 13-5.

Surface structure at the Summit field is a broad, open anticline, but the structure at the

level of the Lower Devonian Oriskany formation is faulted. The crestal portion of the anticline is depressed below both limbs and is bounded on both sides by faults. The faults repeat key beds, thicken the section, and offset structure contours in the way expected in reverse faulting. It is concluded that here as in numerous other fields reverse faults dipping away from the crest of the anticline flank it on both sides. On the northwest flank in this field the faulting appears to be imbricate thrusting.

The Burning Springs anticline, located near the Ohio–West Virginia border, is another structure of particular interest. Here again drilling has supplied subsurface control. The surface expression of the structure is an anticline asymmetrical toward the west, but in one of the wells drilled on the eastern flank of the fold, the Lower Devonian (Onondaga and Helderberg formations) was found repeated four times. Subsurface control indicates a zone of imbricate southeast-dipping thrusts parallel to the fold which terminates abruptly on the south side. This southern termination has been interpreted as a transverse fault. No thrusts are found west of the fold, nor do those thrusts in the fold appear to extend below the Silurian. The edge of the Salinas salt beds of Silurian age occurs just east of the Burning Springs anticline; the salt bed lies to the east. Rodgers (1964) has attributed the development of the faulting and folding in this particular place to its location at the edge of the salt beds.

Interpretation of the mechanics of the origin of the structural pattern in the plateau region revolves around what happens at depth. There is still very little published information con-

cerning the basement in the region, and thus, not too surprisingly, the arguments center around the role of basement in the deformation. Early students of the Appalachians reasoned that the stresses that uplifted and strongly deformed the basement in the Blue Ridge and the sedimentary veneer in the Valley and Ridge region could not have been transmitted far enough through relatively flat-lying Paleozoic sedimentary sequences to cause folding in the plateau. A more reasonable explanation to them was to postulate that folds seen at the surface continued downward, ultimately involving the crystalline complex. A modification of this view to explain the faults found in the subsurface is postulating that these faults are caused by faulting in the basement.

The alternative to involvement of the basement is to have the faults change into bedding faults at depth, in the manner of the Pine Mountain fault. In this case the plate of flat-lying sediments must transmit stresses sufficient to move the plate over the fault. This is not so mechanically difficult as was formerly suspected

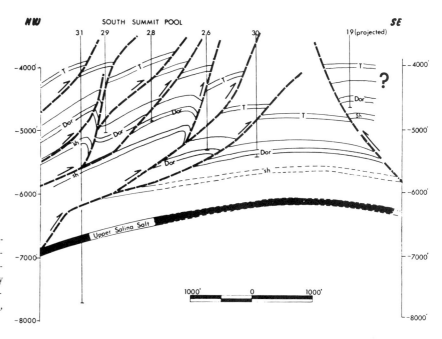

Fig. 13-6 Imbricate thrust faulting and *décollement*, South Summit pool. Dor = Oriskany sandstone, stippled; T = Tully limestone; and sh = lower Helderberg shale. (*From Gwinn, 1964.*)

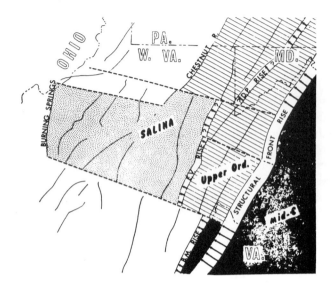

Fig. 13.7 Areas of dominance of specific sole thrust-*décollement* zones in the central Appalachians; the structural front rise marks the zone along which the sole thrusts shear upward from the Middle Cambrain glide zone (cross-hatched) to the Upper Ordovician glide zone (diagonal lines); significant translation on the Cambrian *décollement* occurs in the plateau only near Brown's Mountain (B.M.) anticline; E.V. = Elkins Valley anticline; D.P. = Deer Park anticline. The rise to the Salina *décollement* (stippled) took place beneath and produced most of the shortening in the Elkins Valley anticline and probably in the Deer Park anticline. (*From Gwinn, 1964.*)

if the possible effects of high pore pressure are considered. As we saw, the beds below the salt units near the Burning Springs anticline appear undeformed. Rodgers suggests that this salt is the bed in which the bedding fault lies in this portion of the plateau, and that the development of the anticline and upward imbrication of the fault took place near the edge of the salt because the frictional drag was greatly increased where the fault ran out of the salt. The Lower Cambrian, Upper Ordovician, and Middle Devonian shale sequences provide other sections of weak, incompetent rock units in which frictional drag would be relatively low and which, therefore, would provide probable sites for bedding-plane faults. Gwinn has outlined areas of probable dominance of specific "sole thrust—*décollement* zones in the central Appalachians" (Fig. 13-7). Along the structural front the faults rise from the Lower Cambrian units to Upper Ordovician glide zones, and then farther west to the Salina glide zone. The nature of these rises is shown in the interpreted cross section in Fig. 13-8. It would appear in this interpretation that the sole fault gradually rises in the section toward the west. This rise, plus the well-established southeasterly dip of

the major faults in the Valley and Ridge area and combined with the size of the blocks involved, poses a serious mechanical problem for those who favor the "no-basement hypothesis."

Structure of the South Mountain area, Maryland

South Mountain is situated at the northern end of the Blue Ridge. Just north of South Mountain, Triassic deposits cover the Blue Ridge–Piedmont structure, cutting them off from their northern counterparts, the Reading Prong of the New England highlands, and the metamorphic complex of southern New York state and New England. South of central Virginia, the rocks of the Blue Ridge are in fault contact with the Paleozoic sedimentary units, but in places in northern Virginia, Maryland, and Pennsylvania the transition from the metamorphic to the sedimentary provinces can be studied. One of the classic studies of this transition has been made in Maryland at South Mountain (Cloos, 1947), where structural features in Precambrian rocks can be related to those in the overlying units.

A regional sketch of the South Mountain region, shown in Fig. 13-9, reveals the prominent northeast-southwest structural trends. Rock units of successively younger age occur in belts with the oldest, Precambrian, in the southeast and the youngest, middle Paleozoic, in the northwest. Folding is evident from the geologic map in the sedimentary units. South Mountain is a large asymmetrical anticline overturned to the northwest. Its axis is nearly horizontal and there are many small folds in the sedimentary units at South Mountain as well as to the northwest. The axial traces of many of the small folds are shown in Fig. 13-9. Many of these are also horizontal, all reflect the strong northeast regional trend, and they are broadly curved to form a large salient.

Deformation in the region varied both geographically and with rock type. The modes of folding, for example, are different at South Mountain and in the valley to the northwest. A great variety of rock types, gneisses, schists, slates, sandstones, shales, and limestones, occur in this region. The Catoctin volcanics (metabasalts) and the underlying gneiss are considered Precambrian. The Harpers, Weaverton, and Loudon are unfossiliferous clastic rocks and are classed as Eocambrian.

Cleavages. Rock cleavage is a prominent feature in the Catoctin volcanics and in most of the sedimentary units; however, it is best developed in shales. Recrystallization has partially obliterated it in limestones, and sandstones frequently show no cleavage. Two distinctly different types of cleavage are observed.

Fig. 13-8 Origin of the steep southeast limbs of plateau anticlines; movement on the detachment sole thrust leads to further tightening of the older folds and initiation of new folds above branching splay thrusts; the wedge of competent rocks between the Upper Ordovician and Salina *décollements* is thrust under the northwest limb of the secondary folds, adding on that limb to displacement on the sub-Oriskany thrusts. The latter were generated primarily as a consequence of the concentric folding process, allowing movement of material up and out of the tightening syncline. The net result is relatively greater displacement on the northwest flank fault and steepening of the southeastern flank. Aw and A′w − west limbs of the figured anticlines on the left and right, respectively; AE and A′E = the east limbs; B and B′ = the wedges of pre-Devonian, post-Middle Ordovician rocks being thrust beneath the west limbs. (*From Gwinn, 1964.*)

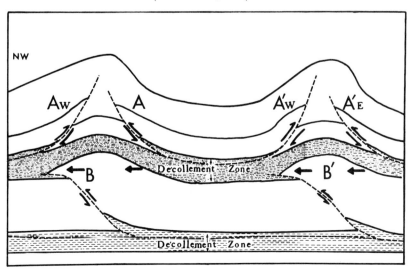

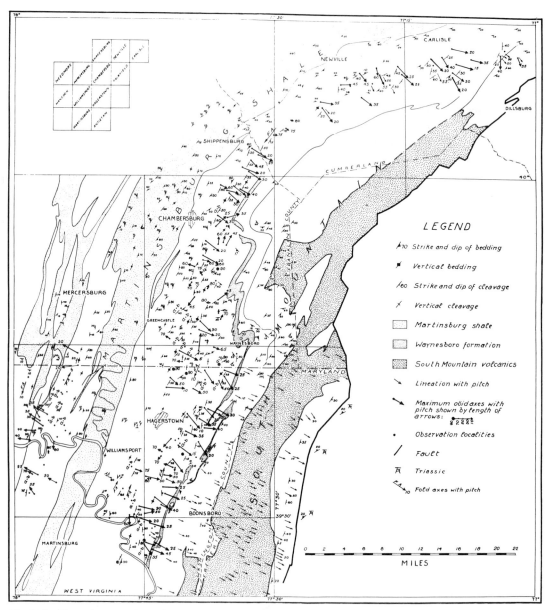

Fig. 13-9   Tectonic map of South Mountain. (*From Cloos, 1947.*)

The cleavage at South Mountain, axial plane cleavage, shows a strong preferred orientation subparallel to the axial plane of the folds. This cleavage is also characterized by the smoothness of the cleavage, its close spacing, and the strong alignment of minerals, particularly micaceous minerals, parallel to it. The second type of cleavage, fracture cleavage, occurs more frequently on folds northwest of South Mountain. Fracture cleavage is not aligned parallel to the axial plane of the folds although the cleavage is essentially parallel to the fold axis (where the axes are horizontal). This cleavage is approximately perpendicular to bedding and it forms rough, uneven surfaces. The two types of cleavage do sometimes occur in close proximity. Axial plane cleavage occurs in the hinge zones of tight folds in the Martinsburg (Ordovician) and Romney (Devonian) shales in the Valley and Ridge, and some fracture cleavage is found in sandstones and quartzites at South Mountain in the northwestern belt. Axial plane cleavage at South Mountain dips more steeply on the upper limb of the folds than on the lower limb. Thus it forms a broad fan which opens toward the west, and all units, even part of the Catoctin metabasalts, show this cleavage.

Lineations. Two lineations are found in this area. One is formed by the intersection of cleavage with bedding. At South Mountain the fold axis and the bedding-cleavage lineation are horizontal. Thus this lineation is in the *b* direction. So consistent is the bedding-cleavage relation that it can be used to determine the position of the axis of the fold if it is unknown. The second prominent lineation lies in the plane of the axial plane cleavage and perpendicular to the fold axes. It is parallel to the *a* direction and is present in a great variety of rock types:

1. In Catoctin greenstones it is composed of lenticular chlorite blebs up to 10 in. long, up to 2 in. wide, and very thin.
2. In metarhyolites the lineation is composed of elongated blebs of sericite in a purple matrix.
3. Precambrian gneisses also show strong lineations (elongated micaceous blebs) of similar orientation.
4. In the Loudon formation (Eocambrian) there are elongated pebbles, lumps, quartz, rods, and streaks.
5. In the Harpers formation the lineation appears as a very fine crenulation and streaking.
6. In limestones near South Mountain the longest axis of ooids in oolitic rocks parallels the lineation.

In almost all instances the bearing of the lineation is S 50–60° E and the plunge is 10–50° SE, but the lineation is absent west of the South Mountain area.

Deformed oolites. Oolites in modern sediments and in older undeformed rocks are almost spherical in shape. Those found in limestones near South Mountain are now deformed. The deformation may be described by measuring diameters in mutually perpendicular directions. The longest direction lies parallel to the strong lineation in the axial plane cleavage in the South Mountain area. Many of the oolites (Fig. 13-10) have centers that are composed of undeformed crystalline micropebbles and detrital carbonate grains. This supports the idea that deformation took place in fairly soft materials. There are also late, post kinematic, undeformed growths on deformed oolites. Cloos measured the percentage distortions (elongations) of the oolites and related them to the

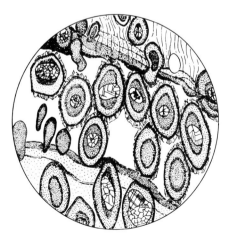

Fig. 13-10 Well-bedded oolite with odd centers and growth aprons as cleavage begins to form (top). Conococheague limestone, Landis Creek, between Hagerstown and Boonshoro. *ac* section, deformation 30 percent. *(From Cloos, 1947.)*

axial plane cleavage (the maximum elongation lies in this cleavage) and to position on the fold (elongation is greatest in the hinge zones).

Interpretations and conclusions. It was concluded in these studies that the nature and intensity of the folding vary and are transitional in nature from the South Mountain fold toward the west and that the folding took place in much softer material (less consolidated) than materials we find now. Folding in the western part of the area produced concentric folds in which fracture cleavages formed perpendicular to the bedding. The folds in the west are more open although tight folds with axial cleavage do occur in some of the thicker shale sequences such as the Martinsburg and Romney formations.

Axial plane cleavage formed in South Mountain and to the east, and this cleavage, which fans out toward the west, was of major importance in the folding. That movements perpendicular to the present fold axis occurred along these cleavages is shown by the very prominent lineation expressed as smeared crystals, elongated oolites, and mineral blebs. Cloos (1947) interprets the deformation as being due to laminar flow on subparallel planes or cleavages. A consequence of this type of folding, as also shown by the elongation of the oolites and crinoid fragments, is that thickness measurements of bedding are not the original true thicknesses. Cloos (1947) describes a technique for estimating original thickness by study of the degree of distortion of the oolites.

Stratigraphic evidence of basement involvement in Appalachian folds

To this point we have examined evidence for the existence of low-angle thrusting in the southern Appalachians and the Appalachian Plateau and the implications that this has for the depth of deformation in the miogeosyncline. Many geologists have taken this evidence to mean that the crystalline basement was essentially rigid and inactive during the deformation

and that its only involvement before the deformation consisted of slow regional subsidence during deposition of the Paleozoic sequences. Not all students of the Appalachians, however, share this point of view. On the basis of stratigraphic studies in the region of southwestern Virginia, Cooper (1964) presents evidence that the basement was involved in the folding.

The evidence of basement involvement is essentially of two types: First, the localization and restriction of certain types of sedimentary facies on synclines and anticlines. Second, variations in thickness which are related to position of the measured section on the structure; synclines have thicker sections than anticlines. Both of these lines of evidence indicate that the structures were in existence during the time of sedimentation. The persistence of these relations for different times on a given structure indicates that the folds continued to form over a very long period of time, and not as a result of *décollement* and buckling during a single period of deformation.

Evidence of thickness and facies variations related to structural position on folds are seen in a number of southwestern Virginia folds. Large open folds occur within this region. Some of the folds lie within areas bounded on all sides by thrust faults, but it is possible in a few places to trace stratigraphic horizons from one fold into folds on either side without crossing fault zones. One such fold is the Bane anticline which has the Rome formation exposed in its center. A well drilled in the Rome formation penetrated only 350 ft of Rome before entering the underlying Shady formation. Thus in one of the most probable places to encounter a bedding thrust like those presumed to characterize the Rome formation in this region, none was found. In the Ordovician exposure around the Bane anticline, red beds associated with the Blackford formation are absent, probably by erosional hiatus, but they are 100 ft thick in nearby synclines. A line of stratigraphic sections taken across the Bane anticline into the synclines on either side has been measured

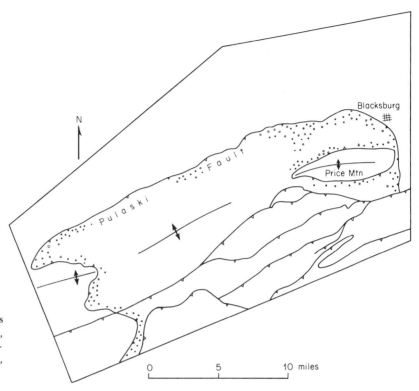

N

Blacksburg

Price Mtn

P u l a s k i   F a u l t

0   5   10 miles

Fig. 13-11 Thrust-fault traces southwest of Blacksburg, Va., showing Price Mountain window. (*Simplified after Cooper, 1963.*)

for the interval from the Blackford to the Moccasin formation. The thickness of the interval in the Sugar Run syncline is 1,375 ft, but the same interval on the Bane anticline is only 570 ft thick. It is of intermediate thickness to the southeast. Thus it is argued that this anticline was present during Ordovician and possibly during Cambrian time.

The Blacksburg-Pulaski synclinorium (Fig. 13-11) is a large synclinorium overridden by the low-dipping Pulaski thrust sheet. Price Mountain is an anticlinal window in the thrust sheet. Beds on the northwestern limb of the synclinorium are well exposed along the New River. Although the southeastern limb of the synclinorium occurs in a more structurally complicated area, the thickness of a portion of the section can be measured in the Barringer window. When a well was later drilled at Price Mountain, that portion of the section which is 2,750 ft at Barringer window is nearly 9,300 ft

thick in the center of the synclinorium, and 4,800 ft along New River (Fig. 13-12). For every unit measured from Ordovician through Devonian, greater thicknesses occur along the axis of the synclinorium. Thus Cooper argues that folding started early in the Paleozoic and continued after the thrusting of the Pulaski sheet which covers Mississippian units in places. According to Cooper's estimates, the folding of the Pulaski fault has been sufficient to create 3,500 ft of closure in the folded surface.

Mention should also be made of the facies associated with the thickness variations on these folds. Not only are the synclinal axes characterized by greater thicknesses, but also they contain ". . . local segregations of special facies including black shales (which suggest stagnant water conditions), green shales, polymictic conglomerates, and poorly sorted coarse clastics . . Anticlinal crests commonly exhibit naturally thinner sections characterized by

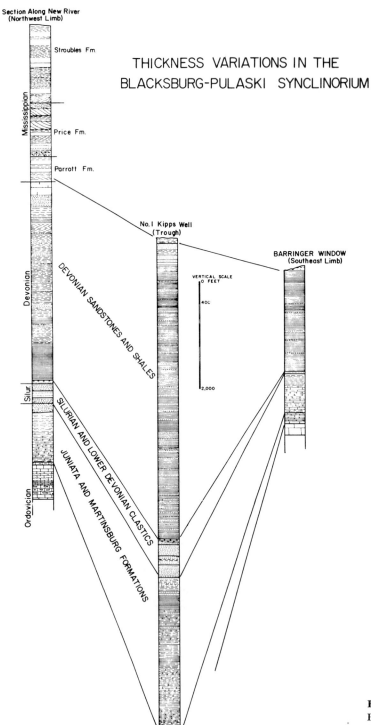

Fig. 13-12 Thickness variations in the Blacksburg-Pulaski synclinorium. (*From Cooper, 1964.*)

prevalence of biostromes and bioherms, abundant desiccation jointing, and thinner well washed and more oxidized sediments." (Cooper, 1964.)

Northern end of the southern Appalachians

The Appalachian Plateau continues northward from West Virginia through Pennsylvania and into New York, but the strongly folded and thrust-faulted belt largely dies out in north-central Pennsylvania and is replaced by broad warps in Devonian units of the northern end of the plateau. However, before this fold belt disappears it exhibits a beautifully intricate pattern of plunging folds involving all the Paleozoic units from Cambrian to Pennsylvanian age (refer to the Geologic Map of Pennsylvania, 1960). There are local faults related to some of the folds, but the repeated thrust slices so typical of the southern Appalachians are absent.

The pattern of structural complexity is greatly increased and the structural relations of the older rocks are partially obscured by extensive areas of Triassic deposits laid down in subsiding fault troughs east of the eastern edge of the Great Valley of Pennsylvania, defined by the broad belt of Ordovician Martinsburg shale exposure. This eastern area may be divided into several parts (refer to the state geological map of Penn. 1960):

1. The extension of the Reading Prong of the New Jersey highland into Pennsylvania, largely an exposure of Precambrian gneisses.
2. The folded and thrust-faulted eastern margin of the Great Valley, an area of known Paleozoic units.
3. The Triassic basins and related high-angle faults.
4. The northern Piedmont area largely underlain by the Wissahickon formation. We will return to a discussion of the problems of interpreting this unit and its relation to the Paleozoic sequences west of it in the discussion of the Piedmont.

A number of important questions arise in the study of this area where there are distinct breaks between the northern and southern Appalachians.

1. Why does the character of the Appalachian Mountain system change?
2. Why does the broad belt of folds die out?
3. Why does the fold system change trend from northeast to east-northeast?
4. Why should the Triassic basins lie across the regional structural trend here, while those to the south and north parallel the trend and lie in the crystalline complexes?
5. Why is the fold belt broken into thrust slices to the south but not in Pennsylvania, Maryland, and northern Virginia?
6. How do we explain the abrupt change from metamorphic to sedimentary rock provinces in the northern Piedmont?

Unfortunately, definitive answers to these questions have not been made, but some plausible suggestions have been offered for consideration. Several of these questions may be resolved in terms of large-scale wrench faulting along an east-west fault located at latitude 40° N. This thesis has been suggested by Drake and Woodward (1963), and evidence for it is found not only in the peculiarities of the continental structures, but in the geology of the Atlantic continental shelf as well. This fault (Fig. 13-13) would thus be located along a line defined by the volcanic peaks of the Kelvin Seamount group, an offset in the submarine topography of the continental shelf, a strong transverse magnetic anomaly, and a pronounced change in the pattern of basement contours off the continental margin. On land the fault would lie along the southern termination of the Reading prong, along the edge of one of the Triassic basins, under the arcuate fold belt of the Pennsylvania Valley and Ridge, and along an offset in isopachs for pre-Mississippian units in the folded belt (Fig. 13-14). It may be that this is but one of a series of transverse fault zones in

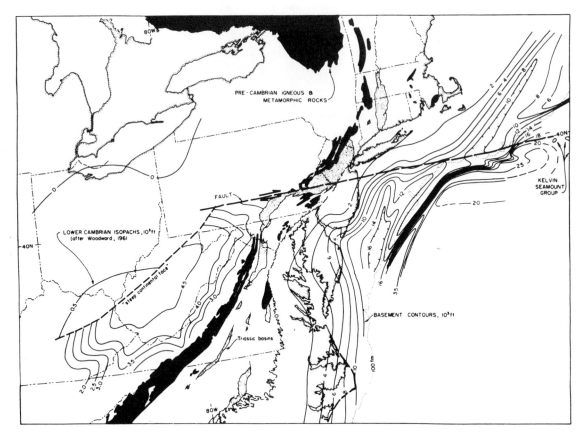

Fig. 13-13 Basement contours on the continental margin of the northeastern United States from seismic refraction measurements. Lower Cambrian isopachs from borehole data after Woodward, 1963. (*From Drake and Woodward, 1963.*)

the Precambrian basement rocks of the Appalachians.

At the present time the idea of a major basement fault seems to offer the best explanation for many of the unusual features of the northern end of the southern Appalachians; however, we must bear in mind several other important factors that would be determinants of variations of structural patterns in a long, folded mountain belt.

1. The original shape of the geosyncline and differences in sediment thickness could be reflected in variation in deformational pattern.

2. Orogenic episodes affected different parts of the geosyncline at different times.

3. Possible variations in magnitude and direction of the forces responsible for deformation.

4. Variations in thermal activity during orogeny.

The northern miogeosyncline

The belt of strongly deformed Paleozoic sedimentary rocks continues from eastern Pennsylvania as a narrow strip into southeastern New York and then northward along the Hudson and Champlain valleys. From Pennsylvania to Albany the belt is bordered on the west by the

little-deformed Devonian deposits of the Catskill delta. Then across the Mohawk valley the
Precambrian crystalline rocks of the Adirondack dome lie on the western edge. The eastern
edge is poorly defined. Along the eastern edge
there are numerous eastward-dipping thrust
faults and klippes bringing metamorphosed
Cambrian units into fault contact with unmetamorphosed sedimentary units. The New York
and Vermont state geologic maps provide the
best regional picture of the complex zone between the New England crystalline complex
and the miogeosynclinal deposits to the west.

The Hudson and Champlain valleys contain
deformed Cambrian and Ordovician units
which are thrown into systems of strongly
asymmetric and overturned folds broken by
eastward-dipping thrust faults. A number of

large klippes of Cambrian and Ordovician units
lie within and on this fold belt and more faults
and metamorphic units lie to the east, but the
Devonian units west of the belt are relatively
undeformed. Folds and small faults are seen
in Lower Devonian units south of Catskill,
N.Y., but above this lies the thick clastic section of the Catskill delta, the famous deposits
laid on the western flank of the mountains
raised in the Devonian Acadian orogeny. The
fact that the Catskill beds themselves are not
deformed raises the strong probability that the
deformation of late Paleozoic age which folded
Pennsylvanian units to the south was not active
in eastern New York. There is little help to be
found in dating many events along the miogeosyncline in New England because post-
Devonian sedimentary rocks are not present

Fig. 13-14 Cumulative isopachs for the pre-Mississippian formations. Although these
are highly generalized, they show a distinct offset of the basinal sag of thickest deposition along the Cornwall-Kelvin displacement. (*From Drake and Woodward. 1963.*)

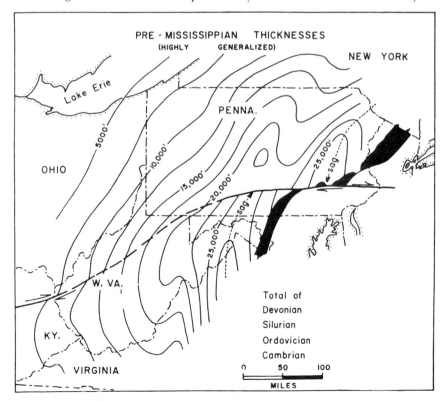

and in most faults and folds it is Cambrian and Ordovician units that are involved.

Evidence for the Late Ordovician Taconian orogeny is found in the clastic sequences of the Queenstown delta of Pennsylvania; in the Green Pond conglomerate located in northern New Jersey, where this Silurian conglomerate lies unconformably on Precambrian crystalline rocks; and in the regional unconformity between Upper Ordovician and Middle Silurian deposits. Thrusting of the massive Taconic thrust sheets into their present position is also usually attributed to Late Ordovician orogeny; however, it is not easy to prove this age more precisely than to say it is late or post-Ordovician, since no younger rocks are involved.

Structures in the miogeosynclinal belt of New England share some similarities with those farther south in that folding and thrust faulting with movements toward the continental interior are prominent. The two regions, however, also have substantial differences. First, there is no recognized equivalent of the upper Precambrian (Ocoee to Chilhowee) clastic sequence, amounting to thousands of feet of section; second, there is no well-defined Precambrian mass which clearly separates the crystalline complex from the sedimentary belt as does the Blue Ridge, and finally a number of major nappes have been recognized in New England metamorphic rocks. The two regions differ in at least one other significant feature. The Adirondack dome has persisted since Precambrian time as a positive area on the edge of the geosyncline and it almost certainly acted as a buttress to deformation in the geosyncline east of it. There is no comparable feature farther south. The Adirondacks are broken by a complex system of major fracture and fault zones, and it is evident that movements did occur along these faults after Ordovician time, but there is no evidence that the dome was ever covered by a sheet of folded and faulted Paleozoic rocks.

East of the miogeosyncline in New England lies a complex terrane of Precambrian crystalline domes, Paleozoic metamorphics, igneous intrusions, and younger sedimentary basins. Low-angle thrust faults, often with imbricate patterns along the western edge of the thrust sheets and asymmetrical recumbent, and even inverted folds, prevail within the miogeosyncline. The Taconic Range, possibly a huge klippe, is situated within this fold belt. Immediately to the east of this belt there are a number of domes and doubly plunging anticlines in which Precambrian crystalline rocks are exposed. These domes, which include the Green Mountain anticline, appear to be northern continuations of the New Jersey highlands. The Triassic basin of the Connecticut River valley is located east of these domes within the metamorphic and igneous complex of New England.

Taconic Mountains—the nature of the problem

The Taconic Mountains pose one of the most interesting and significant problems in understanding the structure of the northern Appalachian geosyncline. The structural feature known as the Taconic klippe is illustrated in Fig. 13-2. As it appears on the 1961 Tectonic Map of the United States, it is a klippe, bounded on all sides by a thrust fault. It is over 150 miles long and on the order of 10 miles wide. The region occupied by the klippe and the structures which are associated with it have long been matters of interest to geologists.

The tectonic map is a simplification of actual fold relations, as is obvious even from the state geologic maps of this region. In place of a single, well-defined major fault, the state maps show numerous faults with intricate fault patterns, and a number of these either die out on a given map or fail to cross state boundaries. From this we may surmise that the criteria for recognition of some of these faults may be questionable.

The answer, at least in part, to the problems involving the Taconic klippe is related to the scarcity of outcrops (about half the region is covered by glacial deposits) and to the rock units involved, slates, shales, and phyllites, some of which are easily confused with one another. The problem is therefore in part a stratigraphic problem.

Bucher (1957, p. 658) summarized the history of the origin of the klippe hypothesis as follows:

> As drawn on the Tectonic Map of the United States (King et al., 1944), the outline of the "klippe" separates two terranes of contrasting lithologies. Outside of it, the Cambrian and pre-Trentonian Ordovician rocks are largely dolomites and limestones. Inside, the same large time interval is represented by quartzites, sandstones, shales, and radiolarian cherts. Interbedded carbonate layers are present only locally and in negligible amounts. The so-called autochthonous carbonate sequence contains practically no argillaceous material up to the end of Chazyan time and so is light-colored. Only the Black River limestones are dark-colored and contain shale partings. The alleged allochthonous terrane, on the other hand, is largely somber-colored, with tints ranging from greenish gray and gray to black with green and red beds in some horizons.
>
> The contrast between these two terranes is so great, the formational units in each maintain their characteristics over such distances, they lie so close together, and transitional beds are so few, that they could not well have been deposited side by side where they now lie.
>
> This led Ulrich to the hypothesis that these and similar belts to the east and north were "deposits in originally distinct troughs that have since been thrust westward over each other" (Ulrich, 1911, p. 443).

Bucher (1957, p. 659) goes on to point out the main flaws in the application of the hypothesis at the south end of the Taconic klippe:

> For 52 miles along the entire master fault which is supposed to mark the western border of the "klippe" on the quadrangles concerned, the Snake Hill shale is shown lying side by side with the Canajoharie shale of the same age, or with the slightly younger Schenectady beds, after an assumed transport of tens of miles. It is unbeliev-

able (1) that the whole western border of the "Allochthonous" sequence could consist exclusively of the youngest formation and (2) that this border should lie in contact only with beds of the same or slightly younger age.

The problem then is to explain the structural and stratigraphic relations of these two strongly contrasting types of Cambrian and Ordovician sedimentary units. The thrust-fault hypothesis which was first proposed by Ulrich is still favored by most students of the region. An alternative suggestion that the two facies were originally deposited in a single trough was rejected by most stratigraphers because the lithologic characteristics of the rock units involved remain so constant for long distances in the region. A second alternative, suggested by Bucher, Craddock, and Weaver (1957), is that in place of a major fault we are dealing with an unconformity of Trenton age and that the strongly dissimilar facies now so close together are due to erosional unconformity later deformed by folding and faulting. It should be pointed out to those unfamiliar with the region that there are asymmetrical, even recumbent folds and thrust in the region of the Taconic klippe. The question is whether these structures were superimposed on rock units in place or whether they involved large-scale transport of a huge thrust mass as well.

The northern end of the Taconic Mountains affords a particularly good location for study of the Taconic klippe. However, the stratigraphic problem remains the same as that farther south. Zen (1961) has summarized the merits, defects, and events in each of three possible hypotheses which might be called on to explain the structure of the northern end of the Taconic Mountains. The three hypotheses discussed are:

1. That there is no klippe; that the deformed slate and phyllite units which now lie within the belt of more typical miogeosynclinal origin are there by virtue of the unconformity as previously discussed. In this case the structure of the northern end of

the Taconic Mountains must be interpreted as consisting of large folds (described by Zen as mushroom folds) which are locally recumbent. There would also be thrusts but with much less movement than suggested in the other hypothesis. This hypothesis has the merit of avoiding large-scale tectonic transport of this mountain mass and the problem of determining its root zone. It has the defects of requiring some eastward movement which is not observable, and it requires rapid facies changes during the deposition of Cambrian and Ordovician units.

2. The second hypothesis is that the structure is that of a klippe composed of a number of thrust slices. In this case the thrust sheets are relatively shallow and were transported from the east, possibly from over the area presently forming the Precambrian exposures in the Green Mountains of central Vermont. This hypothesis is useful in explaining some of the structural peculiarities of the region. The fault traces of the faults indicated on maps such as the Vermont state geologic map indicate low-dipping faults, and this hypothesis makes some of the exposures of miogeosynclinal units within the area of slate and phyllite easily explained as windows.

3. The third hypothesis is that the Taconic area is a klippe but one representing a recumbent fold complex rather than a series of thrust slices. This theory, based in part on stratigraphic relations worked out by Zen and others, is supported by the presence of inverted stratigraphic sections within the allochthonous (out-of-place) mass where its western edge is in contact with the typical miogeosynclinal units. This theory has the advantages of explaining the westerly dip on the east flank of the Taconic Range and some of the east-west-trending structures within the central part of the area.

Each of these hypotheses has defects and merits. The details of the structural and stratigraphic arguments needed to present each case in an unbiased manner would require more space than can be devoted to them here; however, the nature of the problem should be clear. The interpretation of this feature is highly significant in that the character of the deformation here is likely to influence one's concept of the nature of orogeny in the Appalachian geosyncline.

Zen (1967, p. 1) provides a comprehensive summary and synthesis of the work done on the Taconic region and offers a new hypothesis to explain the relationships now documented:

The geologic history of the area is reconstructed as follows: The pre-Normanskill Taconic rocks were deposited in the area of the present Precambrian massifs of the Green Mountains–Berkshire Highlands belt between the clastic, eugeosynclinal east Vermont sequence to the east and the miogeosynclinal synclinorium sequence to the west; they constitute the transitional facies between these two belts. Conditions were relatively stable until early Middle Ordovician time, when the Green Mountain–Berkshire Highlands area began to rise and the area of the present Middlebury synclinorium began to subside. Subsidence took place largely by a series of high-angle longitudinal faults that, as a whole, step down to the west. Argillaceous sediments (the Normanskill Shale) began to inundate the former miogeosynclinal area; because the conditions of sedimentation had become similar, the sediments resembled, in facies, the synchronous Taconic rocks that were being deposited to the east.

Continued rise of the Green Mountain–Berkshire Highlands area led in middle Trenton time to the décollement of the Cambrian and Ordovician sediments into the area of the present Middlebury synclinorium in a series of giant submarine slides. Sedimentation continued at the receiving site throughout the event; sedimentation may also have persisted on the moving slides. The record is found today in the turbidite-laden shale and graywacke in the upper part of the Normanskill Shale of both the allochthon and the autochthon.

Appalachian crystalline complexes

Answers to many of the most intriguing questions related to Appalachian geology must be sought in the crystalline complexes of the Piedmont and New England.

1. Was the deepest part of the geosyncline located in the area of the present crystalline complexes, or was this some type of borderland during the Paleozoic?
2. Were these regions once the highest portions of one or more mountain systems— possibly with peaks comparable to those of modern mountain belts?
3. Was this ever a symmetrical, folded mountain system with a fold and fault belt similar to the Valley and Ridge province on its eastern side?
4. Did the folds and faults in the miogeosyncline develop as a result of gravity sliding off a much higher central mountain uplift in the crystalline complexes?
5. How deeply buried were the rocks now exposed in the crystalline complexes? Is it possible they were once covered by a folded and faulted sedimentary veneer?
6. From what depth has the Precambrian been uplifted and how much horizontal displacement has there been of this uplifted block?
7. Are the metasedimentary rocks direct age equivalents to the Paleozoic rocks in the miogeosyncline? If so, which units are equivalent?
8. Did the igneous activity in the crystalline complex coincide with or precede the deposition of the thick wedges of clastic sedimentary rocks in the miogeosyncline, or are the two unrelated?
9. What is the history of the rocks within the crystalline complex and how is it related to the history of the miogeosyncline?
10. What relation do the small ultramafic intrusions bear to the geosyncline spatially and temporally?

One is certainly tempted to wonder why, in view of the important questions involved, geologists have not found answers by studying the crystalline complexes. The main problems faced are those of age determination and correlation. Correlation by conventional geologic mapping is hampered by the extent of cover and deep weathering in parts of the Piedmont, and radiogenic dating methods reveal a complex thermal history in which early dates are obscured by later thermal events. Thus, despite the efforts of several generations of geologists, any attempt to synthesize Piedmont structure and history at this time would be premature. We can, however, gain some insight into the questions by examining selected parts of the region.

The answers to most of the questions listed above are still being sought. Though not all the answers can now be given, the questions point up the significance of the problems involved.

The two most obvious and striking facts about these areas are:

1. That most of the sedimentary rocks inside these regions are metamorphosed
2. That almost all the Paleozoic igneous activity in the Appalachians appears confined to these provinces (Fig. 13-2)

While it might appear that these two facts are obvious almost by definition, it is nevertheless significant that this crystalline complex is clearly and almost completely separated from the miogeosynclinal deposits. There appears to be complete separation of the two in the Piedmont Valley and Ridge areas of the south; however, Carboniferous sediments do occur in several basins, in Boston, in Narragansett, and in two long synclines extending southwest of Portsmouth within the New England crystalline complex, and the twofold division is not present in Canada.

The answer to the question of why the miogeosynclinal and the present crystalline complexes have experienced such great differences in thermal history is not easy to answer. Certainly some of the metamorphism of sedimentary rocks here is due to the igneous activity, but it is also thought that this eastern belt occupied a position in the more deeply subsiding portion of the geosyncline (the eugeosyncline of Kay, 1951, and others), and that metamorphism here is also due to heating related to the great depth of burial of these units.

Thermal history of the crystalline complexes

The events dated by radiometric dating with uranium-lead, potassium-argon, and rubidium-strontium are usually of two types: date of initial crystallization of igneous intrusions or dates of the most recent heating of the rocks during which recrystallization took place. It is implicit in this that the date obtained from a rock is not necessarily the true age of the rock, but it should be the age of a thermal event in the history of the rock, and it should also provide at least a minimum age for the rock.

Hadley (1964) has compiled a large sample of mineral age determinations from the Appalachian region (the crystalline complexes) (Fig. 13-15) and has discussed the relation of these to sedimentary thicknesses in the miogeosyncline. It is clear that the thermal history in different parts of the Appalachians has not been identical; however, one peak in the Late Devonian does occur in all parts of the Appalachians. This coincides with the Acadian orogeny. It is ironic that a Late Ordovician thermal event is clearly indicated in the central and southern Appalachians but not in the northern area of the geosyncline (which has been the classic region for study of the Late Ordovician Taconic orogeny), while structural features identified with and dated as being Late Ordovician are found in the northern but not in the southern Appalachians. This may be readily explained, however, in terms of the later thermal events in the north which recrystallized and thus eliminated evidence of the Ordovician dates. In the south the Upper Ordovician is represented by

shales and sandstones of the Martinsburg formation which are often severely deformed. These are overlain by massive quartzites which form large concentric folds. Thus the great differences in deformation of the Martinsburg and the overlying Tuscarora could reflect unconformable relations or simply great differences in competence of the two units. It is entirely possible that Late Ordovician structures might go undetected in a region which has been subjected to one and possibly two later major deformations.

The extent of intrusions in the crystalline complexes is illustrated in Fig. 13-2, and the ages of the emplacement of these bodies are indicated. These bodies and particularly the heat associated with them have been important factors in the character of the deformation of the surrounding metasedimentary units; however, a precise evaluation of the effects and timing of the deformation is not now available.

Structural features of the southern Piedmont

The principal divisions of the Piedmont as compiled by King (1951) include (Fig. 13-2):

1. Triassic basin deposits (Deep River, Danville, Richmond, etc.) which were laid in fault troughs after the late Paleozoic Appalachian orogeny and which are accompanied by intrusion of basaltic dikes and sills.
2. Low-grade metamorphic rocks, largely known as the *Carolina slate belt,* situated along the eastern edge of the Piedmont.
3. Metamorphic rocks the age of which seems uncertain. They are interpreted as being primarily Paleozoic on this map, but these units are correlated with the Glenarm series of the northern Piedmont which is most recently interpreted as Precambrian.
4. Paleozoic felsic intrusions and granitic gneisses, undifferentiated. These are middle Paleozoic or older in the Piedmont.
5. Paleozoic mafic intrusions.

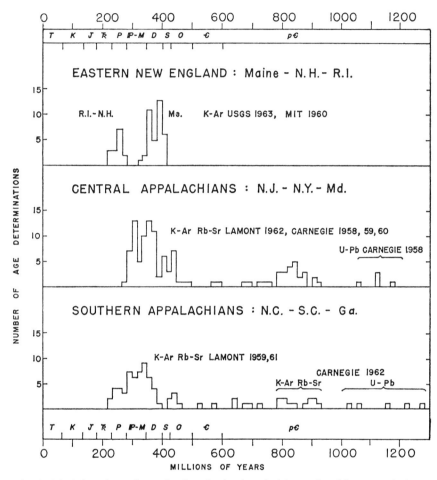

Fig. 13-15 Mineral age determinations in the Appalachian region (histograms in intervals of 17 million years based on data from published sources, 1958 to 1963; geologic time scale from Kulp, 1961). Sources of data: U.S. Geol. Survey—Faul and others, 1963; M.I.T.—Hurley and others, 1960; Lamont—Long and others, 1959; Long and Kulp, 1962; Long, 1962; Kulp and Eckelmann, 1961; Carnegie—Tilton and others, 1958, 1959, 1960; Davis and others, 1962. (*From Hadley, 1964.*)

6. Precambrian metamorphic and metasedimentary rocks primarily located in the Blue Ridge–Smoky Mountain region on the northwestern side of the Piedmont.
7. A number of small ultramafic bodies, peridotite, dunite, and serpentine, most of which are thought to be Paleozoic in age.

The interpretation of Overstreet and Bell (in Dietrich, 1964) of a section across the Piedmont in South Carolina will serve to illustrate the general character of the southern Piedmont. The Piedmont is divided longitudinally into two divisions, an inner and an outer zone. The two are separated by the Brevard fault zone. The rocks of the inner Piedmont are highly metamorphosed sedimentary and volcanic rocks, now altered to staurolite-kyanite and sillimanite-almandine subfacies. Granite masses within this zone are typically layered, folded, and concordant. Three major stratigraphic sequences, the Carolina slate belt, the Charlotte belt, and the Kings Mountain belt, are located between the inner Piedmont and the Coastal Plain. Unconformities have been found separating these three, and presumably another unconformity, not exposed, separates the Kings Mountain belt from a Precambrian basement. Deposition of each of these three sequences is thought to have been followed by folding, regional metamorphism, and igneous activity. The Brevard zone is most often recognized as a zone of mylonite in which even the youngest of the granitic intrusions are crushed, although Triassic dikes cross the zone unbroken. The linearity of the Brevard, the presence of horizontal cataclastic lineations within it, and the contrast of rock types across it suggest that the zone is one of strike-slip movement (Reed and Bryant, 1964). If the lateral offset of bodies of a gneiss (the Henderson gneiss) across the zone is used as a basis for determining movement, then a right-lateral displacement of at least 135 miles has taken place. The extension of the Brevard into Virginia is uncertain, but it is a recognized zone from Virginia to the southwest.

The Kings Mountain belt is a very narrow zone of metamorphosed sediments and volcanics, now greenschist and amphibolite facies. Granites in this and the Charlotte belt (gneisses, migmatite, and mafic rocks of amphibolite facies) cut across the metamorphic rock unlike the concordant bodies of the inner Piedmont. The lowest grade of metamorphism, greenschist, is found in the Carolina slate belt. Each of these belts contains some mafic igneous rocks, both in the form of volcanic ash and lava flows formed during sedimentation as mafic dikes, and in the form of kidney-shaped or circular pipes. These are of at least two ages—the oldest dikes (probably feeder systems for volcanics) are in the Kings Mountain, Charlotte, inner Piedmont and Blue Ridge belts. These older bodies are strongly foliated on their margins, show boudinage, are folded, metamorphosed, and locally intruded by granites. The younger

bodies are coarse-grained and massive and occur in the Charlotte and Carolina slate belts.

The ages of these three belts in the outer Piedmont have been interpreted as follows:

Carolina slate belt: This cycle of sedimentation, metamorphism, and intrusion culminated with intrusions of granite 260 million years ago at the close of the Appalachian orogeny.

Charlotte belt: These rocks were involved in a major thermal event 450 million years ago in Ordovician time.

Kings Mountain belt: This belt is tentatively assigned late Precambrian or Cambrian age on the basis of a thermal event about 560 million years ago.

The northern Piedmont

The northern Piedmont is of critical importance because the Blue Ridge which terminates in South Mountain, Md., does not separate the Cambrian and Ordovician units of the miogeosyncline from the metamorphic rocks in the Piedmont here (Fig. 13-16). Unfortunately, the stratigraphic relationships between the Piedmont and the Paleozoic sedimentary rocks to the west are so complicated even here that the relative ages have long been in dispute. The contact between the two terrains has been termed the *Martic line*—a fault of undetermined sense and amount of displacement. Some geologists have interpreted the metamorphic rocks of the Piedmont as age equivalents of the Paleozoic miogeosynclinal rocks; others believe the metasedimentary units of the Piedmont in this area are of Precambrian age. The age of these metasediments is important because if they are, in fact, Paleozoic, then the structures seen in them must be Paleozoic and related to orogenic features to the west, but if they are Precambrian, then the relationships between the Piedmont and the miogeosynclinal structures may be even more complicated than anticipated, and many of the structures in the metasediments may in this case have predated the miogeosyncline itself. Another aspect of the

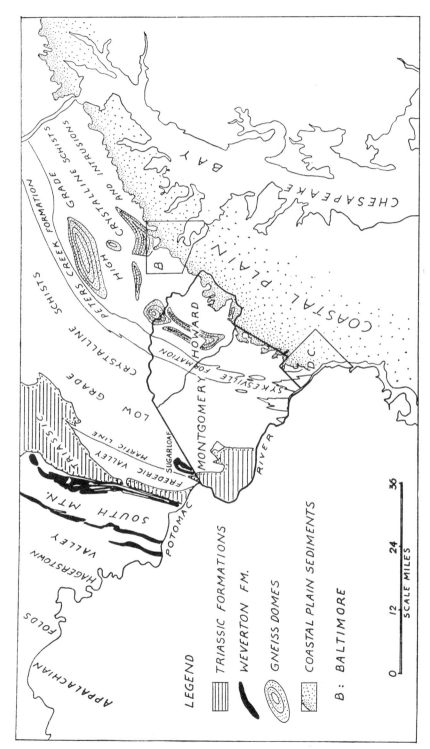

Fig. 13-16 Location of Howard and Montgomery Counties. (*From Cloos and Hopson, 1964.*)

age of these units and their structure bears on the nature of the continental border and the existence or nonexistence of borderlands.

There is no question about the sequence in the Paleozoic stratigraphic succession, but in the Piedmont a succession of metasedimentary rocks known as the Glenarm series is found lying unconformably on the Precambrian Baltimore gneiss, and this succession, although it varies from place to place, consists essentially of the following units:

Glenarm
- Wissahickon formation (Schist mainly, on the order of 20,000 ft. thick)
- Cockeysville marble
- Setters quartzite
- Nonconformity
- Baltimore gneiss

If the Glenarm is Paleozoic in age, the Setters might be equivalent to the Lower Cambrian clastics, the Cockeysville to the Cambrian and Ordovician limestone sequences, and the Wissahickon to the Martinsburg shales. Although the thicknesses vary, the metamorphic units are generally the types of rocks which might be expected as metamorphic equivalents of the miogeosynclinal sequences, and they are in a similar stratigraphic succession.

Hopson (1964) points out evidence which seems to clearly indicate that this interpretation of the Glenarm is in error. Near Baltimore the minimum age of the Glenarm appears fixed by radiometric dates from granitic intrusions which cut into it and are between 570 and 490 million years old. This date would rule out any equivalency between the Martinsburg and the Wissahickon. The maximum possible age of the Glenarm is limited by the age of the Baltimore gneiss (about 1 billion years). Hopson (1964, p. 129) has proposed stratigraphic sequence and facies relations for the Piedmont of Maryland (Fig. 13-17) and summarized the history of the region as follows:

The crystalline basement (Baltimore Gneiss) was eroded to a surface of low relief when Glenarm sedimentation began. Subsidence and flooding were followed by deposition of quartz sand and potassic silt and mud (Setters Formation). Carbonate sediments, largely dolomite, came next (Cockeysville Marble). Together they formed a blanket approximately 1500 feet thick. These sediments reflect deposition under fairly stable tectonic conditions.

The overlying Wissahickon Formation records the development of a deep submarine trough, in which shale, greywacke, and chaotic slide deposits accumulated to a thickness of more than 20,000 feet. The lowest part of the formation was mainly shale, perhaps deposited as the trough gradually deepened. (Thin siliceous beds that may have been chert appear higher in the shale and might indicate periods of starved sedimentation.) Above the lower 1000–2000 feet of the formation thin silty and sandy beds become common and alternate rhythmically with the shale. This characterized the rest of the Wissahickon section, although the proportion of shaly to sandy beds varies widely, and thick intervals of pure shale recur. Slump structures, sandstone dikes, disrupted bedding, and chaotic zones formed by sliding of soft sediments are widespread and may indicate tectonic activity during deposition. These movements culminated in submarine sliding on an enormous scale: the Sykesville and Laurel Formations, perhaps up to 15,000 feet thick, are a wedge of chaotic slide material within the Wissahickon. Evidently great masses of unconsolidated sediment slid from a rising submarine ridge or scarp into a deep, rapidly subsiding trough, forming a thick apron of chaotic debris. This material grades westward into Wissahickon turbidites.

Metasediments in the western part of Montgomery County appear to lie conformably above the Wissahickon and to represent a gradual upward and westward change from deep marine to paralic sedimentation. The Ijamsville Phyllite was chiefly shale, but it contains sandy interbeds that lack the features of turbidites. Among these are quartz sandstones with cross-bedding. The formation is poorly exposed, however, and some argillaceous parts of it may represent the distal end of the Wissahickon, brought up in the crests of anticlines. The Harpers Phyllite is a higher much sandier formation, with cross-bedding, ripple marks, channeling, discontinuous and lensoid bedding, and other features of paralic deposits. The metasandstones are still partly greywacke, but subgreywacke and protoquartzite are also important. Some of the sands and silts are calcareous, and thin lenses of limestone appear locally. Thick beds of massive and cross-bedded orthoquartzite interfinger with the less mature sands and silts and were probably derived from a different source.

Volcanic activity accompanied sedimentation in the western Piedmont. Metabasalts in Frederick and southwestern Carroll Counties are evidently an eastward extension of the Catoctin metabasalt, which is much thicker farther west along the South Mountain (Blue Ridge) uplift. The Ijamsville Phyllite partly interfingers with the metabasalt and more siliceous metavolcanic rocks in Frederick and Carroll Counties and are partly tuffaceous in that area (Stose and Stose, 1946).

Nevertheless, volcanic rocks and tuffaceous sediments form but a small proportion of the strata that fill the Piedmont trough. The Catoctin volcanics, erupted partly from dike swarms along the Blue Ridge (Reed, 1955), encroached upon and interfingered with the western Piedmont sediments, but only after the trough was nearly filled. The filling was chiefly by nonvolcanic sand, silt, and mud. Greenschist and amphibolite derived from mafic aquagene tuffs occur locally in the Wissahickon but comprise only a very small part of the section. Numerous large mafic and ultramafic ophiolitic intrusions are present, however, and the mafic tuffs may be a submarine extrusive phase of the same magma.

[Several geosynclinal sedimentary cycles have been defined in the miogeosyncline.] The Maryland Piedmont reveals another, still earlier cycle. Setters and Cockeysville Formations represent the orthoquartzite-carbonate facies, Wissahickon–Sykesville the Flysch-Wildflych facies, and the current-bedded metasandstone-phyllite formations in the western Piedmont the Molasse facies. The basal part of the Wissahickon, derived chiefly from shale and thin siliceous (chert?) beds, may correspond to the black-shale facies, although there is no proof of euxinic conditions.

An important problem is the source of the clastic detritus that filled the Piedmont trough. Much of it appears to have come from the east. The Sykesville Formation provides one line of evidence. The Sykesville is an immense wedge of submarine slide material that must have slid from a steeply rising ridge or scarp. There is little possibility that this ancient ridge lay west of the Sykesville because of the stratigraphic relations, but it could have been to the east, beneath the present Coastal Plain. Along the Potomac River the mass of Sykesville slide debris thins and lenses out to the west and passes into graded turbidites and then into finer silty and argillaceous beds. This suggests strongly that sliding was to the west. Moreover, the Sykesville contained a larger mixture of coarse sand as well as quartz pebbles and exotic blocks of basement rock. There is no possible source for this coarse debris west of the Sykesville belt, where for many miles the rocks are fine-grained metasandstones and phyllites. Therefore, the coarse debris must have come from the east. If the submarine sliding was directed westward from an elevated area on the east, the Wissahickon turbidity flows probably came from the same direction.

These deductions are supported by observations on Wissahickon slump structures. There is much variation, but in general they indicate westerly downslope movement. Observations on slumping directions are still to few to carry much weight, however.

Still another indication of an eastern source is the westward progression from Flysch to Molasse. In the Alps, Carpathians, and elsewhere the Flysch troughs developed adjacent to the newly rising cordillera, but as uplift continued and troughs became filled the site of paralic sedimentation shifted outward, toward a more marginal position. If this pattern holds for the Piedmont trough the cordillera or tectonic lands that supplied the sediment would have lain to the east.

The present study does not support current opinion that the Piedmont metamorphic rocks are a eugeosynclinal facies of the Paleozoic sedimentary rocks that lie west of the Blue Ridge (Stose and Stose, 1951; King, 1959: Eardley, 1962). (1) The Piedmont sediments are older, probably Late Precambrian. (2) They show the same sequence of sedimentary facies as the Paleozoic strata to the west. The Piedmont rocks therefore appear to be the product of an earlier geosynclinal cycle. This cycle differed from the later

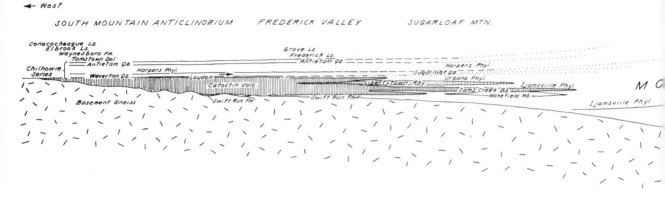

Fig 13-17 Diagram of inferred stratigraphic and facies relations in the Maryland Piedmont. The units are now folded and faulted. Basement rocks are shown by hatched pattern, mafic and ultramafic intrusions by heavy hatching. The Weverton and Antietam quartzites change eastward to rows of dots, representing transition to thinner units which finger out to the east. The arrow in the Weverton shows direction of current transport. The diagram is not drawn closely to scale.

(Paleozoic) ones by having less pre-orogenic and more Flysch sediments, and in being followed by regional metamorphism and plutonic intrusion.

Another conclusion is that the Piedmont trough in Maryland was filled with chiefly nonvolcanic detritus, much of which was derived from metamorphic rocks. This argues against the concept that the Piedmont was bordered by a volcanic island arc (Kay, 1951; King, 1959). A landmass of crystalline rock, east of the present Piedmont, is more compatible with the present data. Perhaps this was the landmass of Appalachia.

If Hopson is correct in his interpretation of the stratigraphic succession within the Glenarm and the position of the Glenarm below the Cambrian and latest Precambrian units, then a large part of the area shown on the 1961 United States Tectonic Map as Paleozoic metasedimentary rock is actually Precambrian. How much of this area is Precambrian is unknown, but a schist belt in the inner Piedmont has often been correlated with the Wissahickon. Certainly parts of it are Paleozoic, as shown by Ordovician fossils found in the Arvonia and Quantico slates in northern Virginia, and a

much larger slate belt of unknown age extends along the eastern edge of the Piedmont in the Carolinas. Higher-grade metamorphism has occurred within the inner Piedmont, but it may be a long time before we know what parts of the metasedimentary rocks there are Paleozoic deposits and what are Precambrian deposits which were recrystallized during the Paleozoic as a result of igneous activity.

Structure within Piedmont metasedimentary rocks

Although it is not possible to date the deformations within the Piedmont metasedimentary rocks accurately, it is possible to examine the character of the deformations. One such study has been conducted along the Susquehanna River in Pennsylvania (Freedman and others, 1964), which affords an excellent outcrop belt across the northern Piedmont. The rock units crossed are part of the same sequences previously described. A number of lineations and foliations of different orientation are found in the area, and these have been related to several deformations. A plot showing typical relation-

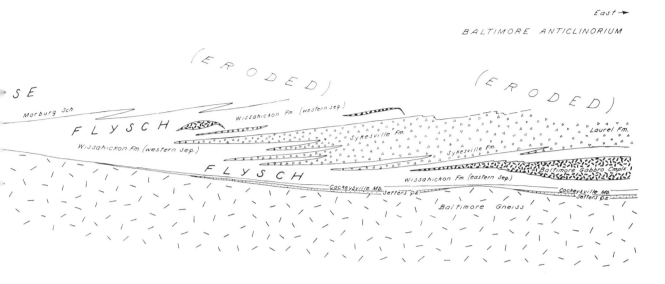

ships of the fabric elements in the mesoscopic analysis are shown in Fig. 13-18. Three phases of deformation are recognized. The first involved the formation of isoclinal folds. These folds vary in orientation systematically across the Piedmont (Fig. 13-19) and possibly indicate a nappe. The second and third deformation resulted in slip folding on *s* surfaces which cut across the earlier isoclinal folds.

Mantled gneiss domes in the northern Piedmont

The Baltimore gneiss, a complex assemblage of quartzo-feldspathic gneisses, amphibolite, migmatite, and gneissic granitic rocks, is generally thought to constitute the oldest crystalline material in the northern Piedmont. Radiogenic dating indicates it was crystallized about 1,000 to 1,100 million years ago. The gneisses occur as a series of oval and doubly plunging domes between Washington, D.C., and Baltimore, Md. (Fig. 13-20). Quartzite and feldspathic mica schists, the Setters formation, usually occur as a rim around the domes where the contacts are unfaulted. Evidence that the gneiss was a basement on which the Setters were deposited lies in the observation that the gneiss is now most commonly rimmed by the Setters. If the gneiss were intrusive it would be hard to understand

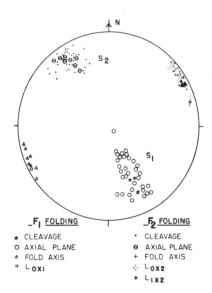

Fig. 13-18 Equal-area plot: multiple folding in Colemanville railroad cut. (*From Freedman, Wise, and Bentley, 1964.*)

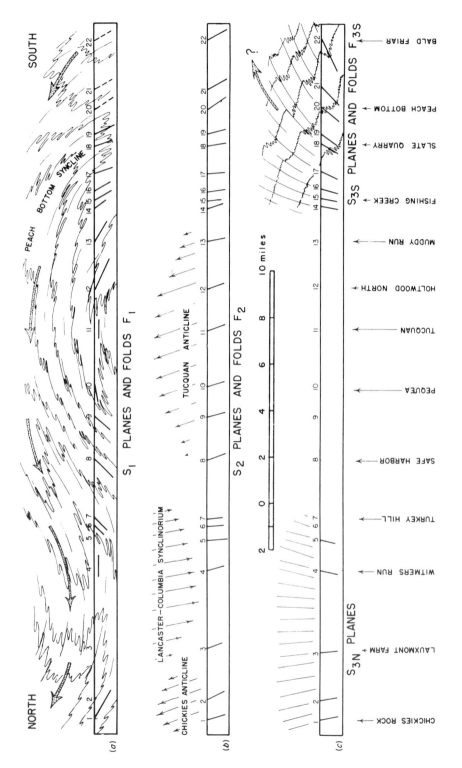

Fig. 13-19 Diagram of dips of S surfaces and axial planes along the Susquehanna River. (*From Freedman, Wise, and Bentley, 1964.*)

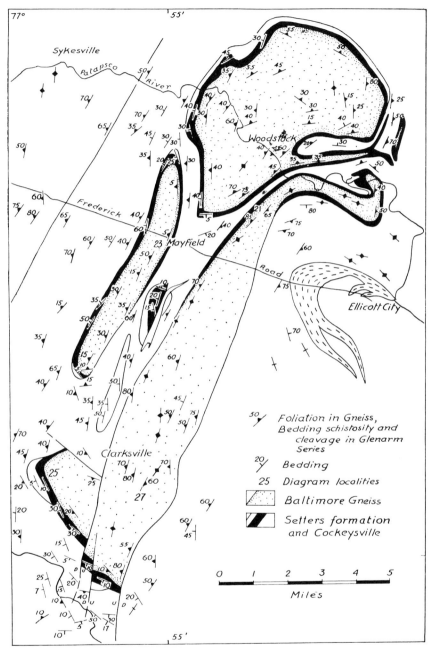

Fig. 13-20 Foliation map of gneiss domes in Howard and Montgomery Counties. The domes are asymmetrically overturned to the east or southeast as shown by the constant dip of foliations to the west or north. The Clarksville dome is partially faulted, and only its northeast and southern portions show the Setters above the gneiss in normal contact. The Mayfield dome is an elongate asymmetrical anticline. The Woodstock domes have risen upward and southward over the adjacent Setters, Cockeysville, and Wissahickon formations. *(From Cloos and Hopson. 1964.)*

why the intrusion stopped at the base of the Setters so consistently. However, in southwestern Baltimore and along the southeastern edge of the Piedmont, banded gneisses are concordantly overlain by a schist that most closely resembles the Wissahickon which is thought to lie above the Setters formation. Also, in at least one place, a granite (the Gunpowder granite) derived from the Baltimore gneiss is intruded into the Setters and other overlying units. Thus it appears that the Baltimore gneiss was the original basement, but that it became mobilized at a later date and moved through and into the overlying units.

In southwestern Baltimore the gneisses are beautifully layered, giving the impression from a distance of evenly stratified sediments, but in most of the domes the gneisses are highly deformed.

"The banded gneiss . . . is often complexly folded, or plastically dragged and smeared out. . . . Some of the folds are simple flexures, but others show thickening and thinning due to plastic flowage. Some have even been smeared out and partly obliterated, and the remnants refolded. As the banded structure becomes increasingly obscured by flowage and recrystallization these rocks grade into migmatite." (Hopson, 1964, p. 37.)

The name *migmatite* is used to refer to a "mixed" metamorphic rock. Migmatites are often products of the invasion of a magma into country rock which begins to flow or become complexly deformed. The igneous-appearing fraction of the Baltimore gneiss forms veins, layers, and cross-cutting bodies in a darker-colored metamorphic rock composed of banded biotite gneisses.

"The migmatization was accompanied by strong deformation but locally outlasted it. The migmatite layering is folded, ptygmatically buckled, stretched, pulled apart, or sheared out and partly obliterated. Large porphyroblasts were crushed, drawn out, and recrystallized. Locally the small scale folding becomes wild, suggesting that the migmatite was in an incompetent, highly plastic condition." (Hopson, 1964, p. 39.)

One of the most striking structures of the gneiss domes is the parallelism of banding and foliation near the margins of the gneiss with bedding in the overlying Setters. Even the folds in the Setters are repeated in the gneisses. This concordance of structures indicates that the gneiss moved with the overlying sediments. The fact that the strong alignment of structures disappears farther away from the contacts suggest that the foliation at the contact may be at least in part secondary and may have formed during the folding. The evidence from the migmatites and folds in the gneisses supports the view that the gneisses were plastic, and indeed such a condition is needed to explain the marginal structures of the domes (Fig. 13-21).

New England crystalline province

The region of igneous and metamorphic rock outcrop in New England occupies a position similar to that of the Piedmont farther south. The two regions are, however, completely separated by the Triassic deposits of the Newark basin. Fortunately, the ages of the crystalline rocks in New England are better established than those of the Piedmont. This is possible because more fossils have been found in the metasedimentary units and because a number of Carboniferous basins are situated within the crystalline complex; the angular unconformity at the base of the Carboniferous sequences provides a marker useful for dating truncated and intrusive bodies.

A tectonic map in Fig. 13-22 shows some of the larger structural features of Vermont and New Hampshire. We have already seen that lower Paleozoic miogeosynclinal deposits are strongly folded and faulted in the region to the west, along the Hudson and Champlain valleys, where the Taconic Mountains are located.

Metasedimentary rocks in the central and eastern parts of New England are also of early Paleozoic age, Cambrian to Devonian, but unlike their age equivalents to the west they are

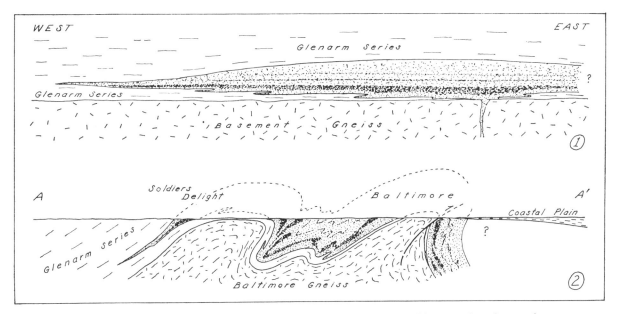

Fig. 13-21 Structural interpretation of the Baltimore gabbro complex. (1) The gabbro complex after emplacement, but before regional deformation; the mass was not yet completely solidified. (2) The gabbro complex after folding, metamorphism, and erosion to the present level. The light stippling is gabbro (including amphibolite), and the heavy pattern is ultramafic rock. The relations are greatly generalized. (*From Cloos and Hopson, 1964.*)

characterized by shale, volcanics, and schists. These associations are of the type generally ascribed to eugeosynclines, and this eastern belt is known as the *Magog eugeosyncline* (Kay, 1951). The eugeosynclinal rocks are now largely recrystallized to slates, phyllites, schists, and quartzites. The present line of contact between these two belts lies within the belt of thrust faults in western New England. One of the main arguments favoring the klippe interpretation of the Taconic Mountains is that eugeosynclinal facies rocks like those of the eastern belt lie within and surrounded by miogeosynclinal rocks of the west. The large elongate dome of Precambrian gneisses which comprises the Green Mountains lies approximately along this zone (Fig. 13-22), and this is the root zone favored by many students of the Taconic klippe.

The outcrop belt of Cambrian and Ordovician rocks, both miogeosynclinal and eugeosynclinal, lies in western New England, while

the later Paleozoic units lie to the east. The pile of metasedimentary rocks in New Hampshire has an aggregate thickness of nearly 3 miles and is composed predominantly of volcanics, conglomerates, impure quartzites, and slates. There are enough fossil localities to document the Silurian and Devonian ages of these sequences. The structure in these consists of a series of anticlinoria and synclinoria (Fig. 13-23) of northwest trend into which several series of igneous rocks have been intruded. These series—the Highlandcroft, Oliverian, New Hampshire, and White Mountain magma series—have been worked out in detail. According to Billings (1937, 1945), these series have the following relations:

White Mountain magma series: The youngest series; rocks of this series occur as ring dikes, stocks, a batholith, and as moat volcanics, tuffs, breccias, and lavas. The series consists of a wide

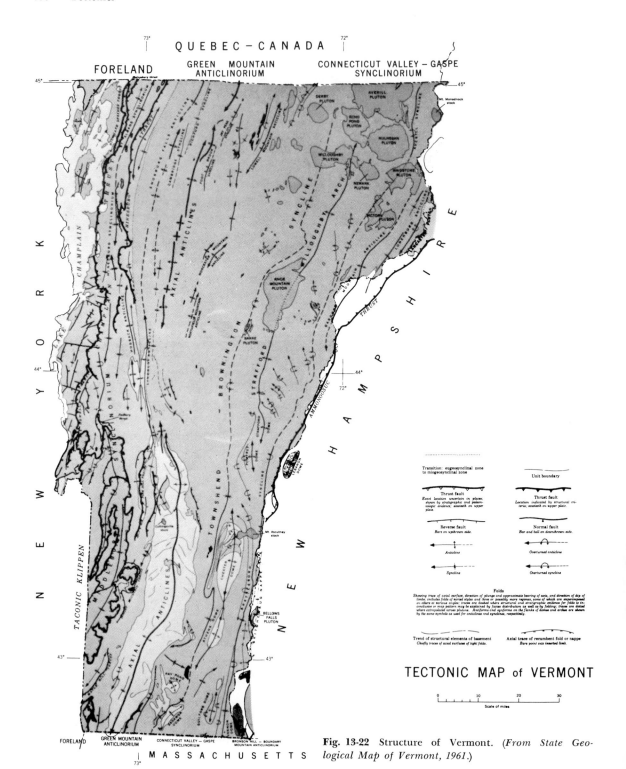

Fig. 13-22 Structure of Vermont. (*From State Geological Map of Vermont, 1961.*)

Fig. 13-23 Structural sketch of New Hampshire. (*Compiled by M. P. Billings; from New Hampshire State Geologic Map, 1955.*)

range of rock types, from mafic (oldest) to felsic (youngest). The age of the series is probably Early Mississippian.

New Hampshire magma series: The intrusives of this series are batholiths and stocks mainly of granodiorite with small bodies of intermediate composition. Its intrusion was contemporaneous with folding of the Silurian and Devonian sequences in the Acadian orogeny.

Oliverian magma series: These granite batholiths were emplaced before the Acadian orogeny.

Highlandcroft magma series: These granodiorite intrusions were emplaced and truncated by erosion before the Middle Silurian Niagaran fossil-bearing beds were deposited over them.

Metamorphism has affected all of the pre-Carboniferous sediments and intrusions in eastern New England, and in a general way the degree of metamorphism increases toward the southeast and the region of the largest of the New Hampshire magma series intrusions which were likely the cause of the metamorphism. The present juxtaposition of different zones across major faults can be explained by later movements on these faults.

The major faults which displace the metamorphic zones in New Hampshire are vertical or reverse faults. The Ammonoosue fault has a stratigraphic displacement of over 7,000 ft locally, and it, like other of the faults in New Hampshire, dips northwest. These late reverse faults dip steeply and appear to have formed after the main orogenic episode in which the direction of tectonic transport was toward the northwest.

REFERENCES

Billings, M. P., 1937, Regional metamorphism of the Littleton-Moosilauke area, New Hampshire: Geol. Soc. America Bull., v. 48, p. 463–566.

——— 1945, Mechanics of igneous intrusion in New Hampshire: Am. Jour. Sci., v. 243A, Daly v. p. 41–68.

Bucher, W. H., 1957, Taconic klippe—a stratigraphic-structural problem: Geol. Soc. America Bull., v. 68, no. 6, p. 657–674.

Cady, Wallace, 1960, Stratigraphy and geotectonic relationships in northern Vermont and southern Quebec: Geol. Soc. America Bull., v. 71, p. 531–576.

Cloos, Ernst, 1947, Oolite deformation in the South Mountain fold, Maryland: Geol. Soc. America Bull., v. 58, p. 843–918.

Cloos, Ernst, and Hopson, C. A., 1964, *in* The geology of Howard and Montgomery Counties: Baltimore, Md., Maryland Geol. Survey.

Cooper, B. N., 1964, Relation of stratigraphy to structure in the southern Appalachians, *in* Tectonics of the southern Appalachians, VPI Dept. Geol. Sci. Mem. 1.

Craddock, J. C., 1957, Stratigraphy and structure of the Kinderhook quadrangle, New York and the "Taconic Klippe": Geol. Soc. America Bull., v. 68, no. 6, p. 675–724.

Dietrich, R. V., 1964, Igneous activity in the southern Appalachians, *in* Tectonics of the southern Appalachians, VPI Dept. Geol. Sci. Mem. 1.

Drake, C. L., and Woodward, H. P., 1963, Appalachian curvature, wrench faulting, and offshore structures: New York Acad. Sci. Trans., ser. II, v. 26, p. 48–63.

Eardley, A. J., 1962, Structural geology of North America: New York, Harper & Row.

Faul, Henry, and others, 1963, Ages of intrusions and metamorphism in the northern Appalachians: Am. Jour. Sci., v. 261.

Freedman, J., Wise, D. U., and Bentley, R. D., 1964, Pattern of folded folds in the Appalachian Piedmont along Susquehanna River: Geol. Soc. America Bull., v. 75, p. 621–638.

Fyson, W. K., 1964, Folds in the carboniferous rocks near Walton, Nova Scotia: Am. Jour. Sci., v. 262, p. 513–522.

Gwinn, V. E., 1964, Thin-skinned tectonics in the plateau and northwestern Valley and Ridge provinces of the central Appalachians: Geol. Soc. America Bull., v. 75, p. 863–900.

——— 1967, Lateral shortening of layered rock sequences in the foothills regions of major mountain systems: Mineral Industries, v. 36.

Hadley, J. B., 1964, Correlation of isotopic ages, crustal heating and sedimentation in the Appalachian region, *in* Lowry, W. D., ed., Tectonics of the southern Appalachians: VPI Dept. Geol. Sci. Mem. 1.

Hadley, J. B., and Goldsmith, R., 1963, Geology of the eastern Great Smoky Mountains, Tennessee and North Carolina: U. S. Geol. Survey Prof. Paper 349-B, 118 p.

Hall, J., 1859, Geological survey of New York: Palaeontology, v. iii, Introd.

Harris, L. D., and Zieta, Isidore, 1962, Development of Cumberland overthrust block in vicinity of Chestnut Ridge fenster in southwest Virginia: Am. Assoc. Petroleum Geologists Bull., v. 46, p. 2148–2160.

Hess, H. H., 1946, Appalachian peridotite belt: its significance in sequence of events in mountain building [abs.]: Geol. Soc. America Bull., v. 51.

Hopson, C. A., 1964, The crystalline rocks of Howard and Montgomery Counties, in Cloos, Ernst, ed., Geology of Howard and Montgomery Counties: Maryland Geol. Survey.

Kay, Marshall, 1951, North American geosynclines: Geol. Soc. America Mem. 48.

——— 1967, Stratigraphy and structure of northeastern Newfoundland bearing on drift in North Atlantic: Am. Assoc. Petroleum Geologists Bull., v. 51, no. 4, p. 579–600.

King, P. B., 1951, The tectonics of middle North America: Princeton, N.J., Princeton Univ.

——— 1959, The evolution of North America: Princeton, N.J., Princeton Univ., 190 p.

——— 1964, Geology of the central Great Smoky Mountains, Tennessee: U. S. Geol. Survey Prof. Paper 349-C.

Miller, R. L., and Fuller, J. O., 1954, Geology and oil resources of the Rose Hill district, Lee County, Virginia: Virginia Div. Mineral Research Bull., v. 71, 383 p.

Osberg, P. H., 1965, Structural geology of the Knowlton-Richmond area, Quebec: Geol. Soc. America Bull., v. 76, p. 223–250.

Pettijohn, F. J., 1957, Sedimentary rocks, 2d ed.: New York, Harper & Row.

Reed, J. C., Jr., 1955, Catoctin formation near Luray, Virginia: Geol. Soc. America Bull., v. 66,
p. 871–896.

Reed, J. C., Jr., and Bryant, Bruce, 1964, Evidence for strike-slip faulting along the Brevard zone in North Carolina: Geol. Soc. America Bull., v. 75, p. 1177–1196.

Rodgers, John, 1953a, Geologic map of east Tennessee with explanatory text: Tennessee Div. Geology Bull., v. 58, pt. 2, 168 p.

——— 1953b, The folds and faults of the Appalachian Valley and Ridge province: Kentucky Geol. Survey Spec. Pub. 1, p. 150–166.

——— 1963, Mechanics of Appalachian foreland folding in Pennsylvania and West Virginia: Am. Assoc. Petroleum Geologists Bull., v. 47, p. 1527–1536.

Scotford, D. M., 1951, Structure of the Sugarloaf Mountain area, Maryland as a key to Piedmont stratigraphy: Geol. Soc. America Bull., v. 62, p. 45–75; discussion by A. J. Stose and G. W. Stose, v. 62, p. 697–699.

Spencer, E. W., 1965, Geology, A survey of earth science: New York, Crowell.

Stose, G. W., and Stose, A. J., 1946, Ocoee series of the southern Appalachians [United States] [abs.]: Geol. Soc. America Bull., v. 57, p. 1233.

Watkins, J. S., 1964, Regional geologic implications of the gravity and magnetic fields of a part of eastern Tennessee and southern Kentucky: U. S. Geol. Survey Prof. Paper 516-A.

Weaver, J. D., 1957, Stratigraphy and structure of the Copake quadrangle, New York: Geol. Soc. America Bull., v. 68, no. 6, p. 725–762.

Williams, Harold, 1964, The Appalachians in northeastern Newfoundland—a two-sided symmetrical system: Am. Jour. Sci., v. 262, p. 1137–1158.

Wilson, C. W., Jr., 1958, Structure of the Cumberland Plateau: Geol. Soc. America Bull., v. 69.

Zen, E-An, 1961, Stratigraphy and structure at the north end of the Taconic Range in west central Vermont: Geol. Soc. America Bull., v. 72, p. 293–338.

——— 1967, Time and space relationships of the Taconic allochthon and autochthon: Geol. Soc. America Spec. Paper 97, p. 107.

14
structural features
of the
north american cordillera

The Cordilleran system of western North America is marginal to the craton, as is the Appalachian system on the east. Thus, we might expect that the two would be similar types of mobile belts differing primarily in age, but if we compare them we find only very general similarities.*

The two are similar in that:

1. Both are marginal to the craton.
2. Both are sites of long-term crustal mobility.
3. Thick geosynclinal sedimentary deposits have accumulated in portions of both belts.
4. Both contain diverse structural elements within the system.
5. Both have been sites of igneous activity.
6. Metamorphism has affected large bodies of rock within each system.
7. Long, relatively narrow belts of strongly folded and thrust-faulted sedimentary sequences occur in portions of both systems.
8. Block faulting affected portions of both systems, and in each case the

---

* The difficulty in outlining the structure of western North America lies mainly in selecting from a vast and excellent literature in all aspects of the stratigraphy, structure, and tectonics of this region. The general framework of the region is here outlined, and detailed features of a few localities and problems are presented. The student is referred to the comprehensive treatment of Eardley (1962), the more abbreviated work of King (1962), and the rest of the selected list of references at the end of this chapter.

block faulting took place after the folding and thrusting.

9. The greatest similarities between the two orogens is found if we compare the Appalachians with the Canadian Rockies. The two are comparable in size, but sharp contrasts exist between the Cordilleran belt of the western United States and the Appalachians.

10. Miogeosynclines and eugeosynclinal divisions are recognized in both belts, and in each case the miogeosyncline lies closest to the craton.

The following are among the differences (refer to the Tectonic Map of the United States and the Tectonic Map of Canada):

1. The two differ in dimensions. At the widest parts within the United States, the Appalachians are about 200 miles wide, the Cordilleran 1,000 miles wide. The ends of the Appalachians are uncertain. The southern end may bend sharply west and connect beneath Coastal Plain sequences with the Ouachitas, but this is not established, and the northern end is lost north of Newfoundland in the ocean. The Cordilleran belt (Fig. 14-1) extends into Alaska, and portions of it seem continuous with the structure of the Alaskan Peninsula which passes into the Aleutian Island arc. The orogenic belt continues south into Mexico, possibly into the Caribbean, then south along the western edge of South America and into Antarctica (Fig. 14-2). There is no young orogenic belt on the eastern side of the South American shield.

2. The age of orogenic activity in the two mountain systems is greatly different. Orogeny took place in the Appalachians through much of the Paleozoic, with the most significant phases in the Ordovician, Devonian, and late Paleozoic (probably Permian). There is no evidence of renewed orogeny after the Paleozoic. Paleozoic orogenic history is somewhat obscure

Fig. 14-1   Position of Rocky Mountains within the Cordilleran system. (*From Shaw, 1963.*)

PRECAMBRIAN SHIELD

ACID PLUTONICS

VOLCANOES ACTIVE OR EXTINCT

STRUCTURAL TRENDS

TRENCHES AND GEOFRACTURES

TERTIARY VOLCANICS

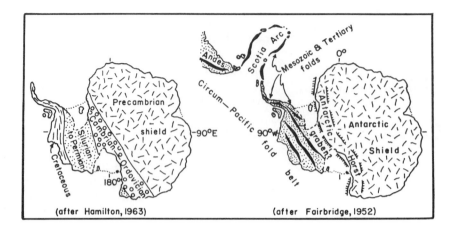

Fig. 14-2 Two interpretations of the tectonic framework of Antarctica. Hypothetical ages of main periods of folding are indicated. *(From Ford, 1964.)*

in the Cordilleran, but from the Jurassic to the present there has been a long, well-documented orogenic history with major phases in the Jurassic, Cretaceous, and Pleistocene. Based on the relative ages of these two North American belts, we might expect to find that the Cordilleran, where orogeny continues at present, would have a simpler structural pattern useful in analyzing the older, more complex Appalachians. This is not the case.

3. The structural pattern of the Appalachians is simpler in almost every respect. It is divisible longitudinally, whereas in the United States the Cordilleran belt is not. The fold and fault belt of the Appalachians is long and continuous over a very large part of its length. The long fold belt of the Canadian Rockies cannot be traced through the United States. It is broken in Montana and is obscured by block faulting south of Wyoming. (It probably continued to the southwest).

4. There is no Appalachian counterpart of the great fault-block mountains of Wyoming, Montana, Colorado, and New Mexico in which Precambrian basement is elevated as much as 20,000 to 30,000 ft. Instead there is a vast basin, the Appalachian basin, situated between the craton and

orogenic belt in the Appalachians, containing thick carboniferous sequences which are largely unfaulted and only broadly folded.

5. There is no Appalachian counterpart of the Colorado Plateau, the Sierra Nevada Mountains, or the block-faulted Basin and Range region.

6. The several Paleozoic orogenies in the Appalachians appear to have been confined to a relatively narrow belt, as was the geosynclinal accumulation. The West Coast is certainly the site of the modern orogeny. The Nevadian (Jurassic) orogeny also was active in the Far West, but the Laramide orogeny affected a belt now located hundreds of miles east.

7. The batholithic intrusions of the Cordilleran belt are much larger than any known in the Appalachians.

8. The effect of the depth of erosion in the Appalachians is one aspect of any comparison which simply cannot be evaluated. It is often assumed that very great thicknesses of rock have been removed from the metamorphic complexes in New England and the Piedmont.

9. Vast quantities of volcanic eruptives and lava flows occur in the Cordilleran. Volcanics and flows are almost wholly con-

fined to the crystalline complexes in the Appalachians.

The pronounced differences in orogenic belts is emphasized by comparison of these two with the Alps. There are some similarities, but each is unique in many respects. Each has followed a different course in its development. We cannot yet be sure whether these differences are the product of differences in initial geography, etc., acting to modify the surface expression of a single basic process which is the cause of all orogeny, or whether the features we find in orogenic belts can be caused by several different processes acting alone in some places and in combination at others. The latter possibility would be the case if, for example, the basic cause of orogeny were mantle convection, and if at the same time continents were drifting or being dispersed by some other process.

SOME MAJOR STRUCTURAL ELEMENTS IN THE CORDILLERAN

The Atlantic and Gulf Coastal Plains obscure areas of vital importance in the Appalachians, and similar limitations due to cover are encountered in the Cordilleran belt. Notable among these are the Quaternary basin fills in the Basin and Range province; Tertiary lava flows and volcanics, particularly in the Columbia River plateau, the Cascade Mountains, and British Columbia; and the large Mesozoic granitic batholiths. All of these impair our reconstructions of structural provinces and tectonic history.

Most geologists agree on which structural features are most important in the sense of regional tectonics, but there are differences of opinion in many cases regarding the nature of the structure and the relative importance of different elements.

The following important features and elements are recognized in the Cordilleran belt in the United States, exclusive of Alaska (Fig. 14-3):

1. The Northern Rocky Mountain fold and fault belt and its continuation south into Idaho and Wyoming
2. The foreland structural features of Montana, Wyoming, Colorado, and New Mexico; the Middle and Southern Rocky Mountains
3. The Colorado plateau
4. The block-faulted structural features of the Basin and Range, including portions of the Columbia River plateau, and associated transcurrent fault zones
5. The large Mesozoic plutons including the Sierra Nevada, Boulder, Idaho, and Coast Range batholiths
6. The Jurassic belt of metamorphics and folds of the Klamath Mountains in California, the Blue Mountains in Oregon, and the northern Coast Range belt in British Columbia
7. The San Andreas fault system
8. The Coast Ranges

THE CORDILLERAN BELT OF CANADA

The northern Cordilleran region is similar to the Appalachians in many respects. Each is readily divisible longitudinally. The arrangement of longitudinal divisions is similar; proceeding from the craton toward the ocean, they are a craton, a regional sedimentary basin, a foreland fold and thrust belt developed in an earlier miogeosyncline, and a belt of Precambrian exposure (Beltian and Blue Ridge) which has been brought up along part of the geosyncline and which lies between the miogeosyncline and the major part of the eugeosyncline with its metamorphic and igneous complexes. The two belts differ, of course, in details.

The evolution of western Canada has been synthesized and is shown, in part, in Fig. 14-5 (McCrossan and Glaister, 1964). Examination of these reconstructions will help in understanding the present distribution of structural

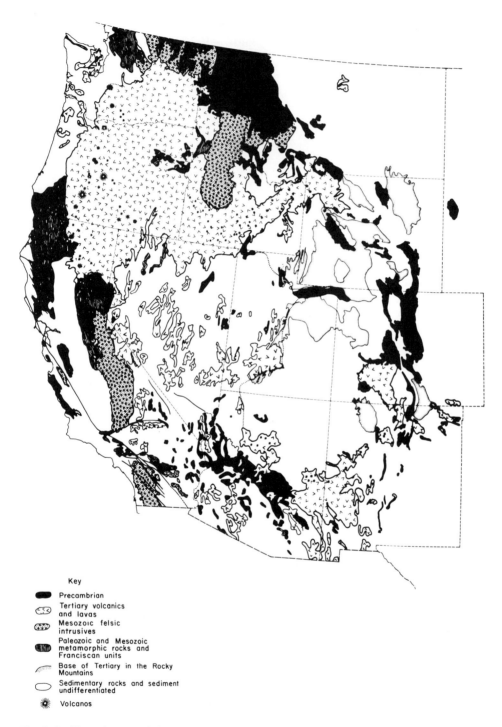

Key

- Precambrian
- Tertiary volcanics and lavas
- Mesozoic felsic intrusives
- Paleozoic and Mesozoic metamorphic rocks and Franciscan units
- Base of Tertiary in the Rocky Mountains
- Sedimentary rocks and sediment undifferentiated
- Volcanos

Fig. 14-3 Tectonic map of the western United States. (*From the United States Tectonic Map, 1961, U.S. Geol. Survey and Am. Assoc. Petroleum Geologists.*

Thrust faults
Strike-slip faults
Normal faults
Undifferentiated faults

Fig. 14-4 Fault map of the western United States. (*Modified after the United States Tectonic Map, 1961, U.S. Geol. Survey and Am. Assoc. Petroleum Geologists.*)

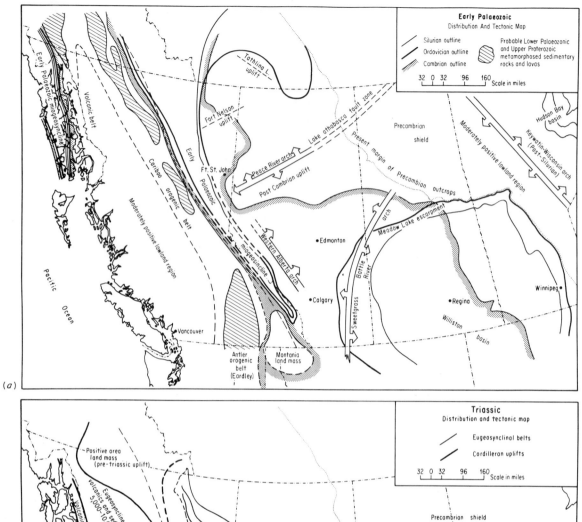

(a)

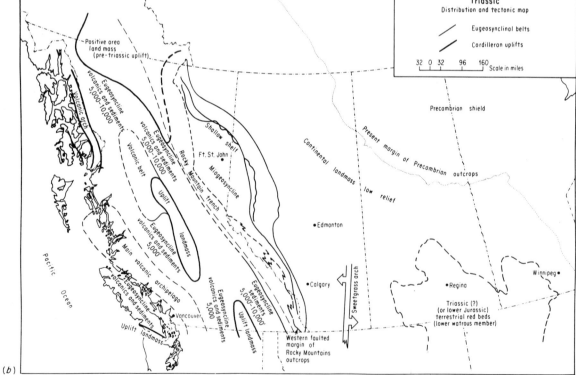

(b)

Fig. 14-5 Synthesis of tectonic evolution of western Canada. (*From McCrossan and Glaister, 1964.*)

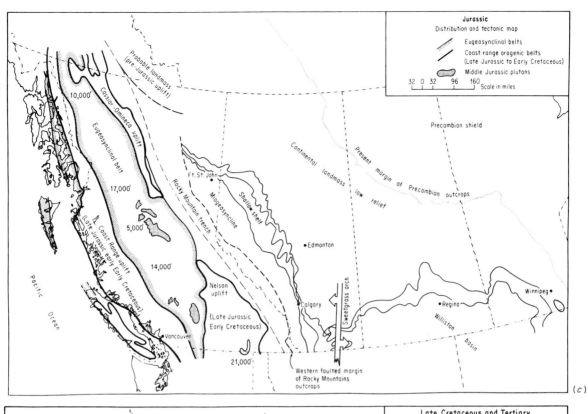

Jurassic
Distribution and tectonic map

Eugeosynclinal belts

Coast range orogenic belts
(Late Jurassic to Early Cretaceous)

Middle Jurassic plutons

32 0   32   96   160
Scale in miles

Probable landmass
(pre-Jurassic uplift)

Precambrian shield

Cassiar-Omineca uplift

10,000'

Eugeosynclinal belt

17,000'

5,000'

Ft. St John

Miogeosyncline

Rocky Mountain trench

Shallow shelf

Continental landmass low relief

Present margin of Precambrian outcrops

14,000'

• Edmonton

Pacific Ocean

Coast Range uplift
(Late Jurassic early Early Cretaceous)

Nelson uplift

• Calgary

Sweetgrass arch

Winnipeg •

• Vancouver

(Late Jurassic Early Cretaceous)

• Regina

Williston basin

21,000'

Western faulted margin
of Rocky Mountains
outcrops

(c)

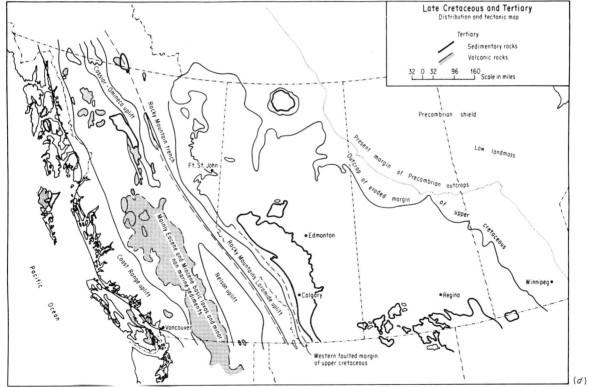

Late Cretaceous and Tertiary
Distribution and tectonic map

Tertiary

Sedimentary rocks

Volcanic rocks

32 0   32   96   160   Scale in miles

Cassiar-Omineca uplift

Rocky Mountain trench

Ft. St. John

Precambrian shield

Low landmass

Present margin of Precambrian outcrops

Outcrop of eroded margin of upper cretaceous

• Edmonton

Pacific Ocean

Coast Range uplift

Mainly Eocene and Miocene basic lavas and minor non marine sediments

Nelson uplift

Rocky Mountains (Laramide uplift)

• Calgary

Winnipeg •

• Vancouver

• Regina

Western faulted margin
of upper cretaceous

(d)

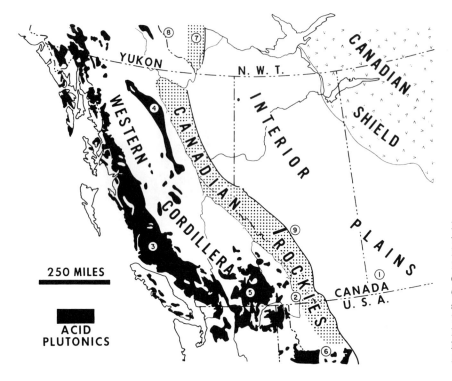

Fig. 14-6 Index map of western Canada. (1) Cypress Hills conglomerate; (2) Kishenehn formation; (3) Coast Range batholith; (4) Cassiar batholith; (5) Nelson batholith; (6) Boulder batholith; (7) Mackenzie Mountains; (8) Selwyn Mountains. (*From Shaw, 1963.*)

elements (Fig. 14-6). The validity of these reconstructions is limited by the outcrop distribution of each age and the state of field data. Several present significant structural features and boundaries are shown superimposed on the paleotectonic maps (Fig. 14-5) in order to establish the relation of these to the older elements. Note particularly the position of the faulted margin of Rocky Mountain outcrops and the Rocky Mountain trench. This trench is a physiographic feature; most of the major rivers of the Canadian Rockies flow along a portion of it, but the trench does not slope continuously in one direction and there are low passes along it. It is drawn here as a single continuous feature over 1,000 miles long, but actually it consists of several distinct lineaments. The northern part is the Tintina trench. Roddick (1967) has compiled the local geology along parts of the Tintina trench (Fig. 14-8). He proposes that a right-lateral movement of about 250 miles is needed to explain the present offset of regional

geologic trends. These lineaments are almost universally interpreted as faults, but the type of fault is yet to be conclusively established. The division of the Cordillera known as the Rocky Mountains lies east of this line of trenches.

The geosynclinal character of the western margin of North America was established in the Precambrian. Thick sequences of clastics were deposited in the late Proterozoic. The Rocky Mountain trench appears to be located approximately along the boundary between the early Paleozoic miogeosyncline and the eugeosyncline. Possibly this was also the boundary between the continental crust of the craton and sima as suggested by King (1962) and by Gabrielse and Wheeler (1961). There are too few Paleozoic outcrops in the western part of the Canadian Cordillera to define its paleotectonic pattern with much precision. The Cariboo orogenic belt which developed from the early Paleozoic eugeosyncline is postulated to be continuous with the Antler orogenic belt identified in Nevada (neither is known in much detail). The Cariboo orogeny took place in the middle Paleozoic, and at that time highlands, including metamorphic and igneous complexes, formed in a belt which is now located between the Laramide Rocky Mountains and the Jurassic Nevadian orogenic belt along the West Coast. Eugeosynclinal conditions of sedimentation persisted in the Alaska panhandle during the Cariboo orogeny, and eugeosynclinal deposits of late Paleozoic age are known in scattered localities throughout the region west of the Rocky Mountain trench. These conditions spread east of the trench in the Permian, but were confined west of the trench in the Mesozoic (Fig. 14-5). The present structural pattern began to emerge in the Jurassic with the Nevadian orogeny which brought uplift, folding, faulting, and emplacement of gigantic granitic plutons in the cugeosyncline, the Coast Range, and the Nelson and Cassiar uplifts. Then in the Late Cretaceous and early Tertiary

the eastern portion of the Cordillera, the miogeosyncline, was uplifted, and great thrusts and nappes moved primarily toward the craton. The structure of a portion of these thrusts has already been described in Chap. 4 This great thrust belt extends into the United States, the famous klippe at Chief Mountain being a part. The eastern edge is formed by the Lewis thrust and the Lombard thrust of Montana. Precambrian belt series rocks are brought onto Cretaceous and Tertiary strata by some of these faults. As in the Appalachian, the thrusts are often very shallow, possibly gravity-glide features, but some of those that bring Precambrian to the surface in high ranges have vertical components of displacement of many thousands of feet. Most of the plates underlain by shallow thrusts have moved east, but there are also numerous high-angle reverse faults, some of which may be thrusts, that dip toward the east. There is no conclusive evidence to demonstrate that shallow, thin-skinned types of deformation acted throughout the Canadian Rockies, or that

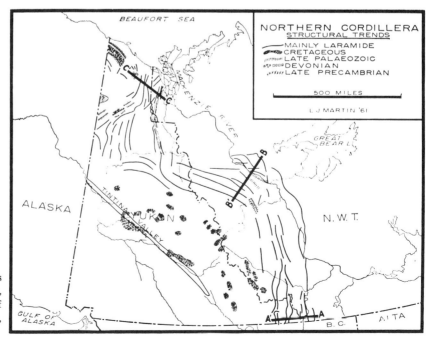

Fig. 14-7 Structural trends of the northern Cordillera, showing five major periods of deformation. (*From Martin, 1963.*)

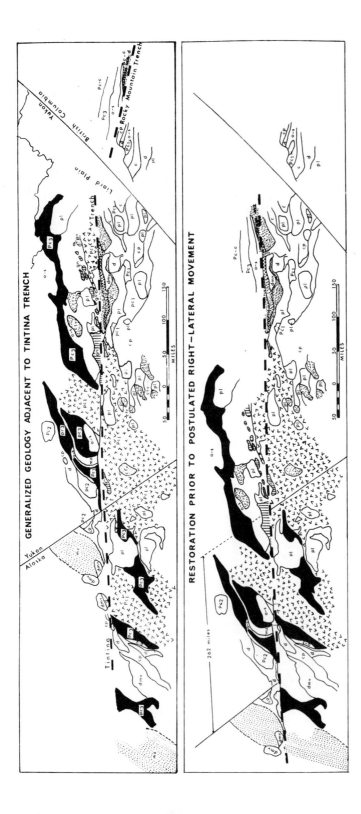

Fig. 14-8 Top—geology adjacent to Tintina trench. Bottom—postulated restoration of geology prior to movement along Tintina trench. pc = Precambrian; pc-c = Precambrian to Cambrian, mainly phyllite; c = Cambrian, limestone and quartzite; o-s = Ordovician and Silurian, black shale and chert; d = Silurian and Devonian to Mississippian, mainly carbonate and dark clastic rocks; dmv = Devonian to Mississippian, volcanic rocks; gm = Mississippian (?), greenstone and related rocks; cp = Carboniferous to Permian, sedimentary rocks; mz = Mesozoic, mainly pelitic rocks; pl = Cretaceous (?), plutonic rocks; ctv = Cretaceous and Tertiary, volcanic rocks Carmacks volcanics.

the long-held view that the thrusts developed in large part from regional compression is valid.

ROCKY MOUNTAIN TRENCH

The trenches are among the most arresting features of the Cordillera. The Rocky Mountain trench can be traced from Flathead Lake in Montana as a nearly straight lineament over 1,000 miles long through British Columbia. The Tintina trench is almost on the same trend in the Yukon Territory, and it is traced 450 miles into Alaska. Both of these trenches have characteristics often associated with strike-slip faults: (1) the trenchlike topographic form, (2) the linearity, (3) separation across the trench of similar lithologies, (4) termination of structural zones which intersect the trench. However, it has not yet been conclusively demonstrated that specific structural or lithologic zones are actually offset as a result of strike-slip movements along the trench, and there is other evidence which is difficult to explain in terms of strike-slip movement. The trench is a sinuous zone near Cranbrook, British Columbia. It

is asymmetrical in cross section, the eastern flank appears to be a youthful fault scarp (Eardley, 1962), and it cannot be traced south of Flathead Lake, Mont. The trench has also been attributed to erosion of a major thrust zone, to normal faulting, and to erosion of zones of weak strata.

There are exposures in the floor of the trench of sheared and highly deformed Belt and Paleozoic strata, including many that are incompetent. What role these weak, easily eroded strata play as compared with erosion along a fault is still uncertain.

The structural pattern near the northern end of the trench (Fig. 14-10) is typical of the complexity of the trench structure. Most of the units east of the trench are overturned toward the northeast, most of the major thrusts dip southwest, and the general sense of tectonic transport is toward the east. But a few folds east of the trench are overturned toward the trench, and thrusts dipping both northeast and southwest are known west of the trench in a structural zone which passes into or is terminated at the trench.

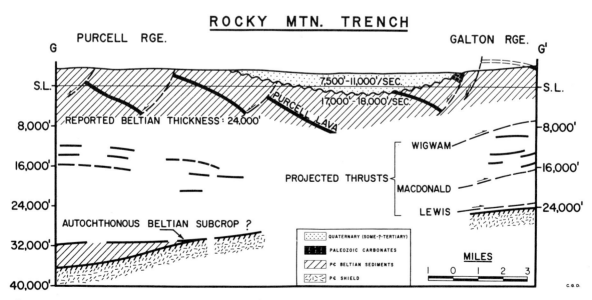

Fig. 14-9 Geological cross section across the Rocky Mountain trench interpreted from seismic reflection profile. (*From Bally and others, 1966.*)

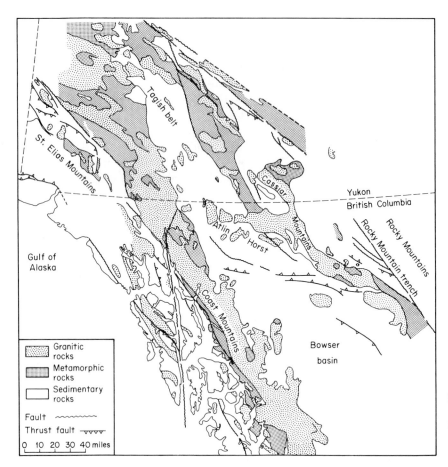

Fig. 14-10 Tectonic sketch of part of the northwestern Cordillera. (*Modified after Gabrielse and Wheeler, 1961.*)

A seismic reflection profile has been taken across the trench near the southern end (Bally, Gordy, and Stewart, 1966). Both sides of the trench are flanked by mountains underlain by generally eastward-dipping Beltian strata in this area, and the trench is characterized by block faulting. The blocks appear to be tilted toward the east. The valley floor contains outcrops of upper Paleozoic carbonate rocks, Miocene sands and gravels, and glacial deposits. Bally, Gordy, and Stewart (1966, p. 356) make the following interpretation of the seismic line and regional geological data (Fig. 14-9):

At the depth, the structure on both sides of the Trench appears to be essentially similar and is layered. The Cambrian event of the Foothills can be traced to the east side of the Trench. On the west side of the Trench we recognize a reflection that is on the regional projection of the Cambrian event of the Foothills. This reflection appears to branch out to the west into two events. . . . Consideration of these geophysical and geological points suggests the propositions (1) that the Trench was formed in Tertiary time and after the main thrusting phase, (2) that the Trench is underlain by an undisturbed gently westward dipping basement, and (3) that location and strike of the Trench is dictated by a complex system of curved low-angle normal faults.

The trenches may be of fundamental importance in the tectonics of the Cordillera.

They do mark a boundary between two provinces that differ in lithologic character and structure. It is essentially a boundary among the unmetamorphosed strata now deformed into great thrust sheets in the Laramide orogenic belt to the east, the long-term miogeosyncline, and the Nevadian orogenic belt to the west with its metamorphic and plutonic rocks. The trench may be located approximately along the edge of the Precambrian craton. If it is a thrust it is one of the longest in the world. If it is a zone of strike-slip movement it may be related to the bend in the Nevadian belt in Washington and Oregon and the great transcurrent movements along the West Coast.

Structural Provinces of the Northern Cordillera*

The Cordilleran region in southern Yukon Territory, northern British Columbia, and southeastern Alaska (Fig. 14-10) may be divided into three northwest-trending belts of unmetamorphosed sedimentary rocks separated by two zones of crystalline metamorphic and granitic rocks. The eastern belt (Pelly, Cassiar, and the Northern Rocky Mountains) is composed mainly of Mississippian and older units. The central belt (Tagish) is composed mainly of Mesozoic volcanic and sedimentary rocks in which numerous granitic plutons are located. The Atlin horst, a complexly faulted block about 250 miles long and composed of late Paleozoic sedimentary rocks, interrupts the Tagish belt near the Yukon Territory boundary. The western belt (St. Elias Mountains) is a complex zone in which granitic plutons intrude sequences ranging in age from Ordovician to Cenozoic. The geology of this part of the Cordillera is known largely through reconnaissance work covering large areas. The crystalline complexes which separate these three belts include the Cassiar batholith in the east and the Coast Mountains in the west.

The structure of the western belt is partially

* After Gabrielse and Wheeler (1961).

obscured by the Pacific, but a central anticlinorium with strongly deformed Paleozoic exposures along its axis and flanked by a synclinorium of Mesozoic strata to the east has been identified. Deformation is also strong near the huge intrusive complexes of the Coast Mountains where beds are isoclinally folded and overturned to the southwest. The regional structure is complicated by strongly developed lineaments, some of which are recognized as fault zones. Many of the longest of these trend northwest with shorter northeasterly zones. St. Amand (1957) concludes that these are dominantly transcurrent faults with right-lateral movement, and recent movements have been of this nature. A right-lateral displacement of 150 miles has been postulated along the combined lineament of Shakwak fault and Chatham Strait, a zone which separates the St. Elias Mountains from the Coast Mountains along most of their length. The St. Elias Mountains include a central zone of metamorphic rocks and an eastern fault zone where thrusts dip southwest and folds are overturned to the northeast. Paleozoic rocks are thrust over Tertiary units along some of these faults. South of the St. Elias Mountains crystalline rocks are thrust to the southwest over Upper Cretaceous and movements dated as Pliocene and Pleistocene have brought about southwestward thrusting.

The Atlin horst interrupts the continuity of structure in the Tagish belt, and large areas are covered by volcanic rocks. The fold and fault pattern reflects a strong northwesterly regional trend which is locally modified near the Atlin horst and near plutons. The intensity of deformation is related to the competence of the rocks throughout the belt, with open folds being prominent in outcrop areas of conglomerate and greywacke, and tight, irregular folds in areas of argillite, limestone, and thin-bedded units.

The eastern belt is characterized by overturned folds and thrust sheets which have moved east.

TRACING THE BELTS SOUTH

The general longitudinal divisions of the northern Cordillera can be followed to the south (Figs. 14-3 and 14-6) through British Columbia and into the northwestern United States. The western deformed belt continues south through Queen Charlotte and Vancouver Islands, but surface outcrops are predominantly Triassic eugeosynclinal sequences. The area of the granitic batholithic complex in the Coast Ranges increases in southern British Columbia, and the number of granitic plutons in the central belt increases in both number and size. A large part of this central belt is covered by Tertiary volcanics. The Rocky Mountain trench continues south through British Columbia, as does the fold and thrust belt east of it which comprises the Northern Rocky Mountains. A notable change is the appearance of a long and wide outcrop of Belt sediments just west of the trench. This belt continues into Idaho and Montana.

Continuity of the belts of the Canadian Cordillera southward is obscured by the Columbia River plateau basalts and the block faulting of the Basin and Range. The character of the eastern frontal structures changes as well in south-central Montana, where the long, narrow, deformed belt gives way to or passes west of a province of block-faulted ranges, major basins, and large anticlinal features.

THE COLUMBIAN ARC

Metamorphosed Paleozoic and Mesozoic eugeosynclinal sequences such as those found in the western and central belts of British Columbia can be traced directly into northern Washington. The structural trends are generally northwest-southeast, and similar rocks outcrop on trend in the Blue Mountains of northeastern Oregon. The trends in the Blue Mountains swing sharply to the west. The next occurrence of these sequences is in the Klamath Mountains of northern California where the trends swing south, and they can be followed into the Sierra Nevada Mountains and in the Transverse Ranges of southern California and Baja, Calif., where granitic plutonic complexes such as those of the Coast Mountains in Canada again reach huge sizes. The belt of Mesozoic metamorphism, plutonic activity, and deformation thus defined follows a long, broad curve down the western North American coast into Washington where it bends sharply to the southwest in a looplike arc called the Columbia Arc. Arcuate swings of this type are not unusual in orogenic belts. They are present in the Alps, they are common among island arcs in Indonesia and the Caribbean, and a swing of this type is necessary to connect the Appalachians with the Ouachitas. The origin of such bends is an unsolved problem. They could be primary or they may be bends imposed on the orogenic belt as a result of deformation.

Paleozoic of the Cordilleran Belt

Paleozoic exposures are scattered through the Cordilleran geosyncline, and although they are not sufficient to yield a definitive picture of the early history, there are enough to indicate some of its major features. Even for the Cambrian, a rather well-defined boundary exists between the region in which great thicknesses of sediment accumulated and a region of shelf deposition (Fig. 14-11). This boundary lies east of a zone that is most often selected to separate eugeosynclinal facies from miogeosynclinal facies (Fig. 14-12); however, neither boundary is exactly the same from period to period through the Paleozoic or Mesozoic. Typical eugeosynclinal deposits of graywacke and volcanics are found in the western belt in every system from the Cambrian through the Cretaceous.

Eardley (1962) has constructed paleogeographic maps of the Cordilleran geosyncline for each period of the Paleozoic.* These give a

---

* A special issue of the Am. Assoc. Petroleum Geologists Bull. was devoted to the sedimentary basins of the Rocky Mountains, Nov. 1965.

general impression of the distribution of major basins and uplifts in the eastern part of the region where outcrops are sufficient for this purpose. Eugeosynclinal facies occurred in western Nevada from the Cambrian through the Permian and presumably involved a much larger area in Washington, Oregon, and California throughout most of the Paleozoic (there are exposures to establish such an extent in the later Paleozoic systems). Major geanticlines and basins occupied the area east of the eugeosyncline. These have regional trends which define a broad arcuate belt extending northeast across Nevada into Utah, where they bend to the northwest and then pass through Idaho into British Columbia. At least one orogenic belt, the Antler belt, passed through Nevada and presumably northward into Canada during the Devonian and Mississippian. A number of northwest elongate basins and geanticlines (central Colorado basin, Uncompaghre Range, Paradox basin) had begun to form in the Colorado, Utah, and New Mexico region by the Mississippian, and these remained as well-defined structures through the Permian. They were aligned with the northern Cordilleran eugeosyncline which bends west of the present Colorado plateau.

Relationship between Igneous and Tectonic Activity

It is a fact that most evidence of igneous activity is found in orogenic belts. The "ring of fire" around the Pacific lies within a belt of modern diastrophism, and most of the known batholiths and volcanic rocks of the United States lie within the Appalachian or the Cordilleran geosynclinal areas. Moreover, the great volumes of intrusions in the Cordilleran were emplaced during time intervals in which orogeny, as dated by unconformities, time of folding, and sediment thickness, was taking place. Many geologists have pointed out this general relationship, and a few have attributed the folding, faulting, and uplift which accompany orogeny to igneous activity, as did Rogers and

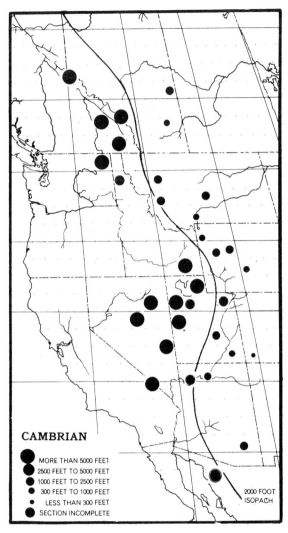

CAMBRIAN

● MORE THAN 5000 FEET
● 2500 FEET TO 5000 FEET
● 1000 FEET TO 2500 FEET
● 300 FEET TO 1000 FEET
· LESS THAN 300 FEET
● SECTION INCOMPLETE

2000 FOOT ISOPACH

Fig. 14-11 Distribution of Cambrian thicknesses in western North America. (*From Kay, 1951.*)

Rogers (1843) and Keith (1923) in the Appalachians. Keith envisioned that the emplacement of magma was forceful and caused the lateral pressures which created the folds in the Valley and Ridge.

Eardley (1960, 1962) and Gilluly (1965) have reviewed the evidence for establishing a temporal or spatial relationship between orogeny and igneous activity in the Cordilleran region. Major intrusions are outlined in Fig. 14-3, and

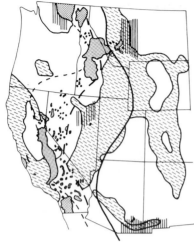

|||||||||| Volcanics, andesitic and more siliceous

▨▨▨ Pluton >70< 140 million years old

▧▧ Orogenic activity

——— Approximate east border of miogeosynclines

— — Approximate east border of eugeosynclines

---- Quartz-diorite line of Moore

Fig. 14-12 Volcanism, tectonism, and plutonism in the Cretaceous in the western United States. *(After Gilluly, 1965.)*

volcanics are shown on the Tectonic Map of the United States. A comparison of the belt in which Nevadian batholiths occur with the major tectonic provinces (Fig. 14-14) leads to the conclusion that the batholiths are entirely confined to the eugeosynclinal portion of the belt. The eugeosyncline was also the site of Paleozoic orogeny. The Nevadian batholiths were emplaced millions of years after these earlier orogenies following Jurassic deformation and metamorphism of the intruded Mariposa formation. The batholiths were emplaced before the main folding in the miogeosyncline to the east. Volcanic rocks, which are prominent on the tectonic maps, are widely distributed over the orogenic belt. The greatest volume is in the Columbia plateau where they are situated on and across the eugeosyncline, but volcanism occurs within the miogeosyncline and even in the eastern foreland provinces in Colorado and New Mexico. These volcanic out-

pourings came after the emplacement of the batholiths and most of the folding in the Tertiary, but they have been affected by block faulting, particularly in the Basin and Range province.

Moore (1959) pointed out that the Cordilleran geosyncline can be divided longitudinally into two petrographic provinces. The western province (Fig. 14-12) contains intrusions of quartz diorite and less siliceous rocks, while the eastern province contains more siliceous intrusions. The boundary between these two lies near but west of the boundary between the miogeosyncline and the eugeosyncline. The largest of the Nevadian plutons lies just east of Moore's line.

Gilluly (1965) proposes several important generalizations regarding the association of tectonism and igneous activity:

1. Basaltic and andesitic volcanics are represented in every system, and in general they cannot be associated with plutons.
2. Siliceous lavas have been erupted widely and in huge volume (probably comparable to that of basalts on the whole) since the Ordovician.
3. Not a single granitic pluton of Phanerozoic age demonstrably older than Early Triassic has been recognized in the western United States, yet Paleozoic orogeny is widely recognized in this same region.
4. Volcanism and tectonism have been more or less continuous at one place or another in the Cordillera throughout Phanerozoic time, but plutonism at a level accessible to later erosion has been essentially independent of both processes in place and catastrophic in time.

STRUCTURAL FEATURES OF THE SHELF REGION IN THE UNITED STATES

The region which constituted the shelf during the Paleozoic lies east of the main belt of

Cretaceous to Eocene folding and thrusting which developed in the thicker miogeosynclinal deposits. This shelf region (Fig. 14-12) includes some of the highest of the Rocky Mountains, starting in Montana with the Beartooth Range and including the Big Horns, the Tetons, the Wind River, Uinta, Laramie, the Colorado Front Range, Wet, Sawatch, the Sangre de Cristo Mountains, and the vast Colorado Plateau. The front of the Rocky Mountain system must certainly be drawn along lines at the eastern edge of these high mountains, but on structural grounds the southern continuation of the Canadian Rocky Mountain fold and thrust belt lies west of all these ranges. There is no structural counterpart of this shelf region in Canada, in South America, or in the Appalachians. We may expect for this reason that the structures here are the product of unique circumstances in the pattern of development or the mechanism of deformation as it affected this part of the Cordilleran geosyncline. Strong cases can be made for each of these premises.

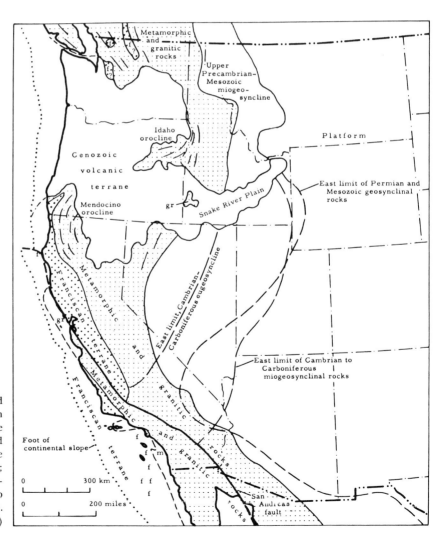

Fig. 14-13 Major Paleozoic and Mesozoic complexes of the western United States. Small and offshore areas of basement rocks are marked by letters: f = Franciscan terrane (and similar rocks in Washington); gr = granitic rocks; m = metamorphic rocks belonging to metamorphic-and-granitic terrane. *(From Hamilton and Myers, 1965.)*

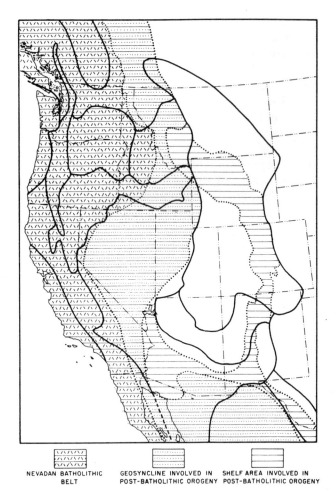

NEVADAN BATHOLITHIC
BELT

GEOSYNCLINE INVOLVED IN
POST-BATHOLITHIC OROGENY

SHELF AREA INVOLVED IN
POST-BATHOLITHIC OROGENY

Fig. 14-14   Relations of tectonic to igneous provinces of western United States (*From Eardley, 1960.*)

This shelf region occupied part of the ancient continental craton. The crustal thicknesses here are greater than those to the west (Fig. 10-9); the Precambrian is well exposed in mountains, where it stands as much as 13,000 ft above sea level, with relief of over a mile. Seismic refraction profiles suggest thicknesses of sialic crust on the order of 12 to 15 miles, with a lower, more mafic, layer of similar thickness. Note on the tectonic map in Fig. 14-3 that very few Precambrian rocks are exposed west of the Rockies. Some students of the region have taken this as a line of evidence to support the idea that the eugeosynclinal belt of the Cordil-

leran was founded on oceanic crust. This idea receives support from geophysical evidence.

The dominant characteristics of the structural pattern of the shelf are:

1. It is underlain by a thick, continental-type crust composed of sialic Precambrian rocks.
2. Large sedimentary basins separated by block-fault mountains, arches, and geanticlines have existed in this region since Precambrian time.
3. The position, shape, and size of these basins have changed as first one and then another area has been elevated or lowered.
4. The vertical component of movement has been great. The structural relief from the top of Precambrian and Cambrian contacts in high mountains to the same contacts penetrated by drilling in adjacent basins is commonly 20,000 ft or more.
5. Many of the positive elements at the present time are bounded by high-angle faults on one or more sides, although monoclines, geanticlines, and local reverse and even thrust faults also occur within the region. The largest of these positive elements is the Colorado Plateau, where Paleozoic and Mesozoic marine sedimentary sequences have been elevated to several thousand feet above sea level over a vast area. The sequences are warped to form spectacular monoclines and structural terraces, and are block-faulted but with little folding or thrusting. Differential vertical movements have clearly dominated the deformation.

Faults of the Rocky Mountains

The region encompassing the Middle and Southern Rocky Mountains and the Colorado Plateau is particularly attractive for purposes of structural study. Good exposures, high relief, and a wealth of subsurface data gradually being released provide excellent control on the shape of the structures. The Precambrian basement in this region (Fig. 14-3) is usually bounded by faults. Many of the faults are at least locally thrusts, and others are nearly vertical. The bordering fault zone may contain normal faults as well. The structural relief measured from the surface of the Precambrian in the Rockies to the top of the Precambrian in adjacent basins is frequently on the order of 25,000 to 40,000 ft in the foreland. Thus the faults of whatever shape have a large vertical component. Tight folding of the type described in the folded and thrust-faulted orogenic belts is absent. We find instead structural terraces, monoclines, and homoclines. All greater fold complexity is confined to local structural features.

Among the lines of evidence which point to vertical tectonics in this region, the thrust margins of the Bighorn Mountains are particularly significant. Local thrusts dipping under the mountains are located on both the eastern and western sides of the mountains. Similar structures occur in the Beartooth Range where the northeastern front is thrust to the north, the eastern front is thrust to the east, and the southwestern corner of the range is thrust to the southwest. Thrusts consistently dip under the mountain uplifts irrespective of their orientation, showing nothing of the strong alignment found in the Canadian Rockies, the Appalachians, the Alps, and other folded orogenic belts. These thrusts must extend to depths of 5 or more miles just in order to account for the Precambrian basement which has come up along them, but the way the fault surfaces are shaped at depth is not obvious. Hypotheses have been based on stress theory (refer to Chap. 4) and on the presence of near-vertical faults in the same region along the border of other ranges, the nature of subsidiary structures along the mountain fronts, seismic evidence, and a few wells which have been drilled through the overthrust plate (Fig. 14-15). The hypotheses advanced are a block-fault uplift along a fault which changes from a thrust near the surface to a high-angle reverse fault, a vertical fault, and eventually possibly a normal fault at depth; uplift along low-angle thrusts with inclinations of 30° or less; and a fold-thrust uplift in which the structure developed from a combination of folding and thrusting (Fig. 14-16). It is not easy to choose among these alternatives. Each can be used to explain such geologic

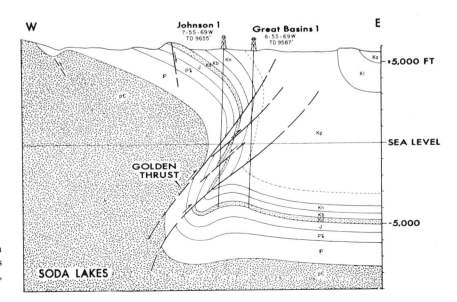

Fig. 14-15 The Golden thrust in the Soda Lakes area, Jefferson County, Colo. (*From Berg, 1962.*)

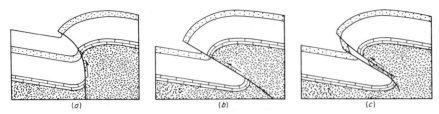

Fig. 14-16 Diagrams illustrating hypotheses of mountain flank deformation: (*a*) = block uplift, (*b*) = thrust uplift, (*c*) = fold-thrust uplift. (*Redrawn from Berg, 1962.*)

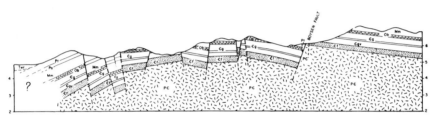

Fig. 14-17 Structure section in Wind River Canyon area, Wyoming. (*From Wise, 1963.*)

facts as: (1) the thrust at the northeast corner of the Beartooth Range which is displaced along tears (Fig. 4-13), (2) the curvature of the cover on the overthrust plate such as that along the flanks of the Bighorn Mountains, (3) normal faulting resulting from extension in the sedimentary cover such as that on the southern margin of the Wind River Range (Figs. 14-17 and 14-18), (4) the presence of cover beneath the overthrust Precambrian crystallines.

An analysis of the gravity anomalies along a traverse across the margin of the Wind River Range (Fig. 14-19) supports the interpretation that the thrust along the margin of this range extends far (about 18 miles) under the range at very low angles. The preferred model does show the fault steepening at a depth of about 10,000 ft below sea level.

Vertical and near-vertical faults such as those shown in section along the Sangre de Cristo Mountains (Fig. 14-20) also clearly exist in this region. A particularly good example of vertical faults is found in the Pryor Mountains and in the Clark's Fork Canyon of the Beartooth Range. Four block-shaped units comprise the

Pryor Mountains of Wyoming and Montana. Each is bounded on two or three sides by high-angle faults. The blocks are tilted, suggesting the opening of four trap doors. The faults intersect at the corners at nearly right angles, a configuration that is hard to obtain by movements along any but very steep faults. At the corner of one of these blocks, the Precambrian is brought up into fault contact with Cretaceous units. The throw decreases laterally along the fault until the covering Paleozoics can be seen to form a passive *drapelike fold* over the fault. This fold then passes along its axis into a monocline and eventually disappears. The development of such structural features may be viewed as a progressive sequence in time (Fig. 14-21).

Big Horn Mountains

The Big Horn Mountains, Wyo., provide an interesting example of the types of structures found in the shelf region. The range has an exposed core of Archean rocks which now stand at elevations over 10,000 ft above sea level over a large area (Fig. 14-22). Paleozoic sections surrounding this core are deformed in highly varying degree. The gross structure of the range is anticlinal, yet the central portion of the eastern limb is overthrust to the east. Paleozoic sequences on the central portion of the west limb dip gently off the flank of the range, but to the north of this central area the western flanking

sections become steeper and eventually overturned and faulted to the west (Fig. 14-23) in the Five Springs Creek area.

The margins of the range are cut by local high-angle faults at numerous places, but these are not continuous along the margins (Hoppin, 1965). The longest major fault, the Tensleep

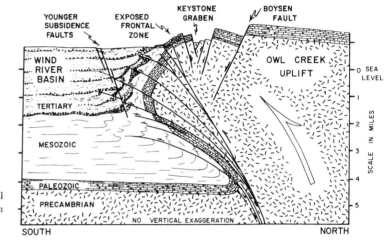

Fig. 14-18 Suggested structure of frontal zone of Owl Creek uplift, Wyoming. (*From Wise, 1963.*)

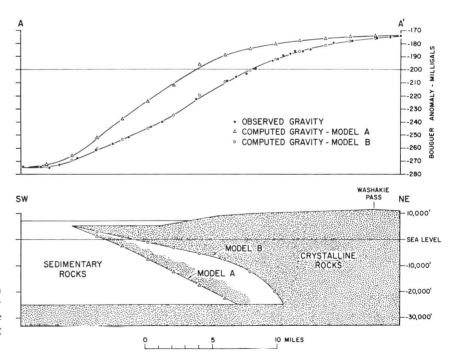

Fig. 14-19 Gravity profiles on the southwest flank, Wind River Mountains, and interpretive structure models. (*From Berg and Romberg, 1966.*)

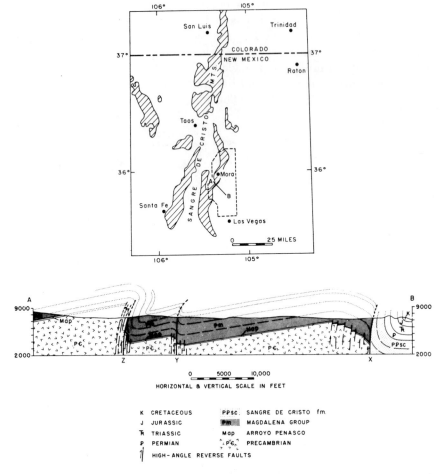

Fig. 14-20 Basement block faulting and related structures in southeastern part of Sangre de Cristo uplift near Mora, N. Mex. Index map of Mora area and cross section AB showing relation between basement block faulting and asymmetrical folds in overlying sedimentary formations. (*From Prucha, Graham, and Nickelsen, 1965.*)

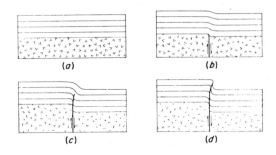

Fig. 14-21 Postulated sequence in deformation of sedimentary rock beds overlying basement fault blocks. (*a*) Before faulting in basement. (*b*) Initial stage of faulting in basement. Sedimentary beds adjust by bending without faulting. (*c*) Intermediate stage in basement faulting. Lower sedimentary beds have exceeded critical degree of bending and are faulted; upper sedimentary beds are bent but not faulted. (*d*) Advanced stage of basement faulting. Faulting extends through sedimentary beds to surface. (*From Prucha, Graham, and Nickelsen, 1965.*)

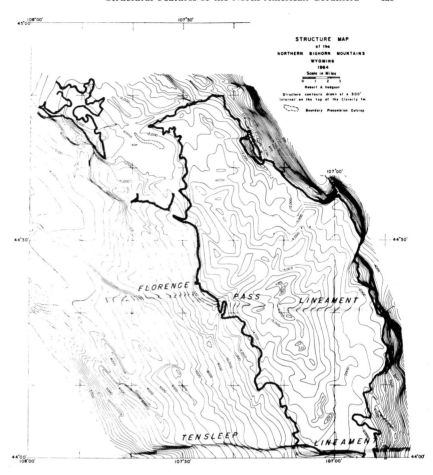

Fig. 14-22 Structure contour map of northern Big Horn Mountains, Wyo., showing location and structural geometries of Tensleep and Florence Pass lineaments. (*From Hodgson, 1965.*)

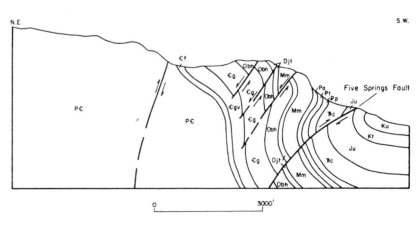

Fig. 14-23 Sketch cross section through Five Springs fault on west side of Big Horn Mountains, Wyo., near State Highway 14. Scale in feet. (*After Osterwald, 1961, Fig. 4; from Prucha, Graham, and Nickelsen, 1965.*)

Ku	Cretaceous undivided	
Kt	Thermopolis shale	
Ju	Jurassic undivided	
Ћc	Chugwater formation	
Pp	Phosphoria formation	

Pt	Tensleep sandstone
Pa	Amsden formation
Mm	Madison limestone
Djt	Jefferson limestone and Three Forks shale
Obh	Bighorn dolomite

Єg	Gallatin limestone
Єgv	Gros Ventre shale
Єf	Flathead sandstone
PЄ	Precambrian undivided

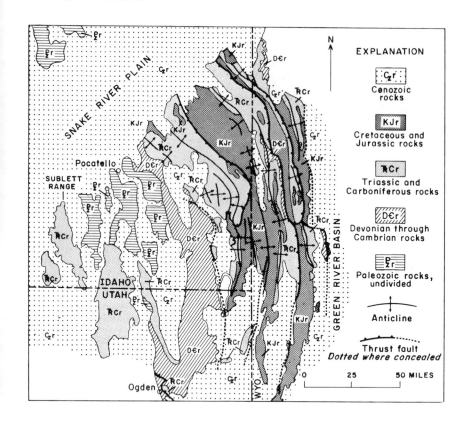

Fig. 14-24 Generalized geologic map of Idaho-Wyoming thrust belt. *(From Armstrong and Oriel, 1965.)*

fault, trends across the range. The magnitude and extent of the thrusting along the margins of the range are subordinate to uplift and arching of the basement. This arching may have been accomplished in large part by movements along closely spaced fractures in the basement rocks. Why the local thrusting has occurred is more difficult to understand. The effect may be analogous to an expansion of the volume of the uplifted mass or to the lateral spreading of the uplifted basement, and it is also theoretically possible that these local faults are cases of high-angle faults which become reverse faults only near the surface.

FOLDS AND FAULTS OF THE MIOGEOSYNCLINE

A wide belt of low-angle thrusts and strongly asymmetrical folds which resemble the Appalachian fold belt is located west of the shelf province and approximately along the line of rapid thickening of Paleozoic and lower Mesozoic sequences. This belt has long been recognized in the Canadian Rockies, in western Montana, and along the Idaho-Wyoming border (Fig. 14-24). These faults bring Beltian rocks to the surface in Canada and Montana, but in Wyoming the oldest sequences thrust to the surface are Cambrian. These thrusts (Fig. 14-25), like the faults in the Canadian foothills, involve large-scale lateral transport, possibly as much as 10 to 20 miles, and their features include imbricate thrust slices as on the Absaroka fault, folded thrust planes, a concentration of movement along bedding planes, and later high-angle faulting which disrupts and offsets the thrusts.

Recent field studies (Roberts and others, 1965; Kay and Crawford, 1964; Miller, 1966;

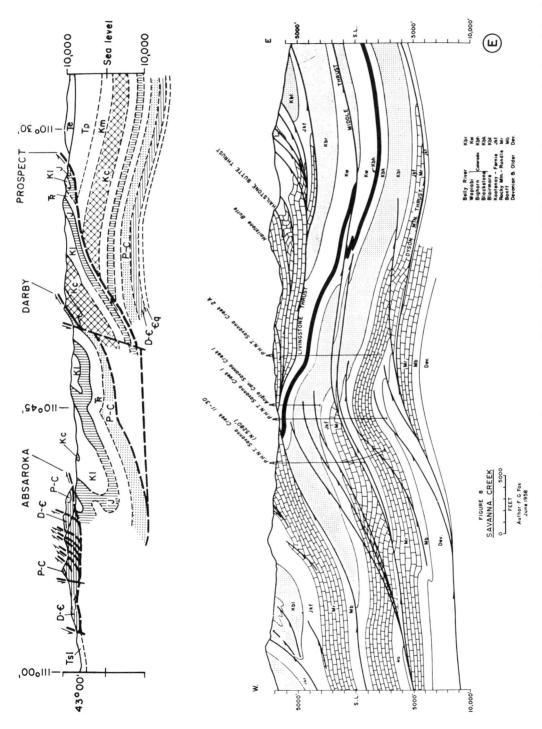

Fig. 14-25 Cross section across the thrust belt of western Wyoming, top *(from Rubey and Hubbert, 1959)*. Cross section across the thrust belt of the Canadian Rockies, below *(from Fox, 1959)*.

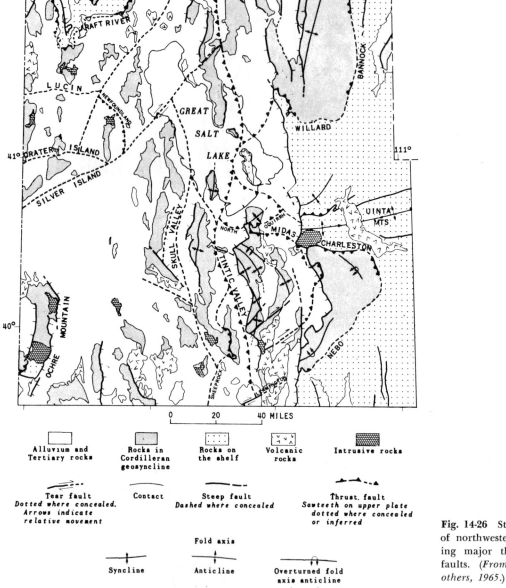

Fig. 14-26 Structural map of northwestern Utah showing major thrust and tear faults. (*From Roberts and others, 1965.*)

Nelson, 1966; and others) have established the continuity of this belt southwest across Utah and Nevada into Arizona. The continuity has been obscured by block faulting in the Basin and Range province which has left only scat-

tered remnants in isolated mountain ranges surrounded by valleys now filled with alluvium deposited from the Pleistocene to Recent times and covered in part by Tertiary lavas. Structural sketch maps of the belt near Great Salt

Lake (Fig. 14-26) and in the Wah Wah Mountains of southwest Utah (Fig. 14-27) illustrate the complexity of the structure. Overthrust plates in both of these examples, and indeed throughout most of the mapped portions of the Basin and Range have moved toward the east, and most of the overturned folds are overturned in the same direction. It is difficult to tie the structural pattern of the deformation together across the Basin and Range because the stratigraphic section involved in the thrusting differs from place to place. Primarily Ordovician through Devonian sequences are involved in the klippes and thrust of the Toquima Range of central Nevada (Kay and Crawford, 1964), but Cambrian is thrust onto Jurassic in the Wah Wah Mountains (Fig. 14-27).

What happens to the miogeosyncline and the thrust belt southwest of the Colorado Plateau remains very obscure. There are very few Paleozoic or Mesozoic sedimentary rocks in this area, and most of these are metamorphosed and belong to the eugeosynclinal associations farther west.

Does this belt of thrusts represent a thin-skinned type of deformation, as has been suggested in the Appalachians? Are these thrusts and folds due to horizontal crustal compression, or are they products of gravity sliding from a higher uplifted core? These questions will doubtless be argued for a long time to come. The present configuration does not lend itself to a conclusive answer. All the thrust plates are in the sedimentary veneer; many of the faults are very flat and they are often bedding-plane faults. Rubey and Hubbert (1959) have applied the theory that pore pressure in sedimentary piles allows thrusting over very

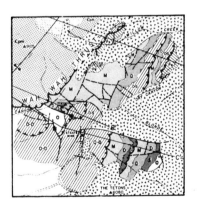

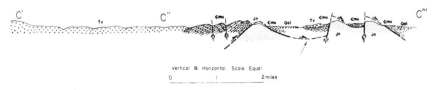

Fig. 14-27 Geologic map of part of the Wah Wah Mountains, southwestern Utah. Letter abbreviations are periods, check pattern in Tertiary volcanics. Section is along line labeled *C'*. (*From Miller, 1966.*)

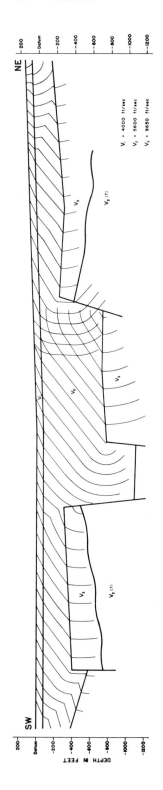

Fig. 14-28 Seismic reversed profile in Summer Lake Valley, Oreg. *(From Donath and Kuo, 1962.)*

low slopes to the Wyoming fault belt, but even though slopes of only a few degrees may be necessary to cause gravitative sliding in such cases, it is still difficult to show that such slopes did, in fact, exist over the vast region involved. Nor can we fail to be impressed by the great stratigraphic throw involved where Beltian rocks are thrust onto Cretaceous rocks.

BLOCK FAULTING IN THE BASIN AND RANGE

The present configuration of the Basin and Range physiographic province is due largely to Cenozoic block faulting. Many of the faults have been active in Pleistocene and Recent times. This must prompt us to examine the possibility of a connection of this block faulting with Cenozoic transcurrent movements along the West Coast.

This Cenozoic block faulting bears no apparent relation to the boundary of the older geosynclinal margins. Extensive faulting along predominantly northwest-southeast lines occurs in the basalts of the Columbia River plateau in Oregon, southern Idaho, northern California, and Nevada. These faults cut across the trend of the metamorphic eugeosynclinal belt of the Nevadian orogeny where this belt is bent (Fig. 14-3). Block faulting is largely responsible for the north-south elongation of the ranges and valleys of Nevada. The Sierra Nevada Range is being uplifted along its eastern edge by Cenozoic fault movements (Christensen, 1966), and steep faults are recognized bounding many of the Precambrian exposures in southern Arizona. Christensen describes the geometry of this movement by means of a structure contour map constructed by use of uplifted Tertiary river channels and volcanic rocks. The latest movements, he finds, began during the Pliocene and since that time have amounted to over 6,000 ft along the eastern (faulted) margin. The block has moved largely as a large unit and differs in this respect from the more closely spaced faulted blocks to the east and west.

Cenozoic uplift on high-angle faults is by no means confined to the Basin and Range; many faults in the shelf region, as in Wyoming at the Tetons, have been active in the Pleistocene also, but the effects have not been nearly so drastic in modifying the regional tectonic pattern as they have been to the west. Block faulting also occurred in the Appalachians after the last major orogeny (the Triassic basins), but the orientation of the basins, the spacing, and the details of the fault patterns are hardly comparable to those in the west. Most of the faults in the Basin and Range region are normal; the structure is essentially that of graben and horst block faulting. Typically, thick tectonic breccias such as those associated with thrust and reverse faults are absent. Drags in the sedimentary and volcanic cover are generally absent; however, folds are sometimes traced into faults or found over faults as described in the Middle Rocky Mountains. The faults dip toward the basins at an angle of 45 to 80°, often as a series of steps. Thrust faults of Cenozoic age are not found associated with the high-angle faults, and in southern Oregon, small volcanic vents are found aligned parallel to the fault direction (Fuller and Waters, 1929). These might be expected to be closed if there had been thrusting or compression.

Geophysical studies have been made across several of the basins. A seismic refraction profile (Fig. 14-28) shows an interpretation from seismic velocities along a reversed profile in south-central Oregon. The faults appear to be very steep, conform in character to those recognized in the region on the surface, and show considerable variation in throw (Donath and Kuo, 1962). Gravity surveys run over Dixie and Fairview Valleys, Nev., indicate that these valleys contain several thousand feet of low-density (Cenozoic) sediments (Thompson, 1959). The visible relief in this area is about 5,000 ft, and thus the structural relief caused by the faulting here is on the order of 2 miles. A gravity profile across one valley is illustrated in Fig. 14-29. Note that the fill is over 5,000 ft thick. This

area was affected by faulting in 1954 and results from studies of movement of triangulation stations indicate that points on opposite sides moved away to the northwest and southeast (Fig. 14-30); the component of extension normal to the fault trace is 5 ft (Whitten, 1956). The west side of the basin dropped by 5 ft also. Dip estimates on the faults range from 55 to 75°. Thompson (1959) concludes that the faulting must be the result of extension, with this movement as the last increment caused by

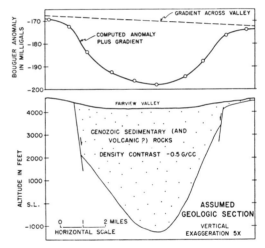

Fig. 14-29 Gravity profile and section across Fairview Valley. (*From Thompson, 1959.*)

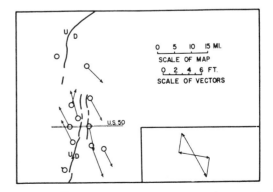

Fig. 14-30 Horizontal movements close to the faults. (*After Whitten, 1956.*)

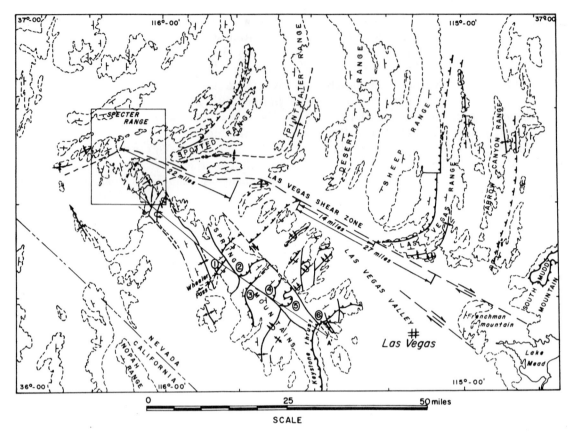

Fig. 14-31 Structure of the Las Vegas shear zone. (*From Burchfiel, 1965.*)

extension across the valley of about $1\frac{1}{2}$ miles in 15 million years (the amount varies depending on the dip used for the fault). If this sample is taken as typical of the Basin and Range, then the total extension in the province would be on the order of 30 miles.

Most students of the Basin and Range province accept the interpretation of the structural pattern as being due to extension. If the extension is approximately normal to the normal faults, it is taking place along northeast-southwest lines in Oregon and along east-west lines in Nevada. The pattern is not so well recognized in southern Arizona, and to the west in California and the Baja Peninsula, transcurrent movements dominate. The necessary extension could arise in several ways—regional

uplift followed by partial collapse, regional extension across the geosyncline, or extension produced as a secondary effect of major transcurrent movements parallel to the elongation of the geosyncline.

Hypothesis of Strike-slip Control of Block Faulting

A number of zones of strike-slip faulting have been identified in the Basin and Range, and many more lineaments are now being considered as possible zones of strike-slip movement (Fig. 14-4). Among these are Walker Lane which trends southeast-northwest in western Nevada and probably continues to the south as the Las Vegas shear zone (Fig. 14-31) and the Death Valley fault zone (Fig. 14-32). All these are right-lateral strike-slip zones, as are the San Andreas and other major faults along the West Coast.

Shawe (1965) analyzed historical faulting in Nevada. He discovered that the recent faults occur in a well-defined arc which transgresses several of the fault-block mountains, and he suggests that these are not formed independently. Faults in the southern portion of this arc are arranged *en échelon*, indicating a pos-

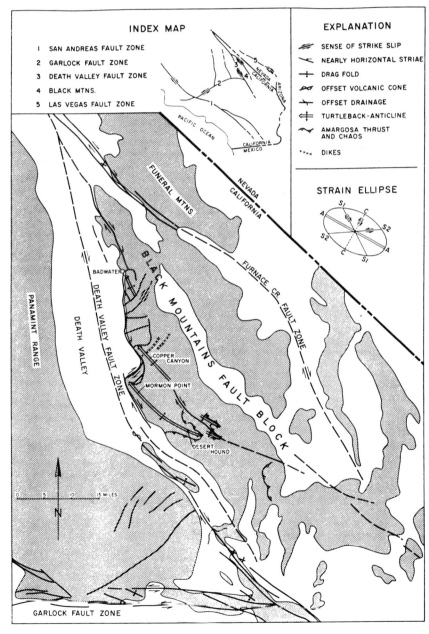

Fig. 14-32 Tectonic sketch map, Death Valley region, California. (*From Hill and Troxel, 1966.*)

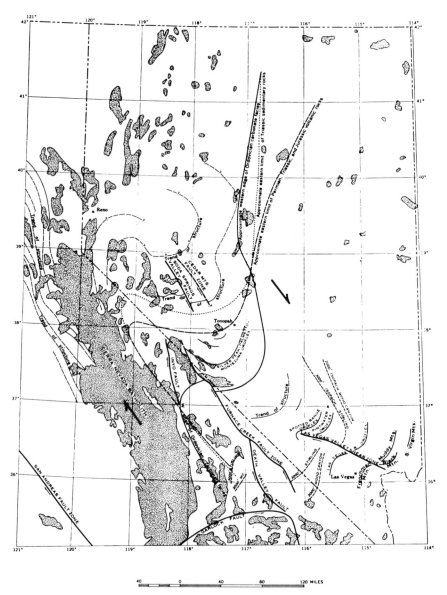

Fig. 14-33 Summary of structural features along the mobile belt east of the Sierra Nevada. Stippled areas are granitic plutonic rocks. *(From Albers, 1967.)*

sible deep-seated shear of right-lateral movement. Some of the faults bounding valleys are dip-slip, others are mainly strike-slip, and a systematic change from dip-slip to strike-slip occurs from north to south. Shawe suggests that the Basin and Range structures have been created as near-surface adjustments in the crust to movements along deep-seated (perhaps extending into the upper mantle), transcurrent faults, which define a conjugate system (northwest zones of right-lateral offset, and northeast zones of left-lateral offset). Stratigraphic evidence (Albers, 1967) also supports a right-lateral movement in the Basin and Range. Albers has shown pronounced sigmoidal bends in the limits of Permian, Triassic, and Jurassic volcanics; Ordovician carbonates; and Triassic sedimentary rocks (Fig. 14-33). These bends coincide with the fault zones along the southwestern border of Nevada.

A similar hypothesis is advanced by Burchfiel and Stewart (1966) and by Hill and Troxel (1966) to explain the fault system of the Death Valley region. As in most of the Basin and Range, it is necessary to project exposed faults for great distances under valleys filled with alluvium in order to make such syntheses. However, if the faults do, in fact, connect in the way shown (Fig. 14-34) and if they are transcurrent, then a mechanical system is possible which allows an easy explanation of the basin and range form. The basins occupy areas of extension and the ranges are the remnants of a once continuous structure which have been shifted laterally apart rather than elevated relative to adjacent lower blocks.

The possibilities of such structures have been investigated by means of scale-model experiments by Tanner (1962). The design of these models allowed horizontal movements in a deep, rigid layer along predetermined breaks (basement shapes included diamond-shaped blocks cut with 60 and 120° angles as well as single cuts). This basement was covered by layers of clay. Movements in the basement were always horizontal, and regardless of the manner of stress application, strike-slip movements in the basement took place. Despite this, accommodating movements in the overlying clay always resulted in vertical movement (scaled values of 1 km vertical movement were common and the maximum was 10 km).

One of the models (Fig. 14-35) produced by a basement strike-slip faulting results in surface effects that are similar to the graben and horst features of the Basin and Range. Undulatory strike-slip fault traces and *en échelon* fault zones were produced in other experiments.

Application of a Rotational Couple to the Cordilleran Geosyncline

Carey (1958) and Wise (1963) have used the concept of a major, rotational (clockwise) couple to synthesize the structure of the Cordilleran geosyncline (Fig. 14-36). The bend of the Mesozoic eugeosynclinal belt (Fig. 14-3) is interpreted as a secondary structure exposed on the belt by this couple. It may be argued that such bending was possible because the rocks were

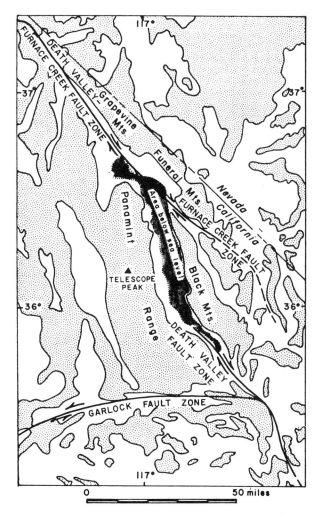

Fig. 14-34 Diagrammatic map showing interpretation of strike-slip movement and area of tension in Death Valley area, California. (*From Burchfiel and Stewart, 1966.*)

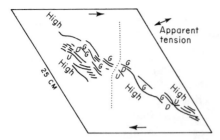

Fig. 14-35 Sketch of compressional model over simple diamond-block basement. Surface fault displacement is about 0.05 times basement offset. Basement failure extended from upper left corner to lower right corner. G = graben; D = down; U = up; dotted line = surface trace which has been doubly curved (drag-type folding) but not broken. (*From Tanner, 1962.*)

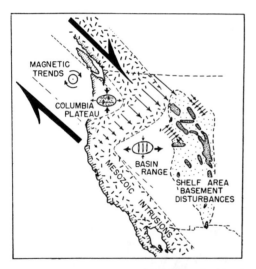

Fig. 14-36 Hypothetical stress distribution in the Cordilleran region. California and Mexico batholith zone on the south. Canadian batholith zone on the north. Strain-ellipsoid orientation for Basin and Range province and for Pacific Northwest indicated. Rotational sense of marine magnetic pattern indicated at northwest. Small arrows in Wyoming indicate combined compression and shear to produce parallelogram pattern. (*From Wise, 1963.*)

not brittle and the region is not underlain by a thick sialic crust. The major zones of transcurrent movement also reflect this couple, and these zones (e.g., San Andreas fault, Walkers

Lane, the Rocky Mountain trench) are fundamental to the overall movement pattern. The extension in the Basin and Range arises as a secondary effect of movement along deep-seated transcurrent faults. The markedly different pattern in the shelf region is attributed to differences in crustal type and thickness. The present tectonic pattern is attributed primarily to horizontal movements along transcurrent faults which penetrate the crust. This idea provides an interesting and in many ways more attractive alternative to the crustal compression hypothesis, which fails to explain the origin of the transcurrent faults and which attributes the bend in the Nevadian eugeosyncline to the primary configuration of the belt.

THE EUGEOSYNCLINE

Pre-Cenozoic eugeosynclinal facies rocks outcrop in northern Washington, the Ochoco–Blue Mountains uplift of Oregon and Idaho, the Klamath Mountains, the Sierra Nevada Mountains, the Coast Ranges, the Transverse Ranges scattered in the western part of Nevada and Arizona, and Baja, Calif. (Fig. 14-37). This belt has been fragmented and regional continuity has been lost as a result of Cenozoic block and transcurrent faulting. A twofold division of these eugeosyncline facies is recognized on the United States Tectonic Map. Largely unmetamorphosed graywacke of Late Jurassic and Cretaceous age, known as the Franciscan group, occurs in the Coast Ranges of California and Oregon. The remaining portions of the belt include eugeosynclinal facies which range in age from Paleozoic to Late Jurassic and include large areas of metamorphic rock and many large batholithic intrusions such as Loon Lake, Colville, Similkameen, Idaho, and the Sierra Nevada intrusive complex. The deformational pattern is complex in all these rocks, and structural relationships between the two major divisions are not yet established although it appears now that the Franciscan was largely formed after the Nevadian orogeny. Franciscan rocks lie adjacent to the metamorphic complex in the Klamath Mountains (Fig. 14-38), but the two are separated there by a fault. The type of fault is uncertain; Irwin (1965) postulates that the fault is an east-dipping thrust, but Dott (1965) prefers to consider this zone part of the transcurrent fault pattern of the Coast Ranges.

Klamath Mountains

The Klamath Mountains are selected to illustrate the nature of the older and metamor-

phosed portion of the eugeosyncline because they have been examined in some detail and knowledge of them has been recently synthesized (Dott, 1965; Irwin, 1960, 1965). Rocks of eugeosynclinal facies have formed in the area now exposed in the Klamath Mountains since the early Paleozoic. The region can be divided longitudinally into several arcuate belts—a western Jurassic belt and eastern and western Paleozoic to Triassic belts separated by a central metamorphic belt (Fig. 14-38). Granitic

Fig. 14-37 Map showing principal structural features of western California and offshore area. Subsurface contours on basement rocks of Great Valley from Merrit Smith (unpublished). The Mendocino escarpment is from Menard (1955b), the Pioneer ridge fault from Menard (1960), and the Murray fracture zone from Menard (1955a). Faults shown in southern California are from Cohee (1961). Areas of underwater bedrock off the coast of southern California are after Emery (1960). Areas of crystalline bedrock off the coast of northern California are after Hanna (1952) and Chesterman (1952). The trend of the crest of the magnetic high of the Great Valley is after Irwin and Bath (1962). The foot of the continental slope is after the U. S. Geol. Survey map of the state of California, scale 1:1,000,000, 1953 ed. (*From Bailey, Irwin, and Jones, 1964.*)

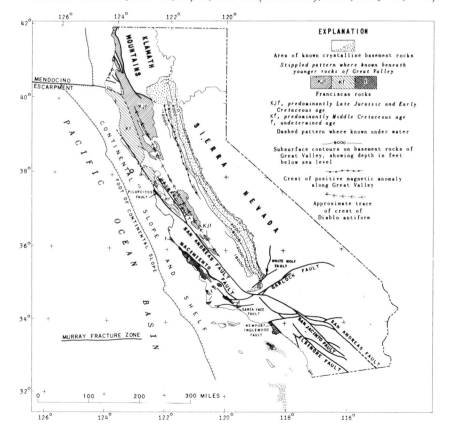

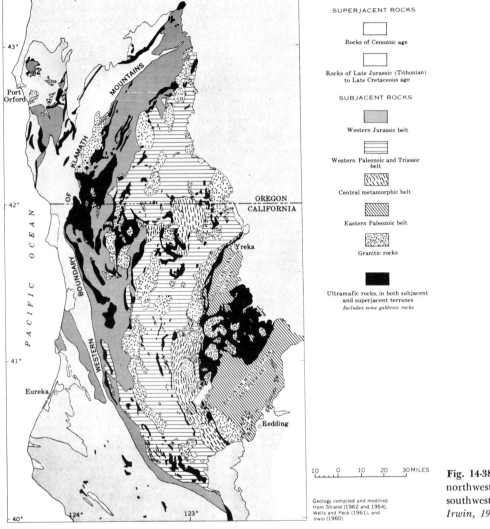

EXPLANATION

SUPERJACENT ROCKS

Rocks of Cenozoic age

Rocks of Late Jurassic (Tithonian)
to Late Cretaceous age

SUBJACENT ROCKS

Western Jurassic belt

Western Paleozoic and Triassic
belt

Central metamorphic belt

Eastern Paleozoic belt

Granitic rocks

Ultramafic rocks, in both subjacent
and superjacent terranes
Includes some gabbroic rocks

10   0   10   20   30 MILES

Geology compiled and modified
from Strand (1962 and 1964),
Wells and Peck (1961), and
Irwin (1960)

Fig. 14-38 Geologic map of
northwestern California and
southwestern Oregon. (*From
Irwin, 1964.*)

plutons and ultramafic rocks occur in all these
belts. The plutonic and metamorphic activity
(Fig. 14-39) culminated in the Late Jurassic
between 135 and 145 million years ago (Dott,
1965) in what is known as the Nevadian orogeny. Each of these outcrop belts appears to be
separated from the next by a fault or a zone of
ultramafic or granitic rocks. The most prominent rock types in the Paleozoic sedimentary
belts are greenstones, graywacke sandstones,

mudstones, and bedded chert; a little limestone and rhyolite occur in several parts of the
section. The central metamorphic belt contains hornblende and mica schists. The western
Jurassic belt is mainly composed of slaty mudstones and graywacke.

Irwin (1965) has postulated that the boundaries between these belts are thrust faults, and
that the arcuate character of the Klamath structural trends is in part a reflection of this

westward-directed thrusting in which each belt is moved over the adjacent western belt (Fig. 14-40), with the resultant development of outliers and windows. The age of the thrusting is younger than Early Cretaceous along the western boundary of the Klamath Mountains if Redwood Mountain (Fig. 14-40) is an outlier of the Klamath rocks, because it is surrounded and, according to this interpretation, underlain by Early Cretaceous rocks. Mapping in southern Oregon has subsequently shown that one of the postulated faults is unnecessary to explain field relations. A gradational contact has been established between schist and an unmetamor-

phosed sequence formerly thought to be separated by a fault (Dott, 1965). Thus it seems possible that future studies in northern California may reveal that Redwood Mountain is not a klippe, and the thrust hypothesis will be significantly weakened. However, at least for the present, the thrust hypothesis must be considered a viable working hypothesis.

Radiometric dates obtained from plutons and metamorphism in the Klamath Mountains indicate a Late Jurassic event, the Nevadian orogeny, but deformation has continued after this deformation. Peridotite bodies locally transect the schists which were recrystallized during

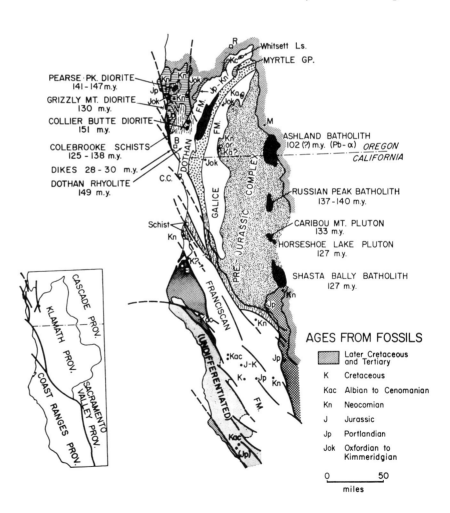

Fig. 14-39 Summary map of age data, regional tectonic patterns, and relations of the geologic provinces of southwest Oregon and northwest California. The "undifferentiated" rocks in the southwest are now included in the Franciscan complex. *(After Bailey, Irwin, and Jones, 1964; from Dott, 1965.)*

PEARSE·PK. DIORITE
141 - 147 m.y.

GRIZZLY MT. DIORITE
130 m.y.

COLLIER BUTTE DIORITE
151 m.y.

COLEBROOKE SCHISTS
125 - 138 m.y.

DIKES 28 - 30 m.y.

DOTHAN RHYOLITE
149 m.y.

Whitsett Ls.
MYRTLE GP.

ASHLAND BATHOLITH
102 (?) m.y. (Pb-α)

OREGON
CALIFORNIA

RUSSIAN PEAK BATHOLITH
137 - 140 m.y.

CARIBOU MT. PLUTON
133 m.y.

HORSESHOE LAKE PLUTON
127 m.y.

SHASTA BALLY BATHOLITH
127 m.y.

AGES FROM FOSSILS

	Later Cretaceous and Tertiary
K	Cretaceous
Kac	Albian to Cenomanian
Kn	Neocomian
J	Jurassic
Jp	Portlandian
Jok	Oxfordian to Kimmeridgian

0   50
miles

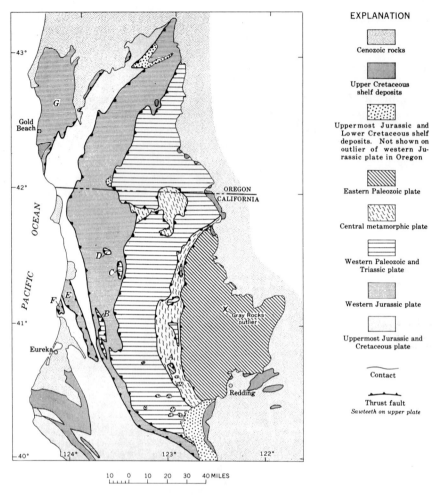

EXPLANATION

Cenozoic rocks

Upper Cretaceous
shelf deposits

Uppermost Jurassic and
Lower Cretaceous shelf
deposits. Not shown on
outlier of western Ju-
rassic plate in Oregon

Eastern Paleozoic plate

Central metamorphic plate

Western Paleozoic and
Triassic plate

Western Jurassic plate

Uppermost Jurassic and
Cretaceous plate

Contact

Thrust fault
Sawteeth on upper plate

10   0   10   20   30   40 MILES

Fig. 14-40 Principal postulated thrust plates of the Klamath Mountains and adjacent Coast Ranges. Thrust outliers are indicated by letter symbol: *E* = Redwood Mountain. (*From Irwin, 1965.*)

the orogeny, volcanism recurred following the Nevadian events (Koch, 1963), and thick conglomerates were widely formed in the Early Cretaceous. These are followed by an unconformity about the middle of the Cretaceous which is related to a deformation unaccompanied by metamorphism or plutonic activity. Notably, the arcuate trends of the Klamath Mountains are present in Dott's reconstruction of pre-Eocene paleogeology. He considers these

arcuate structural trends to be of very early origin and not a product of bending of the orogenic belt in the Late Tertiary and Quaternary when the region was subjected to right-lateral transcurrent faulting.

The Coast Ranges

The Coast Ranges located along the California coast are composed largely of Franciscan rocks and granitic plutons. The structure is dominated by numerous north-northwest-trending subparallel shear zones which have broken, displaced, and fragmented the West Coast south of Oregon. The Franciscan is interesting as an example for the study of sedimentary tectonics.

The Franciscan*

A heterogeneous assemblage of eugeosynclinal rocks found on the San Francisco peninsula has long been referred to as the Franciscan group or series, and other rocks throughout the Coast Ranges have been correlated with these on the basis of lithologic similarity. The predominant rock is graywacke, but shale, altered mafic volcanic rock, chert, and minor limestone are a part of the assemblage. These rocks underlie a major part of western California and are prominently exposed in the Coast Ranges. The total thickness of the Franciscan cannot be determined by normal stratigraphic methods, but is probably more than 50,000 ft. Fossils found at 25 localities establish ages for the rocks ranging from Late Jurassic to at least Late Cretaceous.

The graywacke is predominantly medium-grained and is typically interbedded with minor shale and rarer conglomerate. The physical features indicate rapid deposition of unsorted material, presumably by turbidity currents. Altered mafic rocks consist of pillows, tuffs, or breccias resulting from submarine eruptions, but some massive units may be intrusive. These volcanics range from a few feet to many thousands of feet in thickness.

Chert and a distinctive shale occurring with it are present in minor quantity. They are thought to be chemical precipitates formed by the reaction of magma and sea water under considerable hydrostatic pressure. The chert is usually associated with ultramafic bodies, suggesting a genetic connection. It is possible that the lenses formed from silica, alumina, and iron released by submarine volcanic eruptions that occurred at a depth great enough for the

* Paraphrased from Bailey, Irwin, and Jones (1964).

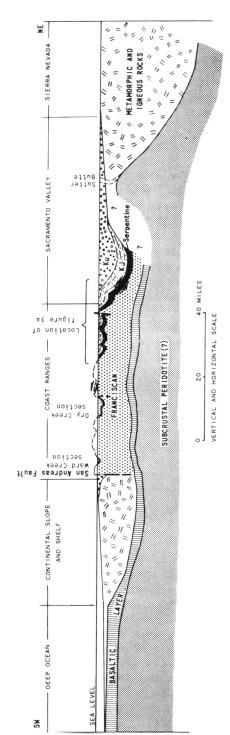

Fig. 14-41 Idealized vertical section across western California and offshore area. Line of section trends southwest through Sutter Buttes and crosses coastline near Fort Ross. Diagram illustrates hypothesis of Upper Cretaceous *Ku*, Lower Cretaceous, and Upper Jurassic *KJ* of Great Valley sequence thrust over the Franciscan, with serpentine along thrust zone. (*From Bailey, Irwin, and Jones, 1964.*)

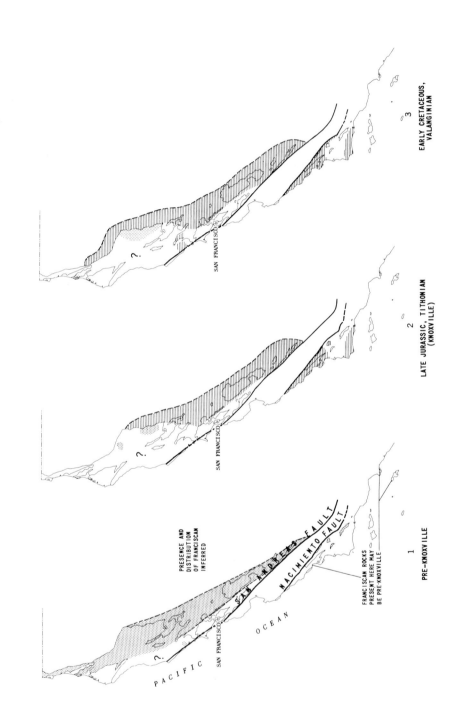

PRESENCE AND
DISTRIBUTION
OF FRANCISCAN
INFERRED

SAN ANDREAS FAULT

NACIMIENTO FAULT

FRANCISCAN ROCKS
PRESENT HERE MAY
BE PRE-KNOXVILLE

PACIFIC OCEAN

SAN FRANCISCO

1
PRE-KNOXVILLE

SAN FRANCISCO

2
LATE JURASSIC, TITHONIAN
(KNOXVILLE)

SAN FRANCISCO

3
EARLY CRETACEOUS, VALANGINIAN

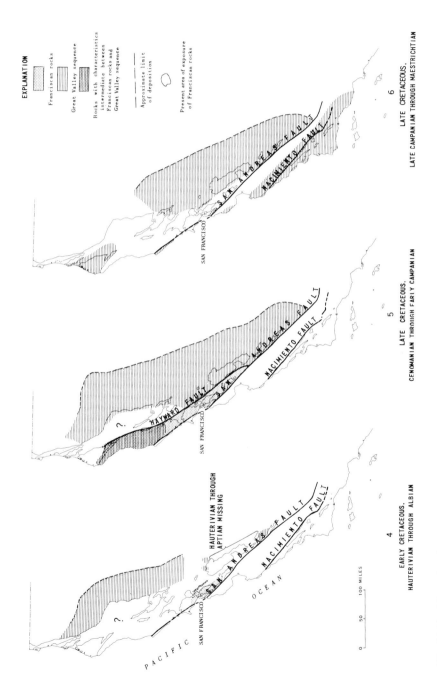

Fig. 14-42 Maps showing areas known or inferred to be underlain by eugeosynclinal Fransciscan rocks and miogeosynclinal rocks of the Great Valley sequence deposited during different intervals. (1) Pre-Knoxville; (2) Late Jurassic; (3) Early Cretaceous; (4) Early Cretaceous; (5) Late Cretaceous; (6) Late Cretaceous. *(From Bailey, Irwin, and Jones, 1964.)*

sea water to be heated to 350°C without boiling. At this temperature and at a pressure equal to 13,000 ft depth of water, over 1,000 ppm of silica can be dissolved in water. Such water would rise, and the silica would be precipitated as a gel and would subsequently crystallize, forming layers and lenses of chert.

Serpentinite and other ultramafic rocks occur widely through the Franciscan rocks. Many of the masses are tabular in form, the largest is 70 miles long and several miles wide, and most of them are concordant with the country rock. The ultramafics are highly sheared and there are no contact metamorphic effects, indicating that they probably were not intruded as magma.

Metamorphic rocks are also present although not in great quantity. These are zeolite, blueschist, and eclogite facies. The blueschist facies (composed of glaucophane, lawsonite, jadeite, stilpnomelane, and pumpellyite) occurs as small isolated patches within and gradational into unmetamorphosed graywacke, as areas several miles wide and tens of miles long suggesting possible regional metamorphism, and as isolated rounded masses of schists up to a few hundred feet in diameter surrounded by nonmetamorphic rocks. The eclogite facies occurs only in this latter form, and these rounded masses are found in shear zones, in serpentine, and in unaltered Franciscan rocks. They probably represent tectonic inclusions. Experimental studies suggest that the blueschists develop under high pressure (5 kbars) but relatively low temperature (under 300°C).

The basement of the Franciscan is not exposed, but as the inclusions brought up in the ultramafic masses are all Franciscan rock types, it is probable that the rocks of the group were deposited on a basaltic or peridotite crust (Fig. 14-41). The Franciscan is highly deformed, but structures within it cannot generally be ascertained because of its persistent heterogeneity and lack of key beds. Most folds trend northwest, but arcuate map patterns around plunging folds are rarely obtained, probably because

of widespread faulting along, and parallel to, the axial part of the folds. The major faults, which have a similar trend, are shear zones that in places are as much as a mile wide. These zones contain large blocks of Franciscan rocks in a sheared matrix, and include tectonic inclusions of schist and sheared masses of serpentine. A fault separates the Franciscan rocks of the northern Coast Ranges from the crystalline rocks of the Klamath Mountains. South of the Klamath Mountains the fault lies covered by the Tertiary sediments of the Great Valley of California.

The eugeosynclinal facies represented by Franciscan units was much more extensive in Jurassic than in later times (Fig. 14-42). The Great Valley sequence is composed of rocks more typical of miogeosynclinal facies. By Late Cretaceous the eugeosynclinal facies was restricted to a zone now exposed between the San Andreas and Hayward faults and before the end of the Cretaceous eugeosynclinal facies disappeared altogether.

Cenozoic Diastrophism on the West Coast

The record of Cenozoic diastrophism is one of shearing along the coast in California and the development of deeply subsiding sedimentary basins, shearing and block faulting in the Basin and Range, uplift and tilting of the Sierra Nevada, folding in the Coos synclinorium in Oregon and Washington, extrusion of the vast lava flows of the Columbia River plateau and their subsequent block faulting, and possibly the bending of the old Nevadian orogenic belt to form the Columbia arc. Dating of events in the diastrophic history of the West Coast indicates almost continuous activity during the Cenozoic with shearing, block-faulting, and fragmentation becoming increasingly significant in the late Cenozoic. Movements on the San Andreas system have been interpreted as starting as early as the Jurassic. A displacement of 350 miles since the Jurassic was suggested by Hill and Dibblee (1953); 225 miles of this is thought to be since Eocene time (see Chap. 4).

Many local Cenozoic basins have developed along these faults. They are usually elongate parallel to the faults, but the deposits in them were derived from easterly or westerly sources. Facies and thickness changes therefore occur across the faults, and these provide the main tool used to infer displacement.

Coastal shearing is prominent as far north as southwestern Oregon, but it is much less well defined in Oregon and Washington. The structural pattern within the Oregon Coast Range is one of broad northeast fold trends in rocks ranging from Jurassic to Eocene age. The lavas of the Columbia River plateau were extruded from late Oligocene to early Miocene, and these were then broadly folded on eastwardly convex trends parallel to those of Mesozoic age before they were overlapped unconformably by Pliocene sediments (Dott, 1965; Lowry and Baldwin, 1952). The Tertiary sediments of the Coos synclinorium folded along north-south trends formed in the late Tertiary. The Willamette downwarp is oriented north-south, and Pliocene and Pleistocene volcanoes of the Cascade Range are aligned north-south in one of the more striking lineaments of the west. This lineament transects the Nevadian eugeosynclinal belt and the earlier Tertiary folds.

Dott (1965) has proposed that the names Cordilleran and Cascadan be applied to the Mesozoic and Cenozoic orogenies of the Cordilleran geosyncline. The Cordilleran would encompass the orogenic episodes of the Laramian, Diablan, Santa Lucian, and Nevadian (Fig. 14-43); the Cascadan would include the Pasadenan and Cascadan, and would be applied to all late Cenozoic block faulting, shearing, and volcanism.

NATURE OF THE CRUST IN THE CORDILLERAN REGION

Recent advances in geophysical work and results from an increasing abundance of seismic refraction, phase velocity, magnetic, and gravimetric data afford us a far better idea of the

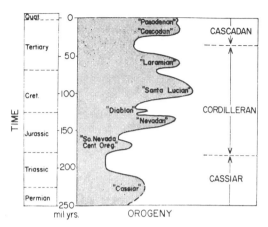

Fig. 14-43 Semiquantitative graph of western orogenesis with time. There is no satisfactory way of establishing absolute relative magnitudes of each already-named event; peaks shown represent judgments of severity of structural disturbance, regional metamorphism, and isotopic age frequencies for plutons. Orogeny is herein interpreted to include any or all of these diastrophic phenomena (see Gilluly, 1963). *(From Dott, 1965.)*

nature of the crust and mantle than has been possible in the past. One important aim of these investigations is determination of the type of crust on which orogenic belts have developed. The answer has direct bearing on the more general idea of continental growth, and the cause and evolution of orogenic belts.

Thompson and Talwani (1964) synthesize the recent knowledge of the crust in the western United States, and interpret the structure of a crustal section extending from the Pacific into the Basin and Range (Fig. 14-44). The thin crust and anomalous mantle are two important conclusions of this interpretation. We have already seen geological evidence that the western portion of the Cordilleran geosyncline developed on an oceanic or intermediate-type crust. It appears that the geosyncline developed on the ocean floor and was later thickened and welded by metamorphism to the continent, with consequent growth by addition of sediments, volcanics, and plutons. The process is still in progress. The mantle under the Cordil-

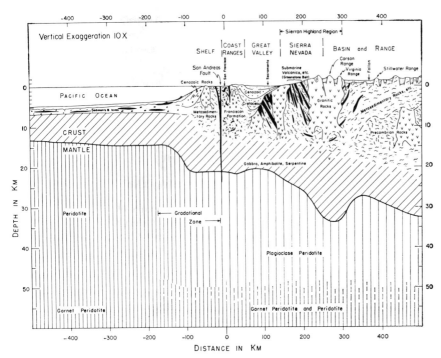

Fig. 14-44 Geologic section of the crust and upper mantle, as interpreted from present evidence. The rock identities suggested in the upper mantle and lower crust are speculative. (*From Thompson and Talwani, fig. 9. Copyright 1964 by the Am. Assoc. Adv. Science.*)

leran region is about 3 percent less dense than is normal, and this extends to depths estimated at 50 km. Anomalous mantle velocities and density also characterize the East Pacific rise which appears to extend under the western United States (Fig. 15-13). Anomalous mantle is likewise associated with modern island arcs, and thus it is closely related to tectonic processes. Convection currents in the mantle and expansion due to phase change in minerals of the mantle under critical temperature and pressure conditions are two explanations often advanced to explain uplift during orogeny. The change of garnet to plagioclase and olivine is accompanied by a 10 percent volume increase, and this is the interpretation favored in Fig. 14-44. Such a transformation is sufficient to explain about 1 km of uplift in the Sierra

Nevada Range. Thus a supplementary process such as compression or convection is needed.

REFERENCES

Albers, J. P., 1967, Belt of sigmoidal bending and right-lateral faulting in the western Great basin: Geol. Soc. America Bull., v. 78, p. 143–156.

Allen, C. A., and others, 1960, Aqua Blanca fault—a major transverse structure of North Baja, California, Mexico: Geol. Soc. America Bull., p. 457–482.

Armstrong, F. C., and Oriel, S. S., 1965, Rocky Mtn. sedimentary basins—Idaho-Wyoming thrust belt: Am. Assoc. Petroleum Geologists Bull., v. 49, no. 11, p. 1847–1866.

Bailey, E. H., Irwin, W. P., and Jones, D. L., 1964, Franciscan and related rocks and their significance in the geology of western California: California Div. Mines and Geol. Bull., v. 183, 171 p.

Bally, A. W., Gordy, P. L., and Stewart, G. A., 1966, Structure, seismic data, and orogenic evolution of southern Canadian Rocky Mtns.; Canadian Petroleum Geol. Bull., v. 14, p. 337–381.

Baltz, E. H., 1965, Rocky Mountain sedimentary basins—Raton and San Luis basins: Am. Assoc. Petroleum Geologists Bull., v. 49, no. 11, p. 2041–2075.

Behrendt, J. C., and Thiel, Edward, 1963, A gravity and magnetic source of the Uinta Mountains: Jour. Geophys. Research, v. 68, no. 3.

Berg, Joseph, Jr., and others, 1961, Seismic profiles in NW Utah Pilot R. and Grouse Creek R. area: Jour. Geophys. Research, v. 66, no. 4.

Berg, R. R., 1962, Mountain flank thrusting in Rocky Mtn. foreland, Wyo. and Colo.: Am. Assoc. Petroleum Geologists Bull., v. 46, p. 2019–2032.

Berg, R. R., and Romberg, F. E., 1966, Gravity profile across the Wind River Mtns., Wyoming: Geol. Soc. America Bull., v. 77, p. 647–656.

Boos, C. M., and Boos, M. F., 1957, Tectonics of eastern flank and foothills of Front Range, Colorado: Am. Assoc. Petroleum Geologists Bull., v. 41, no. 12, p. 2603–2676.

Brown, Robert D., Jr., 1964, Thrust-fault relations in the northern Coast Ranges, California: U. S. Geol. Survey Prof. Paper 475-D, Art. 123, p. D-7–D-13.

Burchfiel, B. C., 1965, Structural geology of the Specter Range Quad., Nev., and its regional significance: Geol. Soc. America Bull., v. 76, p. 175–192.

Burchfiel, B. C., and Stewart, J. H., 1966, "Pull-apart" origin of the central segment of Death Valley, California: Geol. Soc. America Bull., v. 77, no. 4, p. 439–442.

Carey, S. W., 1958, A tectonic approach to continental drift, in Continental drift, a symposium: Univ. Tasmania.

Christensen, M. N., 1966, Late Cenozoic crustal movements in the Sierra Nevada of California: Geol. Soc. America Bull., v. 77, no. 2, p. 163–182, 5 figs., 1 pl.

Churkin, M., Jr., 1962, Facies across Paleozoic miogeosynclinal margin of central Idaho: Am. Assoc. Petroleum Geologists Bull., v. 46, no. 5, p. 569–591.

Clark, L. D., 1960, Foothills fault system western

Sierra Nevada, California: Geol. Soc. America Bull., p. 483–496.

Compton, R. R., 1966, Analyses of Pliocene-Pleistocene deformation and stresses in northern Santa Lucia Range, California: Geol. Soc. America Bull., v. 77, p. 1361–1380.

Corey, W. H., 1962, Effects of lateral faulting on oil exploration: Am. Assoc. Petroleum Geologists Bull., v. 96, p. 2199–2212.

Crowell, J. C., 1963, Displacements along the San Andreas fault, California: Geol. Soc. America Spec. Paper 71.

Curray, J. R., and Nason, R. D., 1967, San Andreas fault north of Point Arena, California: Geol. Soc. America Bull., v. 78, p. 413–418.

Dickinson, W. R., 1966, Structural relationships of San Andreas fault system, Cholame Valley and Castle Mtn. Range, California: Geol. Soc. America Bull., v. 77, p. 707–726.

Diment, W. H., and others, 1961, Crustal structure from the Nevada test site to Kignaw, Arizona: Jour. Geophys. Research, v. 66, no. 1.

Donath, Fred, 1962, Analysis of basin-range structure, south-central Oregon: Geol. Soc. America Bull., v. 73.

Donath, Fred, and Kuo, John, 1962, Seismic-refraction study of block faulting south-central Oregon: Geol. Soc. America Bull., v. 73.

Dott, R. H., 1965, Mesozoic-Cenozoic tectonic history of the SW Oregon coast in relation to Cordilleran orogenesis: Jour. Geophys. Research, v. 70, no. 18, p. 4687–4707.

Drewes, Harold, 1958, Structural geology of the southern Snake Range, Nevada: Geol. Soc. America Bull., v. 69, p. 221–240.

Eardley, A. J., 1960, Igneous and tectonic provinces of the western United States: Norden, Internat. Geol. Cong. Rept., 21st sess., Pt. XIII, p. 18–28.

——— 1962, Structural geology of North America, 2d ed.: New York, Harper & Row.

East, E. H., 1966, Structure and stratigraphy of San Francisco Mtns., western Utah: Am. Assoc. Petroleum Geologists Bull., v. 50.

Fetzner, A. W., 1960, Pennsylvanian paleotectonics of Colorado Plateau: Am. Assoc. Petroleum Geologists Bull., p. 1371–1414.

Fisher, R. V., 1967, Early Tertiary deformation in north-central Oregon: Amer. Assoc. Petroleum Geologists Bull., v. 51, no. 1, p. 111–123.

Foose, Richard, and others, 1961, Structural geology

of the Beartooth Mountains, Montana and Wyoming: Geol. Soc. America Bull., v. 72, p. 1143–1172.

Ford, A. B., 1964, Review of Antarctic Geology: Natl. Acad. Sci., Internat. Geophys. Bull.

Foster, Robert, 1962, Precambrian corundum bearing rocks, Madison Range, Montana: Geol. Soc. America Bull., v. 73, p. 131–138.

Fox, F. G., 1959, Structure and accumulation of hydrocarbons in southern foothills, Alberta, Canada: Am. Assoc. Petroleum Geologists Bull., v. 43, no. 5, p. 992–1025.

Fuller, R. E., and Waters, A. C., 1929, The nature and origin of the horst and graben structure of southern Oregon: Jour. Geology, v. 37.

Gabrielse, H., and Wheeler, J. O., 1961, Tectonic framework of So. Yukon and NW British Columbia: Geol. Surv. Canada Paper 60–24, 37 p.

Gilluly, James, 1963, The tectonic evolution of the western United States: Geol. Soc. London Quart. Jour., v. 119, p. 133.

———— 1965, Volcanism, tectonism, and plutonism in the western U.S.: Geol. Soc. America Spec. Paper 80.

Hamilton, Warren, 1962, L. Cenozoic structure of west central Idaho: Geol. Soc. America Bull., v. 73.

Hamilton, Warren, and Myers, W. B., 1965, Cenozoic tectonics of the western U.S., in The world rift system: Geol. Surv. Canada Paper 66–14, p. 291.

Henderson, C. C. L., and Dahlstrom, C. D. A., 1959, First-order nappe in Canadian Rockies: Am. Assoc. Petroleum Geologists Bull., v. 43, p. 641–654.

Higgins, C. G., 1961, San Andreas fault north of San Francisco, California: Geol. Soc. America Bull., p. 51–68.

Hill, M. L., and Dibblee, T. W., Jr., 1953, San Andreas, Garlock, and Big Pine faults, California: Geol. Soc. America Bull., v. 64, p. 443–458.

Hill, M. L., and Troxel, B. W., 1966, Tectonics of Death Valley region, Calif.: Geol. Soc. America Bull., v. 77, p. 435–438.

Hodgson, R. A., 1965, Genetic and geometric relations between structure: Am. Assoc. Petroleum Geologists Bull., v. 49, p. 935.

Hoppin, Richard, 1961, Precambrian rocks and their relationship to Laramide structure along the east flank of Bighorn Mtns. near Buffalo, Wyoming: Geol. Soc. America Bull., v. 72, p. 351–368.

Hoppin, Richard, and Palmquist, J. C., 1965, Basement influence on later deformation: the problem, techniques of investigation, and examples from Bighorn Mtns., Wyoming: Am. Assoc. Petroleum Geologists Bull., v. 49, no. 7.

Howard, J. H., 1966, Structural development of the Williams Range thrust, Colorado: Geol. Soc. America Bull., v. 77, p. 1247–1264.

Irwin, W. P., 1960, Geologic reconnaissance of the northern Coast Ranges and Klamath Mtns., California, with a summary of the mineral resources: California Div. of Mines [San Francisco] Bull. 179, 80 p.

———— 1964, Late Mesozoic orogenies in the ultramafic belts of northwestern California and southwestern Oregon: U. S. Geol. Survey Prof. Paper 501-C, p. C1–C9.

———— 1965, Late Mesozoic orogenies in the ultramafic belts of NW Calif. and SW Oregon: U.S. Geol. Survey Prof. Paper 501-C, p. C1–C9.

Kay, G. M., 1951, North American geosynclines: Geol. Soc. America Mem. 48.

Kay, G. M., and Crawford, J. P., 1964, Paleozoic facies from the miogeosynclinal to the eugeosynclinal belt in thrust slices, central Nevada: Geol. Soc. America Bull., v. 75.

Keith, A., 1923, Outlines of Appalachian structure: Geol. Soc. America Bull., v. 23.

Ken, J. W., 1962, Paleo. sequences and thrust of the Seetoya Mtns. Independence Range, Nevada: Geol. Soc. America Bull., v. 73.

Koch, J. G., 1963, Late Mesozoic orogenesis and sedimentation, Klamath province, southwest Oregon coast: unpubl. Ph.D. dissertation, Univ. Wisc.

Kupfer, D., II, 1960, Thrust faulting and chaos structure, Silvian Hills, San Bernadino County, California: Geol. Soc. America Bull., p. 181–214.

Kurie, Andrew E., 1966, Recurrent structural disturbance of Colorado Plateau margin near Zion National Park, Utah: Geol. Soc. America Bull., v. 77, no. 8, p. 867–872, 1 fig., 2 pls.

Link, T. A., 1949, Interpretations of foothills structures: Am. Assoc. Petroleum Geologists Bull., v. 33, p. 1175–1501.

Lipman, Peter W., 1964, Structure and origin of an ultramafic pluton in the Klamath Mountains, California: Am. Jour. Sci., v. 262, p. 199–222.

Lofgen, B. E., 1960, Crustal structure in the California-Nevada region: Jour. Geophys. Research, v. 65, no. 3.

Lowry, W. D., and Baldwin, E. M., 1952, Late Cenozoic geology of the lower Columbia River valley, Oregon and Washington: Geol. Soc. America Bull., v. 63.

MacDonald, Gordon J. F., 1961, Gravity measurements over the southern Rocky Mountain trench area of British Columbia: Jour. Geophys. Research, v. 66, no. 8.

Mackin, J. H., 1960, Structural significance of Tertiary volcanic rocks in SW Utah: Am. Jour. Sci., v. 258, no. 2.

Martin, L. J., 1963, Tectonics of northern Cordillera in Canada: Am. Assoc. Petroleum Geologists Mem. 2, p. 243–251.

Mayo, E. B., 1941, Deformation in the interval Mount Lyell–Mount Whitney: Geol. Soc. America Bull., v. 52, p. 1001–1084.

McCrossan, R. G., and Glaister, R. P., eds., 1964, Geological history of Western Canada: Alta. Soc. Petroleum Geologists, Calgary, Alta.

Miller, G. M., 1966, Structure and stratigraphy of southern part of Wah Wah Mountains, southwest Utah: Am. Assoc. Petroleum Geologists Bull., v. 50, p. 858–900.

Moench, R. H., and others, 1962, Precambrian folding in the Idaho Springs–Central City area, Front Range, Colorado: Geol. Soc. America Bull., v. 73.

Moore, J. G., 1959, The quartz diorite boundary line in the western U.S.: Jour. Geology, v. 67.

Nelson, R. B., 1966, Structural development of northernmost Snake Range, Kern Mtns., and Deep Creek Range, Nevada-Utah: Am. Assoc. Petroleum Geologists Bull., v. 50, no. 5, p. 921–951.

Noble, L. F., 1926, The San Andreas rift and some other active faults in the desert region of southeastern California: Carnegie Inst. Washington Yearbook 25, p. 415–428.

Nolan, T. B., 1943, The Basin and Range province in Utah, Nevada, California: U. S. Geol. Survey Prof. Paper 197D, p. 141–196.

Pakisev, L. C., 1960, Transcurrent faulting and volcanism in Owens Valley, California: Geol. Soc. America Bull., p. 153–160.

Parker, Ronald B., 1961, Petrology and structural geometry of pre-granitic rocks in the Sierra Nevada, Alpine County, California: Geol. Soc. America Bull., v. 72, p. 1789–1806.

Peterson, J. A., 1965, Rocky Mountain sedimentary basins—introduction: Am. Assoc. Petroleum Geologists Bull., v. 49, no. 11, p. 1779–1780.

Porter, S. C., 1966, Stratigraphy and deformation of Paleozoic section at Anaktuvuk Pass, central Brooks Range, Alaska: Am. Assoc. Petroleum Geologists Bull., v. 50, no. 5, p. 952–980.

Prucha, J. J., Graham, J. A., and Nickelsen, R. P., 1965, Basement-controlled deformation in Wyoming, province of Rocky Mountains Foreland: Am. Assoc. Petroleum Geologists Bull., v. 49, no. 7, p. 966–992.

Reed, R. D., 1933, Geology of California: Am. Assoc. Petroleum Geologists Bull.

Reed, R. D., and Hollister, J. S., 1936, Structural evolution of southern California: Am. Assoc. Petroleum Geologists Bull., p. 1529–1721.

Reeves, Frank, 1924, Geology and possible oil and gas resources of the faulted area south of the Bearpaw Mountains, Montana: U. S. Geol. Survey Bull. 751-C, p. 71–114.

———— 1946, Origin and mechanics of thrust faults adjacent to the Bearpaw Mountains, Montana: Geol. Soc. America Bull., v. 57, p. 1033–1047.

Roberts, R. J., and others, 1965, Rocky Mountain sedimentary basins—Oquirrh and Phosphoria basins: Am. Assoc. Petroleum Geologists Bull., v. 49, no. 11, p. 1926–1956.

Robinson, G. D., 1961, Origin and development of the Three Forks basin, Montana: Geol. Soc. America Bull., v. 72, p. 1003–1014.

Roddick, J. A., 1967, Tintina trench: Jour. Geology, v. 75, no. 1, p. 23–33.

Rogers, G. S., and Rogers, W. B., 1843, On the physical structure of the Appalachian chain, as exemplifying the laws which have regulated the elevation of great mountain chains generally: Am. Jour. Sci., v. 44.

Rubey, W. W., and Hubbert, M. K., 1959, Role of fluid pressure in mechanics of overthrust faulting, II: Geol. Soc. America Bull., v. 70.

Scholten, Robert, 1958, Paleozoic evolution of the geosynclinal margin north of the Snake River Plain: Geol. Soc. America Bull., v. 68.

Sharp, R. P., 1939, Basin range structure of the Ruby East Humbolt Range, northeastern Nevada: Geol. Soc. America Bull., v. 50, no. 6, p. 881–915.

Shaw, F. W., 1963, Canadian Rockies—orientation in time and space: Am. Assoc. Petroleum Geologists Mem. 2, Backbone of the Americas, p. 231–242.

Shawe, D. R., 1965, Strike-slip control of basin-range structure indicated by historical faults in western Nevada: Geol. Soc. America Bull., v. 76, no. 12, p. 119–162.

Taliaferro, N. L., 1943, Geological history and structure of the central Coast Ranges of California: California Div. Mines Bull., v. 118, p. 119–162.

Tanner, W. F., 1962, Surface structural patterns obtained from strike-slip models: Jour. Geol., v. 70, p. 101–107.

Thompson, G. A., 1959, A study of basin and range structures: Jour. Geophys. Research, v. 64, no. 2.

Thompson, G. A., and Talwani, Manik, 1964, Geology of the crust and mantle, western United States: Science, v. 146, p. 1539–1549.

Wallace, R. E., 1949, Structure of a portion of the San Andreas rift in southern California: Geol. Soc. America Bull., v. 60, p. 781–806.

White, W. H., 1959, Cordilleran tectonics in British Columbia: Am. Assoc. Petroleum Geologists Bull., v. 43, p. 60–101.

Whitten, C. A., 1956, Crustal movement in California and Nevada: Am. Geophys. Union Trans., v. 37, no. 4.

Willis, B., 1938, The San Andreas rift in California: Jour. Geology, v. 46, p. 793–827.

—— 1938, The San Andreas rift in southwestern California: Jour. Geology, v. 46, p. 1017–1057.

Wise, D. U., 1963a, Keystone faulting and gravity sliding driven by basement uplift of Owl Creek Mountains, Wyo: Am. Assoc. Petroleum Geologists Bull., v. 47, p. 586–598.

—— 1963b, An outrageous hypothesis for the tectonic pattern of the North American Cordillera: Geol. Soc. America Bull., v. 74.

Woollard, G. P., 1958, Areas of tectonic activity in the U.S. as indicated by earthquake epicenters: Am. Geophys. Union Trans., v. 39, no. 6.

15
structural features of the ocean basins

Knowledge of the structure of the ocean basins is of paramount importance to an understanding of the structure of the earth, not only because the oceans cover such a large portion of the earth's surface but because oceanic and continental crustal structure are very different, and because the most active belts in the crust occur within and along the margins of the oceans. Until recent years little was known about the structure of the oceans, and unless a program of drilling into the oceanic crust, far more extensive than any now planned, is carried out we are destined to know oceanic crustal structure only indirectly. The methods of approach to studying the ocean's structure include:

1. Study of land areas at the coast in order to know structure where it passes to the sea.
2. Drilling; extensive programs are carried on by petroleum companies on continental shelves.
3. Use of seismic reflection and refraction techniques to construct seismic profiles.
4. Use of gravity measurements, now made at sea both in submarines and on surface ships.
5. Use of measurements of the earth's magnetic field to detect anomalies which are related to near-surface distribution of rocks with different amounts of magnetic minerals, differences in field intensity and polarity.
6. Earthquake seismology is used to outline seismic and aseismic areas, to determine apparent initial directions of movement on faults, and to analyze crustal structure through surface wave dispersion.
7. Heat-flow measurement reveals patterns of abnormal heat flow through

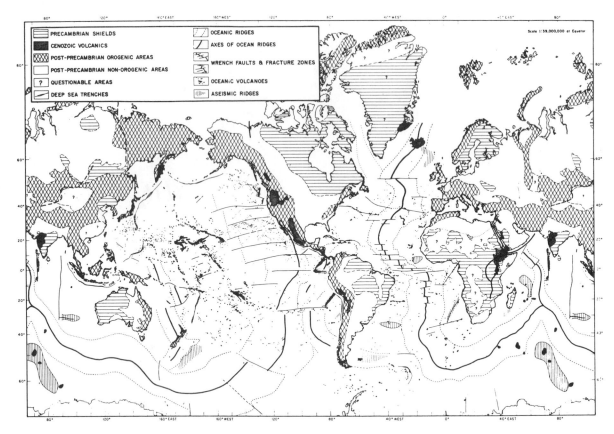

Fig. 15-1 Major geological features of the earth. Most oceanic geological features are taken from Menard (1965), with a few additional data taken from Fisher and Hess (1963), Heezen (1962), and Heezen and Ewing (1963). Geological features on land are compiled from various geological maps. (*From Lee and Uyeda, 1965.*)

the crust which are presumably related to structural characteristics of the crust.

8. Analysis of submarine topography has been one of the most valuable tools, particularly in connection with other methods. The main sources of erosion in the ocean basins are slump, mass movement, and movement of materials by turbidity currents. Many of these deposits have been recognized, and the erosional forms associated with them identified. Since the great variety of agents of erosion on land do not exist in the oceans, the form of submarine topography should reflect crustal structures more accurately than on land

areas except where structure is masked by deposits.

9. Observations from the bathyscaphes may in time contribute to our knowledge of submarine structure.

We shall almost certainly never know the detailed structure of the oceanic crust, but already many of the major features are known (Fig. 15-1) with a reasonable degree of confidence. It is important, however, to bear in mind that many of the illustrations are interpretations arrived at by indirect methods, some of which do not give unique solutions; moreover, the observations in many instances are very sparsely spread over the structure. The data points may be spread as much as tens of miles apart in the case of heat-flow observations; magnetic, gravity, and topography contour maps are prepared from continuous recordings along a ship's track, but these tracks may be very unevenly spread over the areas shown. Seismic observations are usually short, carefully placed profiles located to detail specific areas. Because of these shortcomings we may certainly expect some changes in interpretation as the refinement of techniques and density of observations increase over the years. As in the case of continental structural studies, we will examine the generalized regional interpretations and a few detailed studies selected because there is an unusually large amount of data at that point. The major structures and structural complexes which have been defined are:

1. Continental margins
2. Arcuate islands and topographic ridges associated with deep sea trenches
3. Large fracture and fault zones
4. Midoceanic ridges as exemplified by the mid-Atlantic ridge
5. Oceanic rises
6. Deep sea floors—abyssal plains

LINEAMENTS—FAULT AND FRACTURE ZONES

The strong alignment of islands in the Pacific, both those that lie on arcs and those in midocean that lie on more or less straight lines, has long been recognized. As submarine topography has gradually been elucidated, sea mounts and guyots are also found to be aligned in many instances (Fig. 15-2), and long narrow ridges and depressions in the deep sea floor have been defined. It seems reasonable to expect that the volcanic islands, sea mounts, and guyots owe their alignment to faults or fracture systems in the oceanic crust through which lavas have found their way. Other faults and fracture zones are not covered by volcanic products and are

still clearly defined by offsets in the submarine topography. Zones of this nature occur along the crest of the oceanic ridges, and they have been mapped in the eastern Pacific, along the equatorial portion of the Atlantic, and in the Indian Ocean.

The Clipperton zone (Figs. 15-3 and 15-4) was one of the first major fracture zones to be described (Menard, 1955, 1958). It was recognized by the anomalous topography associated with it. The Guatemala basin, situated at its eastern end, is bounded on the north by a sharp ridge, the Tehuantepec ridge, and on the south by a sharply defined depression which lines up with the Clipperton zone. To the west the zone is represented by a broad welt with a central trough that is between 1,200 and 2,400 ft deep. This is where the zone cuts across the East Pacific rise, the Albatross Plateau. West of this there is a volcano-studded ridge, 60 miles wide and 300 miles long with a narrow trough on the north side which has extreme relief, locally 18,000 ft. Still farther west a broad welt, 10 to 30 miles wide, runs for 900 miles. The north side of this is 150 to 200 fathoms deeper than the south side. This lineament can be traced east-west for nearly 3,300 miles, thus qualifying as one of the longest features in the crust. Submarine topography has been offset along the zone, and volcanoes have formed along one side of it for a long distance. It cuts across the still larger feature, the East Pacific rise, and it ends in the east by intersecting the Middle American trench at the end of the Tehuantepec ridge. The trench is not offset at this point, but it is deflected, the depth to the M discontinuity is altered, the depth of the trench changes, and the character of volcanism is altered (Fisher and Shor, 1958).

The Clipperton is but one of a number of similar east-west structures (Fig. 15-1) now known in the eastern Pacific. The offset on the zones has been inferred by offsets of topography, by seismic studies, and by the use of offsets in contours of magnetic anomalies (Fig. 15-5). The Mendocino zone is one of the most

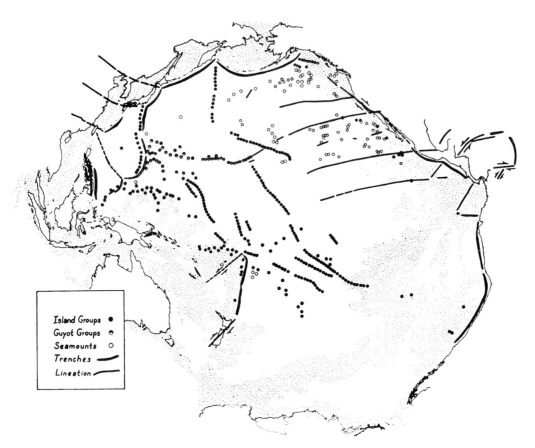

Fig. 15-2 Lineations and trenches in the Pacific basin, shown on equal-area projection. Island and guyot symbols are diagrammatic and merely show the location and trend of groups rather than individual islands and guyots. Stippled area is shallower than 4,000 m. (*From Menard, 1955.*)

spectacular of these zones. The elevation of the sea floor is about 1 km higher on the north side of the fault, which appears often as an asymmetrical ridge with a south-facing escarpment between 1 and 2 miles high. The fault separates two provinces of different structural characteristics. North of it is a province of narrow northeast-trending ridges and troughs, south of it lies a relatively smooth abyssal plain. Seismic work has shown the region south of the fault to be normal oceanic crust, while that to the north is abnormal in that the velocities are not those found normally at the M discontinuity, and in that gravity surveys along the fault

(Fig. 15-6) reveal that there is a thick low-density upper mantle layer north of the fault which probably is chemically different from that south of the fault. The high relief and abnormal mantle across the fault are found most prominent toward the eastern end of the fault. West of longitude 130° W these effects die out (Dehlinger, Couch, and Gemperle, 1967).

The north-south trend of the magnetic anomalies is striking, as are the offsets in it. This pattern has been traced for over 2,500 km, and it may extend even farther west as well. To determine displacements, the anomalies are

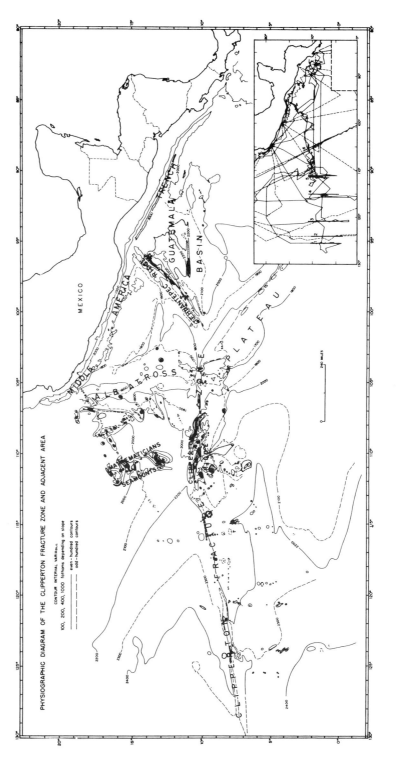

Fig. 15-3 Physiographic diagram of the Clipperton fracture zone and adjacent area. *(From Menard and Fischer, 1958.)*

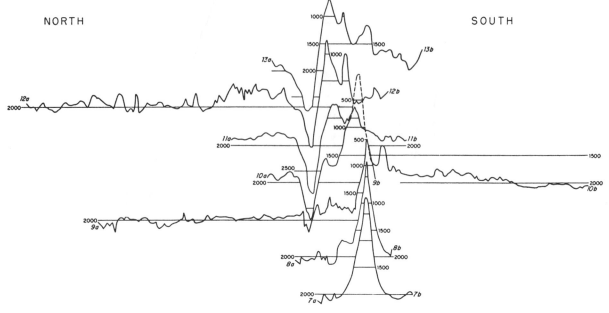

NORTH   SOUTH

Fig. 15-4   Transverse profiles of the Clipperton ridge. (*From Menard and Fischer, 1958.*)

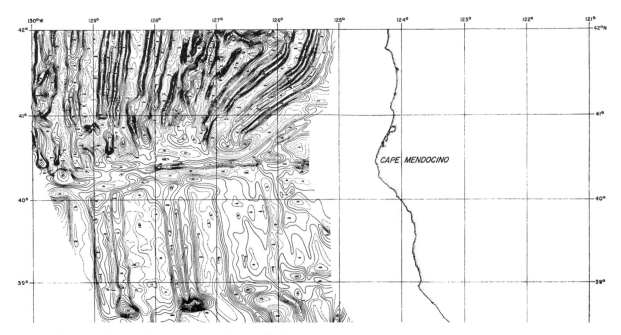

Fig. 15-5   Map of the total magnetic intensity from 32 to 42°N after removal of the regional field. The contour interval is 50γ, and spot values are rounded off to the nearest 5γ beyond the extreme value recorded. (*From Mason and Raff, 1961.*)

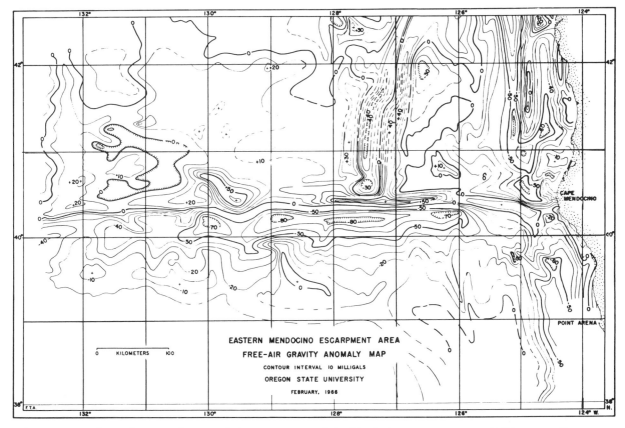

Fig. 15-6 Free-air gravity anomaly map of the eastern part of the Mendocino escarpment area. Solid contour lines are based on reliable anomaly values, dashed contours on sparse data or questionable anomalies. *(From Dehlinger, Couch, and Gemperle, 1967.)*

shifted along each zone until a best fit is obtained. The fits suggested by Vacquier (1959) call for a left-lateral displacement of 1,140 km on the Mendocino zone, left-lateral 260 km on the Pioneer zone, and right-lateral 680 km at one point and 150 km at another on the Murray fault. An alternative to the 1,140-km left-lateral displacement on the Mendocino zone is that the west end of it is displaced 640 miles west and the east end 55 miles to the east. A similar type of movement is suggested for other of the Pacific zones (Raff, 1962). It is suggested that the sense of displacement may be different on either side of the East Pacific rise. (Note that a transverse fault across an

anticline will give this type of displacement if the fold continues to grow on one side of the fault only.)

The following relationships between Pacific faults, lineaments, and island arcs have been noted:

1. The floor of the eastern Pacific is broken by a system of east-west transcurrent faults with displacements measured in hundreds of miles.
2. A second fracture system is indicated by northwest-trending volcanic islands, seamounts, and guyots.
3. Fracture and fault zones intersect island

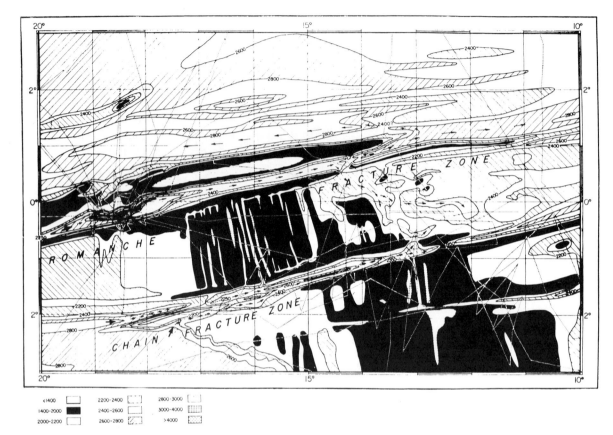

Fig. 15-7 Bathymetric sketch of portions of the Chain and Romanche fracture zones. All available sounding lines are indicated by dotted lines. Arrows indicate a suggested pattern of flow of the coldest bottom water based on interpretation of bottom temperatures, echo soundings, and topographic trends. Basic contour interval is 200 fathoms except below 3,000 fathoms where the slopes are too steep for contour portrayal at this scale and between 1,400 and 2,000 fathoms where topography is too irregular to permit detailed contours with the present control. (Survey of chain fracture zone by Bunce, contours by Heezen.) (*From Heezen and others, 1964.*)

arc systems. Where they do the arc is affected. The Middle American trench is one example. The Emperor Seamount Range intersects the point of junction of the Aleutian and Kurile Island arcs. The point of intersection of the Nansei Shoto and Taiwan-Philippine arcs is intersected by a line extended from the Median trough of the Philippine Sea. The Marcus-Necker rise ends at the point of juncture of the Japan and Marianas trenches. The Caroline swell ends at the junction of the Marianas and West Caroline trenches.

4. Major east-west fracture zones are found in China, in the Pacific, and in the Atlantic.
5. A major transcurrent fault has been proposed to explain the offset of the Tonga trench and the New Hebrides arc (Hess and Maxwell, 1953).
6. Major transcurrent faults on land lie close to the trends of nearby trenches, e.g., the Alpine fault of New Zealand and the Kermadec trench, the San Andreas fault and the Middle American trench, the Visayan rift in the Philippine Islands, and the Mindanao trench.

Atlantic Fracture Zones

Prominent east-west-trending faults have been recognized in the Atlantic as well as the Pacific. The best documented of those in the Atlantic lie just north of the equator where they cut and displace the mid-Atlantic ridge (Heezen, 1964). The Chain and Romanche fracture zones are two of these, all of which show left-lateral displacements. The displacements in this case can be shown by means of detailed topography (Fig. 15-7). The Romanche zone appears as a deep, narrow trench which is about 12 miles wide at a depth of 2,000 fathoms. The walls are very steep, 45° slopes in places, and the floor of the trench is broken by a longitudinal ridge. The maximum depth in the Romanche zone, the Vema depth, is 4,106 fathoms, and thus the fracture zone has local relief of nearly 2 miles. The Chain zone located to the south is similar in trend and depth. From the displacements of topography, it appears that the movement has been in the same direction along the faults. The Chain zone offsets the mid-Atlantic ridge about 180 miles; the Romanche zone offsets it about 300 miles.

Fracture Zones in the Indian Ocean

The fracture and fault systems interpreted from submarine topography by Heezen (1964) show a strong north-south orientation. This trend is reflected in major fault zones, such as the Mozambique, Prince Edward, Malagasy, and Amsterdam, and in the alignment of ridges such as the Ninety East, the Chagos–Laccadive Plateau, and the Mozambique and Madagascar ridges. The fracture zones, like those in the Atlantic and Pacific, cut across and displace the midocean ridge and the rift zone along its crest. These zones are characterized by the trenchlike topography. East-west fracture zones, the Rodriguez and Diamentina, are also recognized, though this trend is not nearly so prominent as it is in the Atlantic and Pacific.

MIDOCEAN RIDGES

Submarine topography is now established in sufficient detail to reveal that a prominent ridge, or more accurately a great submarine mountain range, extends around the world. That portion of this mountain range which

Fig. 15-8 Typical trans-Atlantic profile, Newfoundland to England. The depths indicated in the lower portion of the figure are characteristic of this profile only, as the depths of all provinces gradually fluctuate along the length of the ocean basin. The physiographic provinces have been traced throughout the Atlantic and are believed to extend, in a general way at least, throughout all oceans possessing a median rifted ridge (vertical exaggeration 40:1). (*From Heezen and Ewing, 1956.*)

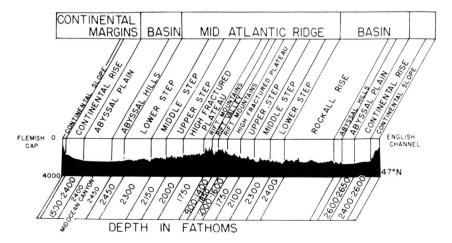

forms the mid-Atlantic ridge was the first part studied, and it is known in much greater detail than other portions (Fig. 15-8). The mountain system known as the mid-ocean ridge extends almost exactly down the center of the North and South Atlantic Oceans and then passes around the southern tip of Africa into the Indian Ocean, near the center of which it splits. One section goes north into the Gulf of Aden and the Red Sea. The other branch runs southeast, south of Australia, across the South Pacific, then northwest by Easter Island toward the Gulf of California. Subsidiary ridges run from the vicinity of Easter Island toward the Cape of Good Hope, from Cape Mendocino in California northward toward the Gulf of Alaska, and from the southwest Pacific toward New Zealand. The north end of the mid-Atlantic ridge in Iceland is traced into the Arctic near Spitzbergen across the Arctic Ocean and into Siberia.

The zone so defined is characterized over most of its length by a distinct topographic ridge, although the character of that ridge varies from place to place. Along the crest of that ridge there is usually a prominent valley defined by inward-facing scarps on either side. The valley thus defined is from 500 to 2,000 fathoms deep and 10 to 20 miles wide. Studies of the distribution of earthquake epicenters in the ocean basins indicate that the great majority of the quakes located near the central portions of the basins lie in or along the valleys on these midoceanic ridges. This relationship is so striking that it was the distribution of epicenters that prompted the investigation of the areas to see whether they lie in valleys which are now generally accepted as rift valleys. Large portions of the sea floor are aseismic; most quakes are located in the island arcs, at volcanoes, or on the midoceanic rift valley. Almost all of the foci for earthquakes in the rift zones are shallow in contrast with those in the island arcs.

The rift system and the associated midoceanic ridge is now traced for a distance of some 40,000 miles around the globe. If it is, as it appears now to be, a continuous feature of essentially the same type of structure everywhere, then it is the longest and largest structural element of the crust.

Details of topography are best known for the central portion of the mid-Atlantic ridge. Heezen has subdivided the range into a number of physiographic provinces (Fig. 15-8). The ridge rises from abyssal plains on either side to a crest that comes to the surface as volcanic islands at a number of places. Thus the relief is over 18,000 ft and the width of the whole ridge province is over 1,000 miles. Heezen has identified plateaulike features on the flanks of the ridge which are called steps and are interpreted as tilted fault blocks. High mountains rise on either side of the rift valley itself. These stand 1,600 to 1,800 fathoms above the adjacent plateaus. Relief on the plateaus and steps is commonly several hundred fathoms. The basins between the top of the steps or plateaus are flat-floored, sedimentary basins interpreted as fault blocks.

The midocean ridge is cut by transverse faults and fracture zones along which it is offset as described in the section on fault zones. Profiles of topography along the ridge are not yet closely enough spaced to show whether the rift valley is a single continuous feature everywhere, or whether it is an *en échelon* zone of rifts, graben and horst structures, and block faults. The zone of rifts is traced into land areas in the Red Sea, Iceland, New Zealand, the Gulf of California, and Siberia. In each of these places the zone is aligned with or near a major crustal fault.

Iceland is located on the rift zone at the northern end of the mid-Atlantic ridge, and a major graben of the same trend is found in central Iceland where modern earthquakes and volcanism are associated with the graben (Fig. 15-9). That this is an active fault zone is also shown by the open fissures found there. These are also indicative of the tensional origin of the faults. Topography north of Iceland is not

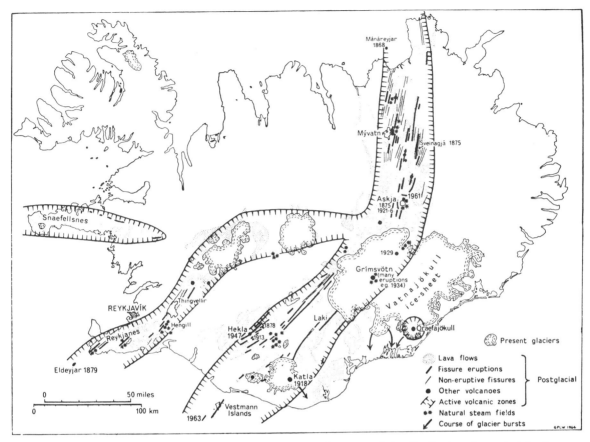

Fig. 15-9 Map of Iceland showing the postglacially active volcanic zones and the distribution of postglacial volcanoes and fissures. (*From Gibson and Walker, 1964, in Thorarinsson, 1965.*)

so high as that to the south, but a ridge with local rift valleys and on which shallow-focus earthquakes · are concentrated can be traced toward Spitzbergen and into the Arctic where a midocean ridge and seismic belt is again identified, although data in this area are few.

Crustal Structure

Seismic refraction, magnetic, gravity, and heat flow measurements have been made at a number of places on the midoceanic ridges. Five such sections are shown (Fig. 15-10), four of which are on the mid-Atlantic ridge and one on the East Pacific rise. It will be noted in these sections that the flanks are about typical for

oceanic crustal sections, but that near the crest they contrast sharply with the typical oceanic section (0.5 km sediment; 2 km of 4.0 to 6.0 km/sec velocity; 3 km of 6.8 km/sec velocity; Moho and 8.0 km/sec velocity), and that there is considerable variation from one section to another. The sections even on the flanks of the ridge are somewhat thinner than normal oceanic crust, and thinning is pronounced over the ridge itself. Abnormally low mantle velocities are found under the crest in most of the sections, including the East Pacific rise which otherwise appears to be primarily a flexure in the crust. The variations in thickness and level of the mid-Atlantic ridge sections are inter-

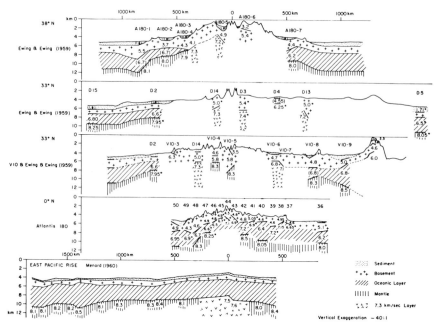

Fig. 15-10 Seismic cross sections of the mid-Atlantic ridge and the East Pacific rise. The topography is schematic, especially between the different stations. (*From Le Pichon and others, 1965.*)

preted as having developed from a broadly warped feature such as the East Pacific rise, which has been fractured and blocks displaced (Le Pichon and others, 1965). It should be further emphasized that none of these sections is like that of the Hawaiian ridge, which is purely volcanic and under which the M discontinuity is depressed. In contrast, there is no thickening of the crust under the midocean ridges and there is an anomalous mantle material.

Gravity measurements over the mid-Atlantic ridge have been interpreted in the light of the seismic data just outlined (Talwani and others, 1965). There is a large Bouguer anomaly, but there is almost no free-air anomaly. In order to provide the necessary compensation for the crestal portion of the ridge, the anomalous mantle material has been postulated to extend laterally under the normal mantle as shown in three possible crustal models (Fig. 15-11). Deeper extensions of the abnormal mantle ma-

terial under the ridge flanks were ruled out by the steep gradient of the Bouguer anomaly.

East Pacific Rise

That portion of the midoceanic ridge and seismic zone that lies in the eastern Pacific is of particular interest because it may be traced into the North American continent. It is also significant that this portion of the ridge system is simpler than that of the Atlantic. The width of the rise, approximately 800 km, is comparable, but the topography of the East Pacific rise is smooth by comparison with the mid-Atlantic ridge, suggesting a simpler crustal structure. This conclusion is born out by the seismic section across it (Fig. 15-12). The East Pacific rise appears to pass into the Gulf of California, under western North America, and back into the Pacific north of Cape Mendocino.

Like other portions of the ridge system, shallow-focus earthquakes occur along the crest of the rise. Heat-flow measurements show ab-

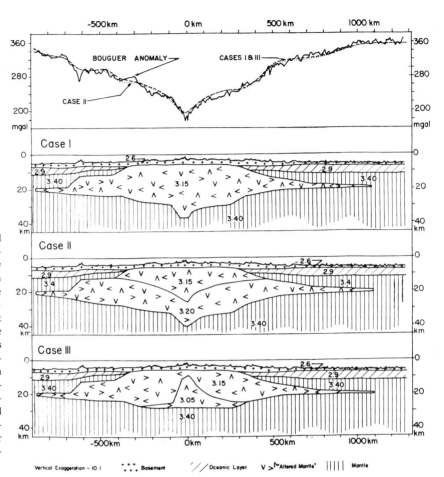

Fig. 15-11 Three possible crustal models across the north mid-Atlantic ridge which satisfy gravity anomalies and are in accord with seismic refraction data. In all three models the anomalous mantle found seismically under the crest of the ridge is assumed to underlie the normal mantle under the flanks of the ridge. In case I the anomalous mantle is assumed to have a uniform density, in case II its density is assumed to increase downward, and in case III the material constituting the anomalous mantle is assumed to be lighter near the axis of the ridge. (*From Talwani and others, 1965.*)

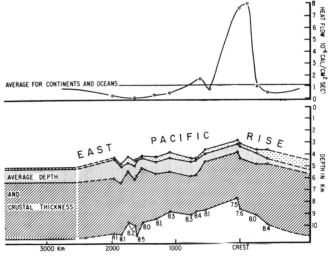

Fig. 15-12 Crustal section and heat-flow profiles of the East Pacific rise. Velocities below the "crust" are in kilometers per second. The crust is thinned under most of the rise, but the region of very high heat flow and anomalous "mantle" velocities is confined to a narrow band on the crest. (*From Menard, 1960. Copyright 1960 by Am. Assoc. Adv. Sci.*)

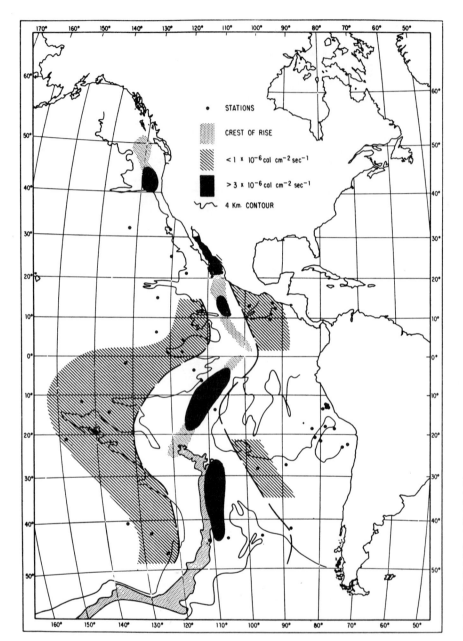

STATIONS

CREST OF RISE

$< 1 \times 10^{-6}\, \text{cal cm}^{-2}\, \text{sec}^{-1}$

$> 3 \times 10^{-6}\, \text{cal cm}^{-2}\, \text{sec}^{-1}$

4 Km. CONTOUR

Fig. 15-13 Correspondence in position of the crest of the East Pacific rise and a pattern of heat flow. The points off the United States are based on unpublished observations by von Herzen. The band of high heat flow, like the crest of the rise, appears to pass through the western United States. (*From Menard, 1960. Copyright 1960 by Am. Assoc. Adv. Sci.*)

normally high values in a narrow zone over the crest (Fig. 15-13), the crust is thinned over the crest of the rise, and abnormal seismic velocities are found in the mantle in a narrow zone below the crest (Menard, 1960). Some longitudinal ridges and valleys are found on the rise. The idea that the rise continues under western North America is supported by the heat-flow measurements (Fig. 15-13) in the Gulf of California and north of Cape Mendocino.

These values are more than three times the average heat flow through the crust of both continents and ocean basins.

The great fracture zones of the eastern Pacific may be related genetically to the rise (Fig. 15-14). They are transverse to it and represent structures of similar scale. It is also significant that the San Andreas fault lies approximately in the position postulated for the crest of the rise under North America. It is interesting to speculate that the thinning of the crust over the rise is due to stretching of the crust. Menard points out that the region with 3.8-km thickness is now 2,800 km in average width, and if this once had a normal thickness of 4.9 km it would have been 2,200 km wide. Thus the amount of stretching, 600 km, is on the same order of magnitude as the estimates of offsets on some of the eastern Pacific fracture zones.

MAGNETIC ANOMALIES

Analysis of magnetic anomalies, such as that illustrated in Fig. 15-5, over the sea floor have revealed some highly significant though unexpected discoveries. Anomalies have been found to have a strong alignment parallel or subparallel to the oceanic rises, although some are offset along what appear to be transcurrent faults. A second important characteristic of these anomalies is the strong variations in the intensity indicated. Vine and Matthews (1963)

Fig. 15-14 Principal fracture zones of the northeastern and central Pacific; equal-area projection. Stippling indicates smooth archipelagic aprons and the belt of equatorial pelagic smoothing; white areas within archipelagic aprons are volcanoes and volcanic ridges. Individual lineations are troughs, asymmetrical ridges, or regional changes in depth; broken-line bands have fracture-zone topography, but information is not adequate for the tracing of individual lineations. *(From Menard, 1967, fig. 2. Copyright 1967 by Am. Assoc. Adv. Sci.)*

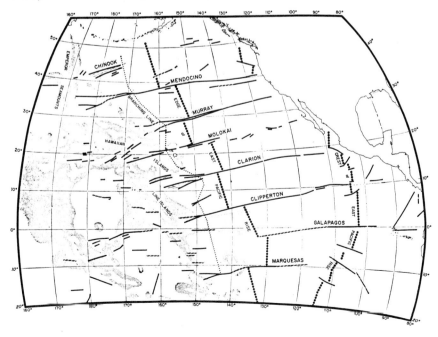

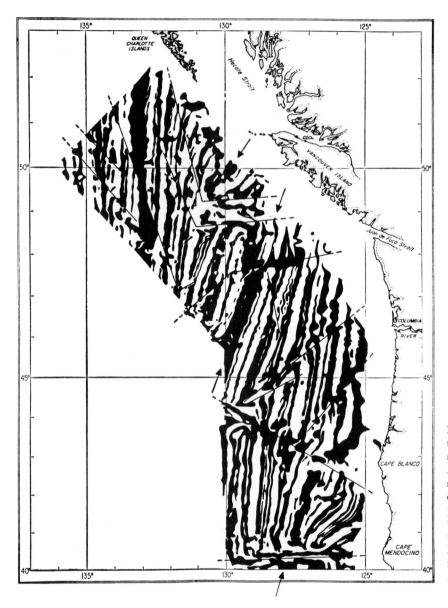

Fig. 15-15 Summary diagram of total magnetic-field anomalies southwest of Vancouver Island. Areas of positive anomaly are shown in black. Straight lines indicate faults offsetting the anomaly pattern; arrows, the axes of the three short ridge lengths within this area — from north to south, Explorer, Juan de Fuca, and Gorda ridges. (*From Mason and Raff, 1961.*)

have interpreted these anomalies as being due to variations in intensity and polarity of the earth's magnetic field which have been "fossilized" in the oceanic crust. This fossilization occurs as new mantle material wells up along the midoceanic ridges or rises and becomes magnetized in the field as it exists at the time of cooling. The intensity and polarity thus become frozen into the new crust and are pre-served as new material rises, forcing the older crust to spread apart.

The anomalies off the western coast of North America (Fig. 15-15) do not obviously lie parallel to a rise; the rise disappears under the continent in the Gulf of California (Fig. 15-13), but similar studies have now been made along the Pacific-Antarctic ridge (Pitman and Heirtzler, 1966), the Juan De Fuca ridge (Mason and

Raff, 1961), the South Atlantic Ocean (Heirtzler and Le Pichon, 1965), and the Reykjanes ridge which is a portion of the mid-Atlantic ridge south of Iceland (Heirtzler, Le Pichon, and Baron, 1965). The patterns over the ridges are often nearly perfectly symmetrical, and trends can be traced for great distances parallel to the ridges. In some cases the spread between matched anomalies is different, but this is interpreted as due to differences in rates of spreading (Fig. 15-16).

Magnetic anomaly belts like those found near the mid-Atlantic ridge do not extend to the continental margins. A rather distinct boundary more or less parallel to the continental slope separates the disturbed from the undisturbed regions of the ocean on both sides of the North Atlantic Ocean. The boundary lies between 2,000 and 2,500 km from the axis of the mid-Atlantic ridge and roughly equidistant from it (Heirtzler and Hayes, 1967). The wide tracts of uniformly magnetized crust could represent a long period during which no reversals took place (possibly late Paleozoic).

The hypothesis of the spreading oceanic crust adds strength to theories of continental drift. Hess (1962) has suggested that if upwelling occurs beneath a continental plate a means is provided for the splitting and eventual separation of the continental plates. Dietz (1961, 1963, 1964) has developed a concept of formation of geosynclines along continental borders where the ocean floor moves down and under the edge of the continental plate. A related idea is that orogenic belts form along the leading edge of a continental plate that is drifting. This idea has been advanced to explain the origin of the North American Cordillera. According to this theory the East Pacific rise has been overridden as North America has moved over the Pacific crust. The theory leaves us to seek other causes for orogeny on the east coast of North America, in such intercratonic belts as the Urals, and for all orogenic systems in the Precambrian.

The various mechanisms advanced for sea-floor spreading provide for the development of new crust in the vicinity of the midocean ridge crest as materials from the mantle rise toward the surface. This new crust might result from long-term upward creep of plastic mantle rock as the upper layers are extended and vertical movements take place to maintain isostatic compensation. More frequently the upward movement is attributed to the rise of material driven upward by a convection current directed upward. On the other hand, the new crust could initially consist of an extensive emplacement of dike swarms beneath the ridge crest. High heat flow over the new crust should accompany the emplacement of this new crust regardless of the mechanism of emplacement. High heat flow is found over the East Pacific rise, but the average heat flow over the mid-Atlantic ridge is within 20 percent of the heat flow in the basins (Langseth, Le Pichon, and Ewing, 1966). This suggests that there has been little or no spreading of the sea floor and perhaps little continental drift in the Atlantic during the Cenozoic.

Determination of the time of initiation of

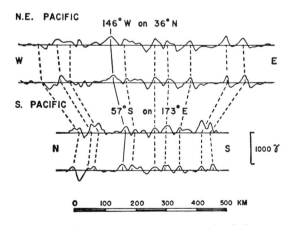

Fig. 15-16 The anomaly pattern correlated between profiles by Peter and Raff in the North Pacific and Christoffel and Ross in the South Pacific. It is suggested that the only difference between the two is the rate of spreading that formed them. (*From Vine, 1960, fig. 16. Copyright 1966 by Am. Assoc. Adv. Science.*)

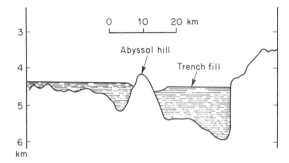

Fig. 15-17 Seismic-reflection profile across the Peru-Chile trench showing undeformed sediments (turbidite beds) deposited around a hill. The age of the sediment is inferred to be Miocene or younger. (*After Scholl, Huene, and Ridlon, 1968, fig. 1. Copyright 1968 by Am. Assoc. Adv. Sci.*)

spreading and its rate are two of the most important problems of the theory and they have yet to be satisfactorily resolved. Two dating techniques have been used, one based on the age of magnetic reversals of the field, the other on distribution of sediment of various ages. Times of changes in polarity of the geomagnetic field have been determined for rocks on continents where the age of the rocks can be closely dated, especially for the late Cenozoic. Pitman and Heirtzler (1966) has proposed a geomagnetic time scale which is used to match the reversals in polarity found over the midocean ridges with geologic time. Spreading rates ranging from 1.25 to 2.5 cm/year over the last 10 million years of geologic time are deduced in this way.

Documentation of the distribution of sediment of various ages is potentially the most fruitful approach to proving or dating the spreading of the sea floor because the age of sediments can be determined by means of fossil correlations much more reliably than the age of polarity changes can be determined. If spreading has taken place, older sediments should be further removed laterally from the midoceanic ridge crest. If the record were completely known we should be able to determine whether spreading has taken place, when it

started, how fast it has occurred, and whether it is continuing. Unfortunately we do not have deep cores from the ocean basins, but the results of shallow penetration coring are becoming available.

Coring programs have been carried out along the East Pacific rise, and Burckle and others (1967) report that only Pleistocene sediments were found on the crest of the rise. Pre-Pleistocene sediments were encountered on the flanks of the rise, and thicker sections of sediment occur on the flanks as predicted by the spreading. But coring in the South Atlantic (Ewing, Le Pichon, and Ewing, 1966) indicates much less sea-floor spreading than has been suggested on the basis of polarity studies.

Miocene sediments have been discovered on one side of the mid-Atlantic ridge within 10 km of the crest. The rate of spreading most frequently suggested is about 2 to 2.5 cm/year. At that rate no Miocene sediment should be found within 500 km of either side of the ridge crest (Ewing, Le Pichon, and Ewing, 1966). The Miocene sediment is not strongly deformed either near the ridge or near the edge of the continents where presumably the oceanic crust must go down under the continental margins (unless the earth is also expanding). Recent studies of the sediment in the Puerto Rico trench and the Peru-Chile trench (Fig. 15-17) show that the sedimentary layers in the bottom of the trenches are flat-lying and largely undeformed. We might expect the sediments to be folded or otherwise deformed if the mantle and oceanic crust actually sank or moved under the continental plate.

TRANSFORM FAULTS

Wilson (1965) proposed the name *transform faults* for those faults that terminate sharply at a place where the movement is transformed into a structure of another type. He has applied the principle primarily to major structures, recognizing transformations of strike-slip faults into midocean ridges, island arcs, or folded mountain belts. Six possible types of dextral transform faults are shown schematically in Fig. 15-18 as they might appear at an early stage of their development and after a period of growth. Wilson suggests that the faults be named for the types of features they connect (e.g., *dextral transform fault, ridge-convex arc type*).

Several basic assumptions and genetic relationships, which are not universally accepted, are implied by the terminology proposed by Wilson. Midoceanic ridges are accepted as expanding to produce new crust, leaving inactive residual traces in the topography; it is assumed that oceanic crust moves down under island arcs, absorbing old crust; and the convex sides of arcs thus advance.

Note in Fig. 15-19 that transform faults differ from transcurrent faults in a fundamental way —the direction of motion on a transform fault is the reverse of that required to offset the ridge.

The concept of transform faults has been applied to the offsets we examined earlier across the mid-Atlantic ridge in equatorial latitudes. Wilson also suggests that the San Andreas fault may be a transform fault—that it connects the East Pacific rise in the Gulf of California with a continuation in the northeastern Pacific. The great rift zones such as the Clipperton may also be interpreted as transform faults.

THE DARWIN RISE

Menard (1958, 1964) gave the name Darwin rise to a vast area of the southwestern Pacific basin where Charles Darwin had recognized regional subsidence from his studies of atolls. Many of the known guyots occur within this region (Fig. 15-20). Menard views it as a subsided rise probably representing a later-stage development of such features as the East Pacific rise and the mid-Atlantic ridge. Using the known elevations of the shelf break of the guyots and the sea floor, a paleobathymetric map was prepared for the time of formation of

the guyots, dated as about 100 million years ago. The result is a shieldlike rise extending from the Tuamotus (Tahiti) to the Marshall Islands. At that time great volcanic activity took place on the rise, volcanic ridges were built, and extensive extrusions of lava took place, building smooth archipelagic aprons. Fractures formed transverse and parallel to the long axis of the rise, creating trough and ridge topography. Seismic soundings show an above-

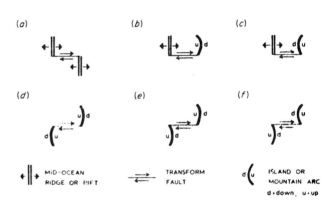

Fig.15-18 Diagram illustrating the six possible types of dextral transform faults. (*a*) Ridge to ridge type; (*b*) ridge to concave arc; (*c*) ridge to convex arc; (*d*) concave arc to concave arc; (*e*) concave arc to convex arc; (*f*) convex arc to convex arc. Note that the direction of motion in (*a*) is the reverse of that required to offset the ridge. (*From Wilson, 1965*.)

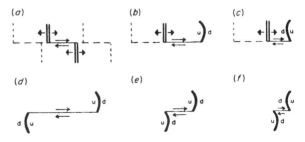

Fig. 15-19 Diagram illustrating the appearance of the six types of dextral transform faults shown in Fig. 15-18 after a period of growth. Traces of former positions, now inactive but still expressed in the topography, are shown by dashed lines. (*From Wilson, 1965*.)

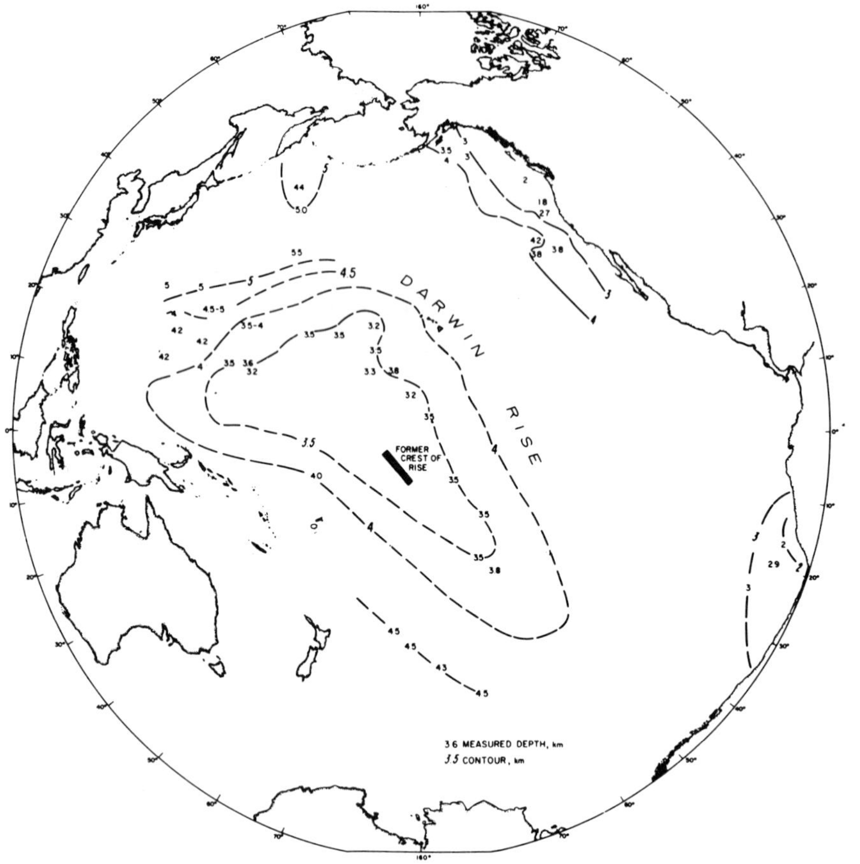

Fig. 15-20 Paleobathymetry of Pacific basin. Contours shown are all shallower than at present, but not necessarily contemporaneous except on Darwin rise. (*From Menard, 1964.*)

average thickness of volcanic rock and an above-average (8.3-km/sec) velocity in the upper mantle.

Menard (1964) compares the Darwin rise, the East Pacific rise, and the mid-Atlantic ridge:

1. *East Pacific rise:* Has high relief and lacks a thick layer of volcanic material; upper mantle velocity is normal.
2. *Mid-Atlantic ridge:* Has high relief and a thick (2 to 3 km) layer of volcanic material now broken by faults; upper mantle velocity is abnormally low.
3. *Darwin rise:* Has a thick (2 to 5 km) layer of volcanic material relatively unfaulted

and originally had high relief now lost; upper mantle velocity is abnormally high.

If these three represent a progression, the East Pacific rise might be young, the mid-Atlantic ridge somewhat older, and the Darwin rise the oldest (Menard, 1964).

REFERENCES

Antoine, John, and Ewing, John, 1963, Seismic refraction measurements on the margins of the Gulf of Mexico: Jour. Geophys. Research, v. 68, p. 1975–1996.

Antoine, J. W., and Harding, J. L., 1965, Structure of the continental shelf, northeastern Gulf of Mexico: Am. Assoc. Petroleum Geologists Bull., v. 49, p. 157–171.

Benioff, Hugo, 1955, Seismic evidence for crustal structure and tectonic activity: Geol. Soc. America Spec. Paper 62, p. 61–74.

Bostrom, R. C., 1967, Ocean-ridge system in northwest America: Amer. Assoc. Petroleum Geologists Bull., v. 51, no. 9, p. 1816–1832.

Burckle, L. H., and others, 1967, Tertiary sediment from the East Pacific rise: Science, v. 157, no. 3788, p. 537–540.

Dehlinger, P., Couch, R. W., and Gemperle, M., 1967, Gravity and structure of the eastern part of the Mendocino Escarpment: Jour. Geophys. Research, v. 72, no. 4, p. 1233–1247.

Dietz, R. S., 1961, Continental and ocean basin evolution by spreading: Nature, v. 189.

——— 1963a, Collapsing continental rises: an actualistic concept of geosynclines and mountain building: Jour. Geology, v. 71.

———1963b, Wave-base, marine profile of equilibrium, and wave-built terraces: a critical appraisal: Geol. Soc. America Bull., v. 74.

——— 1964, Origin of continental slopes: Am. Scientist, v. 52.

Drake, C. L., Ewing, Maurice, and Sutton, G. H., 1959, Continental margins and geosynclines: The east coast of North America north of Cape Hatteras, in Physics and chemistry of the earth, v. 3: New York, Pergamon, p. 110–198.

Drake, C. L., Heirtzler, J. R., and Hirshman, J., 1963, Magnetic anomalies off eastern North America: Jour. Geophys. Research, v. 68, p. 5259–5275.

Drake, C. L., and Woodward, H. P., 1963, Appalachian curvature, wrench faulting, and off shore structures: New York Acad. Sci. Trans., ser. II, v. 26, p. 48–63.

Ewing, John, and Ewing, Maurice, 1959, Seismic refraction measurements in the Atlantic ocean basins, in the Mediterranean Sea, on the mid-Atlantic ridge, and in the Norwegian Sea: Geol. Soc. America Bull., v. 70, p. 291–318.

Ewing, John, Worzel, J. L., and Ewing, Maurice, 1962, Sediments and oceanic structural history of the Gulf of Mexico: Jour. Geophys. Research, v. 67, p. 2509–2527.

Ewing, Maurice, and Antoine, John, 1965, Sediments and structures in the Gulf of Mexico: Am. Assoc. Petroleum Geologists Bull., v.

Ewing, Maurice, Le Pichon, X., and Ewing, John, 1966, Crustal structure of the mid-ocean ridges: Jour. Geophys. Research, v. 71, no. 6, p. 1611–1636.

Fisher, R. L., and Shor, G. G., 1958, Topography and structure of the middle America trench: XX Internat. Geol. Cong. Proc.

Gibson, I. L., and Walker, G. P. L., 1964, Some composite rhyolite-basalt lavas and related composite dykes in eastern Iceland: Geologists' Assoc., London, v. 74, p. 301–318.

Gilcher, A., 1958, Coastal and submarine morphology: New York, Wiley, 274 p.

——— 1963, Continental shelf and slope, in Hill, M. N., ed., The sea, v. iii: New York, Wiley.

Hallam, A., 1963, Major epeirogenic and eustatic changes since the Cretaceous, and their possible relationships to crustal structure: Am. Jour. Sci., v. 261, no. 5.

Hamilton, E. L., 1967, Marine geology of abyssal plains in the Gulf of Alaska: Jour. Geophys. Research, v. 12, no. 16, p. 4189–4213.

Heezen, Bruce C., 1962, The deep-sea floor, in Runcorn, S. K., ed., Continental drift: Internat. Geophys. Ser. 3, New York, Academic, p. 235–288.

Heezen, Bruce C., and Ewing, Maurice, 1956, Arctic oceans: Geophys. Mon. no. 1, p. 75–81.

Heezen, Bruce C., and others, 1964, Chain and Romanche fracture zone: Deep-sea Research, v. 11, p. 11–33.

Heirtzler, J. R., Dickson, G. O., Herron, E. M., Pitman, W. C., III, and Le Pichon, X., 1968, Marine magnetic anomalies, geomagnetic field reversals, and motions of the ocean floor and continents: Jour. Geophys. Research, v. 73, no. 6.

Heirtzler, J. R., and Hayes, D. E., 1967, Magnetic boundaries in the North Atlantic Ocean: Science, v. 157, no. 3785, p. 185–187.

Heirtzler, J. R., and Le Pichon, X., 1965, Crustal structure of the mid-ocean ridges, 3, Magnetic anomalies over the mid-Atlantic ridge: Jour. Geophys. Research, v. 70.

Heirtzler, J. R., Le Pichon, X., and Baron, J. G., 1965, Magnetic anomalies over the Reykjanes ridge: Deep-Sea Research, v. 13, p. 427.

Hess, H. H., 1962, History of the ocean basins, in Petrologic studies: New York, Geol. Soc. America, p. 599–620.

Hess, H. H., and Maxwell J. C., 1953a, Caribbean research project: Geol. Soc. America Bull., v. 64.

——— 1953b, Major structural features of the southwest Pacific: Pacific Sci. Cong. Proc., 7th, v. 2, p. 14–17.

King, E. R., Zietz, I., and Alldredge, L. R., 1966, Magnetic data on the structure of the central Arctic region: Geol. Soc. America Bull., v. 77, p. 619–646.

Langseth, M. G., Le Pichon, X., and Ewing, M., 1966, Crustal structure of the mid-ocean ridges: Jour. Geophys. Research, v. 71, no. 22, p. 5321–5355.

Lee, W. H. K., ed., 1965, Terrestrial heat flow: Baltimore, Am. Geophys. Union Pub. 1288, 276 p.

Lee, W. H. K., and Uyeda S., 1965, Review of heat flow data, in Lee, W. H. K., ed., Terrestrial heat flow: Am. Geophys. Union, Geophys. Mon. ser. 8, chap. 6.

Le Pichon, X., and others, 1965, Crustal structure of the mid-ocean ridges, 1, seismic refraction measurements: Jour. Geophys. Research, v. 70.

Mason, R. C., and Raff, A. D., 1961, A magnetic survey off the West Coast of North America, 32°N to 42°N: Geol. Soc. America Bull., v. 72, p. 1259–1265.

McManus, D. A., 1967, Physiography of Cobb and Gorda rises, NE Pacific Ocean: Geol. Soc. America Bull., v. 78, p. 527–546.

Menard, H. W., 1955, Deformation of the northeastern Pacific basin and the West Coast of North America: Geol. Soc. America Bull., v. 66, p. 1149–1198.

——— 1958, Development of median elevations in ocean basins: Geol. Soc. America Bull., v. 69, p. 1179–1186.

——— 1960, The East Pacific rise: Science, v. 132, p. 1737–1746.

——— 1964, Marine geology of the Pacific: New York, McGraw-Hill, 260 p.

——— 1966, Extension of northeastern Pacific fracture zones: Sience, v. 155, p. 72–74.

Menard, H. W., and Fisher, R. L., 1958, Clipperton fracture zone in the northeastern equatorial Pacific: Jour. Geology, v. 66, p. 239–253.

Moore, D. G., and Curray, J. R., 1963, Structural framework of the continental terrace northwest Gulf of Mexico: Jour. Geophys. Research, v. 68, no. 6.

Murauchi, S., Den, N., Asano, S., et al. 1968, Crustal structure of the Philippine Sea: Jour. Geophys. Research, v. 73, no. 10.

Oliver, J., and Isacks, B. L., 1967, Deep earthquake zones, anomalous structures in the upper mantle, and the lithosphere: Jour. Geophys. Research, v. 72.

Oxburgh, E. R., and Turcotte, D. L., 1968, Mid-ocean ridges and geotherm distribution during mantle convection: Jour. Geophys. Research, v. 73, no. 8.

Patterson, M. S., and Weiss, L. E., 1962, Experimental folding in rocks: Nature, v. 195.

Phillips, J. D., 1967, Magnetic anomalies over the mid-Atlantic ridge near 27°N: Science, v. 157.

Pitman, W. C., III., and Heirtzler, J. R., 1966, Magnetic anomalies over the Pacific-Antarctic ridge: Science, v. 154.

Pitman, W. C., III. Herron, E. M., and Heirtzler, J. R., 1968, Magnetic anomalies in the Pacific and sea floor spreading: Jour. Geophys. Research, v. 73, no. 6.

Raff, A. D., 1962, Further magnetic measurements along the Murray fault: Jour. Geophys. Research, v. 67, p. 417–418.

Raff, A. D., and Mason, R. G., 1961, Magnetic survey off the west coast of North America 40°N latitude to 50°N latitude: Geol. Soc. America Bull., v. 72.

Scholl, D. W., von Huene, R., and Ridlon, J. B., 1968, Spreading of the ocean floor: Undeformed sediments in the Peru-Chile trench: Science, v. 159, p. 869–871.

Sykes, L. R., 1967, Mechanism of earthquakes and nature of faulting on the mid-oceanic ridges: Jour. Geophys. Research, v. 72, no. 8, p. 2131–2153.

Talwani, Manik, 1964, A review of marine geophysics: Marine Geol., v. 2, p. 29–80.

Talwani, Manik, and others, 1965, Crustal structure of the mid-ocean ridges, 2, computed model from gravity and seismic refraction data: Jour. Geophys. Research, v. 70, p. 341–353.

Thorarinsson, Sigurdur, 1965, The median zone of Iceland, in The World Rift System: Geol. Survey Canada Paper 66–14, p. 187–211.

Vacquier, V., 1959, Measurement of horizontal displacement along faults in the ocean floor: Nature, v. 183.

Vacquier, V., Raff, A. D., and Warren, R. E., 1961,

Horizontal displacements in the floor of the northeast Pacific Ocean: Geol. Soc. America Bull., v. 72.

Vine, F. J., 1966, Spreading of the ocean floor: new evidence: Science, v. 154, no. 3755, p. 1405–1415.

Vine, F. J., and Matthews, D. H., 1963, Magnetic anomalies over oceanic ridges: Nature, v. 199.

Von Herzen, R. P., and Uyeda, S., 1963, Heat flow through the east Pacific Ocean floor: Jour. Geophys. Research, v. 68, no. 14.

Wageman, J. M., and Johnson, G. L., 1967, A study of part of the eastern flank of the mid-Atlantic ridge: Jour. Geophys. Research, v. 72, no. 4, p. 1175–1182.

Wilson, J. T., 1959, Geophysics and continental growth: Am. Scientist, v. 47, no. 1.

——— 1965, A new class of faults and their bearing on continental drift: Nature, v. 207, no. 4995, p. 343–347.

16
examples of modern diastrophism

CIRCUMPACIFIC OROGENY

The border of the Pacific Ocean merits special attention because it is the region of most active seismicity, volcanism, and diastrophism. Many hypotheses have been advanced to account for this activity in the Pacific and for the differences among the oceans, but at this point we will review impartially the salient features of the structure of the belt.

The Pacific Ocean basin is separated from continental cratonic shield areas by modern zones of volcanic activity, diastrophism, seismicity, or deep sea trenches around most of its circumference (Fig. 15-1).

The Peru-Chile trench and the Andes separate the South American shield from the ocean basin; the Middle America trench forms the border in Mexico and Central America; a modern belt of diastrophism and the Cordilleran system of North America separate the ocean basin from the Canadian shield; a succession of arcuate island chains and deep sea trenches forms a scalloped and intricately complex border between Asia and Australia and the Pacific basin; finally, in the Antarctic we find that a Mesozoic fold belt separates the shield from the Pacific, but without an intervening volcanic arc or deep sea trench.

ALEUTIAN ISLANDS—ALASKA PENINSULA

The Aleutian Islands form one of the most nearly perfect arcuate belts on the surface of the earth. The belt consists of a chain of volcanic islands that extend from the Alaska Peninsula to Kamchatka; the chain is convex toward the North Pacific Ocean and is bordered along its convex side by an arcuate deep sea trench. The island chain and trench follow the arc of a circle for about 1,400 miles (Murray, 1945). Submarine mountains, some standing

12,000 feet above the sea floor, occur in the Gulf of Alaska, and several are seen on submarine profiles across the trench. Bowers bank, located on the Bering Sea side of the Aleutian ridge, is an unusual topographic feature in that it also lies almost exactly on a circular arc.

Submarine Topography

The submarine topography of the Aleutians is known in considerable detail (Fig. 16-1). The Bering Sea platform, a continental shelf, is less than 100 fathoms deep over most of its area. The edge of this platform intersects the arc at the western end of the Alaska Peninsula. The Aleutian basin, with depths slightly over 2,000 fathoms, lies on the concave side of the Aleutian Islands.

The Aleutian trench, with depths commonly exceeding 3,000 fathoms and over 4,000 fathoms south of the Near Islands, can be followed south and east of the Alaska Peninsula. In this eastern portion the trench diverges from the parallel trend with the volcanic arc. The trench is traced across the Gulf of Alaska and terminates near the end of a submarine canyon out of Yakutat Bay. The eastern end of the trench is shallower than the central and western portions.

Profiles across the trench (Fig. 16-2) show the change from V- to U-shaped profiles in going eastward, but the distance between the walls remains constant at the 5-km depth, and it is probable that this is due to filling by sediment. Slopes on the northern wall of the trench are irregular and locally steep (up to 30°). Two benches at depths of 2 and 4.5 km are persistent, and other features can be followed from one profile to another (Fig. 16-2), although it is impossible to identify the origin of the features with any degree of certainty (Peter and others, 1965).

Surface Geology

There are about 76 major volcanoes and numerous smaller cones located on the Aleutian Islands west of the intersection of the volcanic arc with the continent. Volcanic centers of Quaternary and Tertiary (Miocene and younger) age are known in the islands. The volcanic products of Quaternary volcanoes range in composition from olivine basalt to rhyolite, but they are predominantly of andesitic composition. The volcanic materials are intruded by stocks which range from gabbro to albite granite in composition.

A belt of Quaternary volcanic centers lies somewhat north of the main structural axis of the arc, suggesting that the centers of volcanism have been shifted away from the trench as older centers of activity became extinct (Coats, 1962). The character of the basement on which the Aleutian volcanoes are situated is not revealed on the islands. Pre-Tertiary sedimentary rocks outcrop on very few islands, Adak, Amlia, and Atka. As we will see, geophysical studies indicate that the volcanoes at the western end are built on oceanic crust. The occurrence of boulders composed of granite and metamorphic rocks on several islands near the center of the arc is notable because they are very abundant (Kanaga Island, Coats, 1962), but their source is no longer outcropping on the island. The volcanic arc does extend eastward onto the Alaska Peninsula where the basement materials can be examined. Since the trends of the structures on the peninsula are parallel to the arc, they may continue some distance along the arc as the basement.

The geology of the Alaska Peninsula has been summarized by Burk (1965), as shown in Fig. 16-3. A very large part of the basement geology is covered by Tertiary and Quaternary volcanic materials, but pre-Tertiary rocks, particularly Cretaceous and Jurassic units, are exposed. The sedimentary units are clastic sequences in which feldspathic sandstone and conglomerates are prominent constituents. Flysch-type deposits of probable Cretaceous age are found on islands on the continental shelf. The Lower Jurassic rocks are rich in volcanic products, and in the eastern end of the peninsula large Jurassic granitic plutons are exposed.

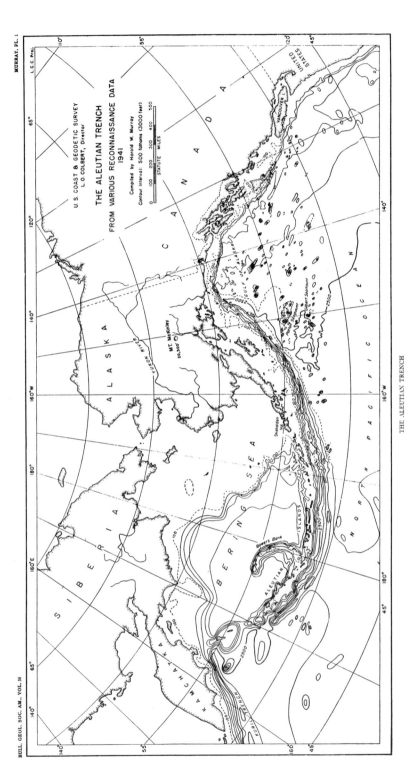

THE ALEUTIAN TRENCH

Fig. 16-1 Topography of the northern Pacific margins. (*Based on the U. S. Hydrographic Office Map of the World, 1961.*)

Triassic cherts are also locally exposed. Thus the more recent volcanic arc has been built on a basement of eugeosynclinal character.

Folds are prominent in the Tertiary and older rocks (Fig. 16-3). The axial traces of these folds parallel the trend of the arc, and most of the folds are broad open structures. Fault traces also show a pronounced parallelism in trend with the folds and volcanic arc. Burk shows one thrust fault which dips north and brings Upper Jurassic into fault contact with Cretaceous units (Oligocene sedimentary units exposed south of the fault are vertical). It appears from the map that this fault does not displace Pliocene rocks. Most of the other faults mapped are reverse faults and the northern side is quite consistently up on these. Normal faults, some of which displace Quaternary units, also are known. Very few of the faults shown on this map are transverse to the trend of the arc, but one exception is the fault which occurs east of Veniaminof volcano and which appears to line up with a chain of cinder cones northwest of the volcano. Coats (1962) shows rose plots of undifferentiated joints and faults on islands in the Aleutians, and these show prominent trends transverse to the arc, some nearly at right angles, others more oblique.

It is interesting to compare the general structural pattern on the peninsula with that in the Near Islands located in the western part of the Aleutians. Studies there (Gates and Gibson, 1956) have led to the conclusions that there is a normal fault along the northern side of the Aleutian ridge and that there is a north-dipping reverse fault on the southern insular slope. Gates also interprets north-dipping thrusts along the inside of the Aleutian bench and in the Aleutian trench. The common occurrence of normal step faults and transverse faults in the Aleutians has also been pointed out (Gibson and Nichols, 1953). There is no clear-cut evidence that any of the faults on the peninsula or in the Aleutians have a large component of lateral displacement such as that postulated for

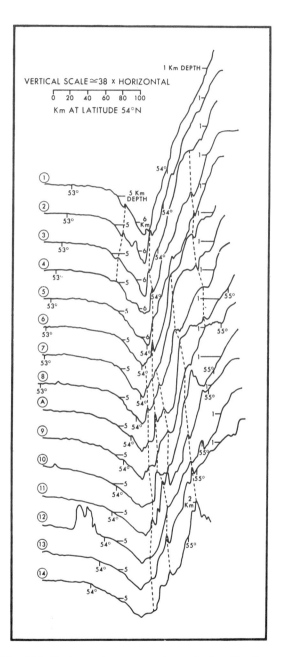

Fig. 16-2 Bathymetric cross sections of the Aleutian trench showing linear topographic trends. Depth in kilometers for each profile is denoted by numbers set off by horizontal tick marks. Numbers set off by vertical tick marks indicate latitude. (*From Peter, Elvers, and Yellin, 1965.*)

Solid black dots are volcanos

Dotted areas – Jurassic sedimentary rocks

White areas – Post Jurassic–largely Tertiary
and Quaternary

ˇˇˇˇ Pattern = Tertiary granitic intrusions

ɔↄↄↄ   = Jurassic granitic intrusions

K   = Cretaceous slate and
graywacke belt

U/D   = High angle fault

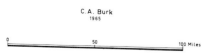

C. A. Burk
1965

Fig. 16-3 Geologic sketch map of the Alaska Peninsula. *(After Burk, 1965.)*

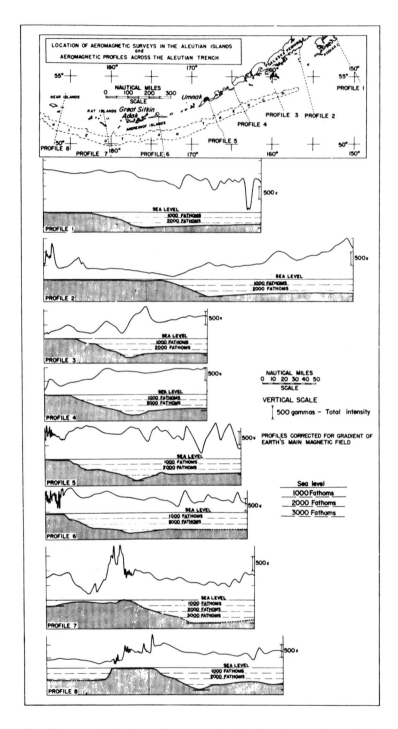

Fig. 16-4 Aeromagnetic profiles across the Aleutian trench. (*From Keller, Meuschke, and Alldredge. 1954.*)

the San Andreas fault and the Alpine fault of New Zealand.

Crustal Structure

A considerable amount of geophysical data has been collected in the Aleutian region (Keller and others, 1954; Shor, 1962; Coats, 1962; Peter and others, 1965). Seismic refraction studies indicate that the crustal sections in the Bering Sea consist of a 2-km sedimentary layer, a 4-km second layer, and a 4-km normal oceanic crustal layer. Large variations in the thickness of the sedimentary layer were found at Dixon entrance on the continental shelf, suggesting the possibility of faulting. The eastern end of the trench shows increased sediment thickness as was suggested by the shallowing and shape of the trench floor. A seismic profile in the Alaska Abyssal Plain showed the M discontinuity at a depth of 10 to 11 km, and it appears to remain at that depth while the sedimentary section thickens toward the land. Near the foot of the continental slope the depth of M discontinuity is somewhat shallower and suggests the outer ridge sometimes found on the seaward side of other trenches.

Additional evidence concerning the crustal structure in the Aleutians has been obtained from magnetic and gravity studies. Eight widely spaced aeromagnetic profiles (Fig. 16-4) show that there is no consistent relationship between the anomalies and the trench, nor are the anomalies due to material distributed in a consistent way along the island arc system (Keller and others, 1954). This leaves us with a number of possibilities to explain the anomalies (e.g., lava flows, the presence of small faults which bring rock with high magnetic susceptibility up). Until detailed studies are made on closely spaced lines, it is difficult to narrow down the possibilities.

More detailed surveys have been made in an area across the trench south of the Alaska Peninsula (Peter and others, 1965). Here the gravity and magnetic anomalies parallel the trend of the trench. A narrow positive magnetic anomaly lies over the trench, and a second positive magnetic anomaly lies along the south rim of the trench. The profile of structure favored by Peter, based on the degree to which it satisfies the gravity and magnetic data, is illustrated in Fig. 16-5. The positive magnetic anomaly over the trench floor is interpreted as a fissure filled with some basic igneous material.

Seismicity

The distribution of earthquake epicenters in the Aleutians as analyzed by Benioff (1954) is shown in Fig. 16-6. Almost all the epicenters are located north of the trench, and within the volcanic arc the shallow-focus quakes lie closer to the trench. Benioff interprets the foci as being located along a fault which dips north about 28°.

KAMCHATKA AND THE KURIL ISLANDS

The peninsula of Kamchatka bears a relation to the Kuril Islands similar to that between the Alaska Peninsula and the Aleutians. The Tectonic Map of Russia (Fig. 16-7) shows Cenozoic fold systems in Kamchatka which parallel (on the northeast) the trend of the peninsula. The modern deformation there began in the Pliocene and continues to the present. A miogeosynclinal zone is situated on the side of the peninsula closest to the Asiatic continent; the eastern side is the site of eugeosynclinal deposits and late Tertiary to presently active volcanism. The number of volcanoes is greatest in the southern end of the region; very few are located north of the point of intersection of the trend of the Aleutian Islands with Kamchatka.

Deformation in the region is still very active, particularly along the eastern part of the Kamchatka Peninsula which is being uplifted, while the shore of the Okhotsk Sea is presently being submerged (Goryatchev, 1962). While the northeast-trending swells and sags are the most prominent Cenozoic structures, there are a

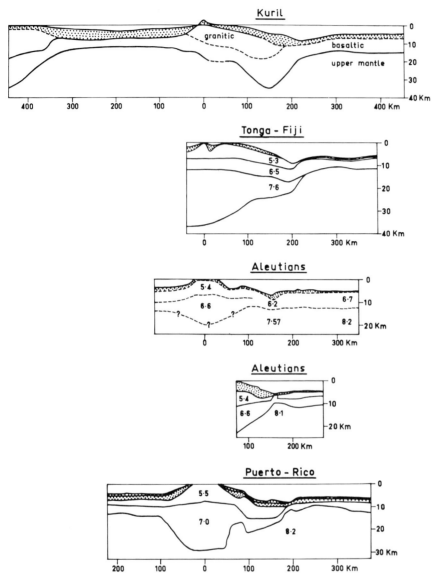

Fig. 16-5 Crustal cross sections across island arcs. Kurils *(from Belyayevskiy and Fedynskiy, 1962)*; Tonga-Fiji *(from Talwani, Worzel, and Ewing, 1961)*; Aleutians *(from Shor, 1962, and Peter, and others, 1965)*; Puerto Rico *(from Talwani, Worzel, and Ewing, 1959)*.

number of sags developed along the arcuate system which trend northwest across the arc (Fig. 16-8). These sags are separated by up-lifted areas on which abrasion and denudation levels can be recognized as having been lifted to different levels. One of these northwest-trending sags occurs where the projection of the Aleutian Island trench intersects Kamchatka.

Several major faults also intersect the arc and cut transverse to it along northwest trends.

The concentration of modern volcanism (which is predominantly andesite) and the seismicity are also connected with these northwest sags. These volcanoes, of which some 285 are known, form an arcuate zone about 50 km wide extending the length of the Kuril Islands and along the eastern side of the peninsula. All 66 of the active volcanoes lie south of the point of intersection with the Aleutians; activity is most intense just south of this intersection and decreases southward. Analysis of the number of eruptions within the last 200 years indicates that the maximum volcanic activity is associated with the western extensions of the

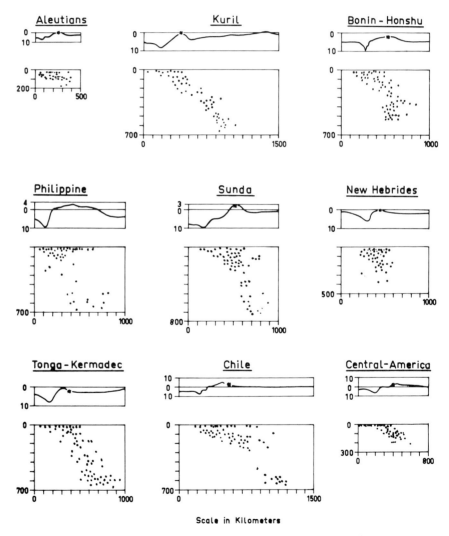

Scale in Kilometers

Fig. 16-6 Foci patterns across island arcs and margins of Pacific. Foci from long sections parallel to the arc have been projected into a single section. (*Modified after Benioff, 1954.*)

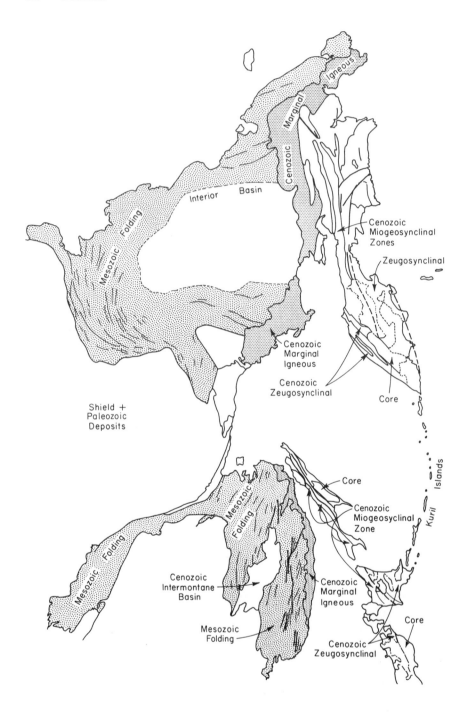

Fig. 16-7 Orogenic belts of western Asia. (*After the Tectonic Map of Russia, 1956.*)

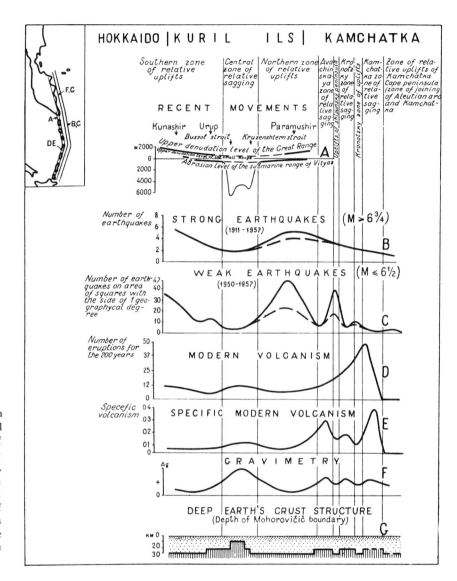

Fig. 16-8 Relationship between the geotectonic and geophysical conditions of the eastern edge of the Kuril-Kamchatka folding zone (modern movements, volcanism, seismicity, gravity anomalies in Bouguer reduction, and deep crustal structure according to the data of deep seismic sounding); on plots *B* and *C* solid lines represent the seismic regime of the zone. *(From Goryatchev, 1962.)*

areas of northwest-trending sags. The transverse sags are also characterized by maximum Bouguer anomalies.

Seismic studies in the region have made it possible to draw isopachs of crustal thickness in the area between the Asiatic continent and the Pacific basin, as shown in Fig. 16-9 (Belyayevskiy and Fedynskiy, 1962). The crust shows

a pronounced thickening under the volcanic arc, but thins toward the oceans and the Okhotsk Sea.

The shallow and intermediate earthquake foci define a zone inclined about 34° toward the continent (Benioff, 1954). There is a good correlation here between the edge of the trench and the zone of concentration of shallow

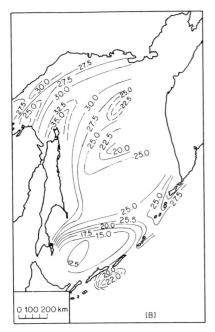

Fig. 16-9 Isopach map of the earth's crust in the zone of transition between the Pacific basin and the Asian continent in the Soviet Far East (in kilometers). *(Redrawn from Belyayevskiy and Fedynskiy, 1962.)*

quakes (Fig. 16-6). The deeper foci lie under the Okhotsk Sea where the zone is inclined more steeply toward the continent.

STRUCTURAL SKETCHES OF THE SOUTHWEST PACIFIC MARGIN

The southwest Pacific margin is one of the most complex structural regions of the earth. Although many parts of the region are poorly known geologically, its importance in regional structural geology and tectonics is great. It is in this region that the two great Cenozoic orogenic belts, the circumpacific and the Alpine-Himalayan, intersect. Critical observations from this region have been used in most orogenic and tectonic theories. Major elements of submarine topography, volcanic, and tectonic belts are summarized in Figs. 16-10 and 16-11.

The effects of Cenozoic and late Mesozoic diastrophism and volcanism obscure the earlier regional structural connections between Australia, New Zealand, and Asia. The vast Precambrian shield of Australia has an early Paleozoic geosynclinal belt running north-south in the center and well-defined later Paleozoic geosynclinal and orogenic belts along its eastern coast. Precambrian gneisses and remnants of a Paleozoic orogenic belt are found in New Zealand also. Scattered Paleozoic outcrops are known in the Malayan Peninsula, Sumatra, western Borneo, on the island of Timor, in New Guinea, and in Japan, but these are too small and too few to provide a basis for anything more than speculation about the early structural history of the region. Metamorphic rocks, largely of uncertain age, are also scattered through the island arcs.

The distances separating the various major structural elements of this region are so great that it is desirable to examine the individual units separately before trying to synthesize the results. It is useful to bear in mind that the distance from New Zealand to southeast Asia is far greater than the entire length of the Appalachian geosyncline. The region is subdivided on the basis of topography and general geological character as follows:

1. New Zealand
2. Kermadec-Tonga-Fiji region
3. New Caledonia and the submarine ridge on which it is located
4. New Hebrides, Solomon, and Admiralty Islands
5. New Guinea
6. Indonesia and the Philippines
7. Taiwan and the Ryukyu Islands
8. Arcuate islands from Palau to Japan

A BRIEF REVIEW OF NEW ZEALAND TECTONICS

The tectonics of New Zealand is particularly interesting because New Zealand is the site of long-term deformation continuing up to the present; because it is unique as a continental crustal element separated from the nearest continent, Australia, by a wide expanse of oceanic-type crust; because it lies along the structural trend of the Tonga-Kermadec Island arc; because it also lies at the end of a long arcuate trend which extends from New Guinea through New Caledonia to New Zealand; and because

an ocean rise with characteristics like that of midoceanic ridges located south of New Zealand terminates in the South Island. It would appear at once to be a small continent, part of an island arc system, and an orogenic belt.

Crustal Structure

The thickness of the crust in the region immediately around New Zealand is comparable

Fig. 16-10 Sketch of major physiographic, structural, and volcanic features of southwestern Pacific. (*Base is the Hydrographic Office Map, The World, 1961.*)

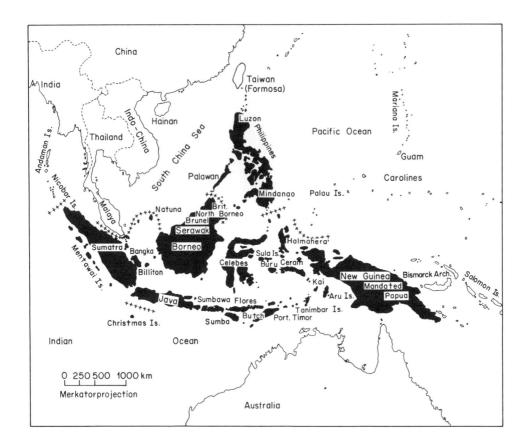

Fig. 16-11A   Sketch map of the islands of the Indonesian region. *(From Van Bemmelen, 1949.)*

to that of continents, 30 to 35 km, and the much larger area defined as the New Zealand Plateau has a crust of intermediate thickness, 20 km+. These thicknesses are determined mainly by surface wave dispersion (Officer, 1955; Adams, 1963; Thomson and Evison, 1962). Brodie (1964) has synthesized the existing data on crustal thickness for the region as shown in Fig. 16-12.

The greatest crustal thickness corresponds with present land areas. The transition from intermediate to oceanic crustal thicknesses occurs rapidly to the west toward the Tasman basin and to the southwest toward the southwestern Pacific basin. This transition occurs where slopes of the ocean floor are relatively steep, about the 2,000-fathom isobath. A large

area of the sea above this depth is 0 to 500 fathoms deep.

A narrow zone of intermediate thickness crust, 20 to 25 km, extends north-northeast from New Zealand to the Tonga Islands. A second zone curves off from the central portion of New Zealand along the Lord Howe rise.

Several islands occur on the New Zealand Plateau and most of these contain outcrops of rock types normally associated with continental crust.

Major Structural Divisions of New Zealand

The larger structural elements of New Zealand are shown on a geologic sketch map in Fig. 16-13. The basement rocks of the North Island consist of a Mesozoic graywacke and argillite complex of undetermined thickness and structure; however, this complex is highly indurated, and the units are thought to be very thick, of geosynclinal proportions. Pillow lavas, sodium rich basalt, chert, and ultramafic bodies associated with the graywacke all point to a eugeosynclinal association. This basement is exposed in the central portion of the North Island as a mountain range and in the Northland Peninsula. The basement is broken by a complex

fault system, along some of which there has been great differential movements. The basement is partially covered by Tertiary and Pleistocene volcanic rocks and sediments. Ultramafic bodies found in fault contact with surrounding sediments are located in the Northland Peninsula. These bodies appear to have been emplaced cold during the early Tertiary. The Mesozoic basement is covered in the north-central portion of the island by a vast area of

Fig. 16-11B Tectonic sketch map of island arcs of the southwestern Pacific. The margins of the trenches are drawn approximately on the 3,000 fathom contour of the U.S. Hydrographic Office map of the world, 1961. The 100-fathom contour is drawn to outline shelf areas. Areas where pre-Cenozoic rocks were undeformed during the Mesozoic and Cenozoic are shown by a wavy pattern. Areas involved in Mesozoic folding are covered by a dot pattern. Areas where pre-Cenozoic rocks were deformed in Cenozoic orogeny, particularly Miocene, are shown by diagonal patterns. Deformed and undeformed Cenozoic sediments are shown blank. The dashed lines mark location of ridges in the submarine topography; *s* designates seamounts; small circles indicate location of volcanos.

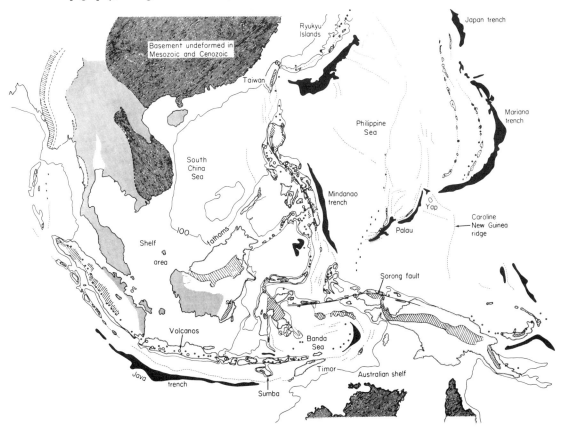

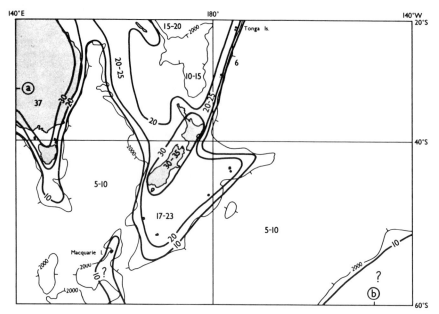

Fig. 16-12 Thickness of the earth's crust (kilometers) in the southwest Pacific region. *(From Brodie, 1964. Based on data in Officer, 1955: Tasman basin, Lord Howe rise, Kermadec ridge, southwestern Pacific basin; de Jersey, 1941 and Doyle, Everingham, and Hogan, 1959: Australia; Thomson and Evison, 1962: New Zealand; Adams, 1962: Campbell Plateau.)*

volcanic rocks. A north-trending system of folded Tertiary units lies along the east coast of the North Island. Recent seismic profiling has revealed the continuation of this fold system on the continental shelf east of New Zealand. Tertiary units west of the central basement ridge are not strongly folded. They occupy a large Tertiary basin, the Wanganui basin, in the southwestern part of the North Island.

The South Island is divided into eastern and western parts by the Alpine fault. East of this fault the basement rock is a thick sequence of Mesozoic graywacke and metamorphic rocks which have a complex internal structure. The Alpine graywacke-metamorphic complex is partially covered by sedimentary deposits from the late Tertiary to the Pleistocene. Taken as a whole, the basement rocks diverge from a trend parallel to the Alpine fault toward the southern

end of the South Island and then bend toward the east. Along the southern edge a large syncline, the Southland syncline of Mesozoic and Tertiary sediments, broadens eastward and closes toward the northwest until it is cut off by the Alpine fault. The southern margin of the syncline is the Fiordland metamorphic complex composed of granitic rock, large parts of which are thought to be Precambrian in age. Along the west coast, west of the Alpine fault, Precambrian metamorphic rocks, strongly deformed lower Paleozoic sedimentary sequences, Cretaceous batholiths, and the presumed continuation of the Southland syncline are located in a region of great structural complexity and poor exposure.

Diastrophic History of New Zealand

Two main periods of deformation are widely documented in New Zealand—the early Cretaceous post-Hokonui (Rangitata) orogeny and the late Tertiary and Pleistocene Kaikoura orogeny. The restricted exposure of Paleozoic and Precambrian rocks and uncertainty about ages of Paleozoic units obscures the early diastrophism of New Zealand, but at least one major Paleozoic (post-Devonian) orogeny is documented in Nelson (the northern part of South Island). Numerous unconformities and episodes of warping or tilting along faults indicate that New Zealand has been active throughout most of the Mesozoic and Cenozoic.

Paleozoic and Precambrian rocks are exposed in Fiordland, east of the Alpine fault, and in

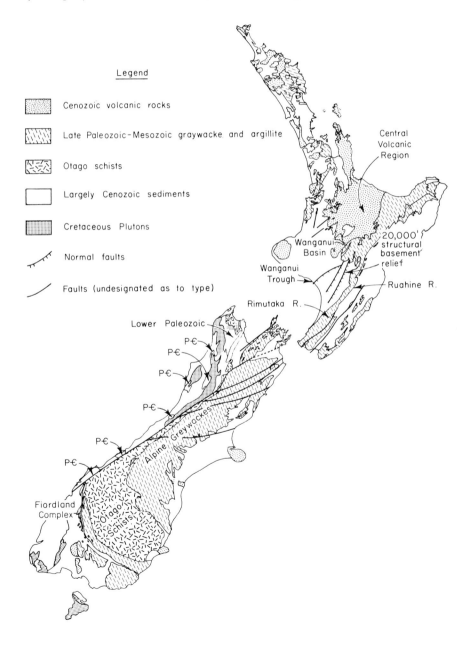

Fig. 16-13 Outline map of New Zealand. (*Based on the Geologic Map of New Zealand, 1958.*)

Nelson, west of the fault. The Paleozoic rocks are complexly deformed and largely metamorphosed. Three periods of folding have been recognized (Grindley, 1961).

Paleozoic folds in central Haupiri are nearly isoclinal and plunge in the direction of the regional dip. Grindley thinks it probable that the plunge of these folds is due to later tilting of the fault-bounded blocks in which they occur. If the tilted blocks are restored to the original position, then the folds become recumbent with southern roots, and the now steep faults would have been low-angle thrust faults.

To the north the Haupiri rocks are inverted and lie over Ordovician schists. To the south the nappes pass back into a para-autochthonous region of east-west isoclinal folds, overturned northwards. The age of this deformation is uncertain, but is possibly Devonian.

The second generation of folds is north-trending with steep limbs and with axial plunges of 10 to 40° south. Drag folds and axial-plane cleavage accompanied this folding. The age is possibly Carboniferous.

Ordovician to Devonian rocks are folded into northeast-trending folds on the eastern side of the Haupiri belt. The main structure is a northeast-trending syncline. The age is possibly late Paleozoic.

Post-Hokonui orogeny

Great accumulations of argillite, graywacke, and associated volcanics, tuffs, pillow lavas, and ultramafics formed in New Zealand during the Permian, Triassic, and Jurassic, and these comprise two systems, the Maitai and Hokonui. Beck has summarized the sedimentary history in the region of Marlborough Sound as follows:

It would appear that a simple sedimentary cycle extended through Carboniferous and Permian times perhaps into the Mesozoic during which time a sedimentary thickness of at least 65,000 feet of sediment was deposited. Greywacke and argillite (in part regionally metamorphosed to schist) comprise the basal 50,000 ft indicating common and typical geosynclinal sedimentation. The upper 15,000 ft of sediment (the Lee River and Maitai Groups) indicate more specialized sedimentary environments such as shallow water . . . indicated by conglomerates and plant remains.

Penecontemporaneous slump and sliding took place during deposition, and much of the material is thought to have been deposited in deep water by turbidity currents. These graywackes and the metamorphic schist and gneisses believed to have formed by regional metamorphism of the graywacke form what we may call the basement in most of New Zealand. No older rocks are exposed in the North Island. The internal structure of these geosynclinal accumulations is complex. Lillie (1964) has mapped large, steeply plunging folds broken by steep faults such as those shown in Fig. 16-14 in the Alpine region graywackes. Wood (1963) has interpreted the structure to the south in the Otago schist in terms of large-scale recumbent folding. The only evidence normally associated with orogenic deformation which can not be documented in New Zealand for this time is intrusion of large plutons accompanying the metamorphism in the geosyncline. The batholiths closest in age are now dated as Cretaceous.

Crustal movements have continued in New Zealand up to the present, and the recent deformation has been most pronounced since the Pliocene. This deformation, known as the Kaikoura Orogeny, has been accompanied by development of broad folds in the eastern fold belt of the North Island, but block faulting and warping of blocks adjacent to the faults have been the most prominent features of the deformation. The Alpine fault has been active during the Pleistocene, as indicated by offset river terraces, but the postulated 300-mile strike-slip movement proposed by Wellman may have accumulated since the Mesozoic. This fault is considered to be of critical importance by many students of Pacific structures; the evidence for it is given in Chap. 4.

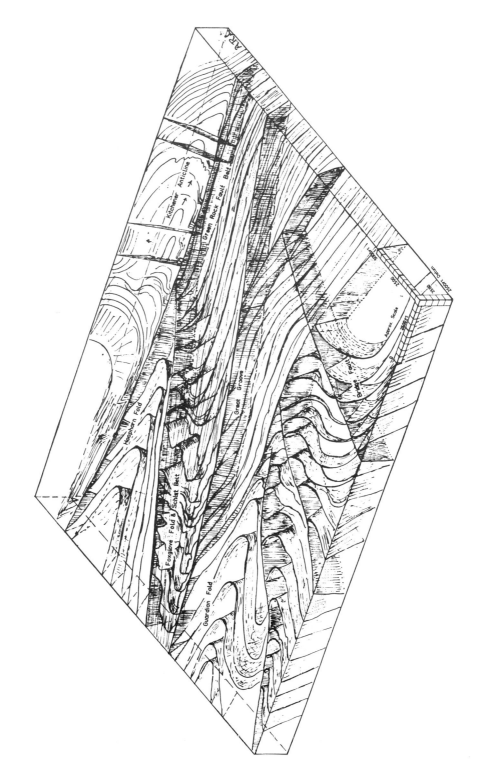

Fig. 16-14 Structural stereogram of the Sealy range, New Zealand. *(Redrawn from A. R. Lillie, 1964.)*

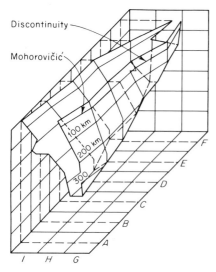

Fig. 16-15 Isometric sketch of the New Zealand subcrustal rift, viewed from its northern end. *(From Eiby, 1963.)*

Seismicity of New Zealand

The pattern of earthquake foci and epicenters for New Zealand is distinctly different from that postulated by Benioff for the volcanic island arcs of the Pacific. A plot of the foci in Fig. 16-15 defines a zone, not a plane, that extends to a depth of 300 km (Eiby, 1964). The zone has the shape of an irregular tetrahedral wedge. Notable features of this wedge are:

1. It is much deeper at its northern end.
2. It trends across surface structure.
3. The southern end is in the vicinity of the Alpine fault.
4. The wedge does not continue along the Alpine fault.
5. The western edge of the wedge is nearly vertical and does not match any feature of the surface geology.
6. The eastern edge is shallow in places but averages a dip of 40 to 50° W.

This wedge has not yet been interpreted in terms of the structure of the crust.

The shallow earthquake epicenters are widely distributed in New Zealand, but they tend to show a degree of concentration along northwest-trending lines which have no surface expression in the geology (Eiby, 1964). It is also interesting to note that while a secondary maximum of activity does occur at one point (Milford Sound) on the Alpine fault, the fault trace is not clearly defined by epicenters. Most deep foci occur east of the fault.

New Zealand seismologists (Adams, R. D., 1963; Eiby, 1964) have postulated that the epicenters do not fall on a plane because earthquakes are not due to elastic rebound associated with faulting. They favor a very rapid phase change resulting in sudden changes in volume of rock.

Gravity Observations

A large negative Bouguer anomaly trends northeast across the North Island and shows no direct correlation with the surface geology, although it crosses the block mountains composed of graywacke at a low angle. Eiby (1964) has examined the possible relationship between the anomaly and the subcrustal rift zone defined by seismicity. Assuming a difference of 0.03 g/cm³ in the density of material in and out of the wedge-shaped zone, the calculated residual anomaly shows a much closer relation to the surface geology. The remaining anomalies can be related to great sediment thicknesses in basins over which they are located. A positive anomaly lies over the central volcanic region, and its fit with this region is improved by Eiby's assumption.

Volcanic Activity

New Zealand has a long history of igneous and volcanic activity. Modern (Quaternary to upper Tertiary) volcanism is most pronounced on the North Island where it is confined west of the central graywacke belt. Rhyolites and welded tuffs occupy a belt in the central part of the island and the Coromandel Peninsula (Fig. 16-16). Andesites and dacites occur in two belts, one along the west coast and a second east of the basalt belt. Basalts occupy a central northland belt that extends south to the Lake Taupo region. A large serpentine body lies within the basalt belt. Volcanic belts are not well defined on the South Island, but both basalt and andesite volcanics lie east of the Alpine fault.

Volcanism on the North Island during the lower Tertiary and the Cretaceous is that of the spilite-keratophyre association, and it oc-

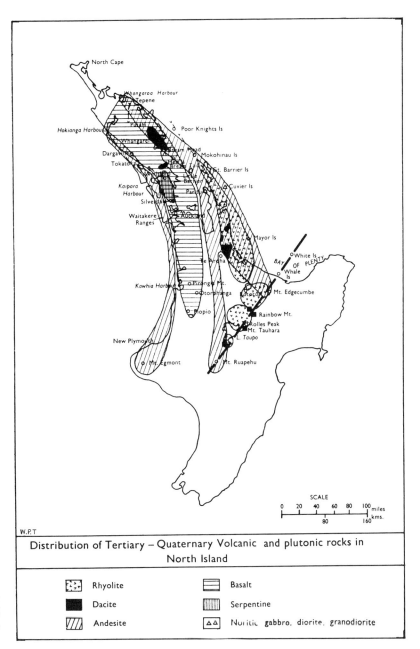

Distribution of Tertiary – Quaternary Volcanic and plutonic rocks in North Island

Rhyolite		Basalt	
Dacite		Serpentine	
Andesite		Noritic gabbro, diorite, granodiorite	

Fig. 16-16 Distribution of Tertiary-Quaternary volcanic and plutonic rocks in North Island. (*From Thompson, 1965.*)

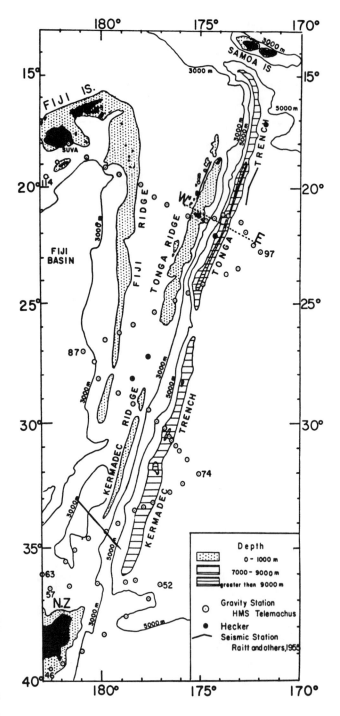

Fig. 16-17 Index map of the Tonga-Kermadec area. (*From Talwani, Worzel, and Ewing, 1961.*)

curs on the central portion of the North Auckland Peninsula. Ultrabasic bodies occur in the eastern part of this Northland Peninsula. The late Paleozoic, Triassic, and Jurassic volcanism is also that associated with eugeosynclinal belts. The pillow lavas and ultrabasics occur in graywackes and are commonly associated with cherts.

Volcanism on the North Island appears to have a definite pattern. The volcanics of various types are distributed in long, relatively narrow concentric belts that follow curves essentially parallel to the Northland Peninsula. The general pattern is one of more basic rocks on the west and more acid volcanics on the east (Thompson, 1965).

KERMADEC AND TONGA REGION

The region north of New Zealand possesses characteristics normally associated with island arcs, but the physiographic features, the Kermadec and Tonga trenches and the ridges topped by andesite volcanoes which lie just west of the trenches, are nearly straight. The Tonga trench, which has a maximum depth of 10,800 m, does, however, hook toward the west at its northern end (Fig. 16-17). A similar hook occurs in the Fiji ridge which diverges northward from the Kermadec ridge.

Seismic and gravity profiles have been taken across the Tonga ridge and trench (Raitt, Fisher, and Mason, 1955; Talwani, Worzel, and Ewing, 1961). Figure 16-5 is a structure section across the ridge and trench based on results of these two studies. The crustal thickness deduced from the gravity is about 20 km below the trench and 36 km under the ridge, a value normally associated with continental crust. The crust from Fiji across the Fiji basin and the Lau basin has been calculated as having a crustal thickness of about 21 km by surface-wave dispersion techniques (Hunkins and Kuo, 1965).

The maps and profiles for the region, compiled by Sykes (1966) (Fig. 16-18), show a clear

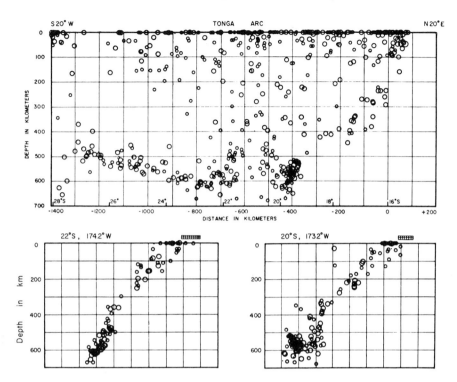

Fig. 16-18 Sections along (top) and perpendicular to (bottom) the Tonga arc showing distribution of foci. (*From Sykes, 1966.*)

spatial separation of shallow, intermediate, and deep foci with shallow epicenters lying just west of the trench and the deepest quakes concentrated under the Fiji basin and the Fiji ridge. The plane zones postulated by Benioff dip at 58 and 64° under the two trenches. The cross section of the Kermadec trench was compiled from data extending well into the region of the wedge-shaped seismic zone described by Eiby (Fig. 16-15), but the two interpretations placed on the shape are markedly different. There is also a clear break in the Kermadec region between foci of shallow and great depth. No foci are shown between 300 and 500 km. This break will be apparent in section across other trenches.

SAMOA

The Samoan Islands are situated in a critical position in relation to the Tonga trench. The trench curves strongly toward the west and separates Samoa from the Tonga Islands. All the rocks on Samoa are volcanic (Pliocene and younger) or reef materials, and the composition of the volcanics places Samoa on the east side of the andesite line. Fiji and the nearer Tonga Islands lie west of the line.

A number of structural trends have been determined on Samoa (Kear and Wood, 1959). The most prominent is N 70° W, which is the alignment of the islands, a number of faults, and rows of cinder cones which mark rifts along which the lava was extruded. The second most common alignment is about at right angles to the first, and several other less well-defined trends are known. Unfortunately, the character of the faults is in general unknown except for one major fault which is normal.

NEW CALEDONIA AND NEW HEBRIDES

The pattern of volcanic islands, trench, and nonvolcanic ridge in the region of New Caledonia departs from such simple arrangements

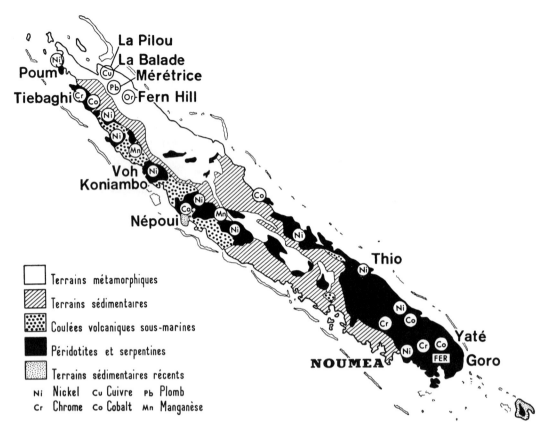

Fig. 16-19 Geologic sketch map of New Caledonia. (*From the Géographic de la Nouvelle-Calédonie, Jean Borgne.*)

as that in the Tonga region. A chain of modern volcanoes occurs in the New Hebrides, but in this case the trench lies between the volcanoes and the nonvolcanic island of New Caledonia. Moreover, the epicenters of shallow and intermediate earthquakes lie in the same region over the New Hebrides, and the fault postulated by Benioff in this case dips toward the ocean basin, 42°. If there is any arc at all here, it is defined by the New Hebrides and the Hunter Island ridge, and it is concave toward the ocean basin.

New Caledonia has a varied geology (Fig. 16-19), of which the presence of large ultrabasic bodies of peridotite, serpentinite, and gabbro forms a conspicuous part. These bodies are interpreted as being in fault contact with

the country rock. The oldest exposed rocks are Permian tuffs which are overlain by thick sequences of graywacke and conglomerates which accumulated in the Permian, Triassic, and Jurassic, and which are now metamorphosed to schists and intensely deformed on the northeastern side of the island. This deformation may be due in large part to Eocene orogeny. These deposits accumulated in a geosyncline known as the Papuan geosyncline which perhaps linked New Zealand with New Caledonia and New Guinea. The clastic sediments in this geosyncline were derived from southern and western sources. The Cretaceous is represented by sandstone and shale deposits which overlie unconformities that may mark a deformation more or less contemporaneous with the New Zealand post-Hokonui orogeny.

The Eocene and Oligocene was a time of orogenic deformation. Within the intensely deformed belt on the north side of the island the rocks are regionally metamorphosed and strongly deformed. Outside this zone a Flysch-like sequence of muds and sands was deposited. Nappes have been postulated which bring the facies of the intensely deformed area over the Flysch, a movement directed toward the south. Glaucophane facies schists are exposed locally within the intensely deformed belt in the northern part of the island.

SOLOMON ISLANDS

Geological work is not far advanced in these islands, but a general outline has emerged. Extremely large gravity anomalies occur here, and the steepest gradient known in the world occurs on Guadalcanal (Bentley and Laudon, 1965). The region is in a state of extreme isostatic imbalance. This belt of islands and the associated submarine topography also lacks the regular geometric distribution of topography so typical of island arcs elsewhere. Elongate deeps occur west of the New Hebrides, in an arc along the north edge of the Solomon Sea, and north of the Admiralty Islands.

Grover (1965) and Coleman (1965) recognize well-defined geologic provinces in the Solomon Islands as follows:

1. The area of deep, partially trenchlike sea southwest of the islands.
2. A region of very high seismicity, largely shallow-focus earthquakes, located between the deep sea and the Quaternary volcanoes, all located along the southwestern side of the island group.
3. A central longitudinal province of block-faulted metamorphic rocks including Eocene schists, possibly some Mesozoic rocks, lavas, gabbroic plutons, and possibly some granitoid plutons.
4. A zone along which serpentine bodies occur. Possibly this zone is a deep-seated fault.
5. A Pacific province in which older Tertiary and Cretaceous volcanic sediments are folded into broad open folds aligned *en échelon* and elongated subparallel to the island group. The zoning of volcanic rocks according to age (young on the south, older on the Pacific side) is emphasized.

Faulting has produced large fault-block ridges and troughs in which Tertiary terrigenous and marine sediments are present; a thickness of about 20,000 ft is found in one such basin on Gaudalcanal.

The most prominent structural trend is parallel to the island chain—the folds are elongated in that direction, many major faults have that strike, hot springs are aligned in that direction, and the longitudinal division of the system is along lines in that direction. Other trends reported are smaller faults, N 80° E and 145 to 180°. Strike-slip movement parallel to the islands is inferred. Grover interprets the fault pattern as a rhomb-shaped pattern with many "sinistrally controlled" small oblique-slip faults. He infers that the region is influenced by a sinistral shear system.

NEW GUINEA AND NEW BRITAIN

New Guinea is separated from the Precambrian Australian shield by the Arafura Sea. Surface-wave dispersion studies indicate that this sea is underlain by continental-type crust, and a thickness of 45 to 50 km is indicated in Papua, New Guinea (Brooks, 1962). This stands in contrast to the 15- to 20-km crust inferred from gravity studies in the Solomon Islands (Woollard, 1962). The southern part of New Guinea is a vast area of Quaternary and Pleistocene deposits. North of this a central zone of complex structure extends the length of the island. Much of this is topographically high, peaks reaching over 10,000 ft; it is largely jungle-covered and large areas are unmapped, but reviews of the geology of most of the island are available (Smith, 1965; Visser and Hermes, 1962). Paleozoic, Mesozoic, and Tertiary rocks occur within the central longitudinal zone. North of this zone large basins containing Quaternary and Pleistocene deposits cover parts of north-central New Guinea.

The present shelf and the southern coastal plain have exhibited long-term stability; 1,800 m of Cretaceous to Pliocene shelf sediment is undeformed; to the north this passed into a miogeosyncline containing 6,000 m of Carboniferous to early Tertiary in a conformable sequence, and then to a eugeosyncline along the northern coast. A fault zone, the Sorong fault (Fig. 16-11), separates the miogeosyncline from the eugeosyncline in western New Guinea. The first major deformation started in the Miocene and two main provinces developed. The western peninsulas developed strongly arcuate fold belts with trends parallel to those of the Banda arc. Along the main axis of the island large geanticlinal masses of Paleozoic rocks rose as the Central Ranges and the Kubor and Bismarck geanticlines to the east. These uplifts are partially enveloped by Mesozoic and Tertiary outcrops. Those in the east are described as horstlike geanticlines (Smith, 1965); Visser attributes the uplift of the Central Range to uplift along south-dipping thrust faults. While the exact nature of the blocks is open to question, the times of uplift, Miocene and Pleistocene, and the idea of strong vertical movement along steep faults appear well established. Following this uplift, basins to either side were flooded with sediment; 5,000 ft of clastics is estimated in the west in places.

Deformation continued and belts of foreland-type folds were produced in the Pliocene and Pleistocene. These belts of long, narrow folds and faults are developed best in the Miocene and Pliocene deposits found along the flanks of the Central Ranges. Again workers have not agreed on the origin of these folds. They are described as shallow structures in the sedimentary veneer created as a result of *décollement* and gravity sliding from the high Central Ranges (Fig. 16-20) and alternatively as resulting from a renewed uplift of the region by movements on steep basement faults which broke through and deformed a passive cover. The argument is very similar to that in the Appalachians.

New Britain has the form of a sweeping arc extending from New Ireland to New Guinea. The island has a central outcrop belt in which Paleozoic and Mesozoic sediments and acid plutons occur. This is partially surrounded by deformed Tertiary deposits, but most of the northwestern coast is covered by basic volcanics.

Active volcanoes extend along the northern coast of New Britain and rise as islands just off the northern coast of New Guinea, defining a long, smooth arc convex to the deep, curved trench (8,000+ m deep) in the Solomon Sea (Fig. 16-11). Active volcanoes also occur at the southeastern end of New Guinea. Granitic plutons occur with the Paleozoic and Mesozoic rocks, and basalts were extruded and intruded as dikes and sills during volcanism which accompanied the Miocene uplift of the Mesozoic geosyncline.

The eugeosynclinal character of the northern coast of New Guinea is indicated by the presence of ultrabasic intrusions, some of which are unusually large. These lie north of the Central Ranges, and many lie north of major faults to which large transcurrent movements have been attributed. The lower Tertiary sediments also contain abundant volcanics, and are of eugeosynclinal character. Basins subsided in the early Tertiary followed by Pliocene and Pleistocene deformation. Pliocene to Recent sediments cover most of the area with sporadic outcrops of older basic intrusions, volcanics, and Miocene sediments.

Transcurrent Movements

Large-scale transcurrent movements have been called on to explain many aspects of the regional structure of New Guinea. These are so important that they deserve special attention. Wegener (1924) pointed to the very unusual disposition of New Britain and the Solomon Sea deep, and explained this as resulting from a large sinistral transcurrent shear. The island of New Britain might in this case be envisioned as having swung from a position formerly aligned with the northern coast of New Guinea. The present deep would be new sea floor exposed by this movement. It is interesting to note that a sinistral shear was also inferred by students of the Solomon Islands.

The Sorong fault is said to have 600-km sinistral displacement (Visser and Hermes, 1962). The evidence for this is largely based on the apparent lateral displacement of the Sulu Islands from a former position postulated as being in western New Guinea. That the Sorong fault is a major feature is shown by its size and character. The zone is 4 to 10 km wide and contains a chaotic jumble of blocks which range up to 10 km in length. On land the fault is best known in western New Guinea. From Sorong west it shows as a strong east-west submarine topographic feature (Fig. 16-11). Because the features are not buried, it seems reasonable to postulate recent movements on it. This is borne out by the blocks in the zone, which include serpentine, gabbro, basalts, spilites, and tuffaceous limestones all derived from the northern New Guinea province; and marl, clays, conglomerates, Tertiary limestones, shales, slates, pelagic limestones, granites, and contact metamorphic rocks derived from the central zone. Some of the granites and metamorphics are not known in outcrops near the fault.

Visser and Hermes (1962) interpret the Waigro-Halmahera arc as a continuation of the northern New Guinea eugeosynclinal province, and the southwestern arc of western New Guinea as part of the Moluccan geosyncline, and the ridge on which Taliabu Island, Obi Island, and Sorong Island are located as a remnant of the central New Guinea zone faulted by transcurrent movement into its present position. This is based on similarities

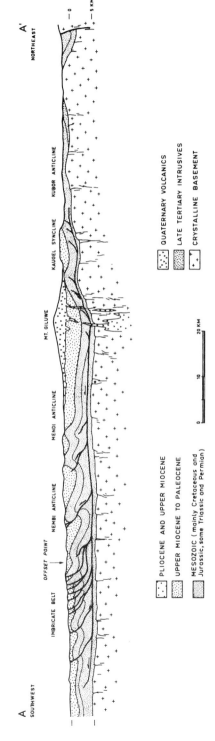

Fig. 16-20 Structure of the Kubor-Bismarck cordillera and the Papuan foreland folded belt, composite section based on the *décollement* principle of foreland folding. *(After Smith, 1965.)*

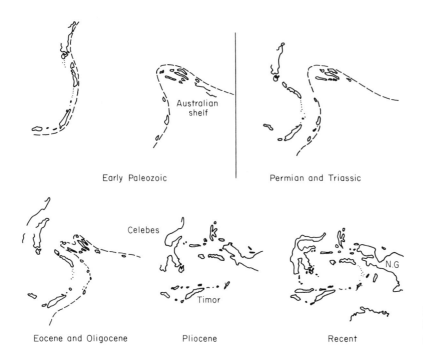

Early Paleozoic   Permian and Triassic

Celebes

Timor

Eocene and Oligocene   Pliocene   Recent   N.G

Fig. 16-21 Evolution of the physiography of eastern Indonesia. *(After Visser and Hermes, 1962.)*

of the stratigraphy. The fault does not extend into Celebes.

The Sorong fault would constitute an element in the great equatorial sinistral shear zone postulated by many students of tectonics. The Indonesian arcs bend around the New Guinea crustal element. Visser and Hermes envision the evolution of the bent arcs and the movements on the Sorong fault as shown in Fig. 16-21. According to this the arcs were highly mobile and bent as a segment of the more rigid continental crust was moved west along the Sorong fault.

SUMMARY OF OROGENIC HISTORY OF SOUTHEASTERN ASIA*

Northern Australia, portions of New Guinea, and the Soela Islands west of New Guinea were being eroded at the opening of the Mesozoic, and marine sedimentation was taking place throughout most of the Indonesian region. The

* See Umbgrove (1949) and Van Bemmelen (1949).

first interruption in this pattern occurred in the Late Triassic when uplift and folding took place in a belt extending down the Malayan Peninsula along northeastern Sumatra and curving into Borneo. This early Mesozoic deformation affected the eastern Asiatic continent, in Korea and Sakhalin. Marine sedimentation continued in Sumatra, Java, and the arcuate chains around the Banda Sea. Seas began to reenter parts of the uplifted areas of Australia, New Guinea, Borneo, and the Celebes in Jurassic time, and this advance continued until most of Borneo and the Celebes were under water by Cretaceous time. During the Cretaceous (toward the end in many places), uplift affected a vast area. Folding of this age is recorded in Java, Sumatra, Borneo, Sumba, the arc from Timor to East Celebes, and the Sulu Islands, but by Eocene time all the areas mentioned were again sites of marine sedimentation.

Mesozoic structural history is partially obscured by Cenozoic sedimentary deposits, superposed deformation, and widespread volcanism.

Deformation dated Miocene to Recent is found in a belt which extends from southeast Asia along the Andaman-Nicobar Islands, along the islands south of Sumatra, through Java, Sumbawa, Flores, Sumba, Timor, around the Banda arc, into the eastern arms of Celebes, and northward into the Philippines and along the Mariana arc. Orogeny also occurred at this time in New Guinea, Halmahera, and the Moluccas Islands.

The orogenic history of the Cenozoic is viewed as consisting of long periods of quiescence interrupted by short orogenic episodes that are nearly synchronous, at Cretaceous, mid-Miocene, Pliocene, and Pleistocene time by Umbgrove (1947, 1949). Van Bemmelen envisions the deformation as a wave which moves progressively through time from the inner belt of Malaya and Borneo to outer arcs in Recent time, as explained in his undation theory. Other geologists take the view that the temporal and spatial relationship of the orogeny has been less well defined. Those who share this view acknowledge orogenic deformation from Miocene to Recent time, but do not view its development as having been clearly defined as a systematic progression of events. This last phase of orogenic history, which is continuing at present, is of prime importance. The Miocene is the time of impact between the New Guinea–Australian block and the geosynclinal belts of Indonesia in the continental drift hypothesis of Carey (1955, 1958).

The Core Area

The region of early Mesozoic orogeny forms a core area around which the later deformation occurs. This core includes much of southeast Asia, western Borneo, Malaya, and presumably most of the shelf area of the Java Sea and the South China Sea.

Character of the Late Mesozoic Orogeny

Paleozoic and Mesozoic rock units are widely distributed through the region of Indonesia, but outcrop belts are rarely continuous for long distances, particularly for Paleozoic units, and even the Mesozoic units are broken by deep and widespread Cenozoic sedimentary sequences, and covered by wide expanses of water and large areas of volcanic extrusives. Even in areas underlain by more or less continuous belts of Mesozoic units, the soil or jungle covers the belts.

Nevertheless, detailed stratigraphic and structural studies (summarized by Van Bemmelen, 1949) have revealed many details concerning a late Mesozoic orogeny of major proportions in Indonesia. Evidence for this orogeny is found widely through Indonesia, but some of the most remarkable structures are found in Sumatra. Here, pre-Tertiary eugeosynclinal deposits are strongly deformed into isoclinal folds and large masses have been thrust toward the southwest. The structure is likened to that associated with the *Schistés lustres* of the Alps. The overthrusts and nappes formed at this time are gigantic; the distance of southwestward overthrusting in the Djambi nappe is about 350 km (Fig. 16-22). Van Bemmelen interprets the formation of this nappe as having occurred in a series of stages in which successive uplifts and gravity sliding propelled the nappe southward. It might be envisioned as riding the front of a huge crustal wave which moved progressively to the south, starting in the Jurassic. Following the orogenesis there was uplift and intrusion of granodiorites.

Mid-Tertiary Deformation

The Tertiary record of deformation is extensive. We will follow the lines of evidence for it through several parts of the Indonesian island arc system, starting at the northwestern end:

1. *Andaman-Nicobar Islands:* There are exposures of pre-Eocene serpentine, large areas of Eocene conglomerate and clastics which are strongly folded, overturned toward the west, and thrust westward. The overlying Miocene deposits are only gently folded, often only warped.

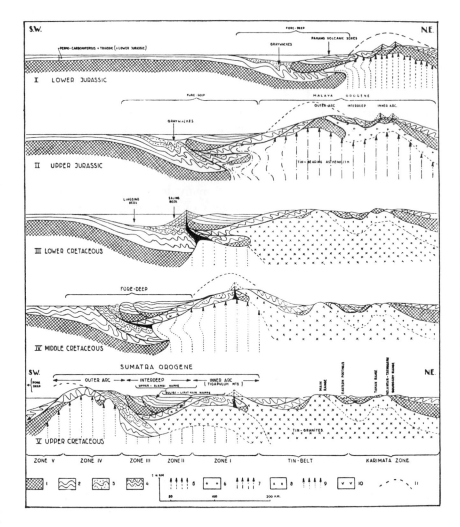

Fig. 16-22 Five schematical sections illustrating the pre-Tertiary evolution of the Malay Peninsula and Sumatra. (1) Pre-Carboniferous and Permian basement complex. (2) Sedimentary epidermis (young Paleozoic and Mesozoic, without further distinction of age). (3) Graywacke formation (Jurassic?). (4) Saling Beds (Lower Cretaceous). (5) Asthenolithic migma and magma zone of the Karimata zone. (6) Same as (5), consolidated. (7) Asthenolithic migma and magma zone of the Tin Belt. (8) Same as (7), consolidated. (9) Asthenolithic migma and magma zone of the Sumatra orogen. (10) Same as (8), consolidated. (11) Outlines which the geanticlinal uplifts from the fore-deeps would have reached, if no bathydermal spreading had occurred. *(From Van Bemmelen, 1949.)*

2. *Sumatra:* The Varisan zone, which had been affected by late Mesozoic orogeny was uplifted a second time in the Miocene, and volcanic and igneous activity took place. Deformation seems to have consisted primarily of arching, block faulting, folding, and thrusting interpreted as results of gravity gliding. The directions of the thrusting and folding are highly variable from place to place. This is used as an argument in favor of gravity sliding.

3. *Java:* Late Miocene folding took place in northern Java. Movement was directed southward but is again associated with gravity-induced movements.

4. *Sumba:* The pre-Neogene deposits are strongly folded, but along highly diverse trends. The Neogene rocks are only gently warped, tilted, and faulted.

5. *Timor:* A pre-Eocene orogenic phase took place in western Timor, causing intra-folding of the Mesozoic and lower Tertiary. There are large nappes and klippes, some indicating movements of 90 km directed toward the south. Unconformities separate the Neogene from these older,

highly deformed units. The Eocene is involved in folding and thrusting in the eastern part of the island. (Later deformation has consisted of gravity sliding, uplift, and block faulting at the end of the Tertiary.)

6. *Banda arc:* An anticlinorium involving Eocene and Miocene units 10 to 20 km wide is found folded and thrust to the east in Tanimbar. Even Mesozoic rocks are brought up along faults at the eastern edge of this belt.

Miocene nappes which moved from south to north are found in Ceram. This involves crystalline schists and upper Jurassic Flysch as well as early Tertiary. Granitic intrusions were emplaced during this orogenic deformation. Burn, the next island west in this arc, is near the end of the arc, and the structures seem intermediate between the strongly deformed zones of Ceram and the Sula Islands to the north, where Mesozoic rocks are only gently folded.

Records of Pliocene and Pleistocene Deformation

Late Tertiary and Pleistocene deposits are deformed in many parts of the island arc systems. Within the Quaternary volcanic belts this diastrophism has taken the form of geanticlinal arching and the formation of longitudinal rift systems, grabens, and block faulting. These long rifts are beautifully developed in Java in the Solo zone (Fig. 16-23). Young block faulting is very widely developed throughout the island arcs, and differential movements along these faults have caused folding in young sediments deposited in the basins formed by the faulting. Folding is also seen in the volcanic tuffs where they were deposited on steep slopes and have begun to slump and slide. Thus the latest phases of deformation are dominated by strong uplift, geanticlinal formation, block faulting often associated with the uplift, and effects of gravity tectonics. Similar zones of uplift and rifting occur along the southwestern side of Sumatra. Several zones of major transcurrent movement have also been recognized in the Philippines and in New Guinea (Fig. 16-11): the Sorong zone which trends east-west through Sorong, New Guinea, passing westward into the central part of the Celebes with an estimated 600-km sinistral movement; and the Ragay zone which passes through the Philippines, also showing sinistral movement. Evidence of recent thrusting is also known.

Diastrophism of the Kendeng zone (Fig. 16-24) of central northern Java is of interest as an example of an area in which strong Pleistocene deformation has taken place. The Kendeng anticlinorium is about 200 km long and 30 km wide, and trends east-west. The folds plunge at the eastern end under young alluvial deposits. The folding occurred through the Pleistocene earlier in the western and very late in the

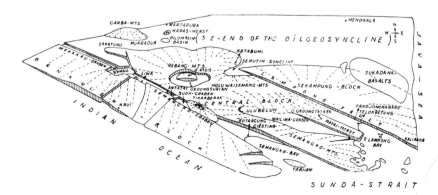

Fig. 16-23 Tectonogram of south Sumatra. *(From Van Bemmelen, 1949.)*

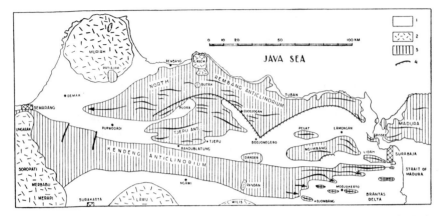

Fig. 16-24 Sketch map of northeast Java, showing the position of the hypothetical faults and flexures in the basement complex of Remband. Key: (1) Alluvial. (2) Quaternary volcanoes. (3) Neogene. (4) Faults and flexures, partly buried by Neogene and Quaternary deposits. *(From Van Bemmelen, 1949.)*

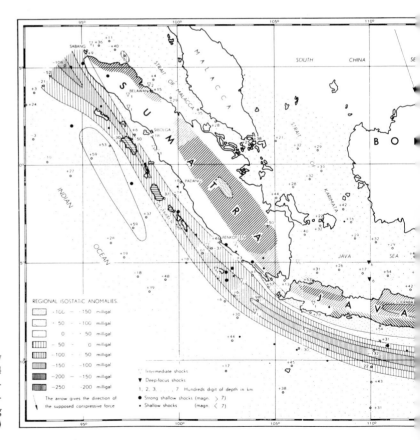

Fig. 16-25 Regional isostatic gravity anomalies (T = 30 km and R = 232.4 km) and geology, according to Umbgrove (1932, 1933, 1934), and earthquakes' foci, according to Gutenberg (1945). *(From Vening Meinesz, 1948.)*

eastern end of the zone. The folding and associated thrusting were directed toward the north. During the Recent the region has been arched upward. (Van Bemmelen interprets the folding as a result of gravity sliding induced by collapse of the Java geanticline, followed by uplift due to magmatic pressures.)

Zonation of Modern Activity

Concentric belts of various types of recent activity that are clear in parts of the region are:

1. A deep trench (i.e., the Java trench).
2. An elevated nonvolcanic ridge. Negative anomalies lie over one or both of these zones.
3. A shallow depressed zone.
4. Active andesite volcanoes.

5. Broad basins of slightly deformed or undeformed Tertiary sediments (termed *idiogeosynclines* by Umbgrove, 1947).

Gravity

Gravity anomalies have figured prominently in island arc theory since Vening Meinesz (1948) formulated the hypothesis of tectogenes caused by convection currents, to explain the strong negative anomalies associated with trenches (Fig. 16-25). The negative isostatic gravity anomaly of this region lies over the Java trench and over the Philippine trench, but it also extends over the islands south of Sumatra and over Sumba, Timor, Tanimbar, Ceram, the eastern Celebes, and the Moluccas Sea. Thus whatever the cause of the anomaly, be it a deeply depressed tectogene, a faulted wedge of

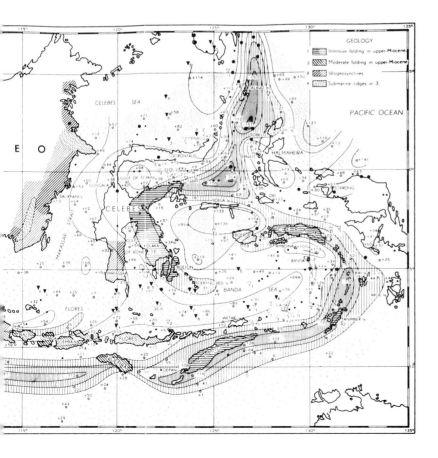

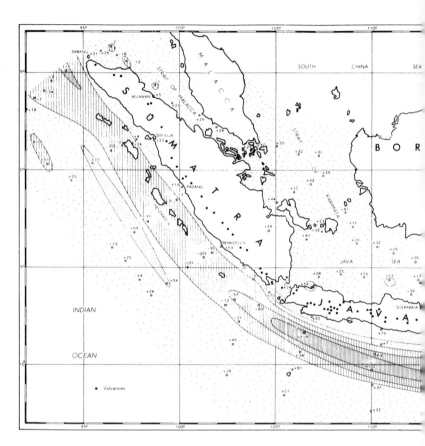

Fig. 16-26 Local isostatic gravity anomalies and volcanoes in the Indonesian archipelago (T = 30 km). *(From Vening Meinesz, 1965.)*

continental material, a zone of the mantle with anomalous density due to alteration, or otherwise, it covers areas of greatly different topography.

If convection currents are responsible, they must now be acting to hold the tectogene down, because we can judge from the rate of recovery of ice-covered areas that significant adjustments may be expected in a few thousand years once the load or force is removed or released.

PLEISTOCENE AND RECENT ACTIVITY IN SOUTHEAST ASIA

Seismicity

Earthquake epicenters (Fig. 16-25) are concentrated in a belt that extends from Taiwan through the Philippines, dividing in the south to form one belt through New Guinea and the Solomons and a second extending between Borneo and Australia and swinging northwestward through Java and Sumatra. Deep-focus earthquakes lie in a belt that extends east-west north of Java into the Banda Sea. A second group is located north of the Celebes and in western Mindanao. Shallow earthquakes occur across the wide belt from the deep trenches into the Sunda and Celebes Seas. Earthquakes of intermediate depth focus are concentrated in a belt extending along the southwestern shore of Sumatra, Java, Flores, Timor; in the Banda arc; in the Gulf of Tomini (northern Celebes); and along the islands from northern Celebes to Mindanao. The scatter of epicenters is so great that it is not possible to correlate them precisely with any geologic features; however, they

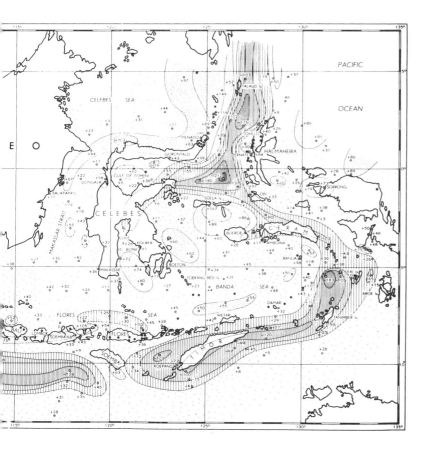

are widely interpreted as marking a deep-seated fault zone dipping from the trenches under the continents as suggested by Benioff (1949). Profiles taken from Benioff's summary (Fig. 16-6) show the nature of the depth concentration. (*Note:* Epicenters from long segments of each arc are shown projected into a single plane.)

Volcanic Activity

The centers of recent active volcanism (Fig. 16-26) are aligned. The products are largely andesitic in composition. Many of these zones are broadly arched and broken by grabens and block faulting. This is particularly well illustrated in Java and Sumatra. The zone of active volcanism is consistently located well inside the axes of the deep sea trenches, often at a distance of 100 to 150 km.

Modern Emergence

The strong negative isostatic gravity anomalies prompt us to examine evidence for recent uplift. Raised terraces and coral reefs point to Quaternary uplift in the Andaman and Nicobar Islands; in the islands west of Sumatra; in Sumba where terraces stand up to 1,800 ft above sea level; in the lesser Sunda Islands, Timor, Roti (up 444 m), and Wetar where terraces stand at elevations of 2,400 ft and reefs are over 700 ft above sea level; in the Banda arc where recent uplift is prominent; and in Ceram where coral reefs are up to 800 ft above sea level. The islands southwest of Celebes (Butang) are also recently uplifted. All these islands are located within the belt of strong negative anomalies. Thus we must conclude that either isostatic adjustments are now going on and causing uplift of very recent origin or that material is being forcefully uplifted due to some tectonic mechanism independent of isostatic adjustment. Such a mechanism for forceful upward ejection of material from the tectogene during later stages of its formation is suggested by the convection current hypothesis.

Celebes

The position of Celebes is critical to an understanding of the structure of the Indonesian Island arcs. The present form of the island is highly suggestive of Cenozoic structural trends. The northern arm is topographically continuous with the Samar arc of the Philippines; the eastern arm is slightly offset from the submarine ridge which connects Sulu, Obi, and Halmahera; the southeastern arm ends in the Banda Sea; and the southern arm is possibly continued to the southwest in the shelf areas of the Flores Sea.

Brouwer (1947) recognizes a zonal arrangement of Celebes—the eastern zone composed of the eastern and southeastern arms; a central zone; and a western zone composed of the northern arm, the western side, and the southern arm. The zones are characterized as follows:

Eastern zone: A region of Mesozoic limestone with some deep sea sediment containing radiolarians. Basic and ultrabasic intrusions are particularly abundant. Cretaceous clays and arkosic sandstones are found unconformably on deformed schist and serpentine. Thrusting, folding, and other evidence of strong deformation are dated at mid-Miocene and late in Pliocene time.

Central zone: This zone is one in which metamorphic rocks, schists, dominate. It is separated from the western zone by a fault, the median line, and the degree of metamorphism decreases from this fault to the east. This zone is one of strongly deformed rocks from thrusts and folding which probably took place in the Tertiary. Spilites occur in the central and eastern zones, but are absent in the west.

Western zone: Schists and other metamorphics also occur in the west, but the sediments are generally of a shallower-water facies than those in the east. Spilites are not present, and evidence of igneous activity, volcanic and plutonic, on a large scale is found from Cretaceous to late Tertiary. Granitic and granodioritic plutons abound. Structures are also complex in parts of the western zone. The plutons are sheared, and tectonic breccias containing granodiorite in lower Tertiary are present. Deformation took place at least as recently as mid-Tertiary.

The southern end of the south arm is unique. There deformed schists and serpentines are unconformably overlain by Cretaceous graywacke, and Eocene lies unconformably over the Cretaceous, but even these do not appear to represent strong deformation. Many of the major faults define a rectangular pattern, and many have been recently active.

The zonal division of the country is complicated by the development of fault troughs, culminations, and depressions. The blocks defined by faults have moved, and fold patterns within basins are influenced by these movements. Movements on many faults have continued to the present.

Recent volcanism is confined to the northeastern end of the north arm, part of the Sulu arc. Recent uplift is indicated by uplifted reef limestone.

Taiwan and the Ryukyu Islands

Taiwan is located at the juncture of the Ryukyu Island arc which extends south from Japan and a broken arcuate submarine ridge which extends south toward Luzon. However, the deep sea east of the Ryukyu Islands does not contain a sharply defined trench, the northern islands are recently active or dormant volcanoes, and deep-focus earthquakes occur in a belt west of the islands. Hess (1948) describes glaucophane schists which are commonly associated with peridotite in the southern Ryukyu Islands.

Biq (1960) describes Taiwan as a double arc

concave toward the ocean. The island is divided longitudinally into zones as follows:

1. *Ocean basin:* Intermediate-depth earthquakes occur on the oceanic side of the island.
2. *Volcanic arc:* Defined by two Pleistocene and Recent andesite volcanoes on the ridge south of Taiwan.
3. *Structural arc:* This arc is a complex of geosynclinal troughs, created and tectonized at the close of the Paleozoic, in the Mesozoic, and early and late in the Tertiary. These troughs contained on the order of 10,000 ft of sediment each, and they are now arranged in a huge imbricated mass. The Central Range has a Paleozoic metamorphic core surrounded by metamorphosed Mesozoic and early Tertiary rocks. Migmatite, metavolcanic, and green schist intruded by orthogneiss and serpentine comprise most of this core, with higher-grade metamorphics toward the northern end. This Central Range is thrust toward the west and broken by a long rift zone on its eastern side. The Coastal Ranges consist of late Tertiary eugeosynclinal rocks that are folded. The foothill zone west of the Central Range is a belt of folded and faulted late Tertiary Flysch-molasse-type deposits which contained volcanics at first but later were free of volcanic materials. Folding in the foothill zone probably does not involve the basement; a shallow *décollement* is inferred from drilling.

The structural arc is folded and sliced into thin thrust plates which have moved west. Many of the thrusts are oblique-slip, the plate having moved southwest. Dextral transverse faults are also common.

Arcuate Islands from Palau to Japan

The islands from Palau to Japan, including Yap, Guam, and the Bonin Islands, form one of the most perfect of the arcuate systems on earth. Trenches separate the islands from the Pacific basin. The Japan trench follows an arcuate course to the latitude of the Bonin Islands where a poorly defined submarine ridge separates it from the Mariana trench. The southern end of the Mariana trench joins the Yap trench but the junction is nearly at right angles. The Yap trench in turn is abruptly terminated by the Palau trench which dies out at its southern end. The nature of these junctions must be significant, but they are yet to be satisfactorily explained.

Several rows of islands and submerged ridges cross the Philippine Sea (Fig. 16-11). Many of the islands closest to the trenches are active or recently active andesite volcanoes from Japan to Guam, and this inner ridge is the location of many deep-focus earthquakes. Hess (1948) interprets the two inner ridges as geanticlines (the Iwo Jima and the Bonin geanticlines), but there are few islands on which to base geologic interpretation. No unmetamorphosed Mesozoic rock has been positively identified in the arc. Schist and amphibolite (pre-Miocene) are known on Yap, and serpentinized peridotite is known in the Bonin and Marianas (three islands only). Where Eocene and younger sedimentary rocks occur they are not strongly folded; however, the Mariana Islands are terraced, and these terraces are tilted toward the west.

Classification of Island Arcs

Wilson (1954, p. 154) has classified island arcs into three types:

1. *Single island arcs* are uniformly curved chains of volcanoes with an oceanic foredeep. The Aleutian and South Sandwich Islands are examples (also Kuril, Japanese, Ryukyu, and Taiwan-Luzon). There are large negative gravity anomalies over the foredeeps and a characteristic arrangement of earthquakes.
2. *Double island arcs* develop where single island arcs approach continents. In them an outer chain of islands composed of folded sedimentary rocks replaces the foredeep. Examples of such islands are Kodiak, Timor and Trini-

dad. This development has been considered to be due to an increasing supply of sediments which first fill the deep and then during orogenetic movements get folded and squeezed up to the surface. The negative anomalies are found over the outer arc of sedimentary islands (Umbgrove, 1947).

3. *Complex island arcs* may be either single or double but display an irregularity of shape and features which is considered to be due to interaction of forces from two directions. The island arcs from New Guinea to New Zealand provide several examples.

Wilson recognizes a systematic change in the island arc structure from northern to southern arcs. The arcs grow smaller to the south; the *en échelon* arrangement becomes more pronounced; the "knots" at the linkages of the arcs, composed of volcanoes in Kamchatka and the islands of Hokkaido, Kyushu, and Taiwan, respectively, become increasingly detached from the continents; the connections become less definite; deep earthquakes are associated with the northern arcs, but do not continue to the south, following the Bonin and Mariana arcs instead.

Wilson (1959) suggested that the young, active, folded mountain belts and island arcs are surface expressions of a great fracture system, deeper and more active than the midocean fracture system. Variation in arcs is attributed to the idea that arcs evolve. Primary arcs, either mountains or island arcs, have the following characteristics:

1. They are parts of circular arcs, concave toward the nearest continent.
2. They are sites of recent andesite volcanic and older granodioritic igneous activity.
3. They are accompanied by the greatest deep trenches.
4. Large negative anomalies occurring along narrow strips lie parallel to them.
5. Most of the world's shallow earthquakes and all deep earthquakes lie in a zone beneath them.

6. They rest upon no basement of more ancient rocks.

Secondary arcs (Taiwan and western Kamchatka are examples) occur with primary arcs. Their characteristics include:

1. They are less volcanic, igneous, and metamorphic.
2. They are made of uplifted older basement and folded and thrust sediments.

RÉSUMÉ OF PACIFIC ISLAND ARC TECTONICS

It is apparent from the brief descriptions of regional geology and geophysics presented here that the framework of the Pacific basin is varied, is structurally complex, and does not readily yield to simple generalities. Yet some generalizations can be defended and some structural patterns do emerge:

1. Cenozoic deformation has been and still is taking place in the zone between the Pacific basin and the cratons of surrounding continents.
2. This deformation involves the edges of the continents themselves on the eastern and southern sides of the Pacific in North and South America and the Antarctic. It involves a fringing island belt from Alaska to New Zealand.
3. The andesite line separates a Pacific basin petrographic (oceanic basaltic) province from the circumpacific marginal belts of volcanics from which a wide range of volcanic products, primarily andesite, is extruded. The andesite line appears to mark the division between continental and intermediate crustal types on one side and oceanic crust on the other.
4. Within the circumpacific island belt, certain structures recur repeatedly. These include arcuate chains of volcanic island

(Aleutian, Kuril, Mariana, and Sumatra-Java Islands) which are separated from adjacent ocean basins by deep sea trenches. A number of other trenches and associated chains of islands, many of which are somewhat arcuate in trend occur in the belt. Larger islands (New Zealand, New Caledonia, Java, Sumatra, Borneo, Philippines, and Japan) on which a more complex geology is exposed lie within this belt also. The peninsulas of Alaska and Kamchatka, like the large islands, have varied geology. However, all are sites of modern earthquakes and volcanism, and all have a history of long-term tectonic activity. Where exposure permits determination of the orogeny, they all show Mesozoic as well as Cenozoic orogeny.

5. One of the repeated patterns of the circumpacific is that of concentric physiographic-tectonic belts.

   a. Trenches occur only with active volcanic island chains. (Without exception.)

   b. The trench is on the oceanic side of the volcanic islands. (Exceptions: Hebrides trench, Solomon Sea Deep, Banda Sea Deep, Flores Sea Deep.)

   c. The trenches and island chains are arcuate. (Exceptions: Tonga-Kermadec, Hebrides trench, Flores Sea Deep.)

   d. Arcuate trenches are convex toward the ocean basin. (Exception: Japan trench.)

   e. Some island chains are single and others are multiple concentric features.

   i. Single volcanic island chains
      Aleutians
      Kuril Islands
      Ryukyu Islands

   ii. Multiple concentric belts
      Tonga–Kermadec (volcanic), with nonvolcanic South Fiji ridge inside
      New Hebrides–Loyalty ridge–New Caledonia
      Solomon Islands–New Guinea's

eastern extension
      Java volcanic–Java–Sumatra inside
      Bonin–Marianas volcanic chain –Mariana ridge–south Honshu ridge

6. A seismic shear zone virtually surrounds the Pacific. Maps and cross sections prepared by Benioff (1954) have demonstrated several general features:

   a. Shallow-focus earthquakes tend to be concentrated near the inner edge of the trenches; intermediate-depth earthquakes occur under the volcanic arc; deep-focus earthquakes occur on the continent side of the volcanic arc.

   b. The shallow- and intermediate-focus earthquakes define an irregular zone in which seismic activity is concentrated. These zones dip an average of 33° in the belts that are marginal to continents (i.e., Peru, Chile, Bonin–Honshu, Sunda, Kuril–Kamchatka, Acapulco–Guatemala, Aleutians, and New Hebrides). The zones dip about 60° in a second class which are not in a marginal position (i.e., Mindanao, Tonga, and Kermadec). These zones are interpreted as fault zones (Benioff, 1954).

   c. The deep-focus earthquakes do not occur along projections of the dips of the above zones. They lie on steeper zones (about 60°) if drawn as continuations of the shallow and intermediate zones.

   d. The deep earthquakes are often separated from the intermediate and shallow earthquakes by an interval between 300 and 500 km deep in which few focuses are known (note the exceptions to this in the Kuril–Kamchatka and Bonin–Honshu arcs). Benioff infers that these deeper foci define a deep seismic shear zone or fault which is planar for the oceanic faults of Tonga–Kermadec and Mindanao, but it has a break in dip along faults in marginal positions.

Movements Inferred from Earthquakes

Methods for determination of movements accompanying earthquakes in the vicinity of the focus have been developed (reviewed by Hodgson, 1962). The methods are based on the principle of determining the pattern of the initial direction of ground motion in the region around the epicenter. Unfortunately, the patterns observed are capable of several interpretations depending on the model one uses for the earthquake mechanism. The two models in use are a fault model based on the nature of the movements on the San Andreas fault, interpreted as an elastic rebound phenomenon, and a collapse model in which the earthquake is viewed as being generated by rock failure through faulting or collapse of a volume of rock on one conjugate plane or a pair of conjugate planes. The orientation of the conjugate planes is determined by three principal stress directions, one of which is *assumed* to be vertical.

Hundreds of earthquakes have now been analyzed, and regional directions of maximum pressure and principal horizontal stress have

been deduced which are in approximate agreement. Conclusions based on the collapse model are that the maximum pressure directions are normal to most island arc systems with the exception of the Tonga–Kermadec, and that the maximum pressure direction acts north-south in California. Fault-model conclusions are that displacements are normal to geologic features where best determined, and that principal horizontal stress acts normal to most island arcs but north-south in the Americas (Fig. 16-27).

It is now possible to distinguish several large areas of the world which are characterized by a predominance of strike-slip or dip-slip faulting as deduced from seismic fault data (Pulpan and Scheidegger, 1965) shown in Table 16-1. Dip slip is dominant in:

1. A belt composed of the Carpathians, the Caucasus, the Hindu Kuch, and the Tien Shan mountains of Asia
2. The Bonin–Marianas arc

Strike slip is dominant in:

1. The East Pacific rim
2. The West Pacific rim with a distinct increase from north to south. New Zealand has a northern strike-slip-dominated region and a southern dip-slip concentration.

Where strike-slip movements are found, the faults are inferred to be vertical or steep, but they lack strongly preferred directional orientation and there is no clear direction of movement.

CARIBBEAN REGION

The Caribbean region is similar to Indonesia in many ways. Both are the sites of modern arcuate volcanic and tectonic island chains; both are framed between cratons which appear to have undergone some sinistral displacement

Table 16-1 Percentage of Earthquakes in Pacific Island Arcs Which Are Interpreted as Having Initial Strike-slip Movements

Site	No. of earthquakes	Percent of strike-slip movement
Aleutians-Alaska	49	0.74
Kamchatka	26	0.39
Kurils	22	0.49
Hokkaido-Sakhalin	5	0.60
Honshu	76	0.61
Ryukyu to Taiwan	7	0.50
Philippines	39	0.77
Celebes-Ceram	28	0.78
Java-Timor	40	0.67
New Guinea-Solomons	32	0.90
Fiji Tonga Kermadec	25	0.92
New Hebrides	18	0.97
New Zealand	14	0.40
Marianas	8	0.25

Source: Pulpan and Scheidegger (1965).

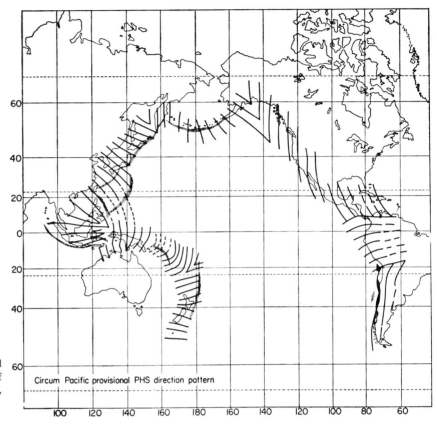

Fig. 16-27 Principal horizontal stresses around the boundaries of the Pacific. *(From Hodgson, 1962, after Lensen.)*

in relation to one another; and both are regions in which sinistral shear is strongly suggested along east-west lines by structural field relations, geophysics, and submarine topography.

The topography of the Caribbean has great relief and strongly developed morphological forms and trends to which structural significance is attributed, although we know that Cenozoic sedimentary deposits may blanket and obscure some of these features. The Florida shelf and the Great Bahama banks separate the arc from the North American craton. The large, high islands of Cuba, Hispaniola, and Puerto Rico form the northern flank of the arc, which continues as the Lesser Antilles and forms a strongly curved lineament ultimately leading to Tobago and Trinidad and into Venezuela. Deep trenches form a second major type of element and include the Cayman trench

(the Bartlett trough is within the Cayman trench) which lies south of Cuba; the Anegado passage, a deep trough which separates Puerto Rico from the Lesser Antilles and is subparallel to the Cayman trench; the Puerto Rico trench, located on the Atlantic side of Puerto Rico and the northernmost Lesser Antilles; and the Leeward trench, north of the Venezuelan shelf.

Geophysical Studies in the Caribbean

Gravity and seismic studies have been made at a number of critical places in this region. A weak negative-gravity anomaly over southern Mexico may be interpreted as part of an east-west belt extending across the southern Gulf (Fig. 16-28) and the northern part of Yucatan and into Cuba. A strong negative anomaly emerges from the eastern end of Cuba and lies over the Puerto Rico trench, and farther south

Fig. 16-28 Gravity anomalies in the Caribbean. The black and diagonally lined areas are negative anomalies where there is a mass deficiency. Such negative anomalies are associated with deep sea trenches in the island arc systems of the Pacific also. (*From Eardley, 1957, redrawn after Hess, 1938.*)

over the Barbados ridge, Tobago, Trinidad, and northeastern Venezuela, where it dies out. The striking characteristic here is that the anomaly lies over both trench and elevated ridge and mountains—indicating a deep source. A second negative anomaly of east-west trend lies along the southern side of the Cayman trench, Jamaica, and the southern part of Hispaniola. A third negative anomaly lies over the Leeward trench north of Venezuela.

Positive anomalies are present over the major basins and notably over the Cayman trench.

Seismic refraction profiles (Fig. 16-29) have established that the main parts of the basins are floored by crustal sections that are of intermediate character between continental-type and oceanic-type sections. They are closer to oceanic type, but sediment thickness is greater and the velocities obtained at depth are mixed with many velocities lower than the 8.0 to 8.2 km/sec associated with mantle materials. The observed velocities (7.4 to 8.0 km/sec) are commonly interpreted as altered mantle. Still lower velocities (6.6 to 7.4 km/sec) are found under islands of the island arcs and under trenches. These velocities could represent a number of types of material: gabbro or other igneous rocks of intermediate to basic composition, hydrated peridotite, serpentine. The intermediate character of these velocities is variously interpreted by adherents of convection current hypotheses and adherents of crustal tension hypotheses, but neither argument is proved conclusively.

Geology of the Large Islands in the Arc

The four largest islands, Cuba, Hispaniola, Puerto Rico, and Jamaica, have a highly varied

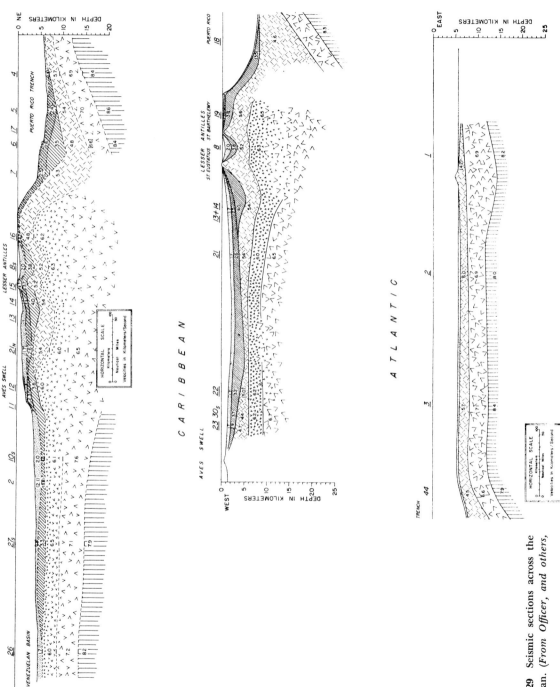

Fig. 16-29 Seismic sections across the Caribbean. (*From Officer, and others, 1957.*)

geology.[*] Although their histories differ in detail, there are a number of similarities. The oldest rocks in each are thought to be Mesozoic and these are crystalline complexes consisting of schists, amphibolites, and granites. This basement is commonly overlain by great thicknesses of Cretaceous tuff. Serpentinized peridotites are found and are of particular interest because Hess (1938) has pointed out their common association with major orogenic belts in which they are emplaced early in the orogenic cycle. The age of the peridotites is not clear. They occur within the exposed belts of Cretaceous tuffs in Cuba and Hispaniola, but they are possibly of Eocene age. They are involved in thrusting that took place in the Eocene and are dated as Eocene in Puerto Rico.

Diastrophism in these islands is dated by means of unconformities. These are not contemporaneous through the region. One part or another seems to have been emergent almost continuously throughout the Cenozoic.

Unconformities occur as follows (after Butterlin, 1956):

Time	Locations
Recent	Cuba
Pleistocene	Cuba, Jamaica
Pliocene	Cuba
Miocene	Cuba, Puerto Rico
Oligocene	Hispaniola-Jamaica
Eocene	Cuba, Puerto Rico, Jamaica
Cretaceous	Cuba, Puerto Rico, Hispaniola, Jamaica

Despite the abundance of unconformities, most evidence points to two major periods of diastrophism, one late in the Mesozoic and another in the Eocene.

Widespread late Mesozoic diastrophism is evident, and it is with this deformation that

* References include: General—Eardley (1962): Maxwell (1948); Butterlin (1956); Donnelly (1964). Cuba—Hill (1959), Wassall (1957). Hispaniola—Hess and Maxwell (1953). Puerto Rico—Kaye (1957); Berryhill and others (1960).

many of the volcanics, granitic intrusions, and ultrabasic intrusions are associated. The geosynclinal accumulations involved at this time were of great thickness, 35,000 ft of Middle Jurassic alone in Cuba.

Folding and thrusting in the late Mesozoic were directed toward the north. A volcanic and clastic sedimentary eugeosynclinal facies was thrust northward over carbonate facies in Cuba. This was later broken by high-angle faults, displaced, and partially eroded.

A mid-Tertiary orogeny is indicated in Cuba (mid-Eocene), Hispaniola (late Eocene), and Jamaica (mid-Eocene). Folding and northward-directed thrusting are attributed to this orogeny. A large early Tertiary batholith occurs in eastern Puerto Rico, and part of the complex fault pattern there has been attributed to the emplacement of this pluton. The distinction between the role of gravity-induced sliding and folding, and deformation of other types is not yet clearly defined. As in Indonesian arcs, block faulting constitutes a major part of Pliocene and Pleistocene deformation. Such faulting is evident in Jamaica where Miocene fault blocks have been rejuvenated, resulting in tilting and uplift probably related to the development of the Cayman trench. The fault pattern in Puerto Rico (Fig. 16-30) is also an old pattern rejuvenated in Pleistocene time. Two major faults here have been interpreted as transcurrent, and the northwest faults as subsidiary tears.

Character of the Lesser Antilles

Puerto Rico is separated from the Lesser Antilles by a major topographic depression which is almost certainly a fault, probably a transcurrent fault as suggested by Hess and Maxwell. Inner volcanic and outer nonvolcanic arcs are present here, as in so many other modern island arcs. The islands of the inner arc are sites of Recent andesite volcanism, although some mid-Tertiary volcanics are also known. The volcanoes are associated with a submarine swell or broad ridge, but they are not on the crest as

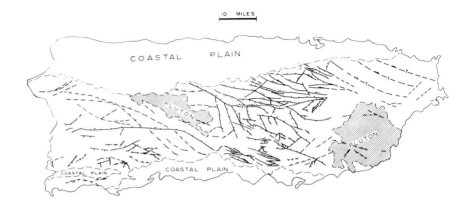

Fig. 16-30 Simplified structural map of Puerto Rico. (*From Donnelly, 1964, after Briggs, 1961.*)

might be expected if the volcanism is the result of tension over the crest of the ridge.

The eastern nonvolcanic islands are largely composed of Tertiary-Quaternary limestone (Maxwell, 1948). Where a basement is exposed on St. Martin, it is strongly folded, metamorphosed tuff with intrusions of diorite. The basement on most of these islands is composed of volcanic debris, tuffs, with lava flows intruded by diorite. This old volcanic activity ended in the Oligocene and the islands have not been much deformed since (Christman, 1953). The structural continuation of this outer belt of islands to the south is a submerged ridge.

Barbados is separated from the volcanic islands by a shallow submarine trough; it lies on a ridge that is directly in line with the Puerto Rico trench to the north. Also, the negative anomalies over the trench can be traced directly over the Barbados ridge. Tobago and Trinidad are probably part of the same structural belt. The oldest rocks on Barbados are strongly folded and thrust Eocene clastic sedimentary rocks. These are overlain by a thick sequence of deep-water sediments, including radiolarian oozes. Apparently the region was submerged rather rapidly (Senn, 1940). Folding has continued into the Pleistocene, and in Recent time there has been uplift (Maxwell, 1948).

Tobago and Trinidad contain outcrops of Mesozoic basement, folded schists of metavol-

canic origin, and intermediate intrusives with some ultramafics. A Late Cretaceous age is probable for the orogenic deformation of the region. The intrusions are thought to be a little younger than the folding, and they are sheared (possibly in late Eocene time). Miocene and younger units lie unconformably and undeformed on the basement in Tobago.

The orogenic history in Trinidad is similar to that in Barbados. There is evidence of upper Eocene and Pliocene deformation as well as the Upper Cretaceous orogeny that affected the Coastal Ranges of Venezuela. An upper Eocene deformation in which granitic plutons were emplaced also took place in northern Venezuela, and folding and southward thrusting are present in the Pliocene. Thus the principal times of deformation in the island arc were contemporaneous with similar events in Venezuela.

REFERENCES

Adams, F. D., 1912, An experimental contribution to the question of the depth of the zone of flow of the earth's crust: Jour. Geology, v. 20, p. 97–118.

Adams, R. D., 1963, Source characteristics of some deep New Zealand earthquakes: New Zealand Jour. Geol. and Geophys., v. 2, no. 6, p. 209–220.

Allan, R. S., 1925, Preliminary account of the geology of the Chatham Islands: New Zealand Jour. Sci. and Technology, v. 7, p. 290–294.

Beck, A. C., 1964, Marlborough Sound, Sheet 14, Geological Map of New Zealand: Dept. Sci. Indust. Research, Wellington, New Zealand, Govt. Printer.

Belyayevskiy, N. A., and Fedynskiy, V. V., 1962, Deep structure of the earth and problems of super-deep drilling: trans, by Joint Publications Research Service, Internat. Geology Rev., v. 4, no. 7.

Benioff, H., 1949, Seismic evidence for fault origin of oceanic deeps: Geol. Soc. America Bull., v. 60, p. 1837–1856.

——— 1954, Orogenesis and deep crustal structure—additional evidence from seismology: Geol. Soc. America Bull., v. 65, p. 385–400.

Bentley, C. R., and Laudon, T. S., 1965, Gravity and magnetic studies in the Solomon Islands: Natl. Acad. Sci., Prog. Rept. United States Program for the Internat. Geophys. Year Upper Mantle Project.

Berryhill, H. L., Jr., et al., 1960, Stratigraphy, sedimentation, and structure of late Cretaceous rocks in eastern Puerto Rico: prelim. rept., Am. Assoc. Petroleum Geologists Bull., v. 44.

Biq, Chingchang, 1960, Circum-Pacific tectonics in Taiwan: Internat. Geol. Cong., 21st, p. 203–214.

Bowin, C. O., Nalwalk, A. J., and Hersey, J. B., 1966, Serpentinized periodotite from the north wall of the Puerto Rico trench: Geol. Soc. America Bull., v. 77, p. 257–270.

Brodie, J. W., 1964, Bathymetry of the New Zealand region: New Zealand Dept. Sci. and Industry Resources Bull., v. 161.

Brooks, J. A., 1962, Seismic wave velocities in the New Guinea–Solomon Islands region, in The crust of the Pacific basins: Am. Geophys. Union Mon. 6, p. 2–10.

Brouwer, H. A., 1947, Geological exploration in the island of Celebes: Amsterdam, North Holland Publishing, 346 p.

Bunce, E. T., and Hersey, J. B., 1966, Continuous seismic profiles of the outer ridge and Nares basin north of Puerto Rico: Geol. Soc. America Bull., v. 77, p. 803–812.

Burk, C. A., 1965, Geology of the Alaska peninsula—island arc and continental margin, pt. 1: Geol. Soc. America Mem. 99, 250 p.

Butterlin, J., 1956, La constitution géologique et la structure des Antilles: Paris, Centre national de la recherche scientifique, 456 p.

Carey, S. W., 1954a, The rheid concept in geotectonics: Geol. Soc. Australia Jour., v. 1, p. 67–117.

——— 1954b, The orocline concept in geotectonics: Proc. Royal Soc. Tasmania, v. 89, p. 255–288.

——— 1955, The orocline concept in geotectonics: Proc. Royal Soc. Tasmania, v. 89.

Christman, R. A., 1953, Geology of St. Bartholomew, St. Martin and Anguilla, Lesser Antilles: Geol. Soc. America Bull., v. 94, p. 65–96.

Coats, R. R., 1962, Magma type and crustal structure in the Aleutian arc, in The crust of the Pacific basins: Am. Geophys. Union Mon. 6, p. 92–109.

Coleman, P. J., 1965, Stratigraphic contrasts in the Solomon Islands and their tectonic implications [abs.], in Australia and New Zealand Assoc. of Sci., 38th Cong.

Donnelly, T. W., 1964, Evolution of eastern Greater Antillean island arc: Am. Assoc. Petroleum Geologists Bull., v. 48, no. 5, p. 680–696.

Eardley, A. J., 1962, Structural geology of North America, 2d ed.: New York, Harper & Row.

Eiby, G. A., 1964, The New Zealand sub-crustal rift: New Zealand Jour. Geol. and Geophys., v. 7, p. 109–133.

Gates, Olcott, and Gibson, William, 1956, Interpretation of the configuration of the Aleutian ridge: Geol. Soc. America Bull., v. 67, p. 127–146.

Gibson, W., and Nichols, H., 1953, Configuration of the Aleutian ridge Rat Islands—Semisopochnoi I to west of Buldir I: Geol. Soc. America Bull., v. 64, p. 1173–1187.

Goryatchev, A. V., 1962, Specific features of recent tectonism along the Kuril Island arc: Internat. Geol. Rev., v. 4.

Grindley, G. W., 1961, Mesozoic orogenies in New Zealand: Pacific Sci. Cong. Proc., 9th, v. 12, p. 71–75.

Grover, J. C., 1965, British Solomon Islands progress in geological and geophysical exploration [abs.], in Australia and New Zealand Assoc. of Sci., 38th Cong.

Hayes, D. E., 1966. A geophysical investigation of the Peru-Chile trench: Marine Geology, v. 4, p. 309–351, Amsterdam, Elsevier.

Hayes, D. E., and Ludwig, W. J., 1967, The Manila trench and West Luzon trough—II. Gravity and magnetics measurements: Deep-sea Research, v. 14, p. 545–560.

Hess, H. H., 1938, Gravity anomalies and island arc structure with particular reference to the

West Indies: Am. Philos. Soc. Proc., v. 70, p. 71–96.

—————— 1948, Major structural features of the western North Pacific: an interpretation of H. O. 5485, bathymetric chart Korea to New Guinea: Geol. Soc. America Bull., v. 59, p. 417–548.

Hess, H. H., and Maxwell, J. C., 1953, Caribbean research project: Geol. Soc. America Bull., v. 64, p. 1–6.

Hill, P. A., 1959, Geology and structure of the northwest Trinidad Mts., Las Villas Province, Cuba: Geol. Soc. America Bull., v. 70, p. 1459–1478.

Hodgson, J. H., 1962, Movements in the earth's crust as indicated by earthquakes, in Runcorn, S. K. ed., Continental drift: New York, Academic, p. 67–102.

Houtz, R., Ewing, J., Ewing, M., and Lonardi, A. G., 1967, Seismic reflection profiles of the New Zealand Plateau: Jour. Geophys. Research, v. 72, no. 18.

Hunkins, K., and Kuo, J. T., 1965, Surface wave dispersion in the Tonga-Fiji region: Seismol. Soc. America Bull., v. 55, no. 1, p. 135–145.

Isacks, B. L., Sykes, L. R., and Oliver, J., 1967, Spatial and temporal clustering of deep and shallow earthquakes in the Fiji-Tonga-Kermadec region: Seismol. Soc. Am. Bull., v. 57, no. 5, p. 935–958.

Kaye, C. A., 1957, Notes on the structural geology of Puerto Rico: Geol. Soc. America Bull., v. 68, p. 103–117.

Kear, D., and Wood, B. L., 1959, The geology and hydrology of western Samoa: New Zealand Geol. Survey Bull., no. 63.

Keller, F., Jr., and others, 1954, Aeromagnetic surveys in the Aleutian, Marshall and Bermuda Islands: Am. Geophys. Union Trans., v. 35, p. 558–572.

Krause, D. C., 1966, Tectonics, marine geology, and bathmetry of the Celebes Sea–Sulu Sea region: Geol. Soc. America Bull., v. 77, p. 813–832.

Lillie, A. R., 1964, Steeply plunging folds in the Sealy Range, southern Alps: New Zealand Jour. Geol. and Geophys., v. 7, no. 3, p. 406.

Ludwig, W. J., Ewing, J., and Ewing, M., 1965, Seismic refraction measurements in the Magellan Straits: Jour. Geophys. Research, v. 70, no. 8, p. 1855–1876.

Ludwig, W. J., Hayes, D. E., and Ewing, J. I., 1967, The Manila Trench and West Luzon Trough—I. Bathymetry and sediment distribution: Deep-Sea Research, v. 14, p. 533–544.

Marshall, E. O., 1909, The geology of Campbell Island and the Snares, in The subantarctic islands of New Zealand: Christchurch, Philos. Inst. Canterbury, v. 2, p. 680–704.

Maxwell, John, 1948, Geology of Tobago, B.W.I.: Geol. Soc. America Bull., v. 59.

Menard, H. W., 1967, Sea-floor spreading, topography, and the second layer: Science, v. 157.

Murray, H. W., 1945, Profiles of the Aleutian trench: Geol. Soc. America Bull., v. 56, p. 757–782.

Officer, C. B., Jr., 1955, Southwst Pacific crustal structure: Am. Geophys. Union Trans., v. 36, p. 449–459.

Peter, G., and others, 1965, Geological structure of the Aleutian trench southwest of Kodiak Island: Jour. Geophys. Research, v. 70, p. 353–367.

Pulpan, Hans, and Scheidegger, A. E., 1965, Statistical analysis of seismic faulting: Pure and Appl. Geophysics, v. 61, p. 89–94.

Raitt, R. W., Fisher, R. L., and Mason, R. G., 1955, Tonga trench: Geol. Soc. America Spec. Papers, v. 62, p. 237–254.

Rodgers, John, 1964, Basement and no-basement hypotheses in the Jura and the Appalachian valley and ridge, in Tectonics of the south Appalachians: VPI Dept. Geol. Sciences, Mem. 1.

St. John, V. P., 1967, The gravity field in New Guinea: Ph.D. thesis, Univ. Tasmania.

Scholl, D. W., von Huene, R., and Ridlon, J. B., 1968, Spreading of the ocean floor: Undeformed sediments in the Peru–Chile trench: Science, v. 159, p. 869–871.

Senn, A., 1940, Paleogens of Barbados and its bearing on history and structure of Antillean–Caribbean region: Am. Assoc. Petroleum Geol. Bull., v. 24, no. 9, p. 1548–1610.

Shor, C. G., Jr., 1962, Seismic refraction studies off the coast of Alaska: Seismol. Soc. America Bull., v. 52, p. 37–55.

Smith, J. G., 1965, Orogenesis in western Papua and New Guinea: Tectonophysics, v. 2, p. 1–27.

Speight, R., 1905, On some rocks from Campbell Island: New Zealand Inst. Trans., v. 37, p. 552–554.

Suess, Edward, 1909, The face of the earth: Oxford, Clarendon.

Sykes, L. R., 1966, The seismicity and deep structures of island arcs: Jour. Geophys. Research, v. 71, no. 12, p. 2981–3006.

Sykes, L. R., and Ewing, M., 1965, The seismicity of the Caribbean region: Jour. Geophys. Research, v. 70, no. 20, p. 5065–5074.

Talwani, M., Worzel, J. L., and Ewing, M., 1961, Gravity anomalies and crustal section across the Tonga trench: Jour. Geophys. Research, v. 66, no. 4, p. 1265–1278.

Thomson, A. A., and Evison, F. F., 1962, Thickness of the earth's crust in New Zealand: New Zealand Jour. Geology and Geophysics, v. 5, no. 1.

Thompson, B. N., compiler, 1965, New Zealand volcanology: New Zealand Dept. Sci. Indust. Research Inf. Ser. no. 49, 102 p.

Umbgrove, J. H. F., 1947, The pulse of the earth: The Hague, Martinus Nijhoff.

————— 1949, Structural history of the East Indies: Cambridge, Mass., Cambridge Univ.

Van Bemmelen, R. W., 1949, The geology of Indonesia, v. I: Govt. Printing office, The Hague.

Vening Meinesz, F. A., 1948, Gravity expeditions at sea: Pub. Netherlands Geodetic Comm., v. 4, p. 1–233.

Visser, W. A., and Hermes, J. J., 1962, Geological results of the exploration for oil, Netherland New Guinea: Holland, Staatsdrukkerij en Uitgeverij Christoffel Plantijnstraat 's-Gravenhage.

Von Huene, R., Shor, G. G., Jr., and Reimnitz, Erk, 1967, Geological interpretation of seismic profiles in Prince William Sound, Alaska: Geol. Soc. America Bull., v. 78, p. 259–268.

Wassall, H., 1957, The relation of oil and serpentine in Cuba: Geologia del Petroleo, Sec. III: Mexico, Cong. Geol. Internac.

Weeks, L. A., Harbison, R. N., and Peter, G., 1967, Island arc system in Andaman Sea: Am. Assoc. Petroleum Geologists Bull., v. 51, no. 9, p. 1803–1815.

Wegener, Alfred, 1924, The origin of Continents and oceans: London, Methuen.

Wilson, J. T., 1954, The development and structure of the crust, in Kuiper, G. P., ed., The Earth as a planet: Chicago, Ill., Univ. Chicago Press.

————— 1959, Geophysics and continental growth: Am. Scientist, v. 47, p. 1–24.

Wood, B. L., 1963, Structure of the Otago schists: New Zealand Jour. Geol. and Geophys., v. 6, no. 5, p. 641–680.

Woollard, G. P., 1962, Gravity anomalies and the crust of the earth in the Pacific basin, in The crust of the Pacific basin: Am. Geophys. Union Mon. 6, p. 60–80.

17
tectonic syntheses

SYNTHESIS AND GEOTECTONIC PROBLEMS

A number of attempts have been made to synthesize large-scale earth structures; only a few are described here, for a full treatment would require a separate book. Some workers have concentrated on trying to explain certain features such as orogeny, the origin of island arcs, and the distribution of continents; others have sought global synthesis in which the origin of all major structural features is derived and related.

The evaluation of geotectonic hypotheses invariably involves processes acting within the interior of the earth which are difficult to refute or prove and many of which depend on interpretations of only vaguely known oceanic structure. That the data are capable of satisfying various hypotheses is dramatically shown by the contrast which exists among present-day hypotheses. Although not all these hypotheses can be right, such syntheses are valuable in that they focus attention on critical questions and problems which become the objectives of future research. The efforts at global synthesis have pointed clearly to the upper mantle and the ocean basins as the areas from which data is badly needed.

These theories must be viewed as working hypotheses to be tested against new observations. An open mind is needed. A number of almost universally accepted concepts have been seriously challenged by results obtained in the last two decades. The ideas of all-sided crustal compression, compressional origin of folded mountain belts, synchronous worldwide orogeny, permanence of ocean basins, the cooling and contracting earth, the fixed position of continents, the origin of earthquakes along faults, the depth of faulting, the origin of thrusts, and homogeneity of the mantle are among these.

The syntheses outlined here are by no means universally accepted. They are continually modified by their adherents to fit new observations, but in a number of instances the hypotheses are in direct conflict. New data from the critical areas of continental margins, ocean basins, Precambrian basement, and the upper mantle are being obtained very rapidly now. Evaluation of the geotectonic hypotheses at this time would be premature, but it is possible to point out some particular problems which are currently topics of concern to geologists and geophysicists, and some aspects of these theories which are being challenged.

Many orogenic belts appear to have similar histories. One widely accepted characteristic is an early stage of geosynclinal development in which great thicknesses of sediment accumulate. Some recent studies in the Alps, however, point to much thinner accumulations than were previously thought. This raises the question of just how significant to the process of orogeny is the thickness of the geosynclinal accumulation.

Closely tied in with this question is the relation of crustal type to orogeny. Are orogenic belts developed along continental margins? Modern orogenic belts can be traced from continents into island arcs as in the Caribbean and Southeast Asia. The belt passes from continental- to oceanic-type crust. While the structural trends continue, the thickness of the crust changes, the layers recognized by seismic velocities change in thickness and character, and deep sea trenches appear. While most of the island arcs are located along continental margins, the chains from Fiji to New Guinea are strewn across deep sea floor. Deep sea also separates the Marianas from Asia, and intermediate or oceanic crustal types lie between many of the island arcs and true continental crust. Thus orogenic belts are not confined to continental margins now, and this must be explained.

The cause of elevation within orogenic belts is still an unsolved question. Among the theories advanced are crustal shortening, compression between convection cells, compression related to transcurrent faulting and differential global rotation, expansion caused by melting and emplacement of plutons, and hydration and alteration of mantle material induced by convection and by crustal tension causing increased volume.

The origin of foreland folds is still not completely settled in two of the best-known areas, the Juras and the Appalachians. Certainly the trend is toward viewing these as superficial folds developed as a result of gravity sliding off uplifted regions. However, there is also convincing evidence that folding in some fold belts has taken place during deposition of the sediments both by basin-directed submarine slump and sliding and by differential movements in the geosynclinal basement.

That all orogenic belts do not have identical histories was shown in our comparison of the Appalachians and the Rockies. The region of the Wyoming Rockies and the shelf area in general in which vertical movements along basement faults have caused displacements of several miles has no counterpart in many other orogenic belts, nor is there a counterpart for the Basin and Range structure in the Appalachians. Such differences are equally apparant when we compare North American orogenic belts with those of other parts of the world.

It has long been thought that plutonic activity and deformation in orogenic belts were closely connected in time. Radiogenic dating has confirmed that this relationship does hold in many places, but the precise timing of the igneous activity is not consistent relative to the time of folding, and it now appears that each may occur independent of the other. The causal relationship inferred from this connection is now in doubt.

The nature of the mantle is highly significant in all geotectonic theories. Seismic and heat-flow studies indicate that the mantle is *not* homogeneous. Phase changes seem probable in the upper mantle; it has been suggested that these rather than elastic rebound cause earthquakes. Continental crusts are distinctly different from oceanic crusts, but seismic profiling is showing increasingly great areas in which departures from these norms are found. The list of abnormal areas now includes midocean ridges, rises, island arcs, continental margins, and at least parts of the seas between island arcs and adjacent continents.

The theory of mantle convection is one of the most widely accepted of all modern hypotheses, but many doubt that the convection reaches near the crust or that it causes the formation of a tectogene as originally proposed. Seismic refraction profiles in island arcs have proved that a great downbuckle of continental crust does not exist under the arcs. There is an anomalous zone reaching depths close to those associated with continents, 25 to 40 km, but the velocities are those of a more basic material than granite and can be explained as resulting from alteration of mantle material.

EVOLUTION OF ISLAND ARC THEORY

It has been hoped that by gaining an understanding of the structure of the modern orogenic belts in the Pacific we might at the same time throw light on the process of orogeny in general. Geologists have long been attracted to the island arcs for this reason, and proponents of most geotectonic theories have sought to explain Pacific island structure. Thus it will be of interest to see how those theories have been applied, and how they have been adjusted to meet the new data.

The first scientists in the Pacific in the eighteenth and nineteenth centuries made their contribution through collection of basic data concerning the geographic distribution of islands and locations of volcanoes, and through description of rock types and determination of ages. A considerable body of knowledge was available when Dana (1875) recognized four major structural lineaments in the Pacific:

1. Hawaii: Marquesas
2. Polynesian chain: Radak, Gilbert Islands to Samoa
3. Australian chain: Admiralty–Solomon–New Hebrides
4. New Zealand chain: Macquarie–New Zealand–Tonga

By the time Suess (1909) published the English edition of his classic work "The Face of the Earth," many of the salient features of the island arcs had been recognized. The arcuate character of the Aleutians, Kuriles, Marianas, and the Indonesian Islands was known, and it was recognized that these are the trend lines of modern mountain belts. Trenches were recognized on the oceanic side of the arcs, and it was conjectured that these were connected with the folding seen on the nearby islands in the arc. Suess postulated that the trenches were analogous to the depressions in front of the recently folded mountain ranges in the Carpathians and Alps, and that they indicate the subsidence of the foreland beneath the folded mountains. The Marianas trench was inferred to be the eastern edge of the Asiatic mountain system. The widespread elevated coral reefs in the Indonesian arcs were recognized as a sign of recent uplift. The existence of two concentric belts, an outer (eastern) ridge dotted with islands of Eocene limestone, old eruptive rocks, and serpentine, and an inner arc of active andesite volcanoes, had been recognized in the Bonin Islands southeast of Japan. A similar division of the Tonga–Kermadec region was pointed out by Lister (1891). Metamorphic rocks were known on Yap, and the elevation of the terraces in the southern Marianas Islands had been identified up to 800 ft above sea level and tilted westward.

Suess visualized three arcuate structural belts, called the Australian arcs:

1. A belt consisting of two concentric zones extending from New Guinea through New Caledonia to New Zealand and from North Mecklenburg through the Solomons and New Hebrides

2. A belt extending from the Caroline Islands through the Gilbert and Ellice Islands to Fiji

3. A belt extending northeast from New Zealand to Tonga and Kermadec

Suess recognized an arc extending northwest through the Tuamotu Islands and the linearity of the Hawaiian chain, and he commented that the greater the distance of the arc from Australia the rarer are the traces of ancient continental land, till at last only volcanoes and atolls remain.

Sollas' Idea of Circular Arcuate Structures

Sollas (1903) demonstrated that many mountain systems and island arcs are clearly parts of circular arcs. Sollas and later Lake (1931) conceived that this shape would be easily explained if a thrust plane defined the base of each of these island arcs; moreover, the angle of dip of the plane could be calculated from the form of the arc (the pole and the radius). If the arc is not now circular, it is inferred that subsequent deformation has changed the original shape.

The way Sollas (1903) envisioned the tectonics of an arc is shown in this quote regarding the Aleutians:

> The numerous mighty volcanoes which characterize the region point to the existence of an extension subterranean reservoir of lava, and to discontinuity of the earth's crust, in the form of a circular crack. It is difficult to look upon this portion of the globe, to avoid the impression that we have before us the remains of a spherical dome or blister, which has broken down along circular and radial fractures. . . .

Further, Sollas pointed out that the poles to the circular arcs lie on a great circle. Lake (1931), inferring the arcs to be thrust faults, concluded that these must be normal to the great circle of their poles and that this must mean that the Asiatic continent is moving relative to the floor of the Pacific, the direction of

movement being normal to the great circle. He described the creep of the Pacific sima toward and under the continents of Asia.

Andesite Line

Marshall (1912) synthesized knowledge of Pacific Ocean deeps, the composition of volcanic rocks, and distribution of petrographic province. He succeeded in demonstrating that there is a boundary generally located along the trenches which separates regions of marked folding in sedimentary and volcanic rocks and andesite volcanism from a region in which the exposed rocks are little deformed and in which coralline limestone and basaltic igneous material predominate. Folding, faulting, earthquakes, and andesite volcanism are concentrated on one side of this line. He marked its location along the Tonga–Kermadec trench, then south of Samoa and westward just north of the Solomon Islands. He later named the line the andesite line (1924).

Convection Hypothesis of Vening Meinesz

Vening Meinesz (1964) has summarized his concept of mantle convection currents and their application to interpretation of crustal structure. Essential elements of this theory and its application to island arcs are discussed in the following paragraphs.

If the crust is subjected to uniaxial horizontal compression exceeding the elastic limit of the crust, plastic deformation occurs in two belts, making about 55° angles with the compression. Crustal deformation starts by the thickening of the crust, but because of isostasy the downward bulge exceeds the upward bulge, causing the layered crust to bend downward. This downward bulge explains the negative-gravity anomalies occurring in island arcs and provides an explanation for the formation of a geosyncline. If the downbuckle is far away from islands or the coasts, the belt shows as a deep trench.

It is concluded that the presence of strong negative anomalies and trenches demonstrates that mantle currents are still keeping at least large parts of the crust under compressional stress. When the half-turn convection currents complete their half turn, the mantle becomes stable again; stress in the crust disappears; readjustments of crustal equilibrium occur in the downpressed belts leading to the development of a mountain range. The Alps have reached the stage of equilibrium; the Indonesian archipelago has not. The theory as applied to the Indonesian arc explains many features of the observed structures. Volcanoes form in the inner volcanic arc at a distance of about 150 km behind the tectonic arc. This occurs in a region of crustal arching in which tensional effects appear to be located behind the zone of thickening and buckling. The magma finds its way up from a zone of shearing due to crustal shortening. Inside (behind or on the side of the nearby continent) the arched belt in the volcanic inner arc, there is a zone of downwarping, the site of the idiogeosynclines (Umbgrove, 1947).

Wrench faulting accompanied by overriding in the wing areas of island arcs (i.e., Philippine Islands), also that in New Guinea and that along the western North American coast, can be explained. Strike-slip faulting in the wing areas of island arcs is due to the movement of a crustal block. The Indonesian block bounded by the Philippine trench on one side and the Java trench on the other defines such a block. Two types of trenches thus exist—the wing trenches due to wrench faulting and overriding, and a central type at the leading edge of the moving crustal block. Gravity anomalies on the order of −50 mgals occur in the downpressed areas while −130-mgal anomalies occur in the downbuckled belts. The reason the eastern end of the Indonesian archipelago is broken is the presence of the New Guinea buttress where the crust is too strong to resist downbuckling. The deep basins in the Indonesian Island area are attributed to small convection cells. The third arcs, such as that in the Banda Sea, are also attributed to these convection cells.

Wide areas of crustal tension such as are found in East Africa and Europe between the Alpine arc and the North Sea are caused by the divergence of a great mantle current system. The gravity field over East Africa is in harmony with the convection current hypothesis.

Island Arc Tectonics According to Umbgrove

Umbgrove (1947, 1949) accepts the convection current hypothesis as postulated by Vening Meinesz, and uses it to explain the tectonics of the Indonesian arcs. He recognizes four zones in the western part of the archipelago which have been prominent during the Cenozoic:

1. A nonvolcanic strip in which the most recent folding is Miocene. Grabens formed along the axes of these trends in Pliocene and Pleistocene time. This zone is thought to be the zone under which the great downbuckling has taken place. The zone would include the islands southwest of Java and Sumatra, for example.
2. A volcanic geanticlinal zone such as that in western Sumatra.
3. A series of idiogeosynclines (broad sedimentary basins of relatively shallow subsidence). Many of these were moderately folded near the end of the Pliocene and then were elevated.
4. Core areas that were folded before the Tertiary, i.e., Malaya and Borneo.

The downbuckle and a contemporaneous geanticline formed to one side of it are attributed to compression. Once the compression is relaxed, isostasy acts to uplift the lighter downbuckled root and creates a furrow between the volcanic and tectonic arcs at the same time. Volcanic activity occurs only on the inner arc, never on an outer arc. The reason for this is that arching is more pronounced on the inner arc, and the subcrust is crowded on the inner side while it is free to expand on the outer, convex side.

Umbgrove concludes that the last strong

compression occurred in the Miocene although a second compression took place at the end of the Pliocene. He attributes all present bathymetric features and topography to Quaternary activity.

Spreading of the sialic downbuckled root is an important process in this hypothesis. Spreading of the root at depth is called on to explain uplifts through isostatic adjustment and to account for the deviations of gravity anomalies from predicted values.

Sumba Island presents a problem because it is not typical of either the outer nonvolcanic arc or the inner volcanic arc. The strong negative-gravity anomalies do not cross over it; they terminate and restart on the other side. An explanation for this is that the segment of the crust where Sumba is located is a section of the downbuckle which has risen.

Observations on the Island Arcs by Hess (1948)

At about the time Umbgrove was publishing his synthesis of Indonesia, Hess (1948) summarized the geology of a large area in the western Pacific north of Indonesia, pointing out additional evidence to support the convection current hypothesis. He noted that the arcs intersect sharply, not as a smooth S-shaped curve. The dating of orogenies in the arcs suggests two major periods of orogeny, one of Late Cretaceous age and another about early Eocene. Positive-gravity anomalies were found on the concave side of the arcs in regions occupied by geanticlines; no evidence of deformation could be demonstrated on the oceanward side of the trenches; an important zone through the Philippines was suggested as a major transcurrent fault; the axis of the negative-gravity anomalies was found to correspond to the axis of the trench from Bonin to Honshu; and zones of peridotite intrusions were found to be parallel to the axis of the inferred tectogene. An older zone of peridotites was traced through Japan, Formosa, western Luzon, Palawan, Borneo, Malay, and Burma. The age of these peridotites in Japan is early Mesozoic. A younger belt of peridotites occurs in New Guinea, the eastern Philippines, Palau, Yap, the Bonin Islands, the Marianas, and Kamchatka.

Modified Convection Hypothesis of Fisher and Hess

Fisher and Hess (1963) propose one of the most recent modifications of the convection current hypothesis. The inaccurate model of crustal thickness and the idea of elastic buckling due to crustal compression used in early convection hypotheses is abandoned in favor of plastic flow of oceanic crust and sediments to depth in response to convection in the mantle.

The idea of crustal extension under trenches first advanced by Worzel and Ewing (1954) is rejected for the following reasons:

1. The negative isostatic anomalies follow the axis of the Puerto Rico trench into the Barbados ridge, indicating that the anomaly is due to deep-seated causes and that isostatic equilibrium does not exist over the trench. A high-density antiroot under the trench does not exist.
2. Any anomaly formed as a result of extension would disappear rapidly. The rapidity of such adjustments is seen in the postglacial movements, and there would be no reason for a negative anomaly to arise in case of extension. In fact, positive anomalies are found where extension is generally accepted in the Red Sea and over the Bartlett trough.
3. The top of Capricorn seamount located on the eastern edge of the Tonga trench is tilted toward the trench, and guyots have been found near the axis of the Aleutian trench with tops 900 fathoms deeper than those south of the trench.
4. The seismic refraction profiles and gravity-derived profiles show Moho going down under island arcs.

It is proposed instead that a crust consisting

of supracrustal sediments, volcanics, and a crust of serpentinized peridotite is drawn down along the descending limb of a convection cell until it reaches a temperature of 500°C where a deserpentinizing reaction takes place, releasing water. The magma and fluids migrate upward and toward the island arc where open fractures tend to form at right angles to the direction of compression.

Role of Hydration in Island Arc Deformation

Donnelly (1964) has proposed a theory which explains deformation in island arcs as being related to processes of hydration and dehydration of the oceanic crust. His ideas grew out of studies in the Caribbean, but they appear to be applicable to island arcs in the Pacific as well. Island arcs generally separate regions of oceanic crustal type from areas of modified crust (the crust behind or inside the arcs is usually slightly thicker and has a lower velocity than that of the ideal oceanic type). One of the simplest explanations for this difference in the crustal plates is that the crust behind the arcs has been partially hydrated. Where these plates join, there is a boundary marked by significant differences of physical characteristics. If compressional stresses are exerted on either or both of the plates, failure is most likely to occur along the boundary. The compressional stresses could be derived from subcrustal drag caused by convection currents, continental drift, or crustal compression. If the stress is oriented at a small angle to the boundary, then strike-slip faulting could occur along the boundary (such faults have been postulated in the Philippines, New Guinea, and other arcs and orogenic belts). If the stress is oriented at a higher angle, 30 to 60°, then both compressional and strike-slip features could result; and if the stress is oriented at a still higher angle, 60 to 90°, thrusting and compressional features result.

The lower limit of the proposed hydration is the top of the 8 km/sec layer, the boundary usually taken as the base of the crust. The depths involved range from 8 to 15 km. If the boundary zone between the two types of crustal plates is brought under compression, a buckle will develop and this zone of abnormal crust will be forced down as a root. As it is depressed, the hydrated crust is subjected to higher temperatures and pressures. Experimental work has shown that dehydration will occur at 500°C by the breakdown of a chloritelike layer of silicate. The thickness of the abnormal crustal layer found under many island arcs is on the order of 30 km (Fig. 16-5), which would reasonably correspond to 8,000 bars of pressure and a 650 to 750°C temperature. As the root is depressed, the water and volatiles released cause rapid thickening of the root. The process of dehydration can be called on to explain the presence of several types of igneous rocks found in island arcs. If dehydration is slow, a limited volcanic effusion is produced, but as the rate increases, first a siliceous magma and then basaltic and mafic magmas could be produced. Yoder and Tilley (1962) found the beginning of melting of four types of basalt at 8,000 bars of pressure and about 700°C. This would correspond approximately to the 30-km depth and could represent the beginning of melting of the dehydrated mantle.

Anomalous Structures in the Upper Mantle under Island Arcs

Oliver and Isacks (1967) have discovered an anomalous zone in the mantle under the Tonga–Kermadec island arc, and it seems probable that a similar zone may be found in other arcs. The anomalous zone is about 100 km thick, and its upper boundary is defined by the highly active seismic zone that dips toward the west beneath the islands. The zone extends to depths of about 700 km. The primary evidence for the presence of this anomalous mantle is that seismic body waves, particularly S waves, propagating in the anomalous zones, are not so subject to attenuation as are similar waves in normal mantle.

It is suggested that the anomalous mantle may actually be continuous with the uppermost

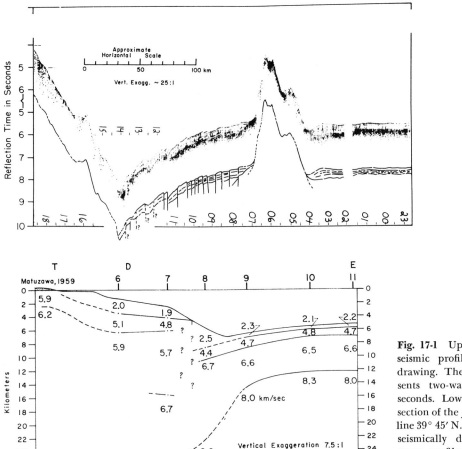

Fig. 17-1 Upper: representative seismic profiler records and line drawing. The vertical scale represents two-way reflection time in seconds. Lower: seismic refraction section of the Japan trench along the line 39° 45′ N. The correlation of the seismically determined layers between profiles 7 and 8 is uncertain, as indicated. The results for profile 8 are tentative. (*Both from Ludwig and others, 1966.*)

mantle material east of Tonga. If this is the case, then the uppermost mantle has been thrust or dragged down beneath the Tonga arc, and mantle elsewhere must be mobile enough to allow the lateral movement necessary.

Tensional Features in Deep Sea Trenches

The widely accepted ideas of crustal compression in island arcs as envisioned in convection theory first came under attack from geophysical arguments in 1954 when Ewing and Worzel interpreted a gravity profile across the West Indies as indicating crustal thinning under the

Puerto Rico trench. The trench might be thought of as having originated through a process not unlike necking on a metal plate or bar that is extended in tension. More recently Ludwig and others (1966) have published crustal sections based on seismic "sparker" and more deeply penetrating seismic refraction profiles of the Japan trench (Fig. 17-1). Numerous steeply dipping faults are found on the sea floor on the eastern side of the trench, and these are interpreted as indicating tension. The relationship is not so clear in the crustal section, however. There the 1.9 to 2.3 km/sec layer and the 4.4 to 4.8 km/sec layer are both displaced; both are up on the side of Japan. It would be easy to interpret a thrust fault dipping from the trench under Japan on the basis of this section. The steep faults on the oceanic side near the surface would then be extensional features caused by the bending of the crust and relative movement of Japan toward the trench.

Sea-floor Spreading

The idea that the sea floor might be moving away from the midocean ridges as a result of the formation of new crust there as suggested by Hess (1962), Dietz (1963), and Wilson (1963) has gained wide acceptance (see discussion in Chap. 15). The idea has been applied to theories of convection, continental drift, and global expansion.

CRUSTAL COMPRESSION—THE CONTRACTION HYPOTHESIS

The theory that the earth is contracting is based in part on thermal considerations. It is obvious that a source of heat energy is required to drive volcanic activity, and it seems logical to seek energy required for diastrophism and other crustal processes from heat derived from the earth's interior. Lord Kelvin developed this point of view, and it found support in the dynamic encounter hypothesis regarding the origin of the earth from a hot gaseous filament drawn out of the sun. Elie de Beaumont (1829) proposed that the earth must be contracting in order to explain the apparent crustal shortening seen in the folded mountain belts. Folds and faults develop in the outer crust of the earth as it accommodates to a cooling and shrinking interior. Jeffreys (1952) has formulated geophysical arguments regarding the cooling rate and has concluded that the cooling of the rock through 100°C or more since solidification would encompass about the outer 600 km of the earth. He goes on to point out that this is also the range of depth of the deep earthquakes, and that it is the range of depth

through which gravity anomalies indicate stress differences comparable with the strength of surface rocks.

We examined many structures which are of compressional origin, but it is impossible to identify them as arising from absolute crustal shortening as implied by this theory. Some compression arises from downslope movement, or gravity sliding, from uplifted areas, and many geologists are now convinced that this is the origin of the foreland fold systems in which measurements of crustal shortening have generally been made. Island arc structures have been interpreted in terms of crustal compressional phenomena, but the convection hypothesis does not require a contracting earth, and the island arcs are viewed as being of tensional origin by proponents of earth expansion.

Contraction of the earth is not proved conclusively by analysis of the surficial structures, although much evidence of local compression exists and too little is known about the heat balance of the earth and the nature of the mantle to allow a positive answer at this time to the question of whether the earth is expanding, contracting, or remaining the same size.

CONTINENTAL DRIFT*

The concept of continental drift has been greatly strengthened in recent years by paleomagnetic studies; some drift is now accepted as a corollary or an essential part of most geotectonic theories. The near-perfect fit between South America and Africa at the 2,000-m line (Carey, 1958) remains the most convincing evidence of drift, but evidence of tensional phenomena under deep sea trenches, the discovery of oceanic-type crust in areas where continents were presumed to have sunk, the

* Paleomagnetism and the continental drift hypothesis have been treated in great detail in a number of significant summaries and symposium volumes in recent years. Refer to Carey (1958), Munyan (1963), Runcorn (1962), Van Hilten (1964), Irving (1965), Garland (1966), and Cox and Doell (1960).

discovery of many large transcurrent faults both on the sea floor and on continents, have lent support to the earlier geological and tectonic theories based on drift. The problems for those who accept drift are how much drift has taken place, when did the drift occur, what caused the drift, and what structures are due to the drift.

Movement of continents is viewed in various ways. Movement caused by the rising and spreading of convection currents is one view. This is modified to favor such views as upward convection under continents, upward convection at midocean ridges causing a push against the continental plate on one side, and the development of new oceanic crust so that the ocean floor spreads. Drifting is also ascribed to expansion of the earth accomplished by the creation of new ocean floor independent of convection, causing drift and dispersal movements of the broken continental plate.

Closely related to the drift hypotheses are those involving differential rotational movements of the crust such as seem implied by the sinistral displacements between Australia and Asia and between South and North America.

The striking differences between the eastern and western margins of the Pacific pose a problem of the type explained by drift. Deep trenches along the eastern edge appear overridden by the young orogenic belts along the continental margins, while most trenches and island arcs on the western rim stand well out away from the continents.

THE GEOMECHANICAL MODEL OF VAN BEMMELEN

Van Bemmelen (1964, 1965) has recently revised and amplified the theory of crustal undations which he used in his analysis of the geology of Indonesia (1949). Five classes of undations, based on their diameters, are recognized: local, 1 km; minor, 10 km; meso, 100 km; geo, 1,000 km; and mega, 10,000 km. These result ultimately from deep-seated mass circuits in the lower mantle. Megaundations result from physicochemical processes in the inner mantle (Fig. 17-2). When heavier constituents are segregated toward the core, the density of the residual matter is reduced. Lighter matter rises and is retarded. Currents in the inner mantle cause bulges in the boundary between the inner and outer mantle. These are transmitted by plastic flow to the surface to form megaundations. Coriolis forces cause moving masses inside the earth to be deflected; rising masses are retarded; subsiding masses are pushed ahead faster.

The undations create potential energy which can be carried off by (1) volcanic activity, (2) spreading of matter by erosion and sedimentation, or (3) gravity tectonics. The maximum height attained by an undation depends on the character of the rock and the rate of uplift. Soft materials spread rapidly, and there is ample time for spread of the largest undations. Maximum height is reached in meso-undations, about 9 km. The lateral spreading does not require pushing, dragging, or passive transporting. Each layer can advance farther sideward under gravity than the layer beneath it. Volcanic spreading was most important in the early phases of earth history, followed by the effects of erosion and sedimentation accompanied by continental crustal development by means of zonal accretion around continental nuclei. Marginal geosynclinal accumulations were transformed into metamorphic and igneous rocks. The eventual effect was the development of Gondwana and Laurasia. The third phase consisted of the breakup and drift of these early continental plates. This process is driven by gravity tectonics.

Drift of continent-size masses is accepted as a proved reality. The mechanism for drift is undation, uplifts, and downwarps of the geoid with diameters measured in hundreds or thousands of kilometers. The highest unit, the *crust*, glides over the next deeper one, the *astheno-sphere*. A wandering continental shield will have a frontal geosynclinal subsidence, followed by orogenesis; extension phenomena will occur on the rear side; and a system of transcurrent, or strike-slip, faults occurs along the sides of the plate. Sideward movement of a plate is accompanied by earthquakes which are sudden releases of accumulated strain. Shallow earthquakes occur in what is known as the *tectonosphere*; medium-depth earthquakes are related to high rates of plastic flow in the asthenosphere; and deep earthquakes are associated with sliding lamellae in the sclerosphere.

If a megaundation occurs in a continental area, the continent can be split as tensional structures develop over the undation. If parts of the continent then lie on either side of the crest of the undation, they may slip apart and allow the opening of a new ocean basin. Voluminous extrusions of plateau basalts accompany the rifting of a continent. Production of the large quantities of basalt is caused by the reduction of pressure on peridotite, causing segregation of basalt as deep portions of the mantle become exposed as a result of the lateral spreading near the surface.

The Darwin rise as described by Menard (1964) is a good example of the growth and decline of a megaundation. It rose in the Cretaceous at which time it was 5,000 km long, 1 km above sea floor level, and cut by longitudinal and transverse fractures which gave rise to volcanic activity. It then subsided in the Cenozoic. The East Pacific rise is a more recent example. The transcurrent faults of the Mendocino type are possibly older results of such undations.

The theory explains the origin of geosynclines as a product of continental drift; depression of the forward margin of the moving plate. When a geosynclinal area is pushed up as a result of the buoyancy of an orogenic asthenolithic root, the reactions are:

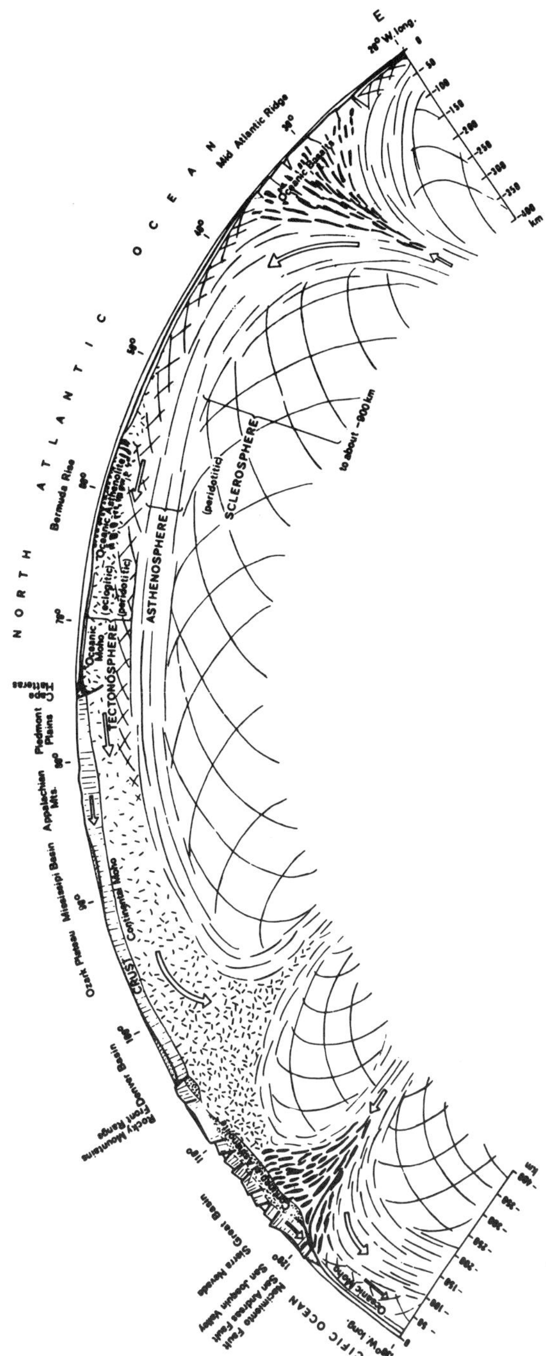

Fig. 17-2 Section along the 37° N parallel from the Pacific Ocean to the mid-Atlantic ridge. Vertical exaggeration 4x. (*After Van Bemmelen, 1964.*)

1. Strata glide toward the basin from the emerging center as helvetic-type nappes.
2. Spreading of crystalline basement causes nappes of east Alpine type.
3. Deeper, where the crust has been mobilized, a sideward mushroomlike spreading is expected.

GEOTECTONIC SYNTHESIS ACCORDING TO OROWAN

Orowan (1964) has proposed one of the most recent and all-inclusive syntheses of tectonics. Since aspects of a number of other syntheses are combined in this one, evidence for and against various parts of it has already been given:

1. Hot convection currents ascend in the ocean basins, causing the midocean ridges to form. These currents are formed in a crystalline mantle which behaves as a plastic at low and moderate temperatures. At higher temperatures (and low strain rate) the mantle materials behave as a pseudoviscous material in which the creep rate is very low until the stress approaches the "creep limit" at which the strain rate goes up very rapidly. The convection is not the type usually envisioned. Movement is largely confined to relatively thin, dikelike layers.

2. Midocean ridges tend to become more or less centered in the ocean because the material brought up in the convection current spreads out to either side. This load is isostatically uncompensated initially, and thus if more of it were built up on one side of the ridge than the other, subsidence on that side would be greater and the mantle material underneath would spread and push the hot dike toward a more central position. The flow away from the central position tends to be more balanced.

3. The sinks for the convection currents occur at the margins of continents. These sinks on either side of North America could hold the continent fixed, but the circumpacific shear zone makes this seem unlikely.

4. The major fault around the Pacific dips under the continents and movement on it is mainly dip-slip. The convection currents slip down under the edge of the Pacific by moving along the deep seismic shear zone at the continental margins.

5. The Atlantic has no such seismic shear zone, and thus the currents move against the continental blocks and shove them to cause continental drift, with North America moving over the Pacific.

6. There is no Atlantic shear zone because there is not enough stress to cause it. Thus the lithosphere behaves as a unit from the mid-Atlantic to the Pacific seismic zone. Presumably shears would also develop on the Atlantic side if the continents were anchored.

7. The low-velocity layer in the upper mantle is a soft shell in which movement occurs. This layer is due to the presence of water, silica, and other low-melting-point and volatile constituents which form pockets or envelopes. Lower in the mantle these are kept dissolved in solid solution. Higher in the mantle they segregate to form glassy boundary envelopes, inducing plasticity and viscosity in magma pockets.

8. Serpentine, water plus olivine, plays a central role in geotectonics. Where the ocean floor glides under the continents, serpentine in the oceanic crust is decomposed at the 500°C isotherm, and the overlying crust is soaked by solutions carrying light and radioactive elements.

9. Water from the shear zone causes plasticity and accounts for serpentine and ultrabasics found in orogenic belts. The water

also accounts for localization of mountains along continental margins.

10. Lava is generated as a result of hydration by decomposition of mantle materials at the seismic shear surface along continental margins. Extrusion of the lava induces subsidence in the region causing the development of a geosyncline.

11. Orogenic uplift is ultimately brought about by long-term hydration under the continental margin, which produces lower-density material. Deserpentinization leads to a density inversion as postulated by Daly (1938). Thus a vertical rise is induced along with magmatic activity in the orogenic belt.

12. Early stages of folding in the orogenic belt occur from horizontal compression due to flow from the midocean ridges during formation of the geosyncline.

13. If water, silica, and other materials continue to be produced for some time after the major orogeny, then a renewal of uplift takes place and causes the brittle crustal materials to break; a phase of deformation characterized by block faulting occurs.

GLOBAL EXPANSION

Evidences of crustal extension have long been recognized on continents. Extension appears necessary to explain the structure of the Basin and Range area in the western United States, the great rift system of East Africa, the Triassic basins of the Appalachians, and numerous other large grabens. Block faulting is prominent in sonic profiles of the Japan trench (Fig. 17-1), and rift systems are now widely recognized along the crest of the globe-encircling midocean ridges. Such rifting may be a result of local extension; extension effects are produced over a dome; it is possible that even the rifts over the midocean ridges result from local uplift, possibly as a result of upwelling of mantle material

where convection currents rise. But as the number and size of extensional features grow, we are led to give more consideration to the hypothesis that the earth is expanding.

As early as the 1930s Hilgenberg pointed out that continental drift could be accomplished by means of expansion of the earth's interior. Rifts would develop within any early crust and continental blocks would be dispersed as the zones between the continental plates, the deep oceanic crust, grew. Much recent work in the oceans suggests just such growth, with new oceanic crust being added along the midoceanic ridges and older oceanic crust being spread farther apart (see Chap. 15). One marked advantage of this idea is that it is unnecessary to seek forces to move the thick continental plates over or through oceanic crust in order to explain continental drift. The continents remain essentially in place and ride passively on the mantle.

Several lines of evidence support global expansion.* Egyed (1955) sought to prove expansion by means of a paleogeographical argument in order to support his theory that the earth's core is composed of an unstable high-pressure phase material that is undergoing a steady transformation to a lower-density phase, resulting in a volume increase for the earth. Egyed selected two sets of paleogeographic maps (Termier and Termier, and Strahov) and measured the areas of the continental plates, including shelf areas that are shown covered by water, for each period. These are plotted against time (Fig. 17-3), and it appears in both plots that the areas of continents covered by water have decreased steadily since the start of the Paleozoic. This has apparently happened in spite of an increase in the volume of water on earth through time. The curve may be explained in terms of an increase in the size of the oceans.

* See Holmes (1965) for an extended discussion of the hypothesis.

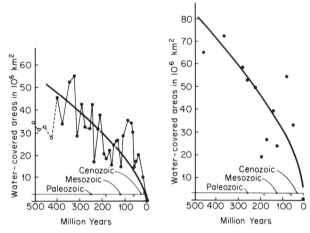

Fig. 17-3 Progressive emergence of continental massifs with time. (*Redrawn from Egyed, 1957.*)

Probably the most comprehensive synthesis of global tectonics ever attempted is that of Carey (1958). He used what is basically a tectonic approach to analyze effects of continental drift. In making restorations, he has used major known transcurrent faults and aligned submarine topographic features as guides to movement. Careful attention is given to the interplay of all major structural elements, and ocean depths are taken as indicative of crustal type. Among the first-order structural features defined are:

Orocline: An orogenic belt with a change in trend interpreted as an impressed strain [e.g., the Alaskan, Novaya Zemlya, and Ligurian (Alpine) oroclines].

Rhombochasm: A parallel-sided gap in the sialic crust occupied by simatic crust (e.g., Sea of Japan, East Greenland basin).

Sphenochasm: A triangular gap of oceanic crust separating two cratonic blocks with fault margins converging to a point (e.g., Arctic sphenochasm).

Orotath: A stretched orogenic belt (e.g., Andaman–Nicobar ridge, Kermadec ridge).

Oroclinotath: An orogenic belt that has been both stretched and bent (e.g., Lesser Antilles).

Nematath: Submarine ridges across Atlantic-type ocean floors which mark lines of stretching across sphenochasms or rhombochasms (e.g., Lomonosov ridge).

The method of tectonic analysis used is illustrated in Fig. 17-4 for the Alaskan orocline and the southwest Pacific. Each segment of the earth is analyzed in turn and the reconstruction is finally effected as indicated by the displacement lines in Fig. 17-5. In order to ensure accurate fits Carey plotted all his maps on a spherical map table. After years of careful work he found that all assemblies of Pangaea on a globe with the present curvature of the earth resulted in large gaps. Only when a globe of smaller radius was used did they fit. Estimates from these reconstructions indicate the diameter of the earth in the late Paleozoic was about three-fourths of the present diameter.

A second argument for expansion grows out of these reconstructions. Although proponents of continental drift do not agree exactly on all movements, they do agree that the continents are moving away from one another—North America is moving apart from Europe and Asia, Australia and Antarctica away from Africa and India. All of the continental blocks surrounding the Pacific seem to be moving toward it; yet the Pacific is still by far the largest ocean basin of all. Furthermore, Carey's analysis of the perimeter of the Pacific indicates that it is growing (Fig. 17-6), most of the island arcs being oroclinotaths. Growth of the perimeter of the Pacific under such conditions is possible only on an expanding earth.

DIFFERENTIATION AS A CAUSE OF TECTONIC PROCESSES

Beloussov (1951, 1962) has stressed the importance of vertical movements of an oscillatory nature in crustal deformation. He has summarized the evidence for such movements (1962), examined various hypotheses—contraction, continental drift, etc.—advanced to explain crustal deformation, and found them unsatisfactory or at least incomplete. An hypothesis based on differentiation at various levels within the earth is advanced. Evidence of differentiation of igneous rocks has been found in many petrologic studies of granitic plutons; basaltic magmas in the Hawaiian Islands and Tahiti are found to undergo differentiation; in fact, many petrologists consider it probable that all "granitic" rocks of the continents have been derived by differentiation from mantle material. Beloussov expresses the view that the entire sialic mantle consists of multiple granitic intrusions and the products of their erosion. Geosynclines are envisioned as evolving through a cycle that has an early stage marked by basaltic flows, followed by intermediate and acid lavas. Acidic magmas are injected with the formation of the new central uplift, and surrounding rocks are granitized. Later magmas

of various compositions rise, and finally, when the differentiation products are exhausted, a homogeneous primary basalt pours out.

Differentiation of the basaltic layer occurs in response to changes which affect the physicochemical equilibrium of the system. This system lies in a gravitational field which has mechanical effects on unstable arrangements, and the processes depend on the composition of the various components, and on temperature and pressure distribution. Differentiation may consist of a gravitative separation of more dense components, but conditions giving rise to differentiation in the earth would be vastly more complicated, since they might be governed more by physicochemical processes.

Differentiation processes are accompanied by other processes of great significance in tectonics. For example, if a "bubble" of acidic material rises upward, it is heated by its radioactive ele-

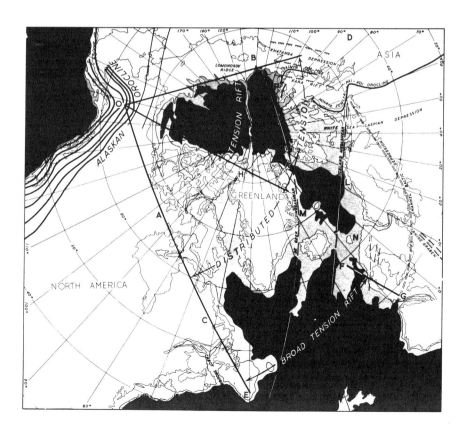

Fig. 17-4 The Alaskan orocline. (*From Carey, 1958.*)

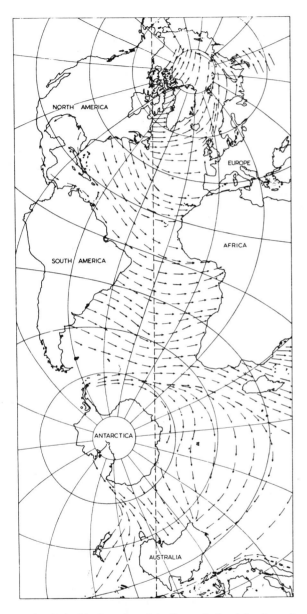

Fig. 17-5 Displacement flow lines of the Atlantic and southwestern Indian Oceans. (*From Carey, 1958.*)

ments, and it expands. The expansion exerts a mechanical pressure on the surrounding masses. In this fashion we find a cause of wavelike oscillatory movements of the crust—the uplifts and subsidence of geosynclines. Thus uplifts

are more frequently associated with acidic magmas and subsidence with basic magmas. Differentiation takes place at many levels in the earth, and the effect at the surface is a result of superimposition of these subsurface variations.

Just as a change in equilibrium of the physicochemical system may cause differentiation of basalt to form acidic magma, a change in the opposite direction may lead to the reverse reaction and granitic rocks may undergo basification. Basification would lead to an increase in density and subsidence, which could provide a process by which continents are converted into ocean basins.

In summary:

> Differentiation is connected with the redistribution of radioactive elements, which, in turn, leads to a difference in temperature: to the heating of some parts of the earth's interior and relative cooling of others. Expansion and compression associated with the temperature changes add to the intensity of the uplifts and cause isostatic anomalies. Finally, it is possible that to all this must be added the chronologically more recent process—whose course runs in the opposite direction—of local increase in the basic components of the earth's crust at the expense of the acidic, with the resulting formation of ocean basins.[*]

DIAPIRISM AS A TECTONIC PROCESS

Maxwell (1968) has suggested diapirism as a possible cause of tectonic activity. The "soft" layer in the mantle, Gutenberg's low-velocity layer, has a low rigidity, apparently because the rocks in that layer are near the melting interval. The plastic nature of the material in this layer and the high temperatures would make this layer have a tendency to become unstable. If the material in the soft layer did become unstable and started to rise in a manner analogous to the rise of salt in the salt basins of Germany and the Gulf Coast, the material would melt

[*] Beloussov (1962).

as it rose in response to the drop in confining pressure. Thus the column of material would have a lower density which would accelerate the process. The material would be driven upward by the sinking of cool, more dense crust outside the zone of upward movement.

Both the midoceanic ridges and the young folded mountain systems are locations of high thermal energy, and both are sites where mantle materials, ultrabasic rocks, have risen. Thus Maxwell postulates that the uplift, the thermal activity in the form of magmas produced, volcanic activity, and metamorphism, and the associated structural features of both oceanic ridges and mountain systems are caused by the same mantle processes. The differences arise

primarily from the differences in the types of crusts (continental and oceanic) which lie above the zones of diapirism. Ten cells of approximately equal size distributed over the surface of the earth are postulated to account for the distribution of ridges and mountain systems; the diapirism takes place along the edges of these cells.

This hypothesis is attractive because it provides a satisfactory explanation for many of the structural features of both ridge and mountain systems and it overcomes the most obvious difficulties of the convection current hypothesis. Its greatest difficulty is that it does not provide a mechanism by which continental drift might be accomplished.

Fig. 17-6 Diagram of tectonics of Southeast Asia (*From Carey, 1958.*)

REFERENCES

Beloussov, V. V., 1951, The problems of inner structure development of the earth: Izvest. Akad. Nauk SSSR Ser. Geograf. Oepiz., no. 7, p. 2, 4–16, 3–19.

—— 1962, Basic problems in geotectonics: New York, McGraw-Hill, 809 p.

Carey, S. W., 1958, The tectonic approach to continental drift, in Continental drift–a symposium: Geol. Dept. Univ. Tasmania, p. 177–355.

Cox, A., and Doell, R. R., 1960, Review of paleomagnetism: Geol. Soc. America Bull., v. 71, no. 6.

Dana, J. D., 1873, On some results of the earth's contraction from cooling: Am. Jour. Sci., Ser. 4, vol. v., p. 423.

Dearnley, R., 1966, Orogenic fold-belts and a hypothesis of earth evolution, in Ahrens, L. H., and others, eds., Physics and chemistry of the earth (7): New York, Pergamon.

De Beaumont, Elie, 1829–30, Recherches sur quelques-unes des revolutions de la surface du globe: Annales Sci. Nat., v. xviii, xix.

—— 1832, Observations et memoires geologiques publies par M. Elie de Beaumont, Professeur adjoint de Geologie a l'École des Mines, In-4°, 4 p. autogr., s.l.n.d.

Dietz, R. S., and Holden, J. C., 1966, Miogeoclines (miogeosynclines) in space and time: Jour. Geology, v. 75, no. 5, pt. 1, p. 566–583.

Donnelly, T. W., 1964, Evolution of eastern Greater Antillean island arc: Am. Assoc. Petroleum Geologists Bull., v. 48, no. 5, p. 680–696.

Egyed, L., 1956, Determination of changes in the dimensions of the earth from paleogeographic data: Nature, v. 178, p. 534.

—— 1957, A new dynamic conception of the internal constitution of the earth: Geol. Rundschau, v. 46, no. 1, p. 101–121.

Ewing, M., and Worzel, J. L., 1954, Gravity anomalies and structure of the West Indies, pt. 1: Geol. Soc. America Bull., v. 65, p. 165–173.

Fisher, R. L., and Hess, H., 1963, Deep-sea trenches, in The sea: New York, Wiley.

Garland, G. D., 1966, Continental drift: Toronto, Royal Soc. Canada Spec. Pub. 9, 140 p.

Hall, J., 1859, Geological survey of New York: Palaeontology, v. iii, Introd.

Heirtzler, J. R., Dickson, G. O., Herron, E. M., Pitman, W. C., III, and Le Pichon, X., 1968, Marine magnetic anomalies, geomagnetic field reversals, and motions of the ocean floor and continents: Jour. Geophys. Research, v. 73, no. 6.

Hess, H. H., 1948, Report of the chairman of the special committee on geophysical and geological study of ocean basins, 1947–48: Am. Geophys. Union Trans., v. 29, no. 6.

—— 1962, History of ocean basins, in Petrologic studies (Buddington volume): Geol. Soc. America, p. 599–620.

Holmes, A., 1965, Principles of physical geology: Ronald, New York.

Irving, E., 1965, Paleomagnetism and its application to geological and geophysical problems: New York, Wiley, 399 p.

Jeffreys, H., 1952, The earth: Cambridge, Mass., Cambridge Univ.

Kay, Marshall, 1967, Stratigraphy and structure of NE Newfoundland bearing on drift in North Atlantic: Am. Assoc. Petroleum Geologists Bull., v. 51, no. 4, p. 579–600.

Lake, P., 1931, Mountains and island arcs: Geol. Mag. [Great Britain], v. 68, p. 34–39.

Ludwig, W. J., and others, 1966, Sediments and structure of the Japan trench: Jour. Geophys. Research, v. 71, no. 8, p. 2121–2137.

Marshall, P., 1912, Oceania: Handb. regional geology, v. 7, no. 2.

Maxwell, J. C., 1968, Continental drift and a dynamic earth: Am. Scientist, v. 56, no. 1.

Menard, H. W., 1964, Marine geology of the Pacific: New York, McGraw-Hill, 260 p.

Munyan, A. C., ed., 1963, Polar wandering and continental drift: Tulsa, Okla., Soc. of Econ. Paleontologists and Mineralogists Spec. Pub. 10, 169 p.

Orowan, E., 1964, Continental drift and the origin of mountains: Science, v. 146, p. 1003–1010.

Oxburgh, E. R., and Turcotte, D. L., 1968, Mid-ocean ridges and geotherm distribution during mantle convection: Jour. Geophys. Research, v. 73, no. 8.

Pitman, W. C., III, Herron, E. M., and Heirtzler, J. R., 1968, Magnetic anomalies in the Pacific and sea floor spreading: Jour. Geophys. Research, v. 73, no. 6.

Poldervaart, Arie, 1955, Crust of the earth—a symposium: Geol. Soc. America Spec. Paper 62.

Runcorn, S. K., ed., 1962, Continental drift: New York, Academic, 338 p.

Scheidegger, A. E., 1967, On the possibility of the

origination of geosynclines by deposition: Jour. Geophys. Research, v. 72, no. 24, p. 6275–6278.

Sollas, W. J., 1903, The figure of the earth: Geol. Soc. London Quart. Jour., v. 59, p. 180–188.

Suess, Eduard, 1904, The face of the earth: Oxford, Clarendon Press.

Umbgrove, J. H. F., 1947, The pulse of the earth: The Hague, Martinus Nijhoff.

——— 1949, Structural history of the East Indies: Cambridge, Cambridge Univ. Press.

Van Bemmelen, R. W., 1964, The evolution of the Atlantic mega-undation: Tectonophysics, v. 1, no. 5, p. 385–430.

——— 1965, The evolution of the Indian Ocean mega-undation: Tectonophysics, v. 2, no. 1, p. 29–57.

Van Hilten, D., 1964, Evaluation of some geotectonic hypotheses by paleomagnetism: Tectonophysics, v. 1, no. 1, p. 3–71.

Vening Meinesz, F. A., 1964, The earth's crust and mantle: New York, Elsevier, 124 p.

Yoder, H. S., Jr., and Tilley, C. E., 1962, Origin of basalt magmas: an experimental study of natural and synthetic rock systems: Jour. Petrology, v. 3.

appendix A
structure maps
and cross sections

CROSS SECTIONS

Cross sections are drawn to show a structure in the subsurface as it would appear if viewed at right angles to some particular line. Usually cross sections are drawn at right angles to the strike or trend of the structure. Ideally the section is drawn normal to fold axes so that true dips are seen. Most geologic maps are accompanied by cross sections in which the geologist presents his idea of what the structure looks like at depth. In some cases cross sections may be prepared from a wealth of control data (surface exposures, well logs, seismic lines, etc.), but more commonly they are prepared from geologic maps and scattered surface control on strike, dip, and topography. When there is no subsurface control, cross sections must be constructed on the basis of certain assumptions. In this, there is likely to be less general agreement about the assumptions than is true in many other techniques. Thus the resulting cross sections represent one of several possible interpretations. The selection of assumptions depends on the mapper's conception of the geometry and the processes that acted during the formation of the structure. There are several different types of fold geometry, and it is not always easy to determine which type actually exists in any given area. The mapper is likely to subscribe to some current opinion regarding the character of the structural style, and this will be used more often than not in the selection of his assumptions for drawing cross sections. Certainly most cross sections reflect the best efforts of the people who draw them, but the beginning student should be warned against literal interpretation of cross sections prepared without subsurface control. It is wise to regard them as interpretations, with the understanding that interpretations change. Generally, cross sections lack the degree of accuracy found in surface geologic maps. In spite of these shortcomings cross sections are very useful. They are much more easily visualized than surface geologic maps; they do reflect what the person who draws them thinks about the subsurface; they are a useful way of helping to visualize the three-dimensional structural situation. Drawing cross sections will help point up various strengths and weaknesses in particular map interpretations.

Preparing to Draw a Cross Section

Some steps toward drawing a cross section can be taken before any assumption is made. One of these is to prepare a profile of the ground surface along the line of the cross section. If the cross section is not to be exaggerated, the same vertical scale is used as the horizontal scale of the map. Vertical exaggeration should be used only when dips are very low or when the section is long. The profile is drawn by laying a piece of graph paper with a labeled vertical scale at one side along the line. Where contours cross the edge of the graph paper, the elevations are read and plotted. Enough points must be taken to make it possible to draw a smooth line.

The second step involves placing the contacts of formations in their proper position along the profile. If the cross section is being drawn at right angles to the strike of the formations the dip of each unit can be laid off at the point of the contact and drawn as a short line. If the cross section is not drawn perpendicular to strike, the true dips given must be converted to apparent dips (this can be done by use of orthographic or stereographic projections and by means of prepared nomographs, i.e., U. S. Geol. Survey Prof. Paper 120-G by H. S. Palmer). The apparent dip is then drawn below the profile from the point of contact.

From this point, cross sections lacking subsurface control must be drawn on the basis of some assumption regarding the style of deformation and its extension at depth. There is little difficulty when it is reasonable to assume that formational contacts or existing faults may

be represented by a straight line, but when folding is involved, the geometry of the folding must be judged and drawn accordingly. If the section includes igneous or metamorphic rocks, they must be drawn according to some assumption regarding their shape. In the absence of control, hypothetical boundaries of such bodies are used. The shape of these is based on previous experiences or known similar features. One of the most complete descriptions of cross-section preparation is found in Busk (1929).

Down-dip Viewing of Structures

A method for approximating the shape of the cross section of a structure, known as the down-structure method of viewing geologic maps, was first described by Mackin (1950). By looking at a geologic map of a plunging fold from a position in line with the axis of the fold and from an angle that is close to the angle of plunge of the structure, the structure may be seen approximately as it would appear in cross section. The method can be used with most types of structures (Fig. A-1); it helps to clarify probable subsurface shape as well as the form that has been removed from the structure through erosion. It should be evident that the cross section you see when looking down some sloping surface in the down-dip method is not a vertical section, but a section at right angles to the line of sight. One of the other limitations to this method is that in dealing with detailed geologic maps in areas of high topography, contacts of even perfectly planar inclined surfaces may appear on a geologic map in a region of high relief as an intricate pattern. This method works best in regions of low relief or on regional maps of such small scale that relief effects are minimized.

Parallel Folding

A geometrical method is available for use when it can be assumed that the formations within the region of the cross section were originally uniform in thickness and remained uniform in thickness during folding. This method is

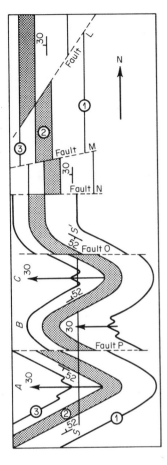

Fig. A-1 Diagrammatic map to illustrate several simple applications of the down-structure method. (*From J. H. Mackin, 1950.*)

2. Using the points of intersection, arcs are drawn with a compass. These arcs are drawn through the contacts and between the lines connecting the two dips with the point of intersection.

3. The compass is then moved to the next point of intersection and the contacts are continued using the new radius for the arc. In this fashion the contacts are drawn across the cross section (Fig. A-2).

One of the characteristics of parallel folding is that the folding dies out with depth and the shape of the folds changes both upward and downward.

Flow Folding

Various combinations of flexure and flow are found in nature. When there is evidence of flowage, the arc method of cross-section construction described above will not produce a true representation of the structure. How far off it will be depends on the amount of flowage. On the gently inclined limbs of flow folds the arc method may work, but the steep limbs are usually thinned and the crests and troughs of the folds are thickened. No geometrical construction has yet been devised that can be applied in the same mechanical way the arc method is used. Instead the geologist must look for as much field evidence as he can find that will suggest the nature of the fold, and he must then try to interpret that data in a cross section that is consistent with the data. This is done freehand or by a combination of the arc method and freehand drawing. In stratified sequences consisting of massive units interbedded with weaker materials such as shale, the shale may be expected to behave differently from the more massive formations.

Compaction Folding

When compaction is the principal process responsible for formation of folds, a method of drawing cross sections known as the *boundary ray method* may be used. This method is based

reasonably accurate in the case of flexural folding (sometimes called *concentric and competent folding*) in which there is little or no flowage within rock units which would cause material to move from the limbs toward the crests of the folds. The procedure following construction of the profile, location of contacts, and insertion of true or apparent dip line along the profile is as follows:

1. Perpendiculars are erected to each dip symbol plotted in cross section along the profile. These are drawn just long enough to intersect the lines drawn from adjacent dips. The points of intersection of adjacent lines are noted.

on the observation that the amount of compaction within a formation at a given point is a function of the dip at that point. A method for drawing cross sections through compacted structures is given in Coates (1945), Gill (1953), and Badgley (1959).

Similar Folding

Folds in which the shape of the fold remains constant from layer to layer are called *similar folds*. The thickness of the layers measured in cross section changes from point to point along the layer as measured normal to bedding, but the thickness of individual layers remains constant if measured along some particular direction. That direction is often the axial plane, or it may show up as a series of closely spaced slip surfaces. Such folds are common in metamorphic rocks.

STRUCTURE CONTOUR MAPS

A structure contour map depicts the shape and elevations on a given surface (often a stratigraphic marker horizon, fault surface, etc.) by means of contour lines. Structure contour maps

are used extensively as a means of depicting structures where subsurface control is available, and they are one of the most useful tools in structural geology. *Form line contours* can be drawn to help in approximating the shape of the structure even when subsurface information is lacking or sparse. These maps are used to create a model of the contact of some particular formation in much the same way that topographic maps are. The maps are independent of topography, although topographic control may be used in their preparation. They provide a three-dimensional picture of the shape of the surface on which they are drawn, and profiles of this contact may be prepared from them along any line. If structure contour maps have been prepared on several contacts in the same area, cross sections can be prepared from them and changes in structure with depth can be detected.

Properties of Structure Contours

The properties of structure contours are similar to those of topographic contours, and the shapes of the contoured surfaces are sometimes similar. As in making and interpreting topo-

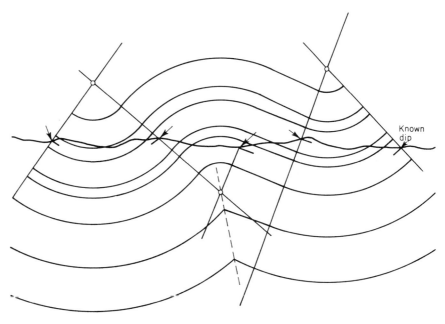

Fig. A-2 Solution to parallel folding.

Known dip

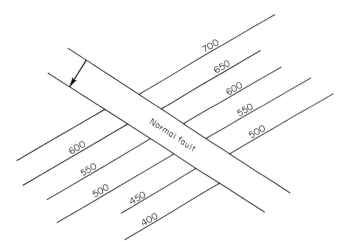

Fig. A-3 Offset of structure contours caused by a normal fault.

graphic maps, the difference between good and mediocre analysis is found in attention given to details, knowledge of the forms to be expected, ability to recognize those forms, and understanding of the way they appear on a contoured map of the structure. Experience in this type of work is indispensable, and the beginning student will learn a great deal by carefully studying structure contour maps prepared by professionals. The following are properties of structure contours and important features of structure contour maps:

1. A structure contour connects points of equal elevation on some surface (e.g., the top or bottom contact of a formation, a dike, vein, fracture, fault, intrusive body, etc.).

2. The elevation of the contour should be specified. The datum may be mean sea level, but a great many structure contour maps are based on other datum levels. Be careful to note negative values on contours if they are present. The negative sign indicates that the contour is drawn below the datum level. On some maps there is a note indicating that all values are depths below the datum, in which case higher

numerical designations signify lower elevations.

3. The contour interval is the vertical distance between contours. Most maps are drawn with a consistent contour interval, but some may have variable intervals reflecting variation in the amount of control available. When variation in contour interval is used, additional contours are inserted between the larger interval used over the entire map, and in this case the additional contours may end abruptly. Particular care should be exercised when first starting to study structure contours on the Tectonic Map of the United States. Structure contours on this map have been drawn on different contacts in different parts of the country. The regions contoured on a certain contact are surrounded by dotted lines along which the stratigraphic horizons used are indicated. In a few areas more than one set of structure contours drawn on two different stratigraphic horizons is shown.

4. Structure contours can cross themselves and other contours. This is not common in regions where the structures are broad and open, and it happens that most structure contour maps are drawn in regions of open structures. However, contours may be expected to merge or at least come very close together on the steep limb of an *asymmetrical fold*. If the fold is *overturned* even slightly the contours will merge and cross on the overturned limb, and they will cross for any *recumbent fold*. Contours on the surface of salt structures may merge and cross at the overhanging edge of a salt dome. A *reverse fault* provides another situation giving rise to merging and crossing of contours. Consider a reverse fault which dies out along strike. Contours may reflect a slight fold where the fault disappears, but as the amount of displacement increases along the fault, the contours on the *downthrown block* first

merge and then pass under those on the overriding thrust or *upthrown block.*

5. Spacing between contours is a function of the dip or inclination of the surface on which they are drawn. True and apparent dips can be measured from structure contour maps. At any given point a tangent to a structure contour is the strike of the contact. True dip must be measured at right angles to that tangent. Apparent dips can be determined along any direction. The dip may be found graphically by using the vertical and horizontal distance between two contours along the selected line, reading the difference in elevation, and solving the right triangle.

The density of contours depends on the contour interval selected, the scale of the map, and the steepness of slope. It is desirable to show as much detail as the field

data allow, but the map must be legible. Care should be taken in selecting a contour interval to keep these factors in mind.

6. Special notations are placed along some contours to aid in interpretation. Every fifth contour is sometimes made heavier to make reading more rapid. Where closed depressions, which bottom at less than the contour interval, occur below the last shown contour, that contour has hachures pointing toward the depression.

7. When the contoured surface is faulted, the fault should be indicated. In the case of *normal faults* (dip slip or oblique slip), there will be a gap produced in the contoured pattern (Fig. A-3). Reverse faults produce overlapping contour patterns. When there is sufficient control, the fault may also be shown by contours (made heavier or lighter to allow distinction

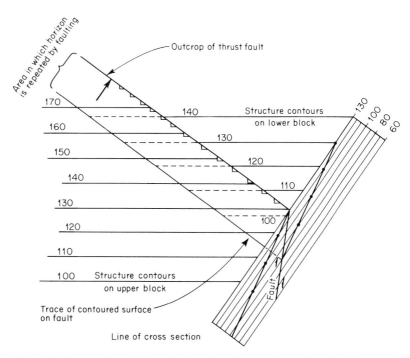

Fig. A-4 Cross section of thrust fault and a plane marker surface showing repetition of marker.

from the others). Usually folds are formed in connection with faulting, and these will be reflected in the contours.

Structure Contours on a Plane Dipping Surface

One simple use of structure contours which has a very important application in connection with *orthographic projections* is the construction of structure contours on an inclined plane surface. Such a surface is defined by its *strike* and *dip*. Consider first a situation in which this plane surface or contact intersects a perfectly flat horizon, as in very flat topography, or some arbitrarily selected horizontal surface. The intersection (outcrop) of the contact in this horizontal surface is the strike of the contact and is shown by a straight line with a specific compass direction. The dip of the inclined contact can be viewed in a cross section drawn at right angles to the strike. If the vertical and horizontal scales are the same, the true dip will appear undistorted. One way of representing this is illustrated in Fig. B-2. In this representation the line along which the cross section is drawn is the line perpendicular to the strike and in the direction of the dip. The horizon on which the strike is shown appears as a line in the plane of the cross section. Now any number of other horizontal planes at different elevations could be represented in this section. A set of horizons can be selected at a fixed interval of vertical separation, the contour interval. The point where each of these planes crosses the inclined contact in the section marks the position of that structure contour. The projection of these points of intersection to the original horizon indicates where structure contours will appear there. On such a plane all structure contours are parallel to the contact line since they are all strike lines.

An application of this idea is to find the outcrop pattern of a plane dipping contact in an irregular topography. This can be done if a topographic map is available, the strike and dip are known, and there is at least one known out-crop of the contact. The procedure is to draw a strike line through the known outcrop to the edge of the map. Prepare a cross section using the same vertical scale as the horizontal scale of the map. Fix the cross section so that it lies along a line perpendicular to the strike line and so that the strike line intersects the cross section at the point in that section which has the same elevation designation as the outcrop. Now any point along the original strike line which has the same elevation as the outcrop will also contain the contact. Additional structure contours can be constructed for as many elevations as are needed, and points falling along those contours, which have the same topographic elevation as the structure contour, will contain contacts.

Preparation of a Structure Contour Map

Various methods are used for the preparation of structure contour maps, depending on the amount and type of information available. The contact to be mapped may or may not outcrop at the ground surface. There may be topographic and surface geologic maps available. There may be strike and dip information for surface outcrops or from wells which have penetrated the contact. There may be good subsurface control from actual wells which penetrate the contact or some overlying formations. Seismic lines showing profiles of a contact or its adjacent contacts may give control. If the data are consistent, the more data there are available the more reliable the structure contour map constructed from it should be. However, for reconnaissance purposes, form line maps may be constructed which in some cases are based entirely on photogeologic studies. A good mapping horizon is selected and traced, strikes and dip on it are estimated, and form lines are constructed as accurately as possible. Badgley (1959) provides many useful hints in preparing maps when various types of data are available. Only the more general problems are discussed here.

1. When both a topographic and a geologic map are available the elevation of the contact may be read directly by placing a transparent overlay of the contact over the topographic map. The two must, of course, be drawn to the same scale. Each point where the elevation is determined becomes a control point.

2. Strike and dip information on the contact may be used not only at the contact but for some distance on either side of it. The assumption is made that the dip remains relatively constant (knowledge of the types of structures found in the region and other control data has to be used to test the validity of this assumption). This assumption is usually relatively safe if dips are known in overlying and underlying formations and they remain constant. On large *monoclines, homoclines,* and other broad flexures, this assumption may be safe for great distances. If the elevation of the contact, the dip at the contact, the scale of the map, and the contour interval are known, a set of multiple dividers or a ruler may be used to lay off a series of points above and below the contact through which structure contours will pass if the dip is constant.

3. Many structure contour maps are drawn on the basis of well logs. Lithologic, electric, and radioactivity logs all may be used to pick formational contacts. These logs will show the depth of the contact below the ground surface. In plotting the data, all readings must first be reduced to the elevation above or below the selected datum. Once the figures are reduced and plotted, contours may be drawn.

4. If seismic data are available they may be extremely valuable. Older seismic surveys provided spot determinations of depth and dip, but some of the modern methods allow construction of continuous profiles. In either case the data are reduced to the datum level in use and plotted on the map as a series of control points.

Drawing Structure Contours

Once all available data have been plotted on the map, contouring is done in much the same manner as contouring of any set of numerical values. But these are not just a set of numerical values. They represent information on a naturally formed surface. If the person drawing the contours understands what the various types of surfaces generally look like, he is much more likely to draw the contours through areas of little control in a more meaningful and realistic way. Any set of numerical values can be contoured in a great many different ways, and even the most experienced geologist may change initial contours many times as he begins to envision the structure represented by the data points. Just as streams help guide topographic contouring, the use of knowledge of the shapes of various known structural features may help guide structure contouring. For example, it may be possible to pick and use as a guide the crest or trough of a fold, a fault, reefs, or salt structures present in the formation. Unless there is control suggesting otherwise, contours should be drawn as smooth easy flowing lines, not as intricate patterns. Similarly, contour spacing should be even, and changes in spacing should appear as gradual changes rather than sudden breaks, unless control dictates a sudden break (in some cases this may be indicative of a fault).

FORM LINE CONTOURING

When there are insufficient data to construct a structure contour map, a map showing lines which reflect the probable structure may be prepared. This type of map can be made in the absence of a known contact, without topographic control if the topography does not have great relief, and without subsurface control. It is only fair to ask what good such a map may be expected to accomplish. Its main function is as a reconnaissance technique in areas where there is little or no ground control. It has come into use mainly through photogeology. In its simplest form this map is drawn from a control map showing only strike and dip symbols. Even though none of the form lines may have elevation control they can be drawn at an arbitrary interval from any arbitrarily selected datum. The technique is to select a contour interval, and if the angle of dip and scale of the map are known, the contour spacing can be found. Contour spacing marks are made on either side of each strike and dip symbol on the assumption that the dip is constant. Spacing marks from one symbol are not extended beyond the next data point on either side. It is assumed that the shape of the structure remains constant vertically so that the dip at any point on the surface is a reasonable guide to the dip of underlying units. With all the contour spacings indicated, an initial contour is drawn. This should be drawn in that part of the map where there is the maximum amount of strike control. Other contours may be drawn from this initial contour using the spacing marks to keep the interval constant.

ISOPACH MAPS

An isopach map depicts the thickness variation between two selected contacts by means of contours drawn through points of equal thickness. It follows that a zero isopach marks the edge of a unit where the upper and lower contacts come together. Isopach maps may be constructed when there is good subsurface control, or in areas of high relief and abundant outcrops. The main sources of the necessary thickness information are measured stratigraphic sections exposed at the ground surface, well data, and seismic sections. If structure contour maps have been prepared from two horizons in the same region, an isopach map can be made for the intervening units by subtracting the differ-

ence in elevation of the two structure contours at each point of intersection when the two are superimposed.

The thickness of a stratigraphic unit is measured at right angles to the top and bottom contacts. Care is usually taken to correct for dip of the units when sections are measured at the ground surface, but thickness information from well logs is usually the thickness of a unit that was actually penetrated. This will vary with the dip of the unit and the inclination of the hole. Thus penetration thicknesses are true thicknesses only when the contacts are horizontal and the well hole is vertical. If the dip of the contact is known, then the penetrated thickness must be reduced to true thickness before it is used for preparation of an isopach map. If there is not enough information to show the dip of the contacts in the well or the inclination of the hole, then a map similar to the isopach map may be prepared with the penetrated thicknesses. Such a map is called an *isochore map* (a contour map showing distribution of thicknesses penetrated at depth).

Isopach maps are particularly useful when several can be drawn for the same area. They are used for regional studies in which they provide an insight into the shapes of large basins (Fig. A-5) and the amount and rate of subsidence in different parts of those basins. In detailed studies they are used to outline reefs and salt domes or buried topography over which there has been thinning of rock units. When several isopach maps are prepared for the same area, they can be used to interpret the structural evolution of that area.

A large part of the sedimentary record with which we deal was formed along continental margins, particularly the continental shelves. One of the lasting impressions from the study of historical geology is the extent to which these marginal seas have advanced and retreated throughout geologic history. If the two datum planes selected for preparation of an isopach map are at all close to representing time-

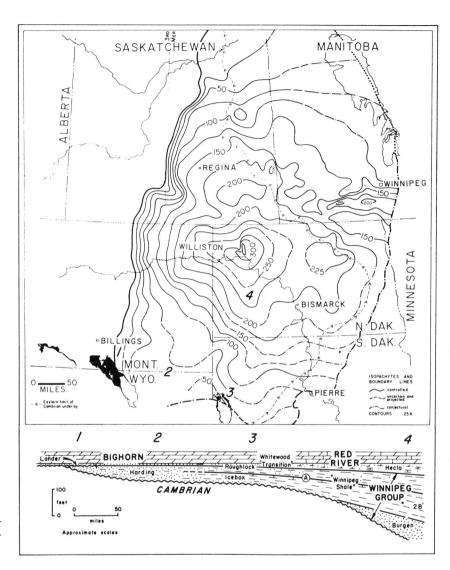

Fig. A-5 Isopach map of Winnipeg group in the Williston basin. (*From Fuller, 1961.*)

synchronous horizons, the isopach map may show the margin of the sedimentary basin. The average rate of subsidence is indicated by the thickness of the intervening strata at any point. The greatest thickness indicates the axis or center of the basin, and thinned places reflect structural highs or positive areas. Preparation of successive isopach maps will reveal the shifting of the centers and axes of subsidence

through time. The assumption made in this type of interpretation is that within a basin the upper level of the sediment is a surface of low relief. Such an assumption would be satisfactory in considering many, but not all, modern continental margins and other sedimentary basins. Maps showing variations in lithology, *lithofacies maps,* are used most often in connection with isopach maps. The two are used together to reconstruct the sedimentary environment. An isopach map drawn between two horizons in the region of a former continental margin would not clearly indicate a distinction between the shallow-water continental shelf and the much-deeper-water continental slope. The lithofacies map might make this relation clear, and then it would be possible to reconstruct the geologic setting at the time of deposition with regard to water depth as well as amount of subsidence.

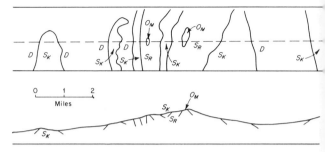

Prob. 1   (*After Lesure, 1957.*)

EXERCISES

Problem 1.   A strip geologic map (1 in. = 1 mile) and a profile along the center line of the map are given. Contacts of formations and the dips of the contacts are given along the profile.

Draw a cross section using freehand, and then draw a second section assuming that the folding is concentric.

Problem 2.   Given a structure contour map, dotted lines, on a marker horizon; four holes have been drilled (at circles) and the depth to the top of the next marker horizon is shown.

Assume a regional uniform change in the thickness and draw a structure contour map on the second marker. (*Procedure:* Determine contours showing change of thickness at 100-ft intervals; superpose these on the structure contour map; determine the elevation on the second marker at each point where the two sets of contours cross; contour the second marker.)

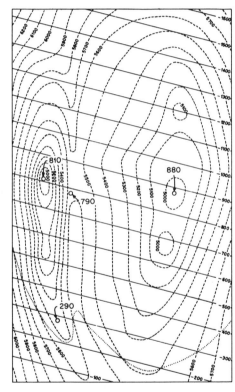

Prob. 2   (*Map from Sugden, 1962.*)

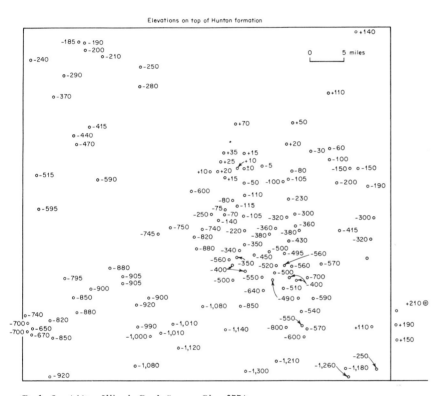

Prob. 3   (*After Illinois Geol. Survey Circ. 377.*)

Problem 3.   Given a map of parts of De
Witt and McLean Counties, Ill., showing subsurface elevations on the Hunton formation.
Draw a structure contour map of the Hunton
and describe the structure.

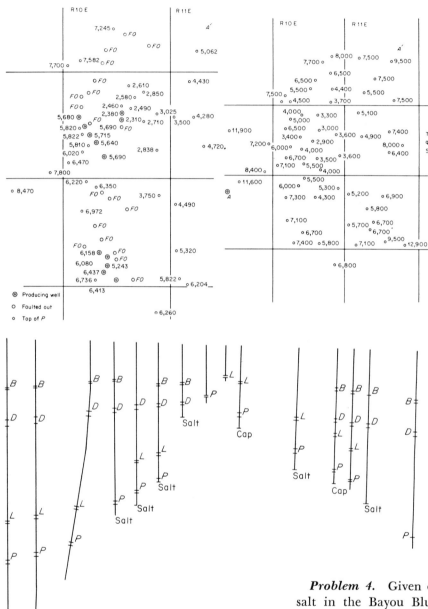

Prob. 4   *(From Mais, 1957.)*

Problem 4. Given elevations on top of the salt in the Bayou Blue salt dome, elevations and location of producing wells on top of the *P* horizon, and a cross section showing wells and the levels in each at which marker horizons have been picked. Draw structure contours on the salt and on the *P* horizon. Then complete the cross section, indicating the positions of faults. Describe the mechanics of intrusion of the salt and the origin of the structure over the dome.

Problem 5. The wells from the Cement-Chickasha area of Oklahoma are shown on a base map. Elevations in each well are given for the top of the Hoxbar, Deese, Atoka, and Morrow formations, all of Pennsylvanian age. All elevations are negative and taken with reference to sea level.

(a) Draw a structure contour map for each horizon.
(b) Determine isochore maps for the Hoxbar, Deese, and Atoka formations.
(c) Draw cross sections across the structure along the lines *A-A'* and *B-B'*.

No.*	Hoxbar	Deese	Atoka	Morrow
1	6,794	10,000		
2	5,588	8,983		
3	4,444	6,964		
4	3,910	Breccia	Breccia	
5	5,119	Breccia	Breccia	
6		4,573	Breccia	12,950
7	Breccia	Breccia	6,500	
8	Breccia	4,292		
9	Breccia	Breccia		8,600
10	Breccia	Breccia	9,272	11,100
11	3,615	6,560	10,400	12,350
12		7,415		
13	5,596	8,876	11,746	13,316
14	6,848	10,358		
15	6,803	10,390		
16	3,492	5,025		
17	3,286	5,023		
18	2,887	5,117	8,209	9,299
19	3,409	Breccia		
20	6,740	11,103	12,173	12,583
21	2,260	Breccia	9,500	9,900
22	2,100	3,282		4,600
23	3,545	6,088		
24	2,960	6,276		
25	2,920	5,410	7,400	8,300
26	2,769	4,555		
27	2,480		6,200, est.	4,452
28	6,945	Breccia		Breccia
29		4,200, est.	4,740	5,400
30	2,156	4,304	6,800	7,800
31	3,856	7,151	10,400	11,600
32		3,639	6,000	7,000
33	6,959	10,594		
34	2,900		10,000	12,000
26'	5,993	Breccia		Breccia
3'	3,402	5,900		
25'	4,224	Breccia		Breccia

* All values negative.
Source: Herrmann (1961).

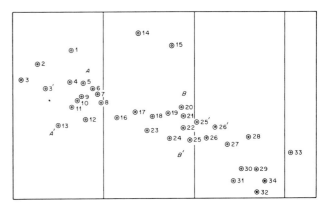

Prob. 5

REFERENCES

Badgley, P. C., 1959, Structural methods for the exploration geologist: New York, Harper & Row.

Belcher, D. J., and others, 1951, A photo-analysis key for the determination of ground conditions: Ithaca, N.Y., U. S. Office of Naval Research, Cornell Univ.

Brown, C. B., and Debenham, F., 1929, Structure and surface: London, E. Arnold.

Busk, H. G., 1929, Earth flexures: Cambridge, Cambridge Univ.

Coates, J., 1945, The construction of geological sections: Geol. Mining Metall. Soc. India Quart. Jour., v. 17.

Compton, R. R., 1962, Manual of field geology: New York, Wiley.

Crowell, J. C., 1948, Template for spacing structure contours: Am. Assoc. Petroleum Geologists Bull., v. 32, p. 2290–2294.

Dapples, E. C., Krumbein, W. C., and Sloss, L. L., 1948, Tectonic control of lithologic associations: Am. Assoc. Petroleum Geologists Bull., v. 32, p. 1924–1947.

Fuller, J. G. C. M., 1961, Ordovician and contiguous formations in North Dakota, South Dakota, Montana, and adjoining areas of Canada and United States: Am. Assoc. Petroleum Geologists Bull., v. 45, p. 1334–1363.

Gabriel, V. G., and Dotson, J. C., 1953, The use of v-concept in structural geology: Am. Geophys. Union Trans., v. 34, no. 6.

Gill, W. D., 1953, Construction of geological sections of folds with steep limb attenuation: Am. Assoc. Petroleum Geologists Bull., v. 37, p. 2389–2406.

Harrington, J. W., 1951, The elementary theory of subsurface structural contouring: Am. Geophys. Union Trans., v. 32, p. 77–80.

Herrmann, L. A., 1961, Structural geology of cement—Chickasha area, Caddo and Grady Counties, Oklahoma: Am. Assoc. Petroleum Geologists Bull., v. 45, p. 1971–1993.

Howard, Richard, 1965, Niagaran reef dolomites De-Witt-McLean Co., Illinois: Illinois Geol. Survey Circ. 377, App. 1.

Krumbein, W. C., Sloss, L. L., and Dapples, E. G., 1949, Sedimentary tectonics and sedimentary environments: Am. Assoc. Petroleum Geologists Bull., v. 33, p. 1859–1891.

Lahee, F. H., 1961, Field geology, 6th ed.: New York, McGraw-Hill, 926 p.

LeRoy, L. W., 1950, Subsurface geologic methods: Golden, Colo., Colorado School of Mines.

Lesure, F. G., 1957, Geology of the Clifton Forge iron district, Virginia: Virginia Polytech. Inst. Bull., v. 50, no. 7.

Low, J. W., 1957, Geologic field methods: New York, Harper & Row.

Lueder, D. R., 1959, Aerial photographic interpretation: New York, McGraw-Hill, 452 p.

Mackin, J. H., 1950, The down-structure method of viewing geologic maps: Jour. Geology, v. 58, p. 55–72.

Mais, W. R., 1957, Peripheral faulting at Bayou Blue salt dome, Iberville Parish, Louisiana: Am. Assoc. Petroleum Geologists Bull., v. 41, p. 1915–1951.

Melton, F. A., 1959, Aerial photographs and structural geomorphology: Jour. Geology, v. 64, no. 4.

Miller, V. C., 1950, Rapid dip estimation in photogeological reconnaissance: Am. Assoc. Petroleum Geologists Bull., v. 34, p. 1739–1743.

Palmer, H. S., 1918, New graphic method for determining the depth and thickness of strata and the projection of dip: U. S. Geol. Survey Prof. Paper 120.

Shearer, E. M., 1957, Stereo-structural contouring: Am. Assoc. Petroleum Geologists Bull., v. 41, p. 1694–1703.

Simpson, Brian, 1960, Geological map exercises: London, Philip.

Sugden, W., 1962, Structural analysis, and geometrical prediction for change of form with depth, of some Arabian plains-type folds: Am. Assoc. Petroleum Geologists Bull., v. 46, p 2213–2228.

Thurrell, R. F., Jr., 1953, Vertical exaggeration in stereoscopic models: Photogramm. Eng., v. 19, p. 579–588.

appendix B
geometric projections

ORTHOGRAPHIC PROJECTION

In the application of structural geology, quantitative as well as qualitative results are often needed. For example the depth of an ore body localized along the intersection of a fault with a limestone unit may determine whether or not that body can be mined for a profit. If the ore is offset along a fault, the amount and direction of the displacement will be decisive in determining whether to go after it or not. These and many other problems can be solved by graphical methods. Solid or analytical geometry can also be used, but the precision of such methods is not necessary for geological problems in which attitudes and shapes of rock bodies and structures only approximate the geometrical models used to represent them. The more complicated problems are more easily solved by graphical techniques than by mathematical analysis. The most important reason for using graphical methods is their usefulness in aiding the geologist to obtain a three-dimensional picture of the structure. When there are several structural elements involved in a problem, the interrelationships are much easier to see with a graphical approach.

For quantitative treatment of problems the orthographic projection is useful. The perspective of block diagrams is lost, but the projection is drawn to a consistent scale. The *orthographic projection* is a means of representing regular geometrical shapes (i.e., a dipping plane, an inclined line) on a plane (a piece of paper) in such a way that their dimensions and angular relations are not distorted. This is done by folding vertical planes containing the lines or planes of the feature into the plane of the projection which is taken as a horizontal plane.

Many structural problems consist of determining relationships among lines, points, and planes. In many instances formational contacts, fractures, faults, unconformities, dikes, and sills can be approximated by planes. The intersection of any two of these features forms a line. Movements within

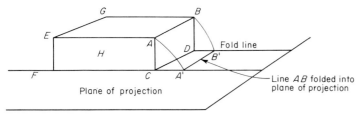

Block Diagram

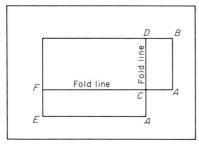

Orthographic Projection

Fig. B-1   Representation of a block by orthographic projection.

fault zones are often translational and along well-defined lines of movement. When structures can be approximated by lines and planes, problems involving angles or distances among various elements can readily be solved by use of the orthographic projection.

In such a projection, lines and planes are projected only in a single plane (usually a horizontal plane in geologic problems). This is done in much the same way a cardboard box would be flattened, by cutting all edges and folding the sides and any interior partitions down. All the lines or planes in a problem can be projected to a single plane in this manner. The lines along which the folding is done are called *fold lines* (Fig. B-1). In the following examples some common problems encountered in geology are solved by orthographic projections. Orthographic projections can be used in geologic problems when:

1. The elements of the structure can be approximated by lines and planes.
2. Quantitative distance measurements are needed. (The stereographic projection offers an easier way to solve problems involving angular relations only.)
3. A true scale model is required.

The plane of the projection is almost always a horizontal surface simulating the flat ground surface, a level in a mine, or a given level through a structure. Because most geologic problems involve features with strike or bearing, the projection surface approximates a map and should be oriented with respect to a compass. North should always be labeled, and all lines actually lying within the plane of the projection should be laid off with their strike direction or bearing. A scale must be selected which will allow a convenient working-size model.

Orthographic Projection of a Single Plane

Any horizontal plane or line will lie within the plane of the projection. It is possible to project a line from within some other plane into the plane of the projection. Going back to the model of the cardboard box and assuming that the bottom of the box is the plane of the projection, the top edges of the box all lie within a plane parallel to the bottom but at a distance above the bottom which is equal to the height of the box. These edges can be placed within the bottom plane by folding the sides of the box down (Fig. B-1). Note that the fold lines must be shown on the plane of the projection and that the height of the box must be scaled using the same scale as that used for lines actually in this plane.

A vertical plane shows up within the plane of the projection as a straight line. Any portion of the vertical plane can be rotated into the plane of the projection by using this straight line as a fold line.

The general case is that of an inclined plane —a dipping contact, for example. This plane or contact appears in the projection as a straight line (the strike line of the contact). The direction of dip may be shown by a line drawn perpendicular to the strike line in the direction of dip. The amount of dip is shown by folding the vertical plane which contains a right-angle cross section of the dipping plane into the plane of the projection. The fold line in this case is the line showing the direction of dip. Use of any other line would have shown an *apparent dip* which would have been less than the true dip. (Note: It is extremely important that the student learn the definitions of *strike, dip, bearing,* and *plunge* and apply them rigorously.) The inclined surface is completely defined by the strike line, the line showing direction of dip, and the sectional view of the dipping surface folded into the plane of the projection. It is often desirable to show, in addition, structure contours or some particular structure contour. A contour at some given depth below the level of the projection can be found by reference to the section which has been folded into the projection. Because this is a vertical distance, it is measured perpendicularly from the fold line down to the projected dipping line. The structure contour for any depth will be parallel to the strike line (Fig. B-2).

Finding an Apparent Dip

When the true strike and dip are given, the plane can be shown on the projection. To find the angle of apparent dip along some given line the bearing of this line is drawn on the projection (if this line is not specified as to location it may be drawn anywhere so that it crosses the strike line of the inclined surface). Since the apparent dip of the inclined plane could now be seen if a section were cut along this new line, the apparent dip is used as a fold line. One or more structure contours are drawn, using the section showing the true dip. The depth to the inclined surface below any point

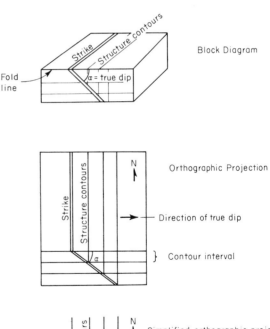

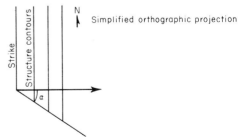

Fig. B-2 Block diagram of a dipping strata and an orthographic projection of the same.

where one of these structure contours crosses the fold line of the apparent dip is known. This depth, drawn to scale, is laid off perpendicular to the line along which the apparent dip is to be found. Then a line representing the cross section of the inclined plane is drawn from this depth back to the point of intersection of the strike line and the line along which the apparent dip is desired. The apparent angle of dip can then be measured directly.

Finding True Strike and Dip from Apparent Dips

Situations may arise in which apparent dips can be measured but true strike and dip are not known. For example, three drill holes penetrate a certain contact. The strike and dip of the contact can be determined from this information if the holes are not in a straight line and if the contact is a true plane. If the plane is inclined then the contact will be penetrated in one hole (A) at a lower depth than in the other two (B and C). This in itself provides some idea of the direction of dip. The apparent dips along the lines AB and AC can be drawn on an orthographic projection, using the horizontal plane which contains A as the plane of the projection. The strike of the contact will be known if any two points on the contact and at the same elevation can be found. Two points on the fold lines AB and AC, directly above points at the same elevation on the sections showing apparent dips of the contact, can be easily located (Fig. B-3). A line connecting such points on the fold lines AB and AC defines the strike direction and actually represents a structure contour at some specific depth. True dip must be measured perpendicularly to the strike; thus, a new fold line in the direction of dip is drawn perpendicularly to the strike (the problem is simplified if the new fold line is drawn so that it passes through point A, where the elevation is already known). The elevation of the contact at two points directly above or below and on this line must be found. This is found from structure contours. Then it is possible to construct the section showing the true dip, and the amount of true dip can be measured directly.

It is also possible to find the true dip when the strike and one apparent dip are given. The method involved is a slight modification of that outlined above. The main difference is that it is unnecessary to find the strike.

Thickness Determination with Orthographic Projections

If a unit is platelike, dips vertically, and outcrops on a flat surface, its thickness can be measured directly on the ground surface along a line perpendicular to the upper and lower contacts. If such a unit is horizontal, the thick-

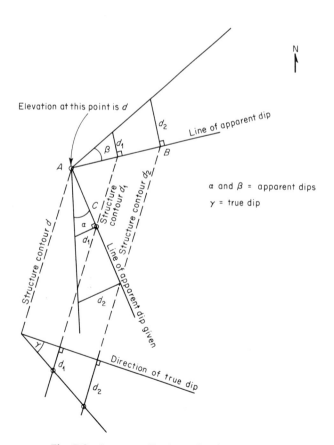

Fig. B-3   Apparent dip determination.

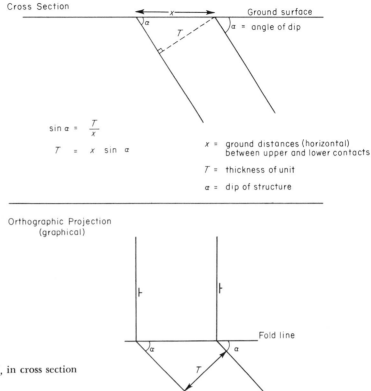

Fig. B-4   Thickness measurement, case I, in cross section and by orthographic projection.

ness can be found by determining the elevation of the upper and lower contacts and then subtracting. More often, however, the ground surface will be sloping, and the unit will be dipping.

Case I.   Ground horizontal, unit dipping

It is simple to solve such a case by use of trigonometry. The thickness and width of outcrop form two sides of a right triangle with one angle being the angle of dip (Fig. B-4). The orthographic projection may also be used in this case. A fold line is drawn perpendicular to the two contacts in the plane of the projection. A cross-sectional view is then drawn by laying off the dips of the two contacts and extending them. If the dips of the two contacts are not identical, the wedge shape of the unit will be reflected in differences in thickness. (Note: In the case of a wedge the orthographic projection

of structure contours on the two contacts will not remain parallel unless thickness increases directly down dip.)

Case II.   Ground surface inclined

As in the above case, the object here is to draw a cross-sectional view perpendicular to the strike of the unit. This view must show, to scale, the direction and amount of slope of the ground surface as it appears along the fold line (perpendicular to the strike), the location of the contacts along this slope, and the angle of dip of the contacts. Once this construction is completed, the thickness can be measured. Apparent thicknesses along any line (e.g., a vertical well hole) can also be measured directly. These thicknesses can also be calculated by using trigonometric relations as indicated in Fig. B-5.

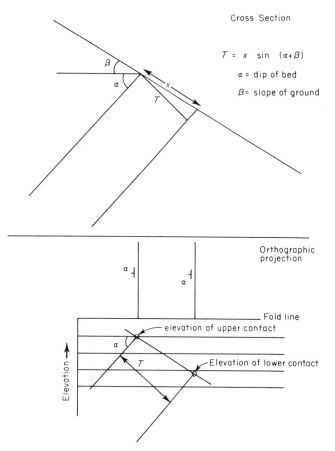

Cross Section

$$T = x \ \sin \ (\alpha + \beta)$$

α = dip of bed

β = slope of ground

Orthographic projection

Fold line

elevation of upper contact

Elevation of lower contact

Fig. B-5 Thickness determination, case II.

Intersection of Planes and Pitch

Plunge: The plunge of a line is the angle between the line and its horizontal projection measured in a vertical plane.

Pitch: The pitch of a line in a plane is the angle between the line and a horizontal line in the plane measured in the plane.

The field geologist is often confronted with problems involving the intersection of two planes. Ore or oil may be concentrated at such intersections, as when mineralizing solutions moving up a dike or fault hit a limestone for-

mation. The position of this line of intersection then has practical importance. The solution of fault problems and the analysis of fracture systems also employ the methods outlined here.

In the most general case there are two inclined planes of different strike and dip. Enough field data must be obtained to determine the strike, dip, and location of the two planes. Once the two have been plotted to scale with orthographic projections of the dips shown, the line of intersection is found by use of constructed structure contours. One point on the line of intersection occurs within the plane of the projection where the two strike lines cross. A second is located by constructing a structure contour at some particular depth on the two planes. The horizontal projection of this second point is located where the two structure contours cross. The line drawn through these two points defines the *horizontal projection* of the line of intersection, and its bearing can be measured directly. The *plunge* of this line can then be determined by using it as a fold line, rotating the line of intersection to the plane of the projection. This is accomplished, as before, by measuring or knowing the depth of the second point (where the structure contours crossed) on the line below the horizon and plotting that distance to scale on a line drawn perpendicular to the fold line and through the point on the fold line which lies vertically above the point of known depth (Fig. B-6). A line drawn from this point through the point of intersection of the contacts is the orthographic projection of the line of plunge. The angle of plunge is then measured with a protractor (Fig. B-6).

It is sometimes desirable to measure the angle of pitch of a line within a plane. The best way to measure this directly with the orthographic projection is to rotate the plane containing the lineation into a horizontal position so that a protractor can be used. To find out what happens to a line within a plane that is rotated back to the horizon around its strike, project one or two points of known depth on that line into the section which shows the true dip of the plane (use structure contours). When the plane is rotated these points will be rotated to a position perpendicular to the original strike line at a distance from the strike line equal to their former distance from the strike line measured in the true dip section (Fig. B-7).

Solution of Fault Problems

The orthographic projection is uniquely adapted to the solution of fault problems. Here it is clearly superior to mathematical solutions, which become complicated, slow, and difficult to follow and which lack the visual aid of seeing the relationships and their direct application to the field problem. Fault problems involving rotations of the blocks on either side of the fault relative to one another are most easily solved by use of orthographic and stereographic projections together. The stereographic projection is used to determine changes in strike and dip after rotation, and the orthographic projection is used to depict the problem in scale and to make distance measurements which cannot be made with the stereographic projection. Examples of rotational fault problems are given after discussion of the stereographic projection.

When faults involving translational movements are considered, there are four variable elements:

1. Attitude of the fault
2. Attitude of the beds, which it will be *assumed* remains constant on both sides of the fault
3. Amount of movement, which is uniform in all parts of the fault
4. Direction of movement, which is uniform in all parts of the fault

Problems are most likely to involve finding:

1. The dip of the fault
2. The position of a displaced vein, dike, or contact

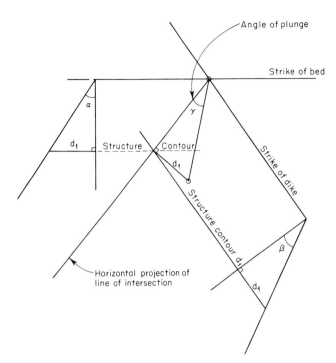

Fig. B-6 Finding the line of intersection of two planes.

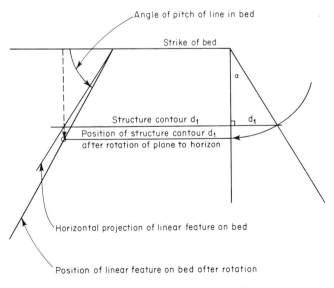

Fig. B-7 Determining the pitch of a line in a plane.

3. The direction of displacement

4. The amount of displacement

Obviously there are numerous variations on fault problems. The following discussions will outline some pertinent general considerations in finding solutions.

Care must be taken at the start of any fault problem to consider what information has been given and to be sure that all pertinent information is indicated on the initial drawing of the problem. If the attitude of the fault, a contact, a dike, or a vein is given, it should be represented by orthographic projection on the drawing. It will usually be helpful at the start to draw the trace or traces of any contact in the plane of the fault (e.g., the trace of the contact of a dike, formation, or vein in the fault). This will continually remind you of the position of that bed, etc., in the fault as you consider possible solutions.

If movements within the fault plane are translational, all points which were originally adjacent on opposite sides of the fault have been displaced by the same amount and in the same direction. If slickensides are present, they indicate the direction of that movement, and it will be helpful to show on the plot the bearing of the slickensides in the fault plane. Movements in translational faults are *strike-slip, dip-slip,* or *oblique-slip.* Slickensides would indicate which of these had taken place. Strike-slip faults do not cause the surface on opposite sides of the fault to be displaced vertically, but in the other two types of movement one side of the fault has been displaced above the plane of the projection. The effect on the drawing of the projection is the same as if the upthrown side had been eroded down to a level surface after faulting. The amount and direction of movement in the fault can be found if any two points which were adjacent before faulting can be identified and located. For example, where a fault cuts across a sedimentary sequence which has earlier been invaded by a dike or vein, the dike intersects the contact of a bed

in a line. This line intersects the fault plane at a point. If this line is cut by the fault, the points which were originally together on opposite sides of the fault may be located and their *displacement* measured.

Tips on the Solution of Translational Fault Problems

1. *Dip-slip movement.* Movement takes place directly down the fault, perpendicular to its strike. The amount of movement can be measured directly in the section showing the true dip of the fault. Any inclined contacts in the plane of projection which are on the upthrown side of the fault and which do not parallel the fault will have migrated in the direction of their dip. The lower the dip, the greater the amount of migration. If an intersection of a bed with the fault is known at one point on the surface, and if the trace of the displaced bed on the fault is known, the amount of movement is found by measuring the distance (within the fault plane and along a line down the dip of the fault) between the two.

2. *Strike-slip movement.* Originally adjacent points are displaced laterally. Displacement of outcrops in the plane of the projection and along the traces of contacts on the fault (strike separation) is due solely to fault movement.

3. *Oblique-slip movement.* The amount of displacement must be measured within the fault plane, but not in the section at right angles to the fault. It must be measured in a section that includes the horizontal projection of the line of movement (e.g., the horizontal projection of slickensides). If the bearing of this section is known, its angle of plunge can be drawn by using structure contours. The amount of movement may be found from separation of contacts or displacement of points that were originally adjacent. If the problem calls for location of a displaced con-

tact and gives the amount and direction of movement, then it is well to remember that the traces of the contact on either side of the fault are parallel, and the directions of strike and dip of the displaced contact are parallel on either side of the fault.

4. *Faulting of two intersecting planes.* This condition arises when two dikes or veins, or a dike or vein and a formation, are faulted. This type of problem can be solved with less than the usual amount of information. The intersection of any three different planes occurs only in a point (e.g., intersection of the fault and two dikes). Plot all contacts and the traces of these contacts on the fault. A unique point is located where the traces of two contacts on the same side of the fault intersect. If the same thing can be done on the other side of the fault, two originally adjacent points are known and the distance between them can then be measured in a section constructed along the horizontal projection of the line connecting them.

STEREOGRAPHIC PROJECTION

The student confronted with difficult structural problems involving angular relations between planes or rotational faults will be pleased to find that there is a simple and rapid graphical method available to solve these relations. The orthographic projection and stereographic projection together can be used to solve most structural problems involving three dimensions. Usually these methods are much faster than trigonometry, solid geometry, or tabular compilations. In addition, the stereographic projection is used for representation and statistical study of large populations of planar and linear features. It has long been used in mineralogy and has now come into widespread use in analysis of joints, foliation, and all types of lineations. Bucher (1944), Donn and Shimer (1958), and Badgley (1959) summarize the char-

acteristics of the projection and cite a number of examples which demonstrate its application.

The projection (Fig. B-8) is a means of showing three-dimensional linear and planar relations on a single plane. This representation is achieved essentially by projecting lines of longitude and latitude, or more precisely meridians and parallels, from a hemisphere (one produced by cutting a sphere through its poles) onto a flat surface. These lines are drawn on the plane of the projection as they would appear if viewed from a position on the sphere vertically above the center (Fig. B-8). Assume that the hemisphere being viewed is the lower hemisphere, so that when you look down on the projection from above everything appears as it would if you were looking into such a hemisphere. This projection is used to determine angles between lines and planes. It cannot be used to measure distances. In order to measure angles between these elements, they must all have a common point of intersection, the center of the projection (this point is represented by a dot in the center).

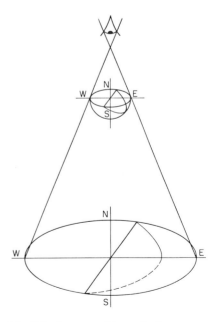

Fig. B-8 Stereographic projection.

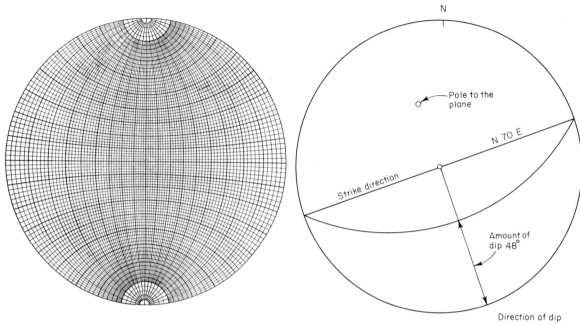

Fig. B-9 Stereographic projection.

Fig. B-10 Representation of a plane by stereographic projection.

Lines in the stereographic projection are laid off just as lines of longitude and latitude would be. The circle representing the outer edge of the hemisphere is divided into four quadrants, and these are divided into nine 10° intervals, as is the distance from the center of the projection out to the edge. This choice of divisions allows strike, dip, bearing, and plunge measurements to be plotted easily. One of the poles of the hemisphere is labeled north, the other south; east is 90° to the right of north, and west is on the opposite side. Thus the outer circle becomes a representation of the horizon. Any line which lies in the horizontal plane appears as a straight line crossing the circle through the center with a given bearing. A vertical line passes through the center but appears as a dot.

Imagine how an inclined plane will appear that passes through the center of a hemisphere (Fig. B-10). On the projection it appears as a straight line passing through the center of the projection to its edges and an arcuate line con-

necting the ends of the straight line. That arcuate line represents the intersection of the plane with the outer edge of the hemisphere. Since the straight line passing through the center of the projection is horizontal, it accurately represents the strike of the plane. The dip must be measured at right angles to the strike, and the stereographic projection allows an easy way of reading or of plotting the dip. Angles of dip, inclination, or plunge can be read along either the north-south or the east-west axis of the projection. Because a great variety of strikes and dips must be handled, and since dip can be measured only along these two axes, the fastest way to handle the projection is to use a piece of tracing paper attached to the projection by a pin placed through the center. North must be recorded on the tracing paper so the paper can be reoriented each time a bearing or strike direction is to be read. Drawing a plane of given strike and dip is accomplished by drawing a straight line across the projection with the given strike direction while north on the tracing is oriented over north on the projection. The tracing is then rotated until the line of strike lies along the north-south axis. In this position the dip direction is along the east-west line. If the plane dips east of north, the amount of dip is plotted along the east-west line on the right side of the center by counting the number of degrees of dip from the outside of the projection toward the center. A meridian line passing through this point or very close to it is now used to trace the arcuate outline of the line of intersection of the plane with the hemisphere. With the plane in this position, it is easy to plot a single point which represents that particular plane. This point is the point of intersection of a line perpendicular to the plane with the hemisphere, called the *pole* of the plane. This point will lie on the east-west axis 90° from the point initially located to determine the dip (Fig. B-10).

Before going on to specific applications it will be helpful to review the features of the projection, the various types of rotations which may be made, and the lines along which these rotations can be made.

1. The outer circle functions as a compass. With north properly oriented, all bearings and strike directions are read from it.

2. Dip is measured from the outside of the projection toward the center. This is done along the north-south or east-west axes because these are the only two radial lines drawn on the projection. (*Note:* A properly scaled ruler could be used to plot dip amount and direction.)

3. Intersections of planes with the outside of the hemisphere are conveniently drawn by use of the meridian lines which represent such intersections for 2° intervals of dip. (Lines of parallel, except for the center parallel, do not pass through the center of the projection and thus cannot be used.)

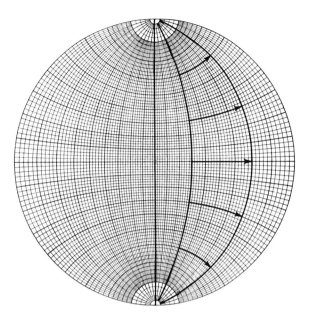

Fig. B-11 Rotation of a plane by 40° around its strike line.

4. Poles to planes can be constructed by allowing a point representation of a plane. This is useful in some of the more complicated problems.

5. The manipulations which are possible with the projection may be thought of as occurring in much the same way as movements of a gyroscope. The movements of points on the edge of a plane can be followed along lines in the projection if the plane is rotated around a vertical axis or around the north-south horizontal axis. Imagine that there is a vertical plane with strike of due north. This plane appears as a straight line on the projection. If this plane is rotated about the north-south axis so that it starts to dip east, movements of points along its intersection with the hemisphere can be followed along the parallels (Fig. B-11). (*Note:* A similar relation does not exist with respect to the east-west axis. Thus rotation of a plane

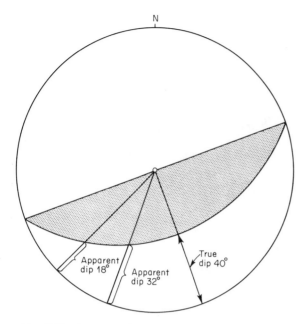

Fig. B-12 Apparent dip determination.

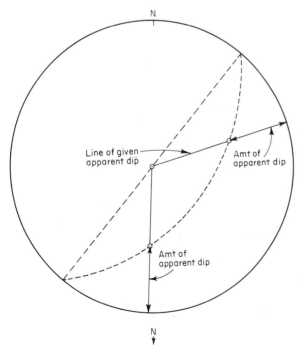

Fig. B-13 Finding strike and dip from two apparent dips.

about its strike must be accomplished by first rotating that plane about a vertical axis until its strike line lies along the north-south axis.)

Application of the Stereographic Projection

1. *To find apparent dip.* If the true strike and dip are given, the plane is sketched. A line with the bearing along which the apparent dip is desired is drawn on the projection. The amount of the apparent dip is the angle between the horizon (the outside of the circle) and the point of intersection of this line with the line of intersection of the original plane with the hemisphere (Fig. B-12). This angle is measured along one of the two axes.

2. *To find true strike and dip from apparent dips.* When two apparent dips are given, the bearings of the lines of these two are drawn, and points are located along them at distances which correspond to their amount of dip. These two points must lie on the intersection of the plane with the hemisphere; thus a meridian line which passes through them will define the true plane. That meridian is found by rotating the points on the tracing overlay until they lie along the same meridian. The two ends of that meridian define the strike of the plane, and its true dip can then be measured (Fig. B-13).

3. *To find the bearing and plunge of the line of intersection of two planes.* Sketch the two planes in the projection. Unless they have identical strikes the lines of intersection of the two planes with the hemisphere will cross at some point. That point is one common point to the two planes, and the center of the projection is another. Thus the straight line between these two points defines the line of intersection. The straight line is, of course, the horizontal projection of an inclined line. Its bearing can be read by extending the line out to the edge of the projection. Its

plunge can be read in the same way a dip is read, by rotating the line to an axis and counting the degrees between the horizon and the point of intersection of the plunging line with the hemisphere.

4. *To find the pitch of a line in a plane.* The angle involved lies within the plane and thus cannot be measured in the horizon unless that plane is horizontal. Angles within dipping planes can be measured along the line of intersection of the plane with the hemisphere. Since the pitch of a line in a plane is the angle between the horizon and that line measured in the plane, it must be measured along a meridian line (the one which contains the arcuate intersection of the plane with the hemisphere) (Fig. B-14).

5. *To find the acute angle of intersection of two planes.* The angle used in such cases is the one that lies in a plane which is mutually perpendicular to the other two. For example, the plane which is mutually perpendicular to two vertical planes is a horizontal plane, and the angle between two such planes may be measured directly with a compass on the projection, if it cannot be determined by simply subtracting one bearing from the other. Generally the two planes involved are both inclined, and thus the plane that is at right angles to them is also inclined. The mutually perpendicular plane must also be perpendicular to the line of intersection of the two planes involved. Start by drawing the line of intersection. Now it is possible to find the plane which is perpendicular to this line by reversing the process of finding a pole to a plane, described earlier. Place the line along the east-west axis; draw in the strike of this plane by tracing the position of the north-south axis; measure 90° along the east-west axis from the end of the line of intersection locating a point which lies directly down the dip of the mutually perpendicular plane and on

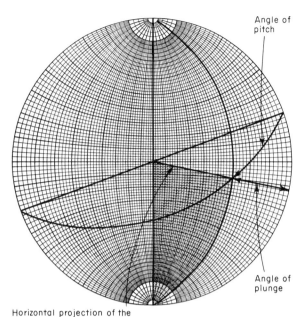

Fig. B-14 Determination of line of intersection of two planes.

the meridian defining it; draw in the meridian line. Once the plane that is mutually perpendicular has been located, the acute angle between the two planes can be measured along the meridian line between the points of intersection of the two original planes with the mutually perpendicular plane (Fig. B-15).

Once the use of poles is fully understood, the above problem can be rapidly solved by finding the pole to each of the two planes involved and then rotating the two poles until they lie along the same meridian. The angle between the two planes can then be read directly along that meridian line.

6. *Rotation of a plane about its strike line.* In this example an inclined plane with a line of known pitch lying in it is rotated about the strike line of the plane. Draw the projection of the plane and the line in it. Rotate the plane until its strike line

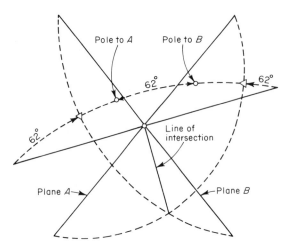

Fig. B-15 Finding a plane normal to two other planes (angle between two planes).

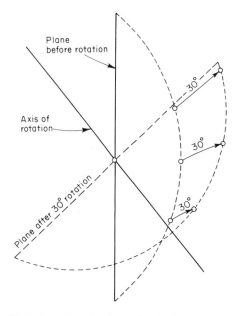

Fig. B-16 Rotation of a plane about a line.

lies on the north-south axis. (The direction and amount of rotation must be given in the problem.) Each point on the line of intersection of the plane with the hemisphere may be traced as rotation proceeds by moving the point the correct number of degrees in the right direction along the parallels of the projection. The point of intersection of a line of known pitch in a given plane with the hemisphere will be among the points moved in this way. Its new position may be found and its new bearing and plunge measured; its pitch, of course, remains unchanged by this operation.

7. *Rotation of a plane about any line.* The principle is the same as above except that some line other than the strike line is the line of rotation. Place the line around which rotation is to occur along the north-south axis. When rotation of a given direction and amount occurs around this line, all points on the given plane will rotate by the same amount and direction. Locate two points on the line of intersection of the plane with the hemisphere, and rotate them by moving them along parallels passing through them in the given direction and by the given number of degrees. These two points can now be used to redraw the line of intersection of the entire rotated plane and the hemisphere by moving them until they lie on a single meridian (Fig. B-16). (*Note:* The problem may arise that points selected for tracing the rotation will lie too close to the outer edge of the projection causing the tracing to run off the edge. To correct this, simply select another point that is farther away from the edge.)

8. *Differential rotation of intersecting planes.* A number of problems (e.g., rotational faults and restoration of beds below an unconformity) involve finding the new strike and dip of a plane which has been rotated around an axis perpendicular to another inclined plane. Consider, for example, a rotational fault problem in which both the fault and the formations that were cut by the fault are inclined. What will be the new strike and dip of beds rotated by a given amount and direction

within the fault plane (around an axis perpendicular to the fault)? This can be solved as follows (Fig. B-17a to e):

a. Draw the fault and a formation contact as it appears before rotation.

b. Rotate the fault to a horizontal position around its strike line.

c. At the same time rotate the beds to their new position resulting from the rotation of the fault.

d. Now redraw the formational contact in a position so that its strike is changed by the number of degrees indicated by the amount of rotational faulting. The dip remains the same.

e. Now return the fault to its original position, tracing out the new position of the formational contact as it is rotated with the fault. You are now ready to measure the new strike and dip of the beds on the rotated block of the fault.

The following key will help the student determine which of the above paragraphs are pertinent to common problems that can be readily solved by the stereographic projection methods.

To find the angle between fractures: No. 5

To find the position (bearing, plunge, and pitch) of a lineation in a plane: No. 3

To find the line of intersection of a contact with a fault: No. 3

To find the line of intersection of two faults, fractures, veins, dikes, etc: No. 3

To find the original strike and dip of beds below a tilted unconformity at the time the unconformity was horizontal: No. 8

To find the amount and direction of rotation of a fault when the attitudes of beds on both sides are known: No. 8

EQUAL-AREA PROJECTION

Since planes and lines can be represented on stereographic projections, the projection is uniquely suitable for statistical analysis of a population of measurements of planar or linear structures such as cleavage, bedding, foliation, fractures, or lineations. A common problem arising in areas where there has been multiple deformation is distinguishing the structural elements that belong to each of the deformations. It is sometimes possible to make this distinction by measuring a large number of the elements, plotting them on a stereonet as poles, and analyzing them, first to see whether they fall into distinct groups and, if they do, to determine the geometric relations among the various groups to see which might logically belong together. This type of analysis makes it possible to eliminate or at least reduce the chance of erroneous subjective judgment. Rarely do we find structures in nature of such rigid consistency that all the structures belonging to a single set have exactly the same strike and dip. If they did, it would not be difficult to measure one and to declare that to be the attitude of the set. Instead there are variations in strike and angle of dip. If two sets appear in a single outcrop, it is not difficult to tell that there are two sets, but the selection of the attitude of each set may be difficult unless they are usually consistent and at large angles to one another. If three or more sets are present, it may be virtually impossible to separate them into related groups unless a large number are measured and analyzed. The stereonet and equal-area projection provide simple ways of making this analysis.

The stereonet has one particular shortcoming for use in this type of study. The area of a degree of latitude and longitude in the center of the hemisphere is quite different in size from that of a degree near the edge of the hemisphere. If the concentration of points on a projection is to be used as a means of determining to which group a given point belongs, projections of areas of identical size should be equal. This is true of the Lambert equal-area projection, also called a *Schmidt net* (Fig. B-18). A comparison of the Schmidt net with the

Rotation of beds within a fault plane

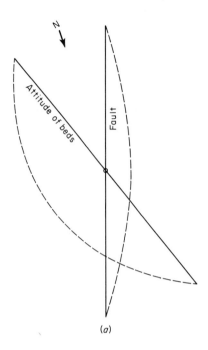

(*a*)

Fault is rotated to horizontal position

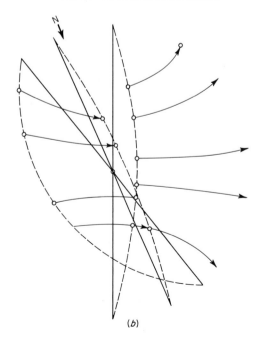

(*b*)

Beds are now rotated around pole to fault

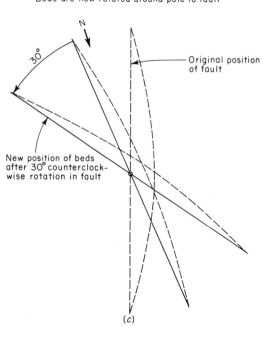

(*c*)

Fig. B-17 Rotational fault problem. The steps illustrated are described in the text.

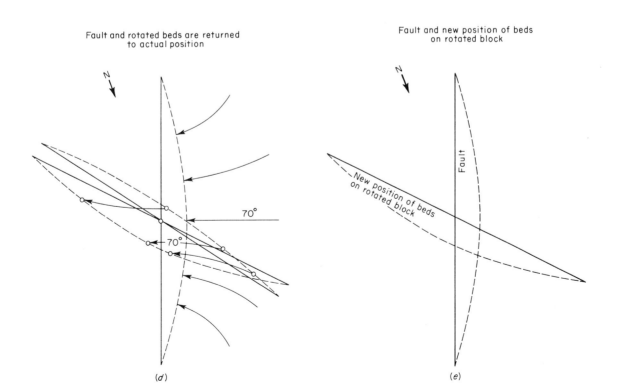

Fault and rotated beds are returned
to actual position

70°

70°

(d)

Fault and new position of beds
on rotated block

Fault

New position of beds
on rotated block

(e)

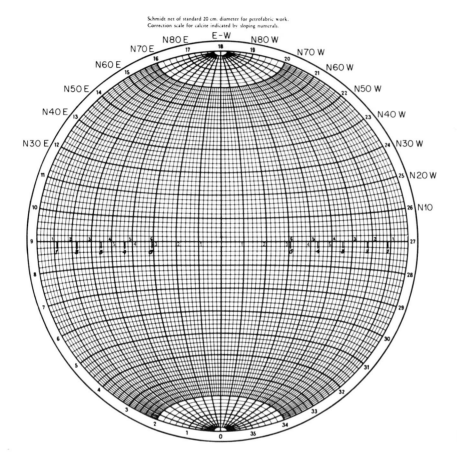

Fig. B-18   Equal-area net.

stereonet shows that the lines have similar general orientation, but the lines on the Schmidt net are distorted.

Analysis of the population of measurements is done through three mechanical steps:

1. Plotting the points (often poles to planes)
2. Counting the points
3. Contouring the counts

Points may be plotted in either the upper or the lower hemisphere. The lower hemisphere is usually used in structural studies. A method for plotting points in the lower hemisphere has already been described, but this method, involving drawing the plane first, is too laborious for plotting of a large sample, and the final

product would be a maze of lines. A number of methods are available for rapid plotting. The following technique, which requires only tracing paper and a Schmidt net, can be used. The 10° indicators in the northern half of the net are labeled as shown in Fig. B-18. East-west is placed at the north position, north-south along the east-west axis, and the 10° markers indicating amount of dip are labeled in reverse with 90° at the edge of the projection. North is marked in its correct position on the tracing paper. In order to plot the pole to a plane of given strike and dip, rotate the north point on the tracing to the strike direction indicated (on the projection). The dip reading is then measured along the newly labeled east-west axis of the projection (the usual north-south axis).

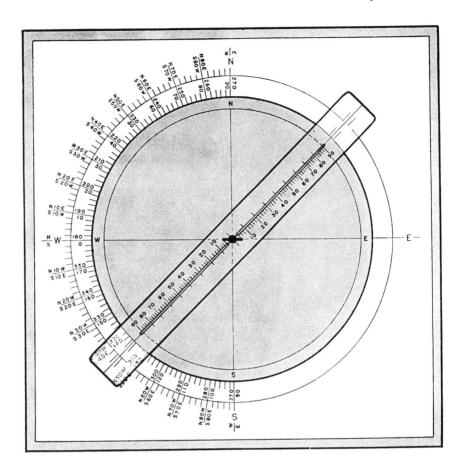

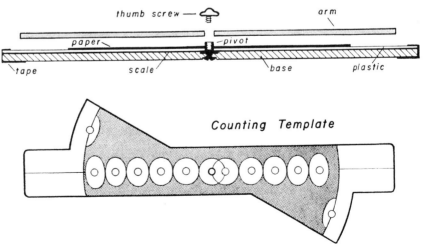

Fig. B-19 Mechanical guide with plotting arm in place. (*From Duschatko, 1955.*)

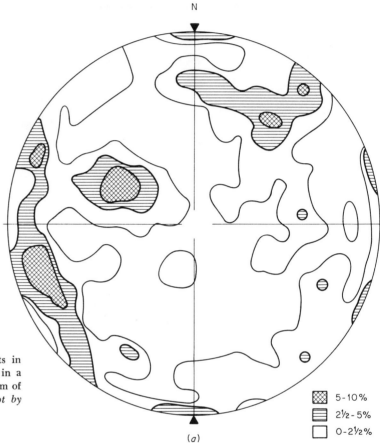

Fig. B-20 (*a*) Count of plotted points in percent of sample representing joints in a basalt dike. (*b*) Contoured point diagram of joints in a basalt dike. (*Data and plot by Poldervaart.*)

5-10%

2½ - 5%

0-2½%

(*a*)

Whether the dip is measured along the top or the bottom half of that axis depends on two things—the direction of dip and the hemisphere in which the point is being plotted. The pole to a plane with attitude N 45° E, 40° SE will appear in the northwestern quadrant of a lower hemisphere projection but in the southeastern quadrant of an upper hemisphere projection. The upper hemisphere is preferred by some because the points appear in the quadrant toward which the planes actually dip. In either case measurement of the dip is done in the reverse manner from that used to find the dip of a plane. The pole to a plane that is vertical will appear at the outer edge of the projection circle (the normal zero dip). Since poles to planes are perpendicular to the plane, the

complement of the dip must be used. This is simplified by locating the pole on a scale which reads the complement of the dip (i.e., one that is 0° at the center of the projection and 90° at the outer edge). A useful tool for rapid plotting is an arrangement such as that described by Duschatko (1955) (Fig. B-19).

Counting points may also be done by several techniques. Counting is necessary in order to contour the points so that exact concentrations can be located. It is not always possible to pick the centers of a cluster of points, and as the clustering becomes less pronounced the difficulty of doing this successfully increases. Most Schmidt nets are printed at a scale such that the diameter of the net is exactly 20 cm. At this scale a circle in the projection that has a

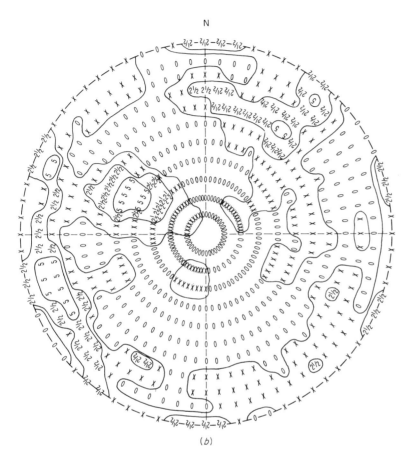

(b)

radius of 1 cm represents 1 percent of the total area of the projection. This simplifies counting because the tracing paper with all the points plotted on it can be placed over a piece of graph paper laid out in 1-cm squares. The grid intersections can be used for locating the center of a counting circle of 1-cm radius. This counting circle can be moved along the grid, and the number of points in each circle can be counted and recorded on the tracing either as the actual number of points or as the percentage of the total number. As the counting circle is moved along, it will overlap previously measured points. This system must be slightly modified along the edge of the projection. For counting these points a peripheral counter is used. The number of points to be counted for a marginal position on the projection is the total of those within the half circles on opposite edges. This total is recorded at both edges. Once all grid corners are tabulated, contouring may begin.

An alternative to the above methods of counting has been described by Duschatko (1955). This method requires a plastic template with a series of overlapping spherical circles (Fig. B-19), and when many point diagrams are to be analyzed it is much faster than the method above. Each of the spherical circles is a 1 percent circle. Counting is done by rotating the template (a 5° rotation each time is generally sufficient).

Contouring of point diagrams is facilitated by drawing in the highest concentration contours first, if there is a well-defined maximum or maxima. Selection of the contour interval may be determined in part by the magnitude of the maxima, but as a general rule it should be 2 percent. The one way in which contouring of point diagrams differs from that of other types of numerical distributions is the unusual shape of the projection. At the edge of the projection any contour which runs off the edge must appear 180° away on the other side, as in Fig. B-20.

EXERCISES

In geometric projection problems 1 to 5, assume planar contacts solve each by orthographic projection, and check by stereographic projection.

Problem 1. A contact between two rock units strikes N 50° E, dips 40° SE. Find the apparent dip along lines bearing
> N 10° E
> N 20° W
> EW

Problem 2. A contact has a strike of N 20° W. The apparent dip along a line bearing N 10° E is 25° NE. Find the true dip.

Problem 3. Apparent dips on a contact are determined to be 30° NE along a line bearing N 60° E and 50° NW along a line bearing N 10° W. Find the true strike and dip.

Problem 4. A dike striking N 15° E dips 40° SE and cuts across a sedimentary contact, striking N 40° W, dipping 30° NE. Find:
> (a) The bearing and plunge of the line of intersection
> (b) The pitch of the dike in the sedimentary contact
> (c) The pitch of the sedimentary contact in the dike

Problem 5. An angular unconformity has been tilted so that the erosion surface strikes N 20° E, dips 18° SE. Beds below the unconformity now strike N 30° W, dip 42° NE. Assume that the erosion surface was nearly horizontal when it formed, and determine the strike and dip of beds below the unconformity at that time.

Problem 6. Outcrops of the basal contact of the Tuscarora formation are located at the three places shown on the topographic map, but no strike or dip information was obtained. Assume that the Tuscarora is homoclinal in this region and construct an orthographic projection of the unit. Determine the strike and dip of the basal contact.

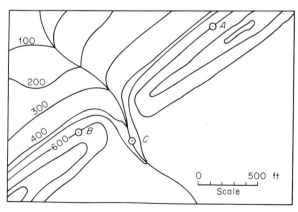

Prob. 6

Problem 7. Three outcrops of the basal contact of the Beekmantown dolomite are shown. Determine the strike and dip of the contact, assuming that the contact is homoclinal in this area. Use the orthographic projection. Check your results using an alternate method.

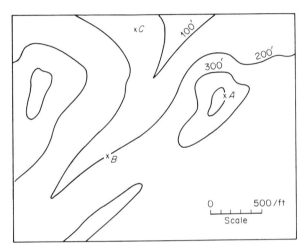

Prob. 7

Problem 8. A dike with strike of N 30° W, dips 25° SW, can be traced until it is cut by an east-west-trending fault. South of the fault the dike is found offset 300 ft to the east. The fault is exposed in one place, where it dips 60° S, and slickensides on the fault indicate dip-slip movement. There is no indication of rotation during faulting. What is the amount of displacement and the type of fault?

Problem 9. A marker horizon is found to strike N 50° E and dip 65° NW on the north side of an east-west-trending fault which dips 40° S. A well is drilled in the position shown and the top of the marker horizon is found at a depth of 150 feet. Locate the outcrop position of the marker on the southern side of the fault trace and determine the amount of strike and dip separation. How would you classify this fault?

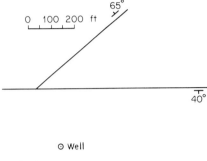

Prob. 9

Problem 10. The strike and dip of two dikes and a fault which offsets them are given on the map. Determine the displacement, strike separation of each dike, dip separation, vertical component of the dip separation of each dike, horizontal component of the dip separation of each dike, and normal separation. (Refer to Chap. 4 for definition of separations.)

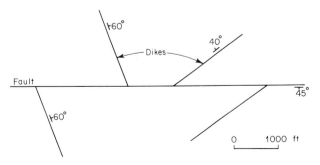

Prob. 10

Problem 11.   Given six drill holes located in the pattern shown. Assume that the ground is flat. The depth to a specific marker horizon is given in each well. Faults are encountered in three of the wells at the depths shown. Make an interpretation of the structure, assuming that the marker horizon has remained planar. Draw a geologic map in this area showing the outcrop of the marker horizon; draw a structure contour map on the marker and a structure contour map on the fault. What type of fault is this? Determine the dip separation at the point on the ground where the fault intersects the outcrop of the marker horizon, and its horizontal and vertical components.

⊙ E   ⊙ C   A ⊙

0 100 200 ft

⊙ F   ⊙ D   B ⊙

Prob. 11

Well	A, ft	B, ft	C, ft	D, ft	E, ft	F, ft
Marker	135	60	115	254		104
Fault	295	105			30	
Marker					104	

REFERENCES

Badgley, P. C., 1959, Structural methods for the exploration geologist: New York, Harper & Row.

Bucher, W. H., 1944, The stereographic projection, a handy tool for the practical geologist: Jour. Geology, v. 52, p. 191–212.

Clark, R. H., and McIntyre, D. B., 1951, The use of the terms pitch and plunge: Am. Jour. Sci., v. 249, p. 591–599.

Dennison, J. M., 1968, Analysis of geologic structures: New York, Norton.

Dickinson, George, 1954, Subsurface interpretation of intersecting faults and their effects upon stratigraphic horizons: Am. Assoc. Petroleum Geologists Bull., v. 38, no. 5.

Donn, W. L., and Shimer, J. A., 1958, Graphic methods in structural geology: New York, Appleton-Century-Crofts.

Duschatko, Robert, 1955, Mechanical aid for plotting and counting out pole diagrams: Geol. Soc. America Bull., v. 66, p. 1521–1524.

Hughes, R. J., Jr., 1960, A derivation of Earle's formula for the calculation of true dip: Southeastern Geology, v. 2, no. 1, p. 43–48.

Rodgers, John, 1956, Trigonometric solution for determining the plunge of the intersection of two dipping planes: Am. Geophys. Union Trans., v. 37, no. 6.

Satin, Lowell R., 1960, Apparent-dip computer: Geol. Soc. America Bull., v. 71, no. 2, p. 231–234.

Woolnough, W. G., 1957, Graphical determination of the dip in deformed and cleaved sedimentary rocks: Jour. Geology, v. 65, no. 4.

This book was set in Baskerville by Monotype Composition Company, Inc., and printed on permanent paper and bound by Von Hoffman Press, Inc. The designer was Dale Maix; the drawings were done by J. & R. Technical Services, Inc. The editors were Bradford Bayne and Janet Wagner. William P. Weiss supervised the production.